D1626780

mathematical process models in iron- and steelmaking

mathematical process models in iron- and steelmaking

Proceedings of the conference on 'Mathematical process models in
iron- and steelmaking', organized by The Iron and Steel Institute,
held in Amsterdam on 19–21 February, 1973. This volume also contains $[P\ 158]$
papers from a specialist mathematical symposium sponsored by
Hoogovens, held at the Technical University of Delft.

The Metals Society

Text set in 10/12 Monophoto Times New Roman 327. Article titles set in 24/30 Monophoto Times New Roman 327.
Printed by J. W. Arrowsmith Ltd, Bristol

The following papers are included :
(State page range)

39369

× Mathematical Models
× Furnaces Electric Arc
× BOS
× Hot Strip Mills

Contents

Chapter 4: Teeming and solidification

Chapter 5: Heating furnaces

Chapter 6: Hot and cold rolling

Foreword

The second mathematical models conference, of which this volume is the proceedings, was attended by some 170 delegates from many countries, including the USA and Japan. It was most successful with regard to both the number and quality of the papers and the extent of the discussion, and confirms the current wide interest in mathematical modelling and its value in iron- and steelmaking.

A comparison of the papers presented at this conference with those presented at that held in 1969 shows some interesting changes. First, the scope and usefulness of the conference has been widened considerably by the inclusion of control models. Further, although models based on the purely physical processes of heat and mass transfer still predominate, there is a trend to more active consideration of complex models involving chemical reaction, and a paper on thermal modelling of liquid steel flow is included (as distinct from flow modelling), and is therefore a new technique as far as this conference is concerned. Also, a number of subjects dealt with in 1969 are either now no longer of technical interest in the modelling sense, or there has been no significant improvement in the techniques available for dealing with them and so they do not appear among the present papers. These include blast-furnace stoves, coil annealing, rapid heating, decarburization, and the cooling and reheating of ingots after teeming.

A number of subjects which were introduced at the first conference have been developed further and are reported in this volume. 'Solidification mechanisms in steel' was the title of a paper in 1969. In 1973 some of the techniques describing the mechanisms of solidification and segregation discussed in this earlier paper have been worked up and developed to the stage of being practically useful in steelmaking. In 1969 it was also noted that there was no satisfactory model of the LD, and now there are two, albeit both demanding more experimental verification, refinement, and practical application. There are also papers on hot and cold rolling. However, there has been little progress in some areas; for example, the paper in 1969 which dealt with bedding and bunkering has not been followed up. One wonders if there is no demand to develop or apply these models, and also those of crushing, grinding, and the segregation of materials which already exist to some degree in the literature, or if the problems of mathematical description of naturally occurring materials are so difficult that the development of models giving generally applicable results is not possible.

Looking to the future, if a third conference were to be held four years from now, one might predict that the trend towards development and refinement of chemical-reaction models would continue, and that without significant technical breakthrough, some subjects discussed at this present conference would not appear. These would include reheating furnaces, continuous casting, and perhaps blast-furnace models in their present form. A number of technically interesting areas which have not previously been examined, though some are dealt with briefly in the four review papers, would probably be included. For example, no model of the sinter strand has been presented and there is no good arc-furnace model, although discrete parts of the latter process have been modelled. It is possible that the total combination of arcing, electrode wear, refractory wear, and

steelmaking in one vessel is too complex to be dealt with in a model of manageable size. Pollution problems have virtually been ignored at both conferences. Air pollution and chimney models are perhaps already well developed, but the state of development and usefulness of river, esturial, and tidal models is less clear. These must have significant importance now that large steelworks are concentrated at coastal sites, and one wonders whether mathematical modelling has a bigger part to play here than the conferences have suggested; or if big water models are still essential. The basic kinetics data are available to enable the writing of models describing the technically newer process of iron and steel manufacture, for example the various direct-reduction and continuous-steelmaking processes, and they would very likely appear in the future. Development of modelling techniques also continues, and the resultant increase in mathematical power may in the future stimulate interest in some processes currently too difficult to handle. For example, Monte-Carlo methods are already useful in both radiation interchange and business forecasting models, and finite-difference techniques of solving the linked flow and heat-transfer equations are being developed. Both these techniques could lead to renewed interest in furnace heat transfer. Finally, in the same way that control models have been included in the present conference, in the future one might see multi-unit process models being used to help make business decisions, for example the optimum arrangement of processes and the supply of energy and raw materials to meet a particular market demand from a large works, corporation, or country.

The development of mathematical models in iron and steel manufacture has gone hand in hand with the development of the computer and measurement techniques on the plant; measurement has provided knowledge which, used with the model, has led to understanding. The developments suggested above presuppose availability of computer power that will allow the very large and complex models to be operated economically and their results to be presented in an easily assimilated form. Good plant measurements for information and calibration purposes are also assumed to be available. While there is every indication that computing power for the same cost will increase dramatically over the next few years and in principle there should be no difficulty, it is well known that increasing the model size demands a disproportionately longer running time, and effort will be necessary to keep the models no larger than is absolutely necessary. Indeed, considerable software development will be necessary before the largest models envisaged can be handled efficiently.

F. Fitzgerald
British Steel Corporation
Corporate Advanced Process Laboratory

Organizing committee

Dr J. M. van Langen (Chairman)
H. S. Brown
Dr F. Fitzgerald
Y. Morillon
A. E. Pengelly
Dr K. Polthier
R. Sevrin

chapter 1: ironmaking

Review of mathematical modelling for ironmaking

J. M. van Langen

The industrial ironmaking processes all include simultaneous heat and mass transfer and phase changes which needed to be described in descriptive models. The transport phenomena and reaction-rate equations have also to be known or at least guessed in order to describe the processes. Finally, if the models are to be used for studying the dynamic behaviour of the processes, the mathematical path of solution must follow the sequence of operation in the process as occurs in practice.

The engineer constructing the model has to apply art in making plausible assumptions where there is a lack of information and in finding mathematical procedures that result in a satisfactory ratio between computer time and real process time as the processes involved have long characteristic times. Processes that are relevant in ironmaking are:

(i) homogenization of raw materials
(ii) coke making
(iii) sintering
(iv) pelletizing
(v) hot-blast production
(vi) the blast-furnace operation.

HOMOGENIZATION

Models of the homogenization of raw materials by bedding and by using bin systems are given in References 1–3.

COKE MAKING

The description of the conventional coke-oven process presents great difficulties in describing the softening, fusion, and volatilization of the coal as a function of temperature and particle size. Further, the behaviour of the tar and the path of the evolved gases leaving the coking chambers have not yet been described in the

literature. The actual coking process is at present simulated by using experimental coking chambers on the laboratory scale. This equipment provides information such as what heating cycle is needed to produce a given quality of coke from a specific coal blend.

Thermal mathematical models can then be used to determine what heating conditions need to prevail throughout the coke-oven battery, taking into account the refractory construction of slots, doors, and regenerators and the layout of the burner arrangements and combustion-air distribution.[4] The work on the model coke ovens can be partly replaced by the empirical statistical relations between parameters describing properties of the coal mixtures as established by the school of Simonis, of the Institut für Aufbereitung Brikettierung und Veredlungstechnik of the Technical University of Berlin.[5] The optimization of benzol plants using mathematical models has been described by Furman.[6]

SINTERING OF IRON ORES IN MOVING STRANDS

The modelling of this process is still less satisfactory than is the case for coke making. The bonding together of the particles by slag fusion or crystal growth is a phenomenon that apart from temperature depends so strongly on the mixture under consideration that the number of variables is practically infinite. As in the case of the coke oven, laboratory experiments are helpful. A pot-grate test is used in which the sinter mix to be studied is subjected to the same conditions of temperature and gas composition for the same time as has been found to exist in the plant in question and again attempts have been made to lay down some general rules.[7]

A mathematical model of the temperature fields in the sintering mass as a function of time can be found in articles by McStewart and Saville and by Muchi and Higuchi.[8]

The author is with Hoogovens, IJmuiden

3

PELLETIZING

The pelletizing process is divided into three parts, i.e. grinding, balling, and induration. Grinding seems to be a highly empirical subject, and a mathematical description based on first principles is not easily available. A. J. Lynch,[9] describes a study made of the optimization of an existing mill. H. E. Rose and R. M. E. Sullivan[10] present a dimensional analysis of the grinding process.

Balling

There is no model available. See P. C. Kapur and D. W. Fürstenau[11] for balling theory.

Induration

Pellet induration on a straight grate is a process comparable to sintering on moving strands. The state of the art is also comparable. All laboratories active in the field have pot-grate installations. However, in this case one can go much further towards a good mathematical description of the process, as the main mechanism of joining the particles is crystal growth. Moreover, the permeability to gases of a bed of spheres as a function of composition, mass transfer and temperature offers hope for success and the present conference contains an attempt in this direction.[12]

A similar model for the induration of pellets in the grate–kiln–cooler process has not been found in literature. However, this could be achieved by combining part of the above model with a kiln description by K. W. Pearce.[13]

HOT-BLAST PRODUCTION

Fully dynamic mathematical models are available for the regenerative heating of air for the blast furnace. A good description of the model is given by A. J. Willmott.[14] U. O. Stikker and H. Broekhuis describe the application of this approach in actual plant.[15]

BLAST FURNACE

Recent descriptive mathematical models of the blast-furnace process have been published by: I. Muchi,[16] R. Wartmann,[17] B. I. Wood,[18] and a dynamic model presented by G. A. Flierman and H. Oderkerk.[19]

The shaft part of these models can be treated thoroughly, based on published data by R. Johnson,

A. Rist, and the study group of the VDEh. On the reduction mechanism of single pellets recent publications by Turkdogan and co-workers, Szekely and co-workers, and Von Bogdandy and Engell[20] give detailed information.

For describing the processes in the melting and combustion zones of the blast furnace, authors have been obliged to make intelligent guesses (hypotheses) which, included in the model, results in agreement with results obtained in practice. In order to obtain a model suitable for simulating the dynamic behaviour of the process it is necessary to design a mathematical solution path, which follows the actual phenomena from step to step. If also a limited calculation time on the computer is to be realized the mathematical problem requires much effort for solution.

REFERENCES

1 A. L. VAN DER MOOREN: 'Mathematical models in metallurgical process development', 1970, London, The Iron and Steel Institute
2 W. A. BEMELMAN: Paper of 47th Iron Steel Eng. Group, Jun., 1963
3 A. W. JENIKE: *Bull. Univ. Utah*, 1961, **52**, (29)
4 K. TASHIRO *et al.*: 'Computer analyses of heat transfer in coke ovens', *Techn. Rep. Fuji Steel*, 1969
5 K. HOFHERR AND W. SIMONIS: *Technikum und Betrieb Glückauf-Forsch*, 1971, **32**, 35–49
6 A. M. FURMAN *et al.*: *Coke Chem. USSR*, 1969, **1**, 31–5
7 W. DAVIES AND D. W. MITCHELL: International Mineral Dressing Congress, 1957, Stockholm
8 I. MUCHI AND J. HIGUCHI: *Trans. ISI, Japan*, 1972, **12**, (1), 54
9 A. J. LYNCH: AIME conference, Feb. 1972, San Francisco
10 H. E. ROSE AND R. M. E. SULLIVAN: 'A treatise on the internal mechanics of ball, tube, and rod mills', London, Constable
11 P. C. KAPUR AND D. W. FÜRSTENAU: *Ind. Eng. Chem. Process Design Development*, 1966, **5**
12 P. A. M. LEBELLE *et al.*: This volume
13 K. W. PEARCE: 'A heat transfer model for rotary kilns', Symposium on Flames, Sep. 1972, London
14 A. J. WILLMOTT, *JISI*, 1968, **206**, 33
15 U. O. STIKKER AND H. BROEKHUIS: 'Automatic control of a hot stove system', Journées Internationales de Sidérurgie, 1970, Luxembourg
16 J. YAGI AND I. MUCHI: *J. Japan Inst. Metals*, 1968, **32**
17 R. WARTMANN: Conference Mathematische Modelle des Hochofenprozesses, 1971, Düsseldorf
18 B. I. WOOD: *ibid.*
19 G. A. FLIERMAN AND H. ODERKERK: This volume
20 L. VON BOGDANDY AND H. J. ENGELL 'Die Reduktion der Eisenerze', 1967, Berlin, Verlag Stahleisen

Discussion

Prof. P. A. Young (Head of the Department of Mining and Minerals Science, University of Leeds) commented that Dr van Langen had said that so far as theoretical models of sinter plants were concerned, it was unlikely that anything useful could be done, because one was concerned very largely with a kind of mineralogical reconstitution of the material. On the other hand, so far as pelletizing was concerned, the degree of grinding and mixing removed these mineralogical problems and one might very well be able to examine the process without becoming involved in any great amount of pilot plant work. In his later paper Mr Hasenack had not mentioned the metallurgical parameters associated with pellets. They do, however, have a reducibility and there are instances of problems due to swelling and low-temperature degradation etc. **Prof. Young** asked Dr van Langen and Mr Hasenack for their comments on these observations and in particular asked if the metallurgical characteristics of pellets really were not all that important.

Dr van Langen, in reply, said if the processes of sintering and pelletizing were to be examined, then the big problems in both processes were in descriptions of the melting and softening reactions (the metallurgical reactions). In describing the induration stage of pelletizing

the bed has a near-constant permeability, because all the particles have the same size and shape. This is obviously not the case in sintering where the sintered part of the bed has a very high permeability and the unsintered part is clogging as the process proceeds. Due to grinding, the ore particles contained in pellets have more or less the same size. They are very small and, therefore, there are no problems of the propagation of the reactions inside them. They react practically instantly. In pelletizing induration, the heat is transferred from the gas, whereas in sintering it is produced in the bed itself and it is governed by the size of the coke which must be within a critical size range.

There were thus many significant differences between the processes of pelletizing and sintering, and while Dr van Langen could see how the pelletizing process might be described mathematically, he had no real idea how to describe mathematically the more complex sintering process.

Induration process for pellets on a moving strand

N. A. Hasenack, P. A. M. Lebelle, and J. J. Kooy

A mathematical simulation of a pellet-induration process is presented, which gives a numerical description of simultaneous heat and moisture transfer and also heat and oxygen transfer (if magnetite is present), between pellets charged on a travelling strand and a gas flowing through them under isobaric conditions. The mechanisms which control drying and oxidation have been investigated on a laboratory scale. Heat and mass transfer into the pellet are described in terms of two resistances, the surface-film resistance and the resistance to conduction in the solid pellet. These two processes must both be taken into consideration, because first, they are of the same order of magnitude when heat transfer is considered and second, because the temperature distribution inside the pellet depends on processes controlled by mass transfer. The model has been verified by comparing the calculated results with results of plant measurements. Attention is paid to the difficulties arising when establishing a complete flow balance based on plant measurements. Owing to the mathematical complexity of the description used, only stationary states may be computed. The model developed has been used to indicate changes to optimize and to improve the strand cooling. This model will also be used to determine which fans must be enlarged first, and also to what extent, in order to increase the production capacity.

LIST OF SYMBOLS

A	surface area of pellets per unit bed volume	J_H	Colburn j-factor for heat transfer, dimensionless
C_{solid} C_{water}	specific heat of pellets and water, respectively	Q	heat of evaporation
C_g	moisture and oxygen concentration of gas respectively	R	radius of pellet
		r	radial coordinate
C_{g0}	inlet concentration	r_1	location of front in pellet
$C_g(h)$	concentration at level h in the bed	Re	Reynolds number, dimensionless
Cp	specific heat of gas	T	temperature
Cp_g	specific heat of water vapour	t	time
C_R	moisture and oxygen concentration of gas respectively at surface of pellet	T_g	gas temperature
		T_{g0}	inlet gas temperature
$C_{r=r_1}$	moisture and oxygen concentration of gas respectively at front in pellet	$T_g(h)$	gas temperature at level h in the bed
		$T_{r=r_1}$	temperature at front in pellet
D	diffusion coefficient	V	gas flow rate
D_e	effective diffusion coefficient	α	heat-transfer coefficient
E	void fraction of bed, dimensionless	β	mass-transfer coefficient
H	bed depth	ϵ	void fraction of bed, dimensionless
h	height coordinate	λ	thermal conductivity of pellet
		λ_1	thermal conductivity of dry pellet
		λ_2	thermal conductivity of wet pellet

The authors are with Hoogovens, IJmuiden

ρ density of pellet

ρ_c critical moisture concentration per unit pellet volume

ρ_{gas} density of gas

ρ_g density of water vapour

ρ_{O_2} oxygen concentration per unit pellet volume

ρ_{water} moisture concentration per unit pellet volume

T_R temperature at surface of pellet

The favourable performance of the blast furnace when partly charged with pellets is making the practice of pelletizing increasingly attractive to ironmakers. The quality of the pellets produced has to meet stringent requirements if the operation of the blast furnace is to be optimized. Large-scale production mills using a travelling-strand technique are operating in places such as Sweden, the USA, and the Netherlands. For a given supply of green pellets, the operation of the induration plant may be optimized in terms of:

(i) productivity and quality, which both depend on the temperature distribution in the bed

(ii) fuel consumption and cooling efficiency.

INDURATION PROCESS AND ITS PLACE IN THE PRODUCTION OF PELLETS

The pellet process in operation at IJmuiden consists of dry grinding of ore concentrates and ore fines, wetting and balling using drums, induration of the green pellets on a travelling strand, and screening of burnt pellets.

The induration equipment used is shown in Fig. 1. Green pellets coming from the balling plant are loaded on a moving strand via a roller conveyor. The roller conveyor reduces the drop height and screens out broken pellets and fines (smaller than 5 mm), thus preventing blockage of the bed. To protect the moving pallets and grate bars against temperatures that are too high, the wet pellets are spread out on a 5–12 cm thick layer of burnt pellets, covering the bars and pallet sideboards. The charge (total height 40 cm) is first dried, then preheated, indurated, and cooled in the various zones of the strand.

As during the drying process condensation will occur at some point in the charge, and as the green pellets become weaker in this zone, the first drying stage is performed in an up-draught flowing (UDD). The condensation will then occur higher up in the bed where smaller forces are executed on the pellets making the possibility of deformation as low as possible.

The first drying zone is extended to the point where the condensation front appears at the top of the bed. This is followed by the second drying phase. As partly wet pellets cannot withstand the high temperatures prevailing in the following process phases, the second drying stage, the preheating and induration parts are performed in a down-draught (DDD). The top layer will dry very quickly and as condensation in the other layer no longer occurs, blocking of the bed by deformed or exploded pellets is highly unlikely.

As at 800–1 000°C crystal transformation, oxidation, and decarbonization will occur, the heating-up speed in the preheat zone has to be restricted. Normally the first setpoint in the preheating-zone PH, combustion-gas temperature is set at 900°C and is then gradually increased to 1 300°C over the length of the PH zone. After a proper PH period, the induration (I) can be started and it is obvious that this too will happen in a down-draught.

The object of the induration is to achieve in the bottom layers, sintering temperatures which are required for the production of good quality pellets. But also, as the strength of the grate bars decreases rapidly at higher temperatures, care must be taken that the grate bars temperature is well controlled.

The induration zone is divided into two sections, each connected to another fan. This is a device enabling the operator to meet both the pellet quality and the grate-bar temperature requirements. As at the end of the induration zone enough heat has been accumulated in the bed to obtain the required sintering temperature in the bottom layers, the inlet gas temperature in this last stage may be lowered to 900–1 000°C. This zone is the so called 'after-firing zone' (AF). Having accomplished the induration, cooling is started. In order to prevent overheating of the grate bars, an up-draught blowing system by means of a cooling-air fan is used. To make maximum use of the heat involved, the air coming out of the first part of the cooling zone is used as combustion air for the fuel over the induration section. The air coming out of the second cooling zone is used as a drying agent in the DDD zone. The gases leaving the last section of the induration zone are used for UDD. Recycling of the gases creates strong interactions between the various zones, a problem which is dealt with later.

PLANT CONTROL

Figure 2 illustrates the control systems of the strand. The systems are designed for optimal use of the heat from the gases while obtaining the required sintering temperature in the lower layers and at the same time preventing overheating of the grate bars.

To maintain quality and to keep the temperature of the grate bars under control, the average temperature of the gases leaving the windboxes 20, 22, and 24 (in Fig. 1) of the second induration zone (the so called burn-through temperature) is used for a forward control of the flow through the bed via a control of the vane positions of the up-draught drying fan DV1411 and the windbox recuperation fan DV1412. As a change in the position of these vanes will become apparent as a pressure change in the firing hood, the pressure P_3 in the firing hood is used to ensure equilibrium between the supplied and outgoing gases in the induration zone by

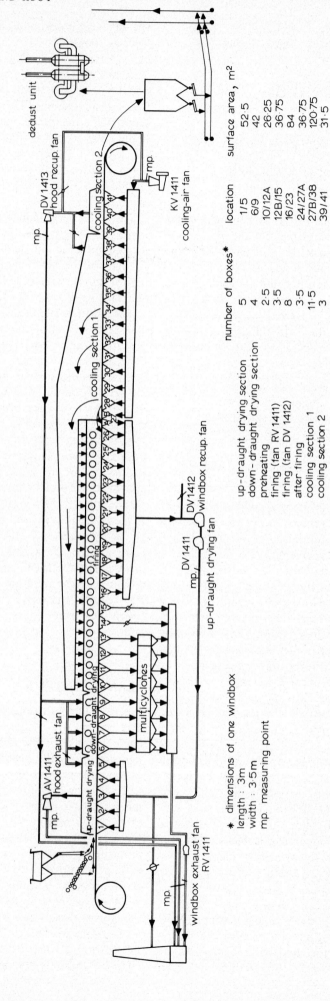

	number of boxes*	location	surface area, m²
up-draught drying section	5	1/5	52·5
down-draught drying section	4	6/9	42
preheating	2·5	10/12A	26·25
firing (fan RV 1411)	3·5	12B/15	36·75
firing (fan DV 1412)	8	16/23	84
after firing	3·5	24/27A	36·75
cooling section 1	11·5	27B/38	120·75
cooling section 2	3	39/41	31·5

* dimensions of one windbox
length : 3m
width : 3·5 m
mp. measuring point

1 Induration plant

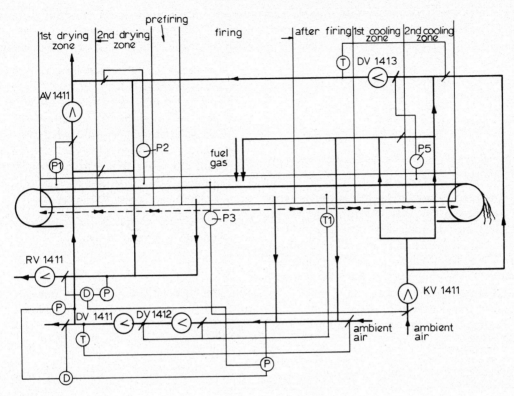

2 Strand control system

using this pressure for a control of the cooling-air fan KV1411.

Bleed-in and bleed-off valves ensure that the gases transported to the UDD zone will meet their temperature and quantity requirements, also taking into account the maximum permissible temperatures for the fans. A pressure controller P_1 in the hood of the UDD zone adjusts the vanes of the hood exhaust fan AV1411, thus obtaining equilibrium between input and output.

The gases leaving the second cooling zone are being used for the DDD zone, and as this quantity is determined by the pressure in the firing hood, care must be taken to obtain the right choice of pressure setpoint P_5 in the second cooling zone, as this controls the vane position of the hood recuperation fan DV1413. Bleed-off, bleed-in valves enable the removal of excessive air and keep the drying-gas temperature below a maximum level. Too low a temperature of the drying gases can be corrected by switching on the burners in the DDD zone. The gases leaving the DDD zone and the first part of the induration zone are removed to the chimney via the windbox exhaust fan RV1411. The ratio/bias module D takes care of the equilibrium of the in- and out-going gases.

Strand speed is controlled by the green pellets supply, which has the advantage that no stockage of the relatively weak pellets is needed. A special device in the supply line takes care that the short term variations in green pellet production will not affect strand operation.

Bed height is not controlled automatically but is kept within limits by choosing the correct bulk density for the wet pellets. Thus rapid variations in the size distribution of the pellets will demonstrate bed-height variations. Level detectors keep the operator informed of the

situation at the charging point. Fuel quantities in DDD, PH, I, and AF zones are controlled by thermocouples along the strand.

FORMULATION AND DESIGN OF THE MODEL

This section consists of five principal subsections, which deal with the following:

(i) a brief report on the mathematical formulation of the heat transfer inside a particle located at any level in the bed and of the rate of heat transfer to a pellet bed, and the heat-transfer coefficient used

(ii) an outline of the mechanisms which are rate controlling during drying and oxidation, followed by a mathematical representation

(iii) a brief survey of the mechanical energy transfer over packed beds

(iv) a report on the integration routines used for the digital computation and an outline of the construction of the model

(v) an outline of the operation with the model.

Mechanisms of heat transfer

Heat transfer in a ball depends on two resistances. The first, convective surface resistance, is a function of the boundary layer, which depends on the gas-flow rate. The second, internal resistance, is fixed by the thermal conductivity and the radius. Under operating conditions, both resistances are of the same order of magnitude. Consequently the temperature history of the solid at any time and at any location in the bed is fixed by integration of Fourier's heat-conduction equation with two boundary conditions.

$$r = R \qquad \alpha(T_g - T_R) = \frac{\delta T}{\lambda \, \delta r}$$

$$0 < r < R \quad \frac{\partial T}{\partial t} = \frac{\lambda}{\rho c}\left(\frac{\partial^2 T}{\partial r^2} + \frac{2}{r}\frac{\partial T}{\partial r}\right)$$

$$r = 0 \qquad \frac{\partial T}{\partial r} = 0$$

The thermal conductivity of granular materials has been extensively investigated, so that a large amount of experimental data and theoretical work in this field is available from the literature (Szczeniowski,[6] Dumes, Cheng and Vachon, De Vries,[16] Jacob,[2] Bratchikov,[7] Beer and Krainer[9]). The data used for the present work are those reported by Bratchikov.[7]

The rate of heat transfer between gas and the packed bed is derived from the thermal balance per unit surface area of the bed.

$$0 < h < H \quad V C_p \frac{\partial T_g}{\partial h} = -\alpha A(T_g - T_{r=R})$$

where A is the surface area of pellets per unit bed volume and equal to $[3(1 - \epsilon)/R]$, where ϵ is the void fraction of bed, $h = 0$, $T_g = T_{g0}$ (inlet gas temperature). The differential heat balance coupled with the Fourier's equation forms an integro-differential system, which can be solved by convenient numerical methods which are discussed later.

According to Lightfoot et al.[1] the correlation between Reynolds and Colburn numbers reported by Yoshida (see Ref. 1), Ramaswani (see Ref. 1), and Hougen et al.[21] is regarded as the most satisfactory.

$$J_H = 0.91 \quad Re^{-0.51} \quad (Re < 50)$$

$$J_H = 0.61 \quad Re^{-0.41} \quad (Re > 50)$$

Drying process

From experiments it became clear that the drying process of a single pellet can be divided into two quite different stages, i.e.:

(i) in the first stage the weight decrease is a linear function of time and the surface temperature of the pellet remains constant

(ii) in the second stage the surface temperature of the pellet rises as evaporation at the surface becomes progressively less. In this stage two steps can be distinguished. In the first, the temperature at the evaporation front is below boiling temperature and the drying process is ruled by the diffusion of the water vapour inside the pellet. In the second, the temperature at the evaporation front has reached the boiling point. The process is now controlled by the heat transfer.

From the computation of the data obtained it was derived that the first mechanism directs the drying process until a statistically constant water concentration $\rho_c = 120 \text{ kg/m}^3$ is reached. In the first drying mechanism the following processes are involved:

(i) heat transfer by forced convection to the external surface of the ball

(ii) heat used for evaporation of the water at the surface and for heating the material by conduction until surface temperature is reached

(iii) liquid water moves to the evaporating surface and this movement is rapid enough to maintain surface saturation; water vapour is transferred from the surface to the gas phase.

Assuming that in the first drying stage the pellet remains homogeneously moistened, i.e.

$$\frac{d\rho_{water}}{dr} = 0$$

the following conditions and equations will describe the previously mentioned processes in the first drying stage:

Conditions

$$t = 0 \qquad T(r) = T_0(r)$$

$$\rho = \rho_0$$

$$t > 0 \qquad \rho_{water} > \rho_{critical}$$

$$\frac{d\rho_{water}}{dt} = \frac{-3\beta(C_R - C_g)}{R}$$

$$r = 0 \qquad \frac{\partial T}{\partial r} = 0$$

$$0 < r < R \quad \frac{\partial T}{\partial t} = \frac{\lambda_2}{(\rho c)_{solid} + (\rho c)_{water}}$$

$$\times \left(\frac{\partial^2 T}{\partial r^2} + \frac{2}{r}\frac{\partial T}{\partial r}\right)$$

$$r = R \qquad \lambda_2 \frac{\partial T}{\partial r} = \alpha(T_g - T_R) - Q\beta(C_R - C_g)$$

where Q is heat of evaporation of water and equals $596 - 0.547 T_R$. C_R follows from the coupling equation of Clapeyron

$$\log C_R = \left[-\frac{13\,425}{T_R} - 22.59 \log T_R + 0.75\,10^{-4} T_R\right.$$

$$\left. + 0.223\,10^{-6} T_R^2 + 94\right]\frac{1}{4.5757} + \log\frac{18}{22.4}$$

Depending on the sign of driving force $C_g - C_R$, either condensation or evaporation may occur. The differential system related to one single pellet when a given temperature and a given moisture concentration of the gas stream are concerned is coupled to the differential systems associated to an infinitesimal layer at location h. The equations are given below:

Conditions

$$t > 0$$

$$0 < h < H$$

$$h = 0 \qquad C_g = C_{g0} \qquad T_g = T_{g0}$$

Moisture balance

$$\frac{\partial \mathring{V} C_g}{\partial h} = -A\beta(C_g - C_R)$$

Conservation of carrier gas

$$\partial\left(\mathring{V}\left(1 - \frac{C_g}{\rho_g}\right)\right) = 0$$

Heat balance

$$\mathring{V} C_p \frac{\partial T_g}{\partial h} = -A\left(\alpha - \frac{C_{\rho g}}{\rho_g}\beta(C_g - C_R)\right)(T_g - T_R)$$

Because the temporal water concentration in the second drying stage has reached the critical value, the capillary forces become neglectable and the diffusion of water vapour becomes the controlling factor. The driving force of the transport is a concentration gradient between the evaporation front moving inward towards the centre of the pellet and the surface, coupled with a concentration gradient between gas phase and surface. The transportation of moisture depends on the way heat is transferred. The temperature and the moisture concentration at the boundary of the wet core interact with each other (Clapeyron's law). It is obvious that $d\rho_{\text{critical}}/dr = 0$ owing to the fact that a negligible temperature gradient exists between evaporation front and the centre of the pellet. By neglecting the heat of the steam between front and surface, the following equations can be written for the first step of the second drying stage:

Conditions

$t > 0 \qquad \rho_{\text{water}} = \rho_{\text{critical}}$

$\qquad\qquad T_{r=r_1} < 100°C$ (diffusion is controlling)

Heat transfer

$$r = 0 \qquad \frac{\partial T}{\partial r} = 0$$

$$0 < r < r_1 \qquad \frac{\partial T}{\partial t} = \frac{\lambda_2}{(\rho c)_{\text{solid}} + (\rho_c c)_{\text{water}}}$$
$$\left(\frac{\partial^2 T}{\partial r^2} + \frac{2}{r}\frac{\partial T}{\partial r}\right)$$

$$r = r_1 \qquad -Q\rho_c \frac{dr_1}{dt} = \lambda_1\left(\frac{\partial T}{\partial r}\right)_{r>r_1}$$
$$- \lambda_2\left(\frac{\partial T}{\partial r}\right)_{r<r_1}$$

$$r_1 < r < R \qquad \frac{\partial T}{\partial t} = \frac{\lambda_1}{(\rho c)_{\text{solid}}}\left(\frac{\partial^2 T}{\partial r^2} + \frac{2}{r}\frac{\partial T}{\partial r}\right)$$

$$r = R \qquad \lambda_1 \frac{\partial T}{\partial r} = \alpha(T_g - T_R)$$

Moisture transfer

$$r = r_1 \qquad C = C_0 = f(T_{r=r_1}) \text{ (Clapeyron's law)}$$

$$r_1 < r < R \qquad \frac{\partial C}{\partial t} = D_e\left(\frac{\partial^2 C}{\partial r^2} + \frac{2}{r}\frac{\partial C}{\partial r}\right)$$

$$r = R \qquad D_e\frac{\partial C}{\partial r} = \beta(C_g - C_R)$$

Coupling equation

$$r = r_1 \qquad D_e\frac{\partial C}{\partial r} = \rho_c\frac{dr_1}{dt}$$

where dr_1/dt is the velocity of the front moving inward towards the centre of the pellet. The effective diffusion coefficient has been related to the diffusion coefficient of steam in a gas mixture by using a labyrinth factor of about 2·8. The incorporation of this step of the drying process into the differential balances of the packed bed is basically the same as given for the first drying stage.

In the second step of the second drying stage, the diffusion process becomes neglectable as the boiling point is reached at the boundary of the wet core; the driving force now turns over in a pressure gradient and the drying process only depends on the heat transfer.

Assuming $d\rho_c/dr = 0$ the condition $t > 0$ $T_{r_1} = T_0 = 100°C$ can be given. The formulation of the heat transfer inside the pellet is based on the previously reported Fourier's law integration. It should be noted, however, that the boundary condition for $r = r_1$ cancels and turns over in $r = r_1$ $T = T_0$ with the coupling equation:

$$\lambda_1\left(\frac{\partial T}{\partial r}\right)_{r>r_1} - \lambda_2\left(\frac{\partial T}{\partial r}\right)_{r<r_1} = -Q_0\rho_c\frac{dr_1}{dt}$$

where Q_0 is the heat of evaporation at the boiling point.

The differential moisture and heat balances turn consequently over in:

$$\frac{\partial \mathring{V} C_g}{\partial h} = -A\rho_c\left(\frac{r_1}{R}\right)^2\frac{dr_1}{dt}$$

$$\mathring{V} C_p\frac{\partial T_g}{\partial h} = -A\left(\alpha - \frac{C p_g}{\rho_g}\left(\frac{r_1}{R}\right)^2\rho_c\frac{dr_1}{dt}\right)(T_g - T_R)$$

The temperature distribution and the moisture concentration distribution as well as location and travelling speed of the evaporation (or boiling) front are determined by using the method developed by Murray and Landis. The basic techniques of the method, mentioned above, are briefly reviewed later.

Oxidation process

Quantitative expressions for the oxidation rate of magnetite pellets have been reported by Tigerschiöld,[14] and Edström.[18] They were based on the observation that the penetration of oxidation into the pellets is marked by a distinct boundary between oxidized layer and unreacted core. Tigerschiöld deduced that the oxidation time of a single pellet in air at 1 230°C follows Fick's law, i.e. that the resistance to diffusion through reacted material controls the rate of reaction. To be able to obtain a workable set of equations the following assumptions have been made:

    (i) the chemical reaction does not control the oxidation process

(ii) oxygen is not transported into the pellet at temperatures below 500°C

(iii) the effective diffusion coefficient of oxygen is only related to the diffusion coefficient in a multi-component gas system by the labyrinth factor σ; the order of magnitude of this parameter can be determined by matching the model to the experimental data obtained under controlled conditions. The mathematical formulation will be limited to the oxygen transfer inside one single pellet. It is obvious that the internal heat transfer, as well as the differential transfers related to any infinitesimal pellet layer at location h, are represented by means of differential systems, analogous to those related to the second drying mechanism. Of course some signs will be reversed. With these assumptions, the mathematical formulation of the oxidation process is given by:

$$t > 0 \; T_R \geqslant 500°C$$

$$\frac{d\rho_{0_2}}{dr} = 0 \; (\rho_{0_2} \text{ is derived for the magnetite content})$$

$$r = R \qquad \beta(C_g - C_R) = D_e \frac{\partial C}{\partial r}$$

$$r_1 < r < R \qquad \frac{\partial C}{\partial t} = D_e \left(\frac{\partial^2 C}{\partial r^2} + \frac{2}{r} \frac{\partial C}{\partial r} \right)$$

$$0 \leqslant r < r_1 \qquad C = C_0 = f(T_{r=r_1}) \quad \text{(Clapeyron)}$$

with the coupling equation:

$$r = r_1 \qquad D_e \frac{\partial C}{\partial r} = -\rho_{0_2} \frac{dr_1}{dt}$$

To determine the effective diffusion coefficient, preliminary experiments were carried out in the laboratory to record the temporal exit oxygen content in a gas stream flowing to a packed column under controlled conditions as well as the magnitude of each parameter involved. In matching the model to experimental data, the only parameter, the labyrinth factor, was adjusted to fit the data. By giving this parameter an average overall value of about 100, a satisfactory agreement was found between predicted and measured data. However, an attempt can be made to explain the discrepancy, which remains at the beginning and at the end of the curves (it should be noted that it is uncertain whether the discrepancy found is attributable to the model or the inaccuracies inherent in measurements).

The order of magnitude of the labyrinth factor suggests that the intermolecular collisions inside the pores do not fully govern the oxygen transfer. It should be convenient to include the Knudsen diffusion by using a more general expression

$$D_e = \frac{D}{\sigma}(1 - e^{-D_k/D})$$

where D_k is the Knudsen coefficient depending on the packing of the sintered pellet. An average overall labyrinth factor cannot be applied owing to the fact that the diffusion path increases as the temperature increases in relation with the sintering process.

Relation between flow rate and pressure drop under non-isothermal conditions

The pellet process is carried out at constant pressure difference so that the resistance against flow depends on the temperature distribution and on the mass transfer. At any location on the strand, the flow rate is deduced from the integration of the differential mechanical energy balance.

$$\frac{1}{\epsilon} \mathring{V} d\mathring{V} + \frac{dp}{\rho_{\text{gas}}} + F \, dh = 0$$

where F represents the friction term expressed by the Ergun correlation.

For the present work it is assumed, that the density is not pressure dependent (maximum pressure drop 500 mm w.g., compared to 10·33 m w.g). More detailed information on flow phenomena under non-isothermal conditions is discussed by Knudsen and Katz,[19] Lightfoot et al.,[1] and Szekely and Carr.[20]

Review of methods and solutions used

The unsteady diffusion equation $\partial T/\partial t = \nabla^2 T$ with two boundary conditions is solved by means of the classical implicit finite difference method based on a fixed network spacing. The one-dimensional diffusion equations involving a moving boundary (evaporation or oxidation front) are solved by the method developed by Murray and Landis. The method used is based on a travelling space network depending on the location of the moving boundary. Basically, the function-time derivative of each travelling point is given by

$$dT = \frac{\partial T}{\partial r} dr + \frac{\partial T}{\partial t} dt$$

where the travel velocity of each point is related to the rate of shrinkage of the moving boundary by employing equally sized space increments in both the reacted region and the unreacted core.

Vertical temperature and concentration distributions in the bed at any time increment are obtained by simultaneously integrating the differential heat and mass transfer equations. The '2/3' Adams–Bashford type predictor corrector reported by Hamming has been chosen to perform the simultaneous integration of the ordinary differential equations mentioned. The starting method is that of Runge Kutta. To check the feasibility of the selected methods, the numerical results of the analytical solution published by Rosen[3] were used. The temporal exit gas flow temperatures predicted by the model showed excellent agreement with those derived analytically.

Operation of the model

The following independent input variables may be derived from above:

(i) strand speed
(ii) bed depth and hearth-layer thickness
(iii) pellet diameter
(iv) pellet density
(v) void fraction of the bed
(vi) water content of the feed
(vii) temperature of the feed
(viii) magnetite and carbonate content of the pellets
(ix) the pressure difference to be applied over the bed in the UDD, DDD, PH, and first induration section
(x) temperature of the gases entering the bed in the various zones
(xi) type of fuel and the humidity of the ambient air
(xii) surface area of the sections and the location of the windboxes connected to the various process fans.

By selecting the above mentioned variables, the problem is completely defined and therefore the following data can be calculated:

(i) the pressure drop over the second induration and the after-firing zone
(ii) the average gas composition of the gases entering and leaving the bed in the various zones
(iii) the pressure drop over the first and second cooling zone
(iv) the temperature and flow of the gases leaving the bed at any place along the strand
(v) the average temperature and flow per section and per process fan
(vi) the temperature distribution over the bed at any place along the strand.

Owing to the recirculation of the gases many interactions exist between the various zones. In order to check to what extent the model can be simplified, the influence of each of these interactions on the temperature profile at the end of the zone is calculated.

The difficulties arising around the gas recirculation, and the method of solving them for the model, are described next.

Gas compositions in the up-draught drying zone

As the drying gas for the UDD zone originates from the last part of the induration section, variations in the fuel consumption in the induration zone will change the humidity of the drying gases, thus influencing the drying speed. Model calculations show, however, that for a given ore mixture the actual variations in humidity at low and at high rates of production do not significantly influence the temperature distribution over the bed height at the end of the firing zone. Therefore an average humidity of the up-draught drying gases can be applied, thus avoiding elaborate iterations.

Choice of pressure drop in the second induration zone

To obtain the pressure difference to be applied over the bed in the last part of the induration section, the burn-through temperature for two arbitrarily chosen pressure drops is calculated. The required pressure drop for a given burn-through temperature can then be determined by interpolation. Therefore instead of a quality demand for the bottom layer of the bed, in the model is inserted a requirement for the burn-through temperature (i.e. the average gas temperature in the windboxes 20, 22, and 24).

To check whether this is allowed, elaborate calculations on ore mixtures with varying hematite/magnetite ratios were made. The results proved the existence of a strong relationship between the so-called 'burn-through temperature' and the temperature profile over the bed at the end of the induration section. Assuming that for good quality in the bottom layer at least during one minute 1 280°C has to be reached, it appears from the calculations that the burn-through temperature must be kept at 800°C. By doing so, the maximum temperature of the gases leaving in the last part of the soaking period results in temperatures being 1 100°C or lower, thus indicating that the stringent demand to avoid overheating the grate bars is executed also.

Interaction between the DDD, PH, I, AF, and C sections

As can be concluded from the plant-control system, the composition of the gases entering the bed in the DDD, PH, and I sections is governed by the quantity and temperature of the air leaving the two cooling sections and by the required hood temperature. To check whether this necessitates complex iteration calculations, the effects of the entering gas composition on the temperature profile in the bed have been calculated. The results indicated that for a given strand-speed an average gas composition can be chosen and by this, iterations are made superfluous.

Pressure drop over the bed in the cooling zone

As the air leaving the first and second cooling sections is used as combustion air for the induration and downdraught section, the pressure difference over the cooling sections must be chosen to match the requirements in these zones. As the temperature profile over the charge when entering the first cooling zone is known, the quantity and temperature of the outgoing air for a given pressure drop over this section can be calculated. The results of two arbitrarily chosen pressure drops are then fed to a secondary program. By inserting into this program the gas flow and temperature of the induration section together with the air/fuel ratios and the combustion-gas quantities matching two arbitrarily chosen combustion-air temperatures, the right pressure drop over the cooling section can be determined by making use of simple heat and flow balances. The pressure drop obtained is then fed to the main program to establish the temperature profile over the cooling sections.

The same procedure is used for establishing the pressure drop over the second cooling zone.

Verification

In order to verify the model properly, elaborate measurements concerning flow, pressure, and temperature distribution had to be made. All measurements were carried out during a three-hour verification period in which the plant was running at a high speed and as close to steady as possible. Detailed information about the process conditions and limits of variation can be seen in Table 1.

TABLE 1   Process characteristics during verification period

Pellet mixture			
Magnetite content	%	37·7	
Grinding fineness	−45 μm %	63·5	
specific surface	m²/g	0·2256	
Bentonite to dry mix	%	0·4	
Green-ball characteristics			
Drop test		8·2 ±	1·0
Compression strength (wet)	g	1 090·0 ±	70·0
Screen-analysis size			
+15 mm	% wt	15·4	
−15 +13		30·0	
−13 +11		33·8	
−11 +9		17·8	
−9 +5		2·2	
−5		0·8	
Pellet diameter	mm	11·7 ±	1·0
Moisture content (wet basis)	%	8·0 ±	0·4
Density dry pellet	kg/m³	3 350·0 ±	150·0
Production data			
Throughput wet pellets	t/h	613·0 ±	2·0
Specific production	t/m² 24 h	31·5	
Strand speed	cm/s	7·42 ±	0·03
Total bed height	cm	40·0 ±	1·0
Hearth layer	cm	9·0 ±	0·5
Void fraction of bed	%	40·0 ±	2·0
Burning-through temperature	°C	400·0 ±	20·0
Induration conditions			
Up-draught drying zone			
process time	s	202·2	
gas temperature	°C	325	
total pressure difference			
($\Delta p_{bed} + \Delta p_{grate\ bars}$)	Pa	4 460 ±	200
Down-draught drying zone			
process time	s	162	
gas temperature	°C	350	
total pressure difference	Pa	4 660 ±	200
Preheating zone			
process time	s	100·8	
gas temperature	°C	1 000·0	
total pressure difference	Pa	4 660 ±	200
Firing zone 1			
process time	s	141·6	
gas temperature	°C	1 210–1 350	
total pressure difference	Pa	4 310 ±	200
Firing zone 2			
process time	s	324·0	
gas temperature	°C	1 360	
total pressure difference	Pa	3 870 ±	200
After firing zone			
Process time	s	141·6	
gas temperature	°C	1 320	
total pressure difference	Pa	3 820 ±	200
Cooling 1			
process time	s	465·0	
gas temperature	°C	70	
total pressure difference	Pa	4 560 ±	200
Cooling 2			
process time	s	121·2	
gas temperature	°C	70	
total pressure difference	Pa	4 660 ±	250
Electric power				
Hood exhaust fan	AV1411	KW	210 ±	5
Windbox exhaust fan	RV1411	KW	2 320 ±	30
Windbox recup fan	DV1412	KW	1 330 ±	70
Up-draught drying fan	DV1411	KW	1 620 ±	70
Cooling-air fan	KV1411	KW	1 700 ±	100
Hood recup fan	DV1413	KW	247 ±	8
Pellet quality				
ASTM tumble index—0·6 mm		%	8·0 ±	3·0
Cold compression strength				
average		N	2 840	
max.		N	4 700	
min.		N	980	
Percentage				
−1 500	N	%	10	

Apart from the normal routine, measurements were also made of the gas flows in the main ducts leading to or from the process fans (*see* Fig. 1), the temperature time curves at four levels in the pellet bed, and the pressure losses over the grate bars.

Gas flow and temperature through the process fans

Owing to the huge dimensions of the ducts, the gas flow in each of them could not be measured simultaneously, and these measurements had to be spread out over the whole verification period. As Table 1 shows, the plant was not running perfectly in the steady state, and variations could not be eliminated completely by the control system of the strand, as the variation in the burn-through temperature is showing. These variations stand for about a ±5% change in the flow rate. Together with the normal measuring error of ±5% when using pitot tubes, a deviation of about ±7% from the average steady-state quantity, is seen in each of the flows.

As can be derived from Table 2, the total flow balance only shows a discrepancy between the in- and out-going gas quantities of about 3·5%, which is well within the expected limits of error. For the calculations with the model, pressure loss and pellet characteristics of the charge in which the thermocouples are inserted have been used. As it is not very likely that this charge will be

TABLE 2   Total flow balance as measured

In	Nm³/s	Out	Nm³/s
Via cooling-air fan—KV1411	269·0	Via hood exhaust fan—AV1411	116·5
Via natural gas and booster air	6·0	Via windbox exhaust fan—RV1411	176
Via moisture in pellets	17·0	Via bleed off—DV1411	5·6
Via leakages	43·6	Via leakages	25·8
		Deficit	11·7
Total	335·6	Total	335·6

Deficit : 3·5% of the total amount of flow
Leakages : calculated from pressure loss and geometry, friction coefficient = 1·0

TABLE 3 Comparison between measured and calculated flows plus gas temperatures in the main ducts after the process fans

	Calculated gas flows, Nm³/s	Correction for leakages, Nm³/s	Total amount of gas flow, Nm³/s	Measured gas flows, Nm³/s	Error, %	Measured gas temperature, °C	Calculated gas temperature, °C	Calculated gas temperature corrected for leakages, °C	Calculated gas temperature at which the heat consumption in the grate bars is taken into account, °C
Hood exhaust fan AV1411	91	40.9	131.9	116.5	+13	116	47	110	110
Hood recup fan DV1413	57.2	27.8	85.0	97.5	−13	272	428	298	298
Cooling-air fan KV1411	219.4	30.6	250.0	269.0	−7	18	18	18	18
Windbox exhaust fan RV1411	157.9	23.9	181.8	176.0	+3	152	162	188	184
Up-draught drying fan DV1411	103	17.8	120.8	126.9	−5	360	755	654	485

an exact replica of the average situation, this will introduce another source of error, the influence of which, based on earlier experiments, can be estimated to another ±5% in flow.

As the model only gives detailed information about the flow passing through the bed and does not take into account gas leakages from one zone to the other, it is necessary to estimate these leakages in order to calculate the gas quantities flowing through the main ducts. As can be seen from Table 3, these corrections sometimes form an integral part of the total flow, thus adding to the total error. Altogether, one can expect a discrepancy of about ±10% between measured and calculated flow distribution. In Table 3, the results of the comparison show that the measured and calculated flows and gas temperatures in the main ducts are fairly well within the accuracy limits.

An exception concerning the temperatures of the gases flowing through the up-draught drying and the windbox-exhaust fan could possibly be made, but one must bear in mind that the heat-consuming capacity of the grate bars, beams, and pallets is not taken into account. If one does so by using a simplified model of the heat exchange between the gases and the construction parts of the strand, (*see* Table 3) the discrepancies become much smaller and by improving this submodel in which we are now engaged, the discrepancies may be reduced still further.

Temperature distribution inside the pellet bed

As for the removal of the thermocouples, the strand has to be stopped, the temperature measurement inside the pellet bed can only be carried out once, otherwise the steady state would have been disturbed too much.

In spite of the deviation of the steady state, the measured and calculated values are in good agreement as seen in Table 4. However, one observes that the model tends to give too optimistic a value for the bottom layer temperatures at the end of the firing period and also for the top layer at the end of the cooling zone. About 25–30°C of this error of 50–60°C can be explained by the decrease of bed permeability during the induration process. As the pellet quality is mainly governed by the temperature of the bottom layer reached at the end of the firing period, the maximum attainable

TABLE 4 Vertical temperature distributions in the pellet bed at the end of various zones

Bed depth	h = 0.011 m (2 cm above the hearth layer)			h = 0.024 m (middle layer)			h = 0.037 m (top layer)		
	Calculated gas temperature, °C	Calculated surface temperature of the pellet, °C	Measured temperature, °C	Calculated gas temperature, °C	Calculated surface temperature of the pellet, °C	Measured temperature, °C	Calculated gas temperature, °C	Calculated surface temperature of the pellet, °C	Measured temperature, °C
Up-draught drying	255	210	240	80	50	40	55	50	40
Down-draught drying	70	75	60	110	55	65	325	280	345
Preheating	200	150	125	535	380	320	980	920	990
Firing 1	570	455	425	1 010	915	950	1 320	1 280	1 350
Firing 2	1 245	1 210	1 180	1 350	1 345	1 320	1 360	1 360	1 360
After firing	1 315	1 300	1 250	1 350	1 350	1 330	1 325	1 330	1 320
Cooling 1	85	105	90	215	295	330	500	580	655
Cooling 2	70	75	75	110	145	120	275	340	400

production for pellets of good quality can thus be calculated by increasing the preset value of the burn-through temperature by 25–30°C.

APPLICATIONS

Pot-grate tests on the mixtures normally in use at Hoogovens proved that good quality pellets could be obtained at the very high production rate of 35 t/m² 24 h. Beyond that limit, quality deteriorates rapidly. Moreover the pressure difference over the bed in the cooling zones is approximately at the fluidization point, thus making it impossible to produce at higher rates with these mixtures on this particular strand.

To realize this maximum production, optimal use of the strand and the fans has to be made. The model proved useful in determining these, as the consequences of the various alternatives could be calculated. In this way, without any significant change in construction, average daily records of 30 t/m² 24 h have been obtained. To increase production further, the fans have to be enlarged and the model shows that another 13% production gain can be obtained by replacing the fan wheels of the up-draught drying, the windbox recuperator, and the windbox exhaust fan by bigger ones, and by increasing the maximum attainable strand speed from 4·5 m/min to 5·25 m/min. Using these measures, the maximum attainable production (under favourable conditions of bed permeability) would be about 34 t/m² 24 h, i.e. very near to the limit imposed by the pellet quality and bed fluidization. By increasing the production that much, the cooling of the pellets and the situation around the second cooling zone needed further examination.

As the investment concerning these measures appeared to be relatively low compared to the calculated production gain, decisions were made in favour of these proposals.

When operating at about 30 t/m² 24 h, the pellets prove to be rather hot at the discharge end (*see* Table 4), thus causing transport problems by the burning of conveyor belts or alternatively wet-dust and condensation problems when using water cooling.

It is obvious that cooling will be improved by forcing a larger flow through the cooling zones. In the present system the amount of flow through the cooling-air fan is governed by the need of combustion air in the induration zone. The cooling-air fan can only deliver more air when part of the air leaving the first cooling zone is drawn from the system. As the model also showed that even in the extended situation the cooling-air fan still has ample capacity, the plan is adopted to control the bleed-off in the first cooling section in such a way that the cooling-air fan is continuously working at maximum capacity. To be able to carry out this plan, a chimney or a second fan parallel to the existing hood-recuperator fan must be built.

Calculations with the model, covering a wide field of alternatives, enabled the selection of the optimal solution for the blow-off of excess air and the control strategy to follow. The selected solution exists in the erection of a second fan connected to the hoods of both the first and second cooling zone. The air passing this fan is discharged from an extra chimney. The selected control strategy enables both optimal use of the heat of the cooling air as well as maximum use of the cooling-air fan capacity.

CONCLUSION

From the preceding sections it should be clear that the model developed here can be of good use in the designing of new plants, and also in finding the optimal way of operating a given strand for a given mixture.

However, as the accuracy obtained by this elaborate model is not required for all applications, the use of a simplified model, as developed by Eindhoven University of Technology, will be of advantage in certain cases.

To be able to make reliable statements about the grate-bar and pallet material temperatures and the gas temperatures in the process fans, the description should be completed by a model dealing with the heat exchange of the goods between the construction parts of the machine. This submodel is in its last stages of completion.

REFERENCES

1 E. N. LIGHTFOOT *et al.*: 'Transport phenomena', 1960, New York–London, Wiley
2 M. JACOB AND G. A. HAWKINS: 'Heat transfer', I, 1949 II, 1957, New York, Wiley
3 J. B. ROSEN: *J. Chem. Phys.*, 1952, **20**, 387
4 H. KRAMERS: 'Fysische transportverschijnselen', 1955 and 1961, 'Stroming, warmte- en stofoverdracht in het vaste en gefluidiseerde bed', 1956 Lectures of the Technological University Delft, The Netherlands
5 J. FREUND AND R. PINON: *Rev. Gén. Therm.* 1967, **63**, 225–63; *ibid.*, 1967, **64**, 343–52
6 B. SZCZENIOWSKI: *Rev. Gén. Therm.* 1967, **68**, 1 047–72
7 S. G. BRATCHIKOV: Translated from *Izvest. VUZ-Chern. Met.*, Jun., 1961, 157–63
8 H. P. BEER AND H. KRAINER: Report on Fried. Krupp Zenztral-institut für Forschung und Entwicklung, Essen, 1966, **24**, 25–47
9 R. C. REID AND T. K. SHERWOOD: 'The properties of gases and liquids', 1966, McGraw-Hill, New York
10 F. A. MISSENARD: *Rev. Gén. Therm.*, 1966, **50**, 125
11 J. CRANK: 'The mathematics of diffusion', 1956, Clarendon Press, Oxford
12 W. H. MCADAMS: 'Heat Transmission', 1954, McGraw-Hill, New York
13 P. A. YOUNG: 'Packed beds in metallurgical operations'. Symposium on Chem. Eng. in the Metallurgical Industries, Edinburgh, Sept. 25–26, 33–46, 1963
14 M. TIGERSCHIÖLD: *JISI*, 1954, **177**, 13–24
15 H. A. C. THYSSEN: 'Drogen', Lectures of the Eindhoven University of Technology, Eindhoven, The Netherlands
16 D. A. DE VRIES: *De Ingenieur*, 28, 1962
17 RICHARD W. HAMMING: 'Numerical methods for scientists and engineers', McGraw Hill Book Company, Inc., New York Kōgakusha Book Co Ltd., Tokyo
18 J. D. EDSTROM: *Jernkon. Ann.*, 1958, **142**, (7), 407–66
19 J. G. KNUDSEN AND D. L. KATZ: 'Fluid dynamics and heat transfer', 1958, New York, McGraw-Hill
20 J. SZEKELY AND R. G. CARR: *Trans. Met. Soc. AIME*, 1968, **242**, 918–21
21 O. A. HOUGEN *et al.*: 'CPP Charts', 1960, New York, Wiley

Optimization of a pellet-indurating machine by means of simplified mathematical models

J. H. Voskamp and H. Vissers

The aim of the study is optimization of production of a pellet-indurating machine. In order to obtain insight into theoretically optimal process operating conditions, a simple mathematical model is constructed. This makes it possible to recalculate the process performance quickly under various conditions. As an approach to process analysis it appears that linear programming with a linearized differential model represents a useful method. Some results are given and a few problems, other than production optimization, are mentioned as practical questions that can be studied in the same way. The main point of interest, however, is not the exact result in itself, but the fact that the method of linear programming provides the means to analyse the complex problem of the non-linear interactions between the many process variables systematically. The approach may be useful for other types of processes also.

In the last twenty years mathematical models for many types of processes have been developed, often very complex and requiring big and fast computers for simulation. Others, developed by a group of persons in a firm or institute are often used for design, management or control etc. The type of model developed is mainly determined by the computer facilities, the taste and preference of the model builder, and to a lesser degree by the task the model has to fulfil. Therefore, it is difficult to choose the right type of model. The paper tries to illustrate how superfluous work in the analysis of a pellet-indurating machine could be avoided by using models that are simplified but contain the relevant information about the various process variables. Also, models are chosen to show the possibilities of improving process performance and process control of the indurating machine.

It is explained that under many circumstances maximization of production of the indurating machine is a very lucrative affair, but the only way to do this at the moment is by means of a simple trial and error method based on the experience of the process engineer and the process operator.[1] However, as this is very cum- bersome and time consuming, it was decided to start a theoretical optimization study at the same time that process experience was obtained by Hoogovens* in practice. There are about twenty manipulatable variables at the disposal of the operator (later on to be called input variables), and each of these variables has an upper and a lower bound. Because of the number of input variables and the requirements imposed on a number of dependent process variables (to be called output variables) the optimization problem is complicated and a systematic theoretical approach is only possible if a mathematical process description is available by means of which one can calculate simply and rapidly at different process conditions and for different values of the set of input variables.

To accomplish these things, model building was started and it resulted in the construction of a model, to be realized on a digital computer, based on heat and material balances together with simple algebraic equations for fans, valves, and ducts. The basic equations can be found in Ref. 1. The computer results give pellet- and gas-temperature profiles that correspond within a few percent with temperatures calculated by means of the

The authors are with Eindhoven University of Technology, The Nether- lands (T.H.E.)

* Royal Dutch Blast Furnace and Steelworks Ltd

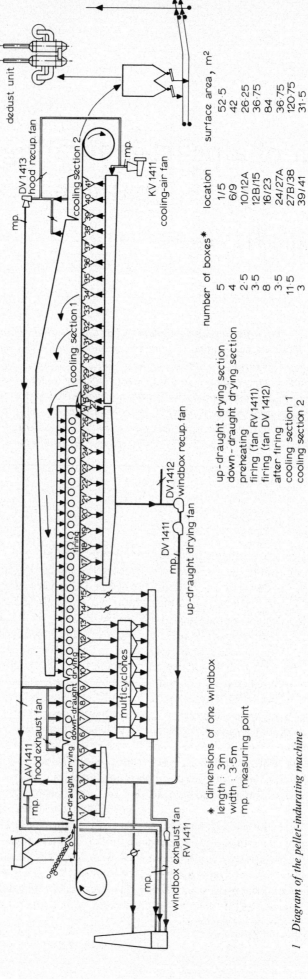

	number of boxes*	location	surface area , m²
up-draught drying section	5	1/5	52·5
down-draught drying section	4	6/9	42
preheating	2·5	10/12A	26·25
firing (fan RV 1411)	3·5	12B/15	36·75
firing (fan DV 1412)	8	16/23	84
after firing	3·5	24/27A	36·75
cooling section 1	11·5	27B/38	120·75
cooling section 2	3	39/41	31·5

* dimensions of one windbox
length : 3 m
width : 3·5 m
mp. measuring point

1   *Diagram of the pellet-indurating machine*

more complicated Hoogoven model that is based to a larger extent on the real physical phenomena.[2]

Since sufficient process-measurement data were not available at that time, a fit of our model had to be made with at least one Hoogoven computer run. In spite of the assumptions made resulting in a simple set of ordinary differential equations together with a set of algebraic equations, computer time was still in the range of 2–3 minutes on the ELX-8 computer of T.H.E.* The model appeared to be accurate enough to provide a very good insight of the relations between the input variables and the resulting output variables, and a number of calculations have been made to trace the effect of various input variables. While doing this work it became clear that for an optimization with a standard optimization technique,[3] with thousands of function evaluations (= computer runs with the model), a computing time of 2 minutes for each evaluation is too much.

The next section gives a description of how by means of some more assumptions, of which linearization is the most important, a linear model can be obtained for optimization purposes and for process analysis. With the linear model it is possible to use the linear-programming technique for the originally very complicated optimization problem. For linear-programming problems standard computer programs are available. These programs have a computation time of no more than a few minutes for solving the entire problem with tens of variables. Production optimization by means of choosing the best process conditions was the first purpose of the study. This, however, is not the only way the model and the linear-programming technique can be used. Design variables as well as process input variables can be incorporated in the linear model. This provides the possibility of studying design and control aspects of the plant at the same time. At the end of this paper some of the problems of this nature, to be studied in the near future, will be stated.

DESCRIPTION OF THE PLANT

A detailed description of the pelletizing plant is given in Ref. 4. Only details of interest for the further analysis will be given in the paper or in the Appendix. A sketch of the indurating machine is shown in Fig. 1. The wet green pellets are conveyed to the grate via a roller conveyor where the smallest pellets (<5 mm) are removed. The remaining pellets form a layer of about 0·3 m on top of the hearth layer of about 0·1 m consisting of fired pellets. The grate with the pellets moves through the various zones of the plant (with a speed of about 4 m/min) where the pellets are dried, fired and cooled to obtain the required physical properties.

In principle, two main gas flows can be distinguished, one flowing upwards through the second cooling zone, downwards through the down-draught drying zone, and with the help of fan RV 1 411 to the stack. The other stream flows upwards through the first cooling zone,

downwards through the firing zone and again upwards through the up-draught drying zone. This stream is divided in the first part of the firing zone where part of the gas is blown to the stack with the help of RV 1 411. A short description of the control system is of importance for the understanding of the list of input variables as discussed in more detail in the Appendix.

In order to prevent leakage of hot gases and damage of the walls of the indurating machine, requirements are imposed on the hood pressure profile. Each of the hood pressures p1–p5 is controlled, but the range of possible set-point values for each is very restricted. The pressures under the first drying zone pu1, under the second drying zone and first part of the firing zone pu2, and under the last part of the firing zone pu3 are each determined by their own control loop.

In order to obtain a constant height of 0·4 m of the total pellet layer the speed of the grate is directed by the green-pellet supply. This means that the production of fired pellets and grate speed are uniquely coupled with the fixed height of the hearth layer. Each burner has its own local temperature-control loop.

PROCESS OPTIMIZATION

An extensive analysis, in part presented in the Appendix, shows that in our model of the IJmuiden plant, 17 input variables are available to influence process conditions (= output variables of the model). All 17 input variables are, of course, constrained. The analysis also shows that 15 output variables are limited either by design or by technical requirements, e.g. a pellet temperature high enough at the end of the firing zone and a pellet temperature low enough at the end of the cooling zone. More requirements exist, however. Schematically the situation is illustrated in Fig. 2.

The problem of static-process optimization requires the values of the 17 input variables to be chosen such that

- (i) the values of the input variables u lie in between the bounds $a_2, a_1 \rightarrow b_2, b_1$
- (ii) the values of the resulting output variables x lie in between the bounds $b_1, b_2 \rightarrow a_1, a_2$
- (iii) the chosen optimization criterion is an extremum.

The optimization criterion may be the net profit of the plant. This criterion contains a great number of factors such as price of fired pellets, price of prepared iron ore, costs of electrical energy and gas etc. A somewhat more detailed analysis shows that the marginal yield of extra

---

* Eindhoven University of Technology

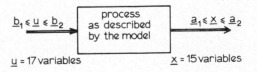

2   *Scheme of the process with input and output variables*

pellets is much higher than the marginal costs, and a useful and practical criterion is maximization of production. A mathematical expression proportional to the total production is:

$$Q = (0.4 - h)V$$

with h being the height of the hearth layer and V being the grate speed. Q now has a simple form and contains only a function of two input variables, i.e. grate speed and height of the hearth layer.

Linearization and linear programming

The tool available for optimization is a.o. the mathematical model as described in the beginning of the paper and programmed for the ELX-8 computer in an ALGOL program. The program integrates a set of ordinary non-linear partial differential equations together with the calculation of many non-linear algebraic equations. Mainly because of the numerical integration computation time is still of the order of a few minutes despite the many approximations and simplifications made. The conclusion is that this model is not directly suitable for a systematic optimization. But the model can be used as a starting point for the construction of a differential model, that is to say when only variations around certain working conditions are considered.

In the linear approximation these variations of the output variables are described as linear combinations of the variations of the input variables. The coefficients in the linear combinations mentioned are the partial derivatives of the output variables with respect to the input variables. These partial derivatives can be found by means of the more complex non-linear ALGOL model. Therefore it is necessary to make 18 runs: one for the working conditions and 17 runs each with a slight variation in one of the input variables. In this way a linearized differential model is obtained and with such a model linear programming can be considered as a suitable method for an optimization analysis. This also means that the criterion Q has to be linearized, but this can be done very simply. The linearized criterion equation is

$$q = (0.4 - h)v - V\Delta h. \qquad . \qquad . \qquad . \qquad (2)$$

The constraints on the output variables are

$$a_1 \leqslant x(u) \leqslant a_2 \qquad . \qquad . \qquad . \qquad (3)$$

or

$$a_1 \leqslant x_0 + \delta x \leqslant a_2$$

or

$$a_1 \leqslant x_0 + J\,\delta u \leqslant a_2 \quad \text{and thus}$$

$$J\,\delta u \leqslant a_2 - x_0$$

$$J\,\delta u \geqslant a_1 - x_0 \qquad . \qquad . \qquad . \qquad (4)$$

with

$$J = J_{15 \times 17} = \begin{bmatrix} \dfrac{\partial x_1}{\partial u_1} & \dfrac{\partial x_1}{\partial u_2} & \dfrac{\partial x_1}{\partial u_{17}} \\[2ex] \dfrac{\partial x_{15}}{\partial u_1} & & \dfrac{\partial x_{15}}{\partial u_{17}} \end{bmatrix} . \qquad . \qquad . \qquad (5)$$

J is the previously mentioned matrix of partial derivatives. With (4) the constraints on the output variables are reduced to constraints on combinations of input variables. The physical constraints on the input variables are:

$$b_1 \leqslant u \leqslant b_2 \qquad . \qquad . \qquad . \qquad . \qquad (6)$$

and can be written as

$$\delta u \leqslant b_2 - u_0$$

$$\delta u \geqslant b_1 - u_0 \qquad . \qquad . \qquad . \qquad . \qquad (7)$$

The optimization problem now is reformulated in a linear-programming problem:

Find the max. of $q(\delta u)$ such that

$$J\,\delta u \leqslant a_2 - x_0$$

$$J\,\delta u \geqslant a_1 - x_0 \qquad . \qquad . \qquad . \qquad . \qquad (4)$$

$$\delta u \leqslant b_2 - u_0$$

$$\delta u \geqslant b_1 - u_0 \qquad . \qquad . \qquad . \qquad . \qquad (7)$$

DISCUSSION OF THE LINEAR MODEL AND OF THE LINEAR-PROGRAMMING TECHNIQUE

At the T.H.E. a standard computer program for linear-programming problems is available. For using this program, called NATHALIE*, no detailed knowledge of the linear-programming technique is required. When matrix J is obtained and the constraints are known, a complete optimization is performed in about 1 minute. Now that the way to obtain results is known it is essential to verify whether these results are useful for the practical problem, i.e. insight in the possibilities of increasing production. A complete verification is difficult, but partly it is done as discussed below. Rather arbitrary working conditions (working point $\{u_0, x_0\}$) with rather arbitrary constraints are chosen. A description of the input and output variables with the values at the working point and with the values of the constraints are presented in the Appendix in Tables 1 and 2. In Table 3 of the Appendix the matrix J is given.

The constraints on the grate speed have been chosen very stringently, namely $-0.1 \leqslant v \leqslant 0.1$ m/min. This is done because it appeared from tentative preliminary calculation that the elements of matrix J strongly depend on the choice of the grate speed, and it is undesirable to obtain a solution that lies too far out of the range in which the linearization is valid. The optimal values of the input variables as obtained by NATHALIE are

---

* Developed by the Group Operations Research, Eindhoven University of Technology

summarized in Table 2 of the Appendix in the first column with the heading 'Results after optimization'. The second column represents the values of the output variables as calculated in the linear-programming technique. The third column represents the output variables as calculated by the non-linear ALGOL model.

The conclusion that can be drawn from these results is that the most valuable aspect is that the results provide rough but reliable information concerning the possibilities to increase production. At the same time insight is obtained as to which constraints are reached or nearly reached and which constraints are no bottle-necks at all. As an example of this information it is mentioned that Table 2 shows that it is permitted to reduce the height of the hearth layer of fired pellets considerably with only small variations of the pressure drops over the firing zone, compared to working point values. Doing this together with the allowed increase of grate speed of 0·1 m makes it possible to produce about 20% more than at the chosen starting point. Of course one ought to realize that this starting point was chosen arbitrarily (clearly at a low production) and only for computation purposes. The calculations here do not say anything about production optimization in practice. It is therefore necessary to choose a starting point much closer to present day operating conditions, as will be done in the next section. Even with a relatively low grate speed the constraint on the grate-bar temperature (GBT) is reached or nearly reached.

The effect of the linearization is to be judged by means of the comparison of the output variables according to the linearized model and according to the non-linear ALGOL model. Generally speaking the differences between the two 'output columns' are small compared to the step made from the starting operating conditions. Only the value for valve V3 is completely wrong, but the valve position V3 is determined by the difference of two nearly equal gas flows and it is easily understood that this may cause errors in V3.

A disadvantage of the method is the fact that also very small effects with only a slight improvement may prescribe considerable input variations. This happens with the last two burners. The increase of burner temperature causes a very slight increase in possible production. In practice these theoretically very small improvements do not make any sense. One draws the conclusion, therefore, that the method provides a framework for an efficient and fast systematic analysis and that within a small region the linear-programming method provides the best step towards more optimal conditions.

THE METHOD AS A TOOL FOR OVERALL OPTIMIZATION

In the previous section arbitrary and narrow constraints are imposed on the grate speed. It is important to investigate how far the described method can be used for an overall optimization over the whole range of operating conditions which may be realized in practice. At first sight the linear-programming method seems of little use because it appears, as stated previously, that the matrix J is very dependent on grate speed (and height of the hearth layer). A stepwise approach seems necessary. This, however, is not true. On basis of the real plant experience it is not difficult to find acceptable working point conditions as starting conditions $\{x_0, u_0\}$ for the calculations, close enough to the optimum so that the linear approximation is mostly valid.

The above is not all there is to say. Also for lower values of the grate speed with narrow constraints on this variable, the method may have its value. It is not always possible or desirable to operate at maximum production. Breakdown of one or more of the preceding rotating production drums or trouble with the belt conveyors may be such circumstances. Then the method can be used to trace the relations between the optimal settings of the remaining input variables for fixed low values of the grate speed. Of course then the criterion is no longer optimum production but something else. With another criterion (e.g. minimal height of the hearth layer) the optimal trajectories of the input variables are found as a function of the grate speed. These trajectories may be of great interest for understanding the performance of the plant. This is generally true because it is not the knowledge about the one optimal point that provides insight in the performance of the plant, but the knowledge about the way to reach the optimal conditions. To illustrate this in detail a few 'trajectory results' will be discussed here.

As an example the minimal available height of the hearth layer has been calculated for $V = 1·6, 3·1, 4·3$ and $4·6$ m/min. In Fig. 3 this height is shown as a function of V. In Fig. 4 the prescribed pressure drops over the firing zone are presented. Figure 3 shows a somewhat surprising aspect in that there exists a minimum for the minimal allowable h. This is to be explained as follows.

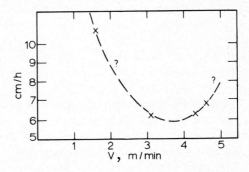

3   Optimal height of the hearth layer as a function of grate speed

Roughly the temperature of the pellets and of the grate bars depends on two parameters, the intensity of the heating-gas stream and the length of time that it is heated. The temperature will be higher with increasing values of both the parameters. With high production and thus a high grate speed the time of heating is shorter, the intensity greater. The total effect on allowable height h is the result of two opposite effects and obviously such that for a relatively high grate speed a smaller value for h is allowed than for very low grate speeds.

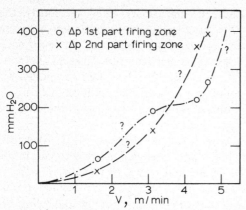

4   *Optimal pressure drops over the firing zone as a function of grate speed*

In Figure 4 it is striking that with a high grate speed the pressure distribution over the two sections of the firing zone is not uniform. Over the second part of the firing zone the pressure drop is nearly twice as high as over the first part. A further analysis shows that this is owing to the fact that with a non-uniform pressure distribution over the two sections better cooling is obtained. Better cooling is necessary in these situations ($V > 4$ m/min) because otherwise the constraint of cooling (COT) is exceeded. Other constraints that are reached with $V = 4.6$ m/min are the drying and firing requirements and the capacity constraints of the fans DV 1 413 and KV 1 411 and the bleed in, in front of the DV 1 412 (*see* Fig. 1).

When applying these results in practice one should of course be aware that the figures are obtained as preliminary results of models which are not completely verified until now with the help of measurements of the real plant. The verification is one of the subjects that is being studied now. Especially the incorporation of leakage between the various zones seems necessary to obtain a better resemblance of the model to the measurements. Also more exact data about the requirement constraints are necessary.

Therefore, the above is more an illustration of the type of information and insight in the relations between the process variables that is obtained. At this moment a few figures must be interpreted somewhat carefully mainly because of lack of real process measurements. However, it is the opinion of the authors that the approach leads to satisfactory results especially if more attention is paid to the problem of adaptation of the model to recently obtained process measurements.

OTHER PROBLEMS TO BE ANALYSED

In the preceding sections the linear-programming method and a cursory synopsis of the results are presented. Little has been said about the nature of the problems one is really interested in. Only the problem of maximization of production has been mentioned and it might suffice to say that every time a recalculation of the optimum according to variations in process circumstances, will be sufficient. This, however, is a little

short sighted. For a realization of the above, a comprehensive on-line or off-line computer system, which will require still several man years of research is necessary. In addition to that it is not proved yet that it will be successful as many problems in the field of accurate measuring of the process circumstances still have to be solved.

On short term, in a different way, advantage can be taken of the models and the linear-programming technique. Earlier it was shown that other questions can also be answered, as for instance the conditions for a minimal height of the hearth layer. In this section the emphasis is placed upon a number of subproblems i.e. problems that are of significance for practical process control or process design. The last aspect is incorporated because in our ALGOL model the manipulatable input variables play exactly the same role as the design variables such as length of zones, dimensions of valves, etc. Integrating in optimization studies, the design and the control aspects make a lot of sense because it may be possible that by a simple change in design a number of problems for the control engineer may be removed.

Therefore, we concluded that the problem is not of overall optimization, but of answering a number of questions concerning problems that can be overlooked by the process engineer or by the process designer without going into too many computations. There are problems such as to find the best way to cool maximally or which is more favourable, an equal or an unequal pressure drop over the two parts of the firing zone. In the latter case what is the right strategy, a large pressure drop over the first part or over the second part?

In the preceding section the weighted sum of two input variables (V, h) was chosen as criterion. Also a situation with only one input variable (h) as criterion was analysed, but in the linear-programming method every linear combination of input and output variables can be taken as criterion. Besides in NATHALIE the possibility exists of parametric programming ($=$constraint analysis) such, that the effect of the various constraints and the sensitivity of the criterion to the various input variables are investigated very easily. The question of how to cool optimally in our analysis is answered theoretically by the linear-programming method by formulating the criterion as:

$$q = \text{COT} = x_4 = \sum_{i=1}^{17} J_{4,i} u_i = \text{minimal}$$

with $V \geqslant 4.5$ m/min

$h \geqslant 0.08$ m

and with the other variables within the 'normal' constraints. In the same manner a number of problems can be analysed as well as the mutual relations between these problems. Further details on this will not be presented here. This paper is confined to the survey of a number of these questions which will be investigated in the near future:

(i)   the results obtained up to now show, until a certain value for V, decreasing height of the hearth layer with increasing grate speed. This has to be verified more thoroughly because the constraint on the grate-bar temperature has been chosen arbitrarily. At the same time the relation with the total bed height (green pellets + hearth layer) is of interest from the designer's point of view. For the design of future pellet plants it is of great importance to know the influence of this total height on the performance of the plant

(ii) the ratio of the pressure drop over the two parts of the firing zone seems of importance for the cooling. Since good cooling with high production is somewhat of a problem, a thorough investigation of all possible ways to improve cooling is desired. Also several small changes in design are possible but until now it is not quite clear which of these is best

(iii) an investigation of the effect of the type of iron ore is important for both future pellet-plant design as for plant performance and control

(iv) the effect of porosity and diameter variations on the problems mentioned and the influence on firing and cooling are of interest especially for control purposes

(v) a study of the right dimensions of the fans, valves, ducts and zones is going to be carried out in the near future. Not only for new plants but also for the plant at IJmuiden this may be of importance. It must be added, however, that the pellet-indurating machine at IJmuiden seemed to be well designed.

CONCLUSIONS

The work described in this paper shows that many questions concerning the performance and the design of a pellet-indurating machine can be answered, at least partly, by means of the mathematical models as developed in our study. More work still has to be done in the field of adapting the model to the process measurements and a more exact investigation of the real process constraints is desirable.

REFERENCES

1 J. H. VOSKAMP *et al.*: *Iron Steel*, 1972, **45**, 635–42
2 P. A. M. LEBELLE *et al.*: This vol.
3 D. J. WILDE AND C. S. BEIGHTER: 'Foundations of Optimization', Prentice-Hall, Inc., 1967
4 A. VAN LATENSTEIN AND J. M. VAN LANGEN: *Stahl Eisen*, 1972, **92**, (3), 101–6

APPENDIX

In Fig. A1 a more schematic diagram of the indurating machine is shown. The meaning of the various variables can be found from this diagram. In forming a list of input and output variables some difficulties were met. These are because the input variables as available to the operator do not exactly correspond with the input variables of the model. This is a difficulty of minor importance to the analysis because it does not change anything in the method. As an example of this type of discrepancies between real process and model inputs it is mentioned that in the real process it is not the pressure under the firing zone that is controlled but the average gas temperature of windboxes 20–22–24, called burning through temperature. Thus the set point of this gas temperature is available to the operator. In the mathematical model the pressure under the firing zone is taken as an input variable. This is done because of computational convenience. What should be done if an optimal setting is found is that with the optimal model input the value of the burning through temperature ought to be calculated and this value must be used as the set

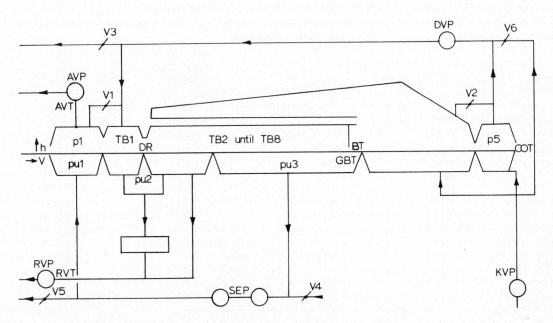

A1   Schematic diagram of the indurating machine with input and output variables

point of the control loop. The following model input variables have been used (*see* Fig. A1):

Hood pressure second cooling zone   p5
Hood pressure up-draught drying zone p1
Pressure under up-draught drying zone pu1
Pressure under down-draught drying
   zone and first part firing zone   pu2
Pressure under second part firing zone pu3
Position of valve between hoods
   drying zones   V1
Position of valve between hoods
   cooling zones   V2

Temperature burner second drying
   zone   TB1
Temperature burners firing zone   TB2 until TB8
Grate speed   V
Height hearth layer   h

Process requirements are transformed to a number of output variables while the value of each has to lie between an upper and a lower bound. For quality requirements this is most difficult because only little is known about the factors influencing quality. Until now in this work the quality requirement has been accounted for by requiring an average temperature over 1 300°C for

TABLE 1   Input and output variables summarized with their lower and upper bounds

Input variable Name	Upper bound	Lower bound	Output variable Name	Upper bound	Lower bound
p5	0 mm H_2O	−50 mm H_2O	DR	5%†	0%
p1	0 mm H_2O	−50 mm H_2O	BT	1 380°C	1 300°C
pu1	600 mm H_2O	0 mm H_2O	GBT	600°C	0°C
pu2	0 mm H_2O	−600 mm H_2O	COT	250°C	0°C
pu3	0 mm H_2O	−600 mm H_2O	RVT	195°C	0°C
V1*	100%	0%	AVT	150°C	60°C
V2*	100%	0%	DVP	400 kW	0 kW
TB1	350°C	280°C	AVP	300 kW	0 kW
TB2	1 050°C	950°C	KVP	2·2 MW	0 kW
TB3	1 380°C	950°C	SEP	4·8 MW	0 kW
TB4	1 380°C	950°C	RVP	2·4 MW	0 kW
TB5	1 380°C	950°C	V3*	100%	0%
TB6	1 380°C	950°C	V4*	100%	0%
TB7	1 380°C	950°C	V5*	100%	0%
TB8	1 380°C	950°C	V6*	100%	0%
V	5 m/min	0 m/min			
h	0·4 m	0·0 m			

* 0% = closed, 100% = opened
† % of the original water content

TABLE 2   Comparison of the working point within the constraints with the results after optimization

Working point		Results after optimization		
Input variable	Output variable	Input variable	Output variable linear-programming method	Output variable ALGOL model
−5 mm H_2O	5%	−50% mm H_2O	5%	5%
−15 mm H_2O	1 326°C	−50 mm H_2O	1 300 °C	1 293°C
150 mm H_2O	546°C	272 mm H_2O	600°C	588°C
−210 mm H_2O	223°C	−190 mm H_2O	225°C	223°C
−110 mm H_2O	153°C	−141 mm H_2O	159°C	161°C
10%	60°C	20%	60°C	65°C
10%	124 kW	0%	115 kW	112 kW
320°C	14 kW	292°C	51 kW	67 kW
1 050°C	565 kW	1 050°C	652 kW	658 kW
1 380°C	495 kW	1 380°C	879 kW	928 kW
1 380°C	536 kW	1 380°C	485 kW	474 kW
1 320°C	15%	1 380°C	100%	55%
1 300°C	80%	1 380°C	100%	90%
1 200°C	55%	1 380°C	0%	0%
1 050°C	40%	1 380°C	46%	42%
3·0 m/min		3·1 m/min		
0·12 m		0·062 m		

TABLE 3 Matrix J

In / Out	p5	p1	pu1	pu2	pu3	V1	V2	TB1	TB2	TB3	TB4	TB5	TB6	TB7	TB8	V	h
DR	0.00	0.124	−0.082	0.103	0.00	0.00	0.00	−0.088	0.00	0.00	0.00	0.00	0.00	0.00	0.00	27	−110
BT	0.00	0.005	−0.008	−0.286	−0.561	0.00	0.00	−0.012	0.086	0.156	0.259	0.088	0.028	0.003	0.00	−48	710
GBT	0.00	−0.070	0.086	−1.354	−2.880	0.00	0.00	0.308	0.171	0.020	−0.029	−0.024	−0.018	−0.011	−0.005	−322	−384
COT	0.459	−0.031	0.039	0.294	1.097	0.00	−0.625	0.117	0.049	0.053	0.054	0.022	0.015	0.011	0.007	120	−38·5
RVT	0.00	−0.195	0.208	−0.019	0.00	0.00	0.00	0.081	0.006	−0.001	−0.001	0.00	0.00	0.00	0.00	−20·1	250
AVT	0.00	−0.073	0.010	−0.016	0.00	−0.049	0.00	−0.027	0.00	0.00	0.00	0.00	0.00	0.00	0.00	−2·4	−28
DVP	−1.584	−0.008	0.00	−0.458	0.236	0.205	0.495	−0.028	0.063	0.033	0.038	0.026	0.012	0.008	0.005	63	−120
AVP	0.00	−0.921	0.037	−0.002	0.00	0.082	0.00	0.00	0.00	0.00	0.00	0.00	0.00	0.00	0.00	0.15	−3·0
KVP	−0.328	0.025	−0.028	−1.176	−3.045	0.00	1.190	−0.076	−0.179	−0.010	−0.002	−0.003	−0.006	−0.008	−0.007	216	−216
SEP	0.00	−0.109	2.062	−1.400	−5.881	0.00	0.00	0.246	0.127	−0.018	−0.074	−0.043	−0.032	−0.021	−0.010	−243	−181
RVP	0.00	−0.253	0.257	−3.581	0.00	0.00	0.00	−0.044	−0.063	−0.018	−0.010	0.00	0.00	0.00	0.00	−26·4	302
V3	−0.850	0.074	−0.119	2.070	0.838	0.460	1.770	0.464	0.223	0.118	0.136	0.058	0.039	0.027	0.015	295	−276
V4	0.00	−0.075	0.093	−1.062	−1.580	0.00	0.00	0.178	0.105	0.00	−0.029	−0.018	−0.014	−0.010	−0.004	−193	−155
V5	0.00	0.605	−0.629	−0.781	−2.520	0.00	0.00	0.138	0.072	0.010	−0.041	−0.024	−0.018	−0.012	−0.006	−138	−100
V6	0.420	−0.046	0.060	0.480	1.742	0.00	−0.790	0.068	0.108	0.096	0.106	0.044	0.032	0.024	0.016	152	−154

2 minutes for the lowest layer of green pellets. A similar type of qualification has to be done for other requirements. The following output variables are incorporated:

Percentage water of the original water content still present at the end of the drying zone	DR
Average pellet-temperature end firing zone	BT
Grate-bar temperature	GBT
Temperature hottest-pellets end cooling zone	COT
Temperature in front of the fan RV 1 411	RVT
Temperature in front of the fan AV 1 411	AVT
Consumed electrical energy DV 1 413	DVP
Consumed electrical energy AV 1 411	AVP
Consumed electrical energy cooling-air fan KV 1 411	KVP
Consumed electrical energy DV 1 411 and DV 1 412	SEP
Consumed electrical energy RV 1 411	RVP
Position of the various valves	V3 until V6

In Table 1 the various input and output variables are summarized with their lower and upper bounds. In Table 2 a rather arbitrary working point within the constraint is presented together with the results after optimization within narrow bounds for the grate speed. Table 3 shows the *J* matrix of partial derivatives for the working point of Table 2.

Mathematical model for the prediction of the residual lining thickness in the stack and bosh sections of a blast furnace

T. A. Bandak

In order to extend the campaign life of a modern blast furnace, it is necessary to ensure a substantial residual thickness of the lining in the stack and bosh regions. Besides choosing a lining material with satisfactory thermal/ chemical properties, the arrangement of coolers in the brickwork to give optimum cooling effectiveness is also desired. To this should also be added the economic factors connected with the cost of lining materials, coolers and water supply which could give optimum results at minimum cost. To achieve this objective, a three dimensional mathematical model was set up to predict the final residual thickness of the refractory for various blast-furnace operational conditions and designs. The results obtained indicate that refractory materials with high thermal conductivity and 'reaction-limit temperature' will give a superior residual thickness. When water coolers are grouped closer together, less expensive refractory with lower thermal conductivity and 'reaction-limit temperature' may be used with equal effectiveness.

During the last decade there has been a significant advance in blast-furnace design and performance. The trend in the industry has been towards building larger blast furnaces capable of producing a large amount of pig iron over a long period of time. This objective exerted great technological demands on both the design and operating practices of blast furnaces.

In a modern integrated steelplant the effect of blowing out a blast furnace for repairs and refractory reline disturbs the sequence of production. There are often no reserve or stand-by blast furnaces as is the case with LD vessels. The continuity of the steelworks' operation will therefore depend entirely on the ability of the blast furnace to maintain a continuous and uninterrupted supply of hot metal. Therefore, the main aim in any design is to secure a long and trouble-free campaign life by keeping the costly and disruptive practice of refractory repairs and reline to the minimum. A substantial contribution to the duration of a blast-furnace campaign life is made by stabilizing the wear in the refractory

lining at the stack and bosh sections of a blast furnace. As a consequence a need arose for a mathematical model which could simulate the wear process in the refractory brickwork. The model that has been set up predicts the lining residual thickness for a given design after the state of equilibrium has been reached. The model was then used to investigate the new lining proposals for the South Wales blast furnaces. Various types of refractory materials and cooler spacings were examined in order to determine the optimum residual thickness for the most economical condition.

The model was verified by measuring the actual residual thickness during the demolition of a furnace in April 1971. Good agreement was obtained indicating the viability of the model and the credibility of the various assumptions and empirical estimations used.

THEORETICAL BACKGROUND

The theory behind the process of refractory wear is based on the investigation carried out by König et al.[1] König and his associates examined the process of refractory

The author is with BSC, Strip Mills Division

wear in the bosh and lower stack of a blast furnace. They discovered that the wear process in the refractory is due mainly to chemical attack by the gases and ferrous slag inside the blast furnace. The corrosive gases carbon dioxide, carbon monoxide, oxygen, and water vapour, the deposition of zinc and carbon, and the reaction of wustite (FeO) and alkalis create the most destructive conditions in the brickwork. Excessive temperature variations in the brickwork induce thermal stresses which in turn create cracks and separation of the joints. Through the cracks and joints the chemically destructive gases penetrate still further in the brickwork and cause further disintegration and collapse. These chemical attacks are governed by a rate of chemical reaction which is, in turn, controlled by temperature. The rate of chemical reaction and hence the rate of wear, decreases as the temperature drops. A temperature, below which the chemical reaction cannot be sustained, will finally be reached. At this temperature, termed by König as the 'reaction-limit temperature', Tu, wear in the refractory will come to an end.

The 'reaction-limit temperature' depends on the nature of the refractory material as well as the environmental conditions. König determined that for carbon and graphite material the temperature below which no evidence of corrosion or deposition occurs is about 800°C. For firebrick and plumbago, the temperature is near to 400°C.

The wear towards a stable residual thickness proceeds gradually. As the lining thickness is decreased, the cooling effectiveness improves and the temperature at the inner refractory wall drops. When the surface temperature finally reaches the reaction-limit temperature, equilibrium conditions will reign and thus stable refractory residual thickness will be established.

METHOD OF APPROACH

The mathematical model for the prediction of refractory wear is based on the two main factors believed by König to be essential for minimum wear, as follows:

(i) the thermal conductivity of the refractory, i.e. a high thermal conductivity will help both in cooling and in countering the influence of thermal fluctuation and stresses

(ii) the reaction-limit temperature, i.e. the higher the temperature at which the rate of chemical reaction 'freezes', the further away from the steel shell will the final wear boundary lie.

The investigation of the refractory wear will therefore be reduced to the determination of the temperature distribution in the brickwork. Utilizing the particular reaction-limit temperature for the refractory material under consideration, the limit of wear can be established by replacing all the lining lying above the reaction-limit temperature with scab and running the model again. If this process is repeated until the reaction-limit isotherm ceases to move within the refractory, then the

equilibrium state is established and with it the final residual thickness in the brickwork.

PROBLEM DESCRIPTION

The model has been used to investigate Nos. 1 and 2 B.F. Llanwern. A cross-section of the lower stack and bosh for No. 1 blast furnace is shown in Fig. 1. The lower stack section lies above the lintel flange and the bosh below it. As shown by the figure, the cooling of the lining is effected by flat insert copper coolers arranged in a staggered configuration. No. 2 blast furnace is similar in form to No. 1, the only exception being in the number of coolers installed. Whereas for No. 1 blast furnace the vertical spacing of the coolers is 380 mm at the bosh, the spacing for No. 2 blast furnace is only 260 mm. Furthermore, beyond the third cooler row up the lower stack, the vertical cooler spacing for No. 2 blast furnace increases from 457 to 533 mm.

Figures 2 and 3 show the lining section in a three-dimensional view. This section shows a high-conductivity backing material sandwiched between an insulating ramming layer and the main firebrick layer. The linings of Nos. 1 and 2 blast furnaces at the bosh sections do not have this high-conductivity layer nor do they have an insulating ramming layer. However, for these blast furnaces, there is a thermal resistance between the brickwork and the steel shell owing to the air gap that exists from the imperfect contact between the bricks and the steel shell.

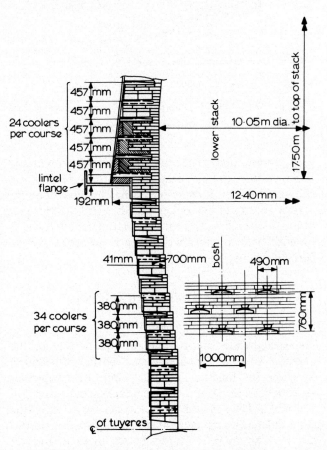

1 Blast furnace No. 1 Llanwern lower stack and bosh

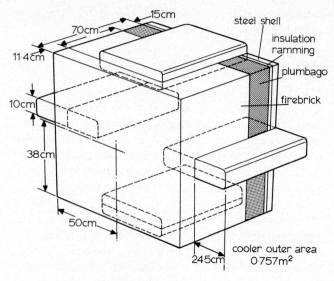

2 *Blast furnace No. 1 Llanwern cooler configuration in bosh section*

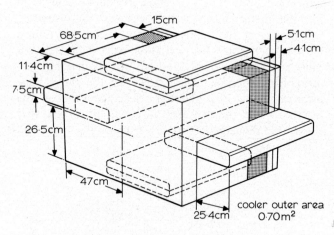

Thermal boundary conditions at the idealized section

3 *Blast furnace No. 2 Llanwern cooler configuration in bosh section*

In order to determine the temperature distribution in this section, a three-dimensional heat-transfer analysis will be necessary. A two-dimensional analysis along the vertical centres of the coolers will disregard the influence of the side-coolers and thus make it impossible to verify the effect of the number of coolers per row on the overall-cooling effectiveness.

MATHEMATICAL CONSIDERATIONS

Steady-state heat-transfer equation

The steady-state heat-conduction equation is of the Laplace form $\nabla^2 T = 0$. In this partial differential equation, the function T is the temperature which is dependent on the three independent variables of direction x, y, and z. The solution of the Laplace equation by the finite difference method results in an approximation to the 'true' solution.[4,5] Physically, the method involves the replacement of a continuous domain by a pattern of

discrete points, each point taken as a representative of a region within the domain. Therefore, instead of obtaining a continuous solution throughout the domain for the function T, only an approximation of T at these isolated points is obtained. By subdividing the continuous three-dimensional domain by a cubed lattice of spacing a, and denoting the typical point of the lattice by i, j, k, the second derivative at this point may then be approximated by the following finite difference relationships.

$$\frac{\partial^2 T}{\partial x^2} = \frac{1}{a^2}[T_{i,j,k-1} - 2T_{i,j,k} + T_{i,j,k+1}] - \frac{a^4}{12}\frac{\partial^4 T_{i,j,k}}{\partial x^4} \quad (1)$$

$$\frac{\partial^2 T}{\partial y^2} = \frac{1}{a^2}[T_{i,j-1,k} - 2T_{i,j,k} + T_{i,j+1,k}] - \frac{a^4}{12}\frac{\partial^4 T_{i,j,k}}{\partial y^4} \quad (2)$$

$$\frac{\partial^2 T}{\partial z^2} = \frac{1}{a^2}[T_{i-1,j,k} - 2T_{i,j,k} + T_{i+1,j,k}] - \frac{a^4}{12}\frac{\partial^4 T_{i,j,k}}{\partial z^4} \quad (3)$$

This is achieved by the Taylor's expansion of the neighbouring functions of $T(i, j, k)$.[5] Combining the above equations, the following expression will be obtained for the Laplace equation at the point i, j, k:

$$\nabla^2 T_{i,j,k} = \frac{1}{a^2}[T_{i,j,k-1} + T_{i,j,k+1} + T_{i,j-1,k} + T_{i,j+1,k}$$

$$+ T_{i-1,j,k} + T_{i+1,j,k} - 6T_{i,j,k}] - 0(a^4) \quad (4)$$

Neglecting terms with fourth and higher powers of a, an algebraic linear equation is generated at the internal point i, j, k for the condition of $\nabla^2 T = 0$

$$T(i, j, k) = \tfrac{1}{6}[T(i, j, k - 1) + T(i, j, k + 1)$$

$$+ T(i, j - 1, k) + T(i, j + 1, k)$$

$$+ T(i - 1, j, k) + T(i + 1, j, k)] \quad . \quad (5)$$

Therefore at each internal point in the lattice, the finite difference approximation to the differential equation provides an algebraic equation which connects the value of T to its neighbouring points.

Boundary conditions

Once the thermal boundary conditions are specified, then the Laplace equation can be uniquely determined. The two main boundary thermal conditions applicable to this problem are:

(i) heat flux at a surface in contact with a fluid medium
(ii) insulated thermal conditions at the surfaces of symmetry.

To apply the Laplace equation in its finite difference form to the boundary, some modification of equations (1) to (5) is in order. Rearranging equations (1) to (3) and including the thermal resistance factor R, the finite difference equation at the boundary becomes:

$$\left[\frac{T(i, j, k - 1) - T(i, j, k)}{R}\right]_x$$

$$+ \left[\frac{T(i, j, k + 1) - T(i, j, k)}{R}\right]_x$$

$$+ \left[\frac{T(i, j - 1, k) - T(i, j, k)}{R}\right]_y$$

$$+ \left[\frac{T(i, j + 1, k) - T(i, j, k)}{R}\right]_y$$

$$+ \left[\frac{T(i - 1, j, k) - T(i, j, k)}{R}\right]_z$$

$$+ \left[\frac{T(i + 1, j, k) - T(i, j, k)}{R}\right]_z = 0 \qquad . \qquad . \quad (6)$$

In matrix notation, i is the layer, j the row and k the column of the element.

Convective boundary condition

The convective boundary condition can be expressed by equation (6) if a fictitious nodal lattice is extended into the fluid medium. For the condition where the boundary occurs at the vertical x–y plane with the node $(i - 1, j, k)$ lying in the fictitious layer $(i - 1)$, the finite difference approximation will take the following form:

$$\frac{1}{2} A \left[\frac{T(i, j, k - 1) - Ts}{a/K}\right]_x$$

$$+ \frac{1}{2} A \left[\frac{T(i, j, k + 1) - Ts}{a/K}\right]_x$$

$$+ \frac{1}{2} A \left[\frac{T(i, j - 1, k) - Ts}{a/K}\right]_y$$

$$+ \frac{1}{2} A \left[\frac{T(i, j + 1, k) - Ts}{a/K}\right]_y$$

$$+ A \left[\frac{Tc - Ts}{1/h}\right]_2$$

$$+ A \left[\frac{T(i + 1, j, k) - Ts}{a/K}\right] = 0 \qquad . \qquad . \qquad . \quad (7)$$

where

$R = \dfrac{a}{KA}$ for heat transfer by conduction

$R = \dfrac{1}{hA}$ for heat transfer by convection

$K =$ conductivity coefficient
$h =$ surface coefficient of heat transfer
$A = a \times a$ for heat conduction between surface nodes, the area is $a \times a/2$
$Ts = T(i, j, k)$
$Tc = T(i - 1, j, k)$, temperature of fluid medium

Rearranging equation (7)

$$Ts = \left[T(i, j, k - 1) + T(i, j, k + 1) \right.$$

$$+ T(i, j - 1, k) + T(i, j + 1, k)$$

$$+ (2)T(i + 1, j, k)$$

$$\left. + 2\left(\frac{ha}{K}\right)Tc \right] \bigg/ \left[6 + 2\left(\frac{ha}{K}\right) \right] \qquad . \qquad . \quad (8)$$

Insulated surface

For an insulated surface, the temperature of the fictitious node outside the boundary is equal to its mirror image node across the boundary. Hence for the condition where the horizontal plane x, z is to be the insulated surface with the upper y node $(i, j - 1, k)$ lying in the fictitious region, then equation (6) becomes:

$$T(i, j, k) = [T(i, j, k - 1) + T(i, j, k + 1)$$

$$+ (2)T(i, j + 1, k) + T(i - 1, j, k)$$

$$+ T(i + 1, j, k)]/6 \qquad . \qquad . \quad (9)$$

Interfacial junction in a composite body

When considering composite bodies, the conductivity coefficient K will vary for the nodes lying in the immediate vicinity of the interfacial junction of the two media. For the case where the vertical x–y plane lies at the interface with layer $i - 1$ having a conductivity $K1$ and layer $i \pm 1$ a conductivity $K2$, equation (6) becomes after rearranging

$$T(i, j, k) = \left[T(i, j, k - 1) + T(i, j, k + 1) \right.$$

$$+ T(i, j - 1, k) + T(i, j + 1, k)$$

$$+ \left(\frac{K1}{KA}\right)T(i - 1, j, k)$$

$$\left. + \left(\frac{K2}{KA}\right)T(i + 1, j, k) \right] \bigg/ 6 \qquad . \qquad . \quad (10)$$

where KA is the average conductivity of $K1$ and $K2$.

Method of solution

The application of the finite difference approximation leads to a set of simultaneous linear algebraic equations equal in number to the reference internal points in the domain. For a very large number of equations, the most attractive procedure is the iteration method[4] using high-speed computing machines. The advantages incurred by using this method are the modest storage requirements in the digital computer and the simplicity of programming. If n internal points are chosen to represent a domain, then n simultaneous algebraic equations of the form shown by equation (5) will be considered. To systematically alter the current value of $T(i, j, k)$ by an improved value is relatively easy to program. During the calculation procedure, only n values

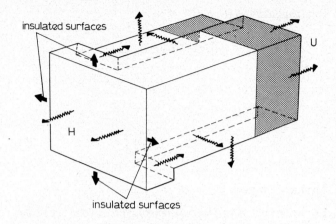

insulated surfaces

U

H

insulated surfaces

4   Blast furnace No. 2 bosh region

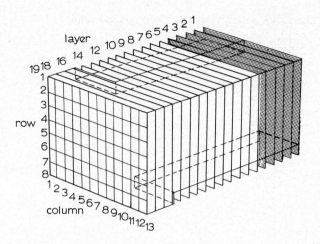

layer

row

column

Subdivisions of the body into nodal grid of layers, rows, and columns

5   Blast furnace No. 2 bosh region composite firebrick plumbago

need to be retained at any instant in the computer storage core.

FORMULATION OF THE PROBLEM

The problem to be treated should be reduced to the idealized form shown in Fig. 4. The figure indicates the following boundary conditions:

(i) the four surfaces of symmetry indicated by the solid arrows
(ii) the cooler bay area with forced convection plus the contact thermal resistance between the copper coolers and the brickwork
(iii) the outer wall with free convection and radiation, together with the thermal resistance of the steel shell and ramming layer or air gap U
(iv) the inner wall with forced convection and thermal radiation H.

With all the boundary conditions specified, the steady-state heat-conduction equations in finite difference form can then be applied to determine the temperature

distribution in the lining. In order to achieve this, the body must be first subdivided into a network of nodes and the finite difference equations assigned to each node.

Definition of node lattice

Figure 5 illustrates how the idealized section has been subdivided by a series of vertical layers placed in parallel between the inner and outer walls. Each of these two-dimensional layers are then subdivided in turn into a network of squares whose dimension is equal to the distance between the layers. The square mesh of two adjacent layers combine to form a cubed lattice with nodes lodged at its eight corners. Every one of the nodes is identified by the layer, i, row j and column k in which it lies. Ideally, the cubed lattice should perfectly fit the body. If this is not possible, then the discrepancy in the fit can be reduced by adopting a smaller cubed lattice.

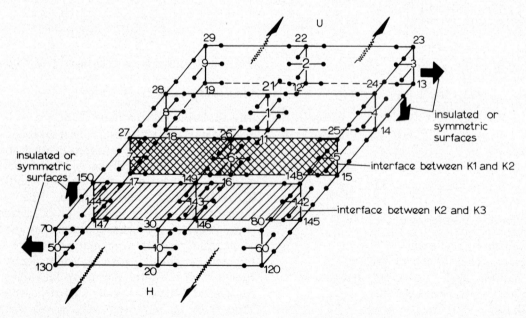

insulated or symmetric surfaces

insulated or symmetric surfaces

interface between K1 and K2

interface between K2 and K3

U

H

6   Nodal code for main body

Node characteristics

A catalogue of nodal configurations has been set up to cover all the possible conditions encountered in this problem. There are about 180 finite difference equations each representing a certain nodal characteristic. Figure 6 shows a catalogue of nodal configurations illustrating the conditions occurring in a composite medium made up of three different materials with insulated and convective boundary conditions. Each node has a code number which stands for a particular finite difference equation. For example, the internal node designated by the code number 1 stands for equation (5). Code 2 at the convective boundary *U* stands for equation (8) while Code 21 at the top of the insulated surface stands for equation (9). Equation (10) at the interfacial junction is designated by the code number 6.

Figure 7 illustrates the nodal code numbers which occur in the cooler's bay section. The top part of the drawing is an enlarged projection of the cooler bay section showing more clearly the nodal layouts. Again, as in the case of Fig. 6 the shaded area represents the interfacial boundary separating two different refractory materials. To obtain a realistic simulation of the curved cavity of the worn refractory, an accurate representation of the interface between the deposited scab and the refractory should be made. Figure 9a–c is a catalogue of

the nodal arrangement which represents the stepwise interface between the slag and the lining cavity.

NODE ARRANGEMENTS IN THE DOMAIN

With this comprehensive catalogue of nodal lattices, the problem then simply becomes the fitting of these code numbers to their appropriate nodes in the grid shown in Fig. 5. In this figure, for example, the nodal element situated in layer 19, row 1 and column 1, lies at the corner of the convective surface. Therefore, from Fig. 6 the code number 70 applies for this node. A layout of all the code numbers for columns 1, 2 and 19 for the domain of Fig. 5 is shown in Table 1. The computer program

TABLE 1 Layout of nodal code numbers

Layer 1

95	95	95	95	95	95	95	63	22	22	22	22	23
63	62	62	62	62	62	62	61	2	2	2	2	3
9	2	2	2	2	2	2	2	2	2	2	2	3
9	2	2	2	2	2	2	2	2	2	2	2	3
9	2	2	2	2	2	2	2	2	2	2	2	3
9	2	2	2	2	2	2	2	2	2	2	2	3
9	2	2	2	2	51	52	52	52	52	52	52	53
19	12	12	12	12	53	95	95	95	95	95	95	95

Layer 2

95	95	95	95	95	95	95	66	21	21	21	21	24
66	65	65	65	65	65	65	64	1	1	1	1	4
8	1	1	1	1	1	1	1	1	1	1	1	4
8	1	1	1	1	1	1	1	1	1	1	1	4
8	1	1	1	1	1	1	1	1	1	1	1	4
8	1	1	1	1	1	1	1	1	1	1	1	4
8	1	1	1	1	54	55	55	55	55	55	55	56
18	11	11	11	11	56	95	95	95	95	95	95	95

etc. for layers 3–18

Layer 19

70	30	30	30	30	30	30	30	30	30	30	30	80
50	10	10	10	10	10	10	10	10	10	10	10	60
50	10	10	10	10	10	10	10	10	10	10	10	60
50	10	10	10	10	10	10	10	10	10	10	10	60
50	10	10	10	10	10	10	10	10	10	10	10	60
50	10	10	10	10	10	10	10	10	10	10	10	60
50	10	10	10	10	10	10	10	10	10	10	10	60
130	20	20	20	20	20	20	20	20	20	20	20	120

reads the nodal code numbers layer by layer. The first layer represents the outer refractory wall and the last layer the inner wall of the blast furnace. The node situated in column 19, row 1 and column 1, and designated in matrix notation $T(19, 1, 1)$ will have, according to the matrix in Table 1, a code number of 70. All these code numbers have the same element address as the node they represent in the domain. The temperature distribution obtained from the program is presented in similar fashion, layer 1 being the temperature distribution at the outer refractory wall.

node code number
51–59 at lower cooler bay for CK2
61–69 at upper cooler bay for CK2
71–79 at lower cooler bay for CK3
81–89 at upper cooler bay for CK3
95–96 for a boundary temperature

7 Nodal code layout for the cooler bay

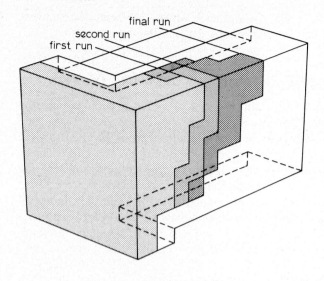

8 Progress of wear in the lining up to the equilibrium state

After obtaining the first temperature distribution, the wear boundary is established by tracing out the reaction-limit isotherm layer by layer. All the nodes above the reaction-limit isotherm are then assumed to be in the newly deposited slag medium. Figure 8 shows how the slag becomes embedded in the lining after the first and subsequent runs. The upper part of Fig. 9 depicts the condition when the slag reaches the innermost part of the lining. This is the layer where the reaction-limit temperature starts to appear as the layers are scanned from the outer wall. From this layer the slag/refractory interface is then established at every one of the subsequent layers until finally the layer is reached where the slag completely covers the whole area. This usually occurs near to or at the cooler tip as shown by the lower part of Fig. 9.

Taking the new lining condition with its embedded slag, a second temperature distribution is obtained from which a new wear boundary is traced out. This process is repeated until the wear boundary ceases to advance in the brickwork with further runs. At this condition, indicated in Fig. 8 by the 'final run', the state of equilibrium is reached.

HEAT-TRANSFER COEFFICIENTS AND ASSUMPTIONS

The boundary conditions due to convection and radiation can be accurately established if reliable heat coefficients are available. In practice it is very hard to obtain heat-transfer coefficients with a great degree of accuracy. In most cases, the values of the heat-transfer coefficients are obtained either empirically or from relevant references.

Heat-transfer coefficient at the outer wall

In the case of the high vertical outer wall, the heat-transfer coefficient due to free convection by the surrounding

air and radiation from the steel plate can be readily determined from the following equations :[2]

$$h_c = 1.25 \, \Delta T^{\frac{1}{3}} \qquad . \qquad . \qquad . \qquad . \qquad (11)$$

$$h_r = 0.983 \, E_f C_f \left[\left(\frac{T_1}{100} \right)^4 - \left(\frac{T_2}{100} \right)^4 \right] \Big/ (T_1 - T_2) \quad (12)$$

$$h = h_c + h_r \qquad . \qquad . \qquad . \qquad . \qquad . \qquad (13)$$

where

h_c = free convection coefficient	W/m² K
h_r = radiation coefficient	W/m² K
h = unit thermal-surface conductance	W/m² K
T_1 = surface-wall temperature	K
T_2 = temperature of the surrounding air	K
$\Delta T = T_1 - T_2$	
E_f = emissivity factor for steel	0·8
C_f = configuration factor	1·0

By taking the thermal resistance of the steel shell and ramming into consideration, the total heat-transfer coefficient is then determined according to the following equation

$$U = \frac{1}{1/h + (x/K)_{\text{steel}} + (x/K)_{\text{ramming}}} \qquad . \qquad . \qquad (14)$$

where x is the thickness of steel or ramming in metres and K is their respective conductivity in W/mK. The temperature at the outer surface of the steel shell has been measured over a period of time and an average value of 66°C was recorded. The temperature of the surrounding air is assumed to be 21°C.

Heat-transfer coefficient at the inner wall

The heat-transfer coefficient at the inner wall of the blast furnace is very difficult to obtain. It depends mainly on the blast furnace operational conditions and as a result its value is exposed to great variation. The influence of the thermal coefficient variation on the lining residual thickness should not be lightly brushed aside. Under the conditions specified by König,[1] it has been shown that a reduction of the convection coefficient by half will more than double the lining residual thickness. Even with a most favourable reaction-limit temperature and thermal conductivity, extremely low residual thickness could be obtained if the convection coefficient is high enough.

König quotes values for the inner-wall convection coefficient varying in range from 117–470 W/m² K. A value of 235 W/m² K was chosen because König's results show that with regard to the residual thickness, this value gave a residual thickness halfway between the two extremes. It should be emphasized at this stage that despite the unreliability of this figure, it is more realistic than assuming an isothermal boundary condition. If a temperature profile at the inner wall is imposed,

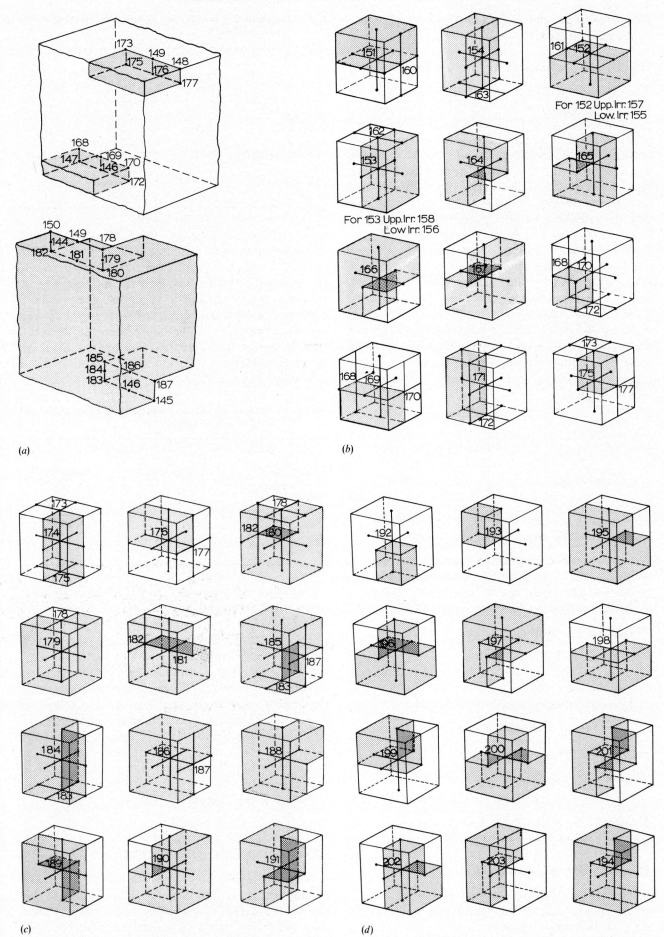

9   Nodal code layout at irregular slag refractory interface

then the influence of the refractory thermal conductivity on the residual thickness could not be ascertained.

Heat-transfer coefficient at the water coolers

The value of the heat-transfer coefficient between the water in the copper coolers and the refractory surface could only be obtained empirically. Great difficulties will be encountered if an attempt is made to evaluate the heat-transfer coefficient from the water velocity distribution inside the winding conduit of the cooler. The water velocity inside the cooler ducts varies greatly as it travels from the inlet to the outlet ports. This, together with the existence of eddy currents and air locks, will further complicate this empirical procedure.

An opportunity arose last year during the reline of No. 2 blast furnace to install thermocouples in the refractory around the water coolers. With this temperature distribution, a balance of the heat flowing into the cooler and the heat flowing out of the cooler can be made by measuring the water flow rate and the inlet and outlet temperatures. The heat flowing out of the cooler can then be determined by the following equation:

$$Q_0 = C_p \times \rho \times m \times dT \text{ watts} \qquad . \qquad . \qquad . \quad (15)$$

where

C_p = specific heat of water 4.187×10^3 J/kg K

ρ = water density   0.998 kg/l

m = water flow rate   Bosh = 26.31/min
    L. stack = 54.51/min

dT = difference between inlet   Bosh = 3.9°C
and outlet temperatures   L. stack = 2.8°C

With the measured temperature distribution around the cooler bay, the overall heat-transfer coefficient can then be determined by equating the heat inflow to the heat outflow according to the following equation:

Heat inflow = Heat outflow

$$Uc \, \Delta A(T_m - T_{arg}) = Q_0 \qquad . \qquad . \qquad . \quad (16)$$

Where

T_m = mean average temperature around cooler bay

T_{avg} = average water inlet and outlet temperature

ΔA = surface area of cooler

and

Uc = cooler overall heat-transfer coefficient, W/m^2 K

A value for Uc of about 170 W/m^2 K was obtained for both the bosh and lower stack coolers.

Thermal conditions and assumptions

Table 2 lists the thermal conductivities of the material under investigation. Where applicable, a list of the material cost and the reaction-limit temperature is included. Owing to the large temperature difference between the inner and outer refractory wall, a variation

TABLE 2 Thermal properties, cost of materials and reaction-limit temperature, Tu

	Price in 1971, £/ft^3	Thermal conductivity, Ws/mK	Tu, °C
Graphite	16–18	93.00	800
Semi-graphite	11.00	32.56	800
Plumbago	14.00	28.81	400
Firebrick (Nettle D)	1.20	1.44	400
Slag	—	11.63	—
Ramming	—	0.23	—
Mild steel	—	45.80	—

in the refractory conductivity value will occur. Table 3 shows the variation in the thermal conductivity for both the semi-graphite and the graphite with temperature. In the model the thermal conductivity was assumed invariant and was taken at a certain mean temperature. For the homogeneous semi-graphite lining, a suitable average temperature was found to lie around the 400°C level. In the case of the graphite backing layer which lies in cooler regions, the thermal conductivity was selected at a temperature of 200°C.

TABLE 3 Variation of thermal conductivity of semi-graphite and graphite with temperature

	Conductivity, W/mK	
Temperature, °C	Semi-graphite	Graphite
200	34.89	93.04
400	32.56	78.88
600	29.00	67.88
800	26.68	58.00
1 000	24.36	51.04

In practice, certain high-conductivity refractory materials are anisotropic in nature, i.e. certain directions are more favourable for the conduction of heat than others. For the case of plumbago for instance, the thermal conductivity across the grain is a third of that along the grain. For the sake of simplification, all the materials were assumed to have an isotropic conducting medium. Furthermore, perfect thermal contact is assumed to occur between all the bricks. In order to simplify the geometrical shape of the wall, the cylindrical curvature of the outer wall and its 5° inclination from the vertical was disregarded. The assumption of a flat and straight wall can safely be made if the wall thickness is small compared to the blast-furnace diameter.

DESCRIPTION OF THE PROGRAM

A flow chart of the program is shown in Fig. 10. The program can be divided into three main parts. The first part reads the input and prepares the data for computation. The second part assigns the finite difference equations to the nodes and determines the temperature distribution. Finally, the program estimates the heat

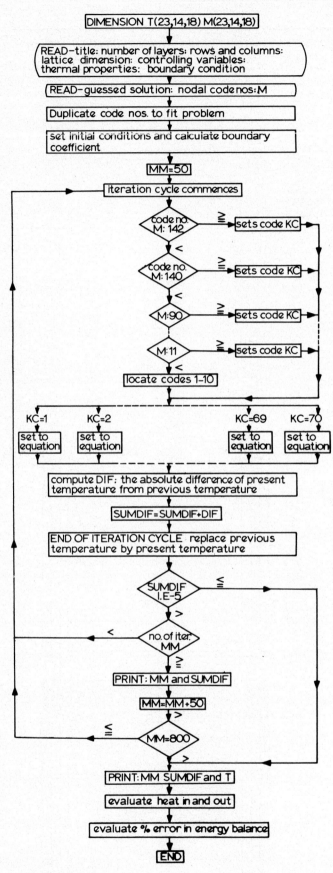

10   Flow-chart diagram

inflow and outflow in the lining and computes the discrepancy in the energy balance.

In the solution of the finite difference equations by the iteration method, some form of criterion is required to terminate the iteration cycle. This has been done by estimating the amount of change in temperature between two successive iterations, adding the differences for the whole grid and then comparing this value to an arbitrary small number. However, the criterion that judges the credibility of the solution is not the smallness of this number but rather the energy balance obtained. If the heat inflow and outflow are approximately equal, then convergence to the solution can be assumed. An intelligent guess of the iteration limiting number will be of advantage, however, in avoiding computer time wastage by over or under iterating.

RESULTS

In all of the calculations, the percentage error in energy balance was not allowed to exceed 5%. A poor energy balance is indicative of erroneous input data, or unrealistic selection of nodal codes.

For ease of representation, the temperature distribution has been plotted on a two-dimensional plane as shown in Fig. 11. Here the isothermal lines before wear commences and the final wear limit at the equilibrium state are depicted for the lower stack of No. 2 blast furnace with a composite firebrick–plumbago lining. Figure 12 shows the condition for the same stack but with a homogeneous firebrick lining. Figure 13 is the condition at the first three cooler rows above the lintel flange of No. 2 blast furnace. These three figures were then combined in the form shown in Fig. 14 in order to give an illustrative comparison of their residual thicknesses. The same representation is made for the bosh section of Nos. 2 and 1 blast furnaces in Figs. 15 and 16. At this section, the existing homogeneous construction of nettle D firebrick was compared with the following three schemes:

(i) a homogeneous lining of semi-graphite
(ii) a composite construction of firebrick backed by a 15 cm layer of high-conductivity graphite refractory
(iii) same as above but with a less expensive plumbago backing material.

The residual thicknesses in the cases investigated have also been tabulated in Table 4.

In considering the results obtained from this model, the following reservations should be borne in mind:

(i) in practice, slag does not completely fill up the cavity in the worn lining nor does it stay stationary in place as has been assumed
(ii) the temperature in the bosh is higher than 1 200°C.

These considerations, together with the inexact method of selecting the heat-transfer coefficients will combine to give a residual thickness which will be in dire need of verification. In April 1971, No. 2 blast furnace Llanwern was blown out after a campaign of $2\frac{1}{2}$ M tons in three years. With the aid of thermocouples positioned at various intervals in the wall thickness of the bosh section, the wear of the refractory was followed by noting

TABLE 4   Residual thickness at the equilibrium state

	Refractory composition	Vertical centre to centre cooler, cm	Horizontal centre to centre cooler, cm	Thickness of section before wear, cm	Residual thickness (from ramming), cm
BF No. 1 Bosh	Firebrick	76	100	70	17
	Semi-graphite	76	100	70	60
	Firebrick plumbago	76	100	70	25
	Firebrick graphite	76	100	70	25
BF No. 2 Bosh	Firebrick	53	94	68·5	31
	Semi-graphite	53	94	68·5	62·7
	Firebrick plumbago	53	94	68·5	30·3
	Firebrick graphite	53	84	68·5	30·3
BF No. 2 L Stack	Firebrick	106·6	152·4	101·6	nil
	Firebrick plumbago	91·4	152·4	101·6	36·5
	Firebrick plumbago	106·6	152·4	101·6	36·5

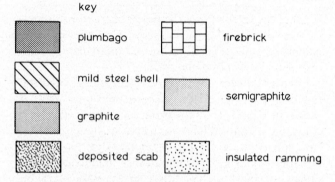

key

plumbago   firebrick

mild steel shell

graphite   semigraphite

deposited scab   insulated ramming

Key to Figs. 11–16

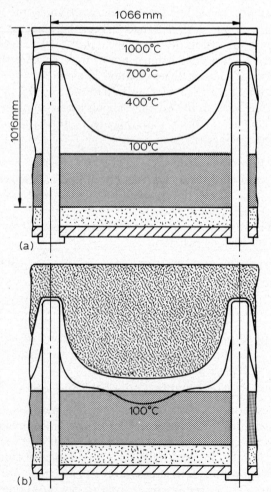

(a)

(b)

a Initial temperature distribution; *b* final wear line

11   Blast furnace No. 2 Llanwern lower stack firebrick–plumbago

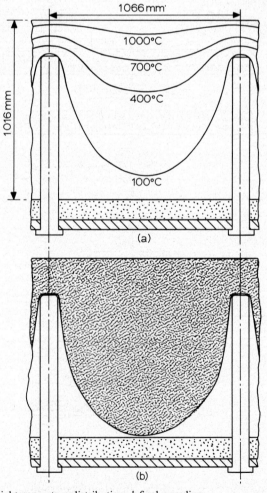

(a)

(b)

a Initial temperature distribution; *b* final wear line

12   Blast furnace No. 2 Llanwern lower stack homogeneous firebrick

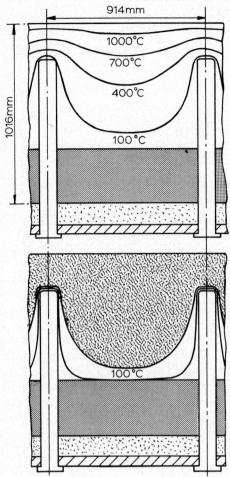

a Initial temperature distribution; *b* final wear line

13   Blast furnace No. 2 Llanwern condition at the first three cooler rows above the lintel flange

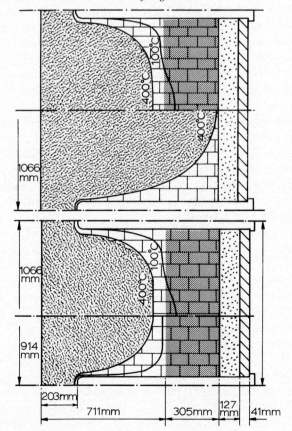

14   Blast furnace No. 2 lower stack Llanwern

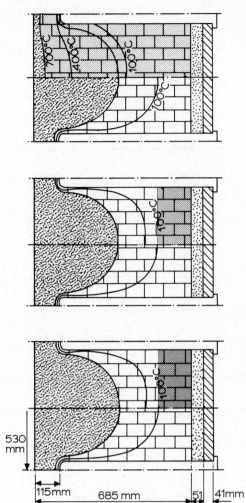

15   Blast furnace No. 2 bosh section Llanwern comparison with homogeneous firebrick lining

the very high rise in temperature followed by the failure of the thermocouple.[6] The final wear profile in the lining was determined at the end of the campaign by measuring the residual thickness during demolition.[6] Figure 17 shows the progress of the wear with time for the bosh lining of the blast furnace compared to the predicted residual thickness. The actual residual thickness should approach the predicted value asymptotically with time. If the actual thickness crosses the predicted line, then some of the thermal coefficients chosen may not represent the realities of the problem and the results obtained from the model are suspect. In this case, the actual residual thickness does seem to approach the predicted value asymptotically. The dashed line is an extrapolation of the curve showing the trend in wear if the blast furnace was allowed to run longer than three years.

Figure 18 shows the actual minimum wear compared to the wear line predicted by the model. This figure shows the variations between the actual and predicted curves delineating the wear boundary. However, what is of interest is the minimum residual thickness which occurs halfway between the coolers. It is this residual thickness that has been tabulated in Table 4. The close agreement

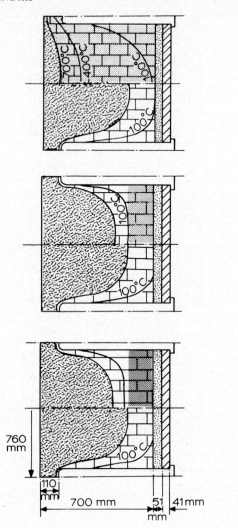

16   *Blast furnace No. 1 bosh section Llanwern comparison with homogeneous firebrick lining*

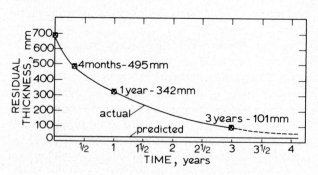

17   *Progress of wear in the bosh section of blast furnace No. 2 Llanwern*

between the predicted and the expected results indicates the validity of the assumptions made and the credibility of the selected heat-transfer coefficients.

DISCUSSION OF RESULTS AND CONCLUSION

The top part of Fig. 14 illustrates the extreme deterioration which occurs in a lining with poor thermal properties and cooling effectiveness. When a 30 cm thick plumbago backing was used, a substantial residual thickness was achieved. It could be stated that for such

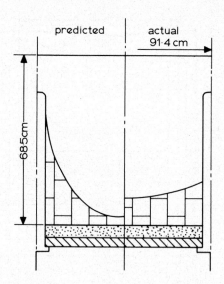

18   *Actual and predicted wear profile in blast furnace bosh section No. 2 Llanwern*

a wide spacing of coolers, the residual thickness will invariably stabilize just ahead of the high-conductivity backing material. The lower part of the figure shows the effect of both the wear and isothermal lines on the lining for a cooler transverse pitch reduced from 1 066 mm to 914 mm. In both cases, the wear is exactly the same. The only difference lies in the somewhat hotter brickwork of the higher cooler pitch as seen by the 100°C isotherm shift towards the outer wall.

Figure 15 compares the refractory wear of three different lining schemes with the homogeneous firebrick lining. It can be observed from the top illustration that the homogeneous semi-graphite with its high reaction-limit temperature and thermal conductivity gives the least wear. For the composite linings of firebrick–graphite and firebrick–plumbago, a 15-cm thickness of the higher-conductivity material will have the same wear as the homogeneous firebrick lining. Therefore, for this cooler configuration, the much cheaper homogeneous firebrick lining will suffice. This indicates that despite the very low reaction-limit temperature and thermal conductivity of the firebrick, intensive cooling will greatly help in providing a safe lining residual thickness. If the residual thickness is to be further improved, then a graphite and plumbago backing thicker than 15 cm should be employed.

Figure 16 illustrates the effect on the lining when the coolers are spaced further apart. In this condition, the results show that for a composite lining of firebrick–graphite or firebrick–plumbago, a 15 cm thick high-conductivity backing improved the residual thickness by 47%. However, as both graphite and plumbago give the same residual thickness, it is recommended that the cheaper plumbago material should be used.

It can be observed from Table 4 that when a cooler's transverse pitch is reduced by 43%, from 76 to 53 cm and the longitudinal pitch is reduced by 6%, from 50 to 47 cm, then the residual thickness of the homogeneous firebrick lining increases by 82%, from 17 to 31 cm, while that of the homogeneous semi-graphite will only be improved by 6%. Furthermore, at this reduced cooler pitch, the homogeneous firebrick lining will have a residual thickness 24% more than the composite lining of the higher cooler pitch. A comparative cost analysis between the extra water coolers required at the low pitch condition and the composite lining required at the higher pitch condition will determine the most economical design to be adopted.

From the above discussion, two main points arise. First, if an advantage is to be made of the very favourable performance obtained from the homogeneous semi-graphite, then either the lining wall thickness should be reduced from the current wall width of 70 cm, or the number of coolers in the lining should be significantly cut down. Thus a saving in both brickwork construction and water coolers can be made. Second, if the plumbago or graphite backing at the lower cooler pitch is to be made effective, then their thickness should be extended beyond the 15 cm limit.

Finally, the accuracy of this model in predicting the lining residual thickness depends to a large degree on the heat transfer coefficients chosen. This mathematical model stands or falls on the judicious selection or determination of the thermal coefficients.

ACKNOWLEDGMENTS

The author wishes to acknowledge the contribution made by Dr John Evans in the supply of relevant information and data. The assistance of the blast-furnace management and staff at Llanwern is also gratefully acknowledged.

REFERENCES

1 G. KÖNIG et al.: *Stahl Eisen*, 1971, **91**,(2), 63–9
2 J. K. SALISBURY (ed.): 'Kent's mechanical engineers' handbook', 12th ed., 3–48, John Wiley & Sons Inc.
3 H. S. CARSLAW AND J. C. JAEGER: 'Conduction of heat in solids', 2nd ed., 1959, London, OUP
4 S. H. CRANDALL: 'Engineering analysis', 1956, New York, McGraw Hill
5 G. D. SMITH: 'Numerical solution of partial differential equations', 1965, London, OUP
6 A. M. WEIGHTMAN: 'Inspection of the blown out lining of No. 2 blast furnace, Llanwern, third campaign', 1971, Report No. 366/D, 3, BSC, Basic Research, Pye Corner

Numerical simulation of the blast-furnace process

G. A. Flierman and H. Oderkerk

A description is given of a dynamic blast-furnace model developed at Hoogovens. The model has been used to survey the possibilities for replacement of a substantial part of the metallurgical coke by heavy fuel oil. It appears that oil injection affects the pig-iron temperature via the flame temperature. Compensation of this effect either by an increased blast temperature or by oxygen enrichment of the blast is discussed. Transient behaviour of the blast furnace following a sudden variation of an input factor has been studied. Coke equivalents of the variations applied have been calculated. Some examples are given of a simulation of blast-furnace incidents and their consequences.

LIST OF SYMBOLS

aSi	silicon activity in liquid iron
$aSiO_2$	silica activity in slag
C, Fe, etc.	mean quantities of solid or liquid material in a cell, kmol
CO, H_2O, etc.	mean quantities of gaseous compounds passing the cell, kmol/min
E_i	activation energy for reaction i, kcal/kmol
F	surface-area factor in silica reduction
f	fraction of a fusible compound that is in the liquid state
g_i	rate constant for reaction i
GAS	mean quantity of gas passing through a cell, kmol/min
h	height above tuyere plane, m
$H_2O(l)$	liquid water in coke, kmol
K_i	equilibrium constant for reaction i
pCO, pH_2, etc.	partial pressures of gaseous compounds, atm
p^*H_2O	saturation pressure of water vapour, atm
$PTOP$	top pressure, atm
R	gas constant, 1·985 kcal/kmol, °C
r	furnace radius, m
r'	radius of deadman, m
t	time step, min
TC	mean coke temperature, K
TG	mean gas temperature, K
TO	mean ore temperature, K
u	relative velocity of liquids with respect to the coke
V_i	rate of reaction i, kmol per cell per min
x	mean degree of oxidation of an ore, atoms O/atom Fe

The blast-furnace process is a continuous counter-current process involving heat and mass transfer. It is also one of the most complicated processes in metallurgy.

First, the number of tasks that have to be performed inside a single reaction vessel is unusually large. Second, the raw materials from which the iron is to be produced contain many impurities which, owing to the high temperatures prevailing in the furnace, often take part in the chemical reactions. Moreover, the composition of the raw materials is not always the same. Third, variations in the gas-distribution pattern cannot be fully prevented even if a movable throat armour is used to improve the burden distribution. Finally, mechanical failures may cause major process disturbances. Consequently, the process is seldom, if ever, in a steady state, which is illustrated by random fluctuations in pig-iron analysis.

The authors are with Hoogovens BV, IJmuiden

The inherent imperfections of the process depicted above can be very disturbing when it is attempted to derive relationships between variables from blast-furnace data. Full-scale trials in which one of the input parameters undergoes a sufficiently large variation to allow calculation of the desired relationship with reasonable accuracy are quite costly, and usually interfere with the interests of the production department.

A suitable mathematical model of the process may be of considerable help in determining whether an industrial experiment is justified. For mathematical models based on reaction kinetics, see Refs. 1–8. However, only the last two models are dynamic in character, i.e., they permit the calculation of transient states as well as the final steady state. Results of the last model are yet to be published.[8]

Fielden et al.[7] have calculated the responses in silicon content and pig-iron temperature as well as the changes in the top gas when blast temperature, coke rate, or oil consumption were varied stepwise. Flierman et al.[2] have calculated the coke consumption as a function of rating, reducibility, coke reactivity, degree of prereduction, hot-blast temperature, and fuel-oil injection rate. The use of the model, however, was limited to the calculation of steady states. Besides, it permitted the use of only one ore at a time. The dynamic model to be presented in this paper suffers from neither of these shortcomings.

OUTLINE OF CALCULATION METHOD

Description of the process in terms suitable for a mathematical model

The blast furnace is described as a reaction vessel with even distribution of both gaseous and solid/liquid flow over the furnace cross-section. The deadman is considered to be impermeable for both liquids and gases. At any time, the actual state of a blast-furnace process can be defined by

(i) the input variables, i.e. the blast conditions, and the amount and compositions of the materials charged at the top

(ii) the characteristics of the furnace itself, such as dimensions and specific heat losses

(iii) the temperatures and concentrations in the furnace as a function of height.

If the variables mentioned above under (i) and (ii) are kept at constant values, the process will in due time arrive at a stationary state, that is to say, the temperatures and concentrations in the furnace at a given level will no longer vary with time. The time whereafter the stationary state is reached will depend upon the magnitude of the difference between the original temperatures and concentrations and those of the steady state to be attained. This state itself obviously depends only on the input variables and the furnace characteristics.

For the purpose of a numerical calculation, the contents of the furnace above the tuyere level (with the exclusion of the deadman) are divided into a large number of layers having the following properties:

(i) all characteristics, such as temperatures and quantities of the various materials, are uniformly distributed within a layer

(ii) each individual layer retains its identity throughout its descent from the stockline to the tuyere level.

A layer being a very small amount of material (i.e. the materials needed to produce 10 kilograms of 'standard' pig iron) it is convenient to combine a number of layers in a cell. The properties of a cell are calculated from those of the individual layers. Once a cell has been formed all properties are again evenly distributed within that cell. The combination of layers to cells is variable. The number of layers in a cell is chosen such that the expected change in gas temperature is about 30°C and that the increment in oxygen content of the gas does not exceed 0·01 g-atom oxygen per mole of gas. The result of this procedure is that the working volume of the furnace above the tuyere plane is divided into about 70 cells, while nevertheless only small quantities of material are being considered where the gradients are large. This is illustrated in Fig. 1.

At the start of the calculation the temperatures and quantities in every cell must be known. A standard set of data representing a reference period of the furnace under consideration is used for this purpose. From the blast conditions, the amount of oxygen per minute available for coke combustion is determined. Subsequently, a calculated number of layers taken from one or more of the undermost cells is split off and the coke content is burned with the hot blast. At a given blast rate, the number of layers, or rather the amount of carbon they contain, determines the length of the time step t, which at present is 10 minutes. Quantities and compositions of pig iron and slag are calculated, and these products are added to the contents of the hearth. The charge column is moved downward until the tuyere level has been reached again. Quantity, composition, and enthalpy of the gas phase are calculated, assuming that the resulting gas contains no H_2O or CO_2. Heat loss at the tuyere level is subtracted from the gas enthalpy, whereafter the gas temperature is calculated.

Subsequently, a new cell l is formed and contacted with the gas. It will be clear that, although the properties of the gas entering the cell are constant, those of the gas leaving it will gradually change. Besides, temperature and concentration gradients will develop inside the cell. For the next cell things will be even more complicated as the properties of the entering gas will no longer be constant.

To avoid the inherent mathematical difficulties the situation pictured above was replaced by a simpler one that is physically equivalent, but very much easier to calculate. In other words, mathematical transformation of the partial differential equations describing the continuous process into finite difference equations is avoided by replacing the process itself by a discrete one. This

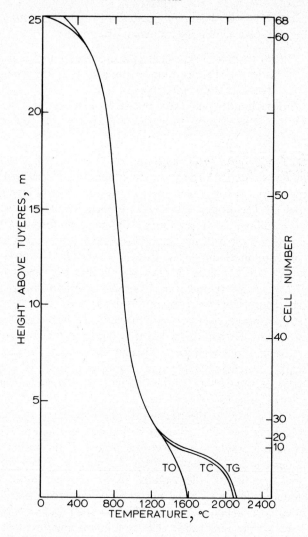

TO temperature of ore, iron, or slag; *TC* coke temperature; *TG* gas temperature

1   Temperature profile for the reference state

discrete process involves complete mixing of the gas phase with the contents of the cell for a period of *t* minutes. Heat transfer takes place under the influence of the mean temperature differences. Similarly, mean concentrations govern mass transfer. After *t* minutes the gas is extracted from the cell and contacted with the next one.

To compensate for the higher descending velocity of the liquid phases compared to the coke a relative velocity *u* with respect to the coke has been introduced. The value of *u* is unity until melting has advanced to some degree, and afterwards increases linearly with temperature. Accordingly, in a cell containing both coke and liquid materials, the liquids undergo heat and mass transfer during *t/u* minutes only. After a cell has been formed the initial temperatures and quantities are known, as well as the properties of the gas that is to enter the cell. An iterative procedure is used to calculate mean quantities and temperatures in the cell after *t* minutes, as well as mean composition and temperature of the gas leaving the cell.

Expected values for the mean temperatures and concentrations needed to start the iteration process are derived from the results calculated for the preceding cells. In the calculations, volume is used as a geometric parameter rather than height. Matter taking volume disappears from the process in the following ways:
Coke

   (i) by combustion with blast oxygen
   (ii) by solution in liquid iron
   (iii) by reaction with the slag constituents FeO, MnO and SiO_2
   (iv) by reaction with CO_2 and H_2O

Ores and solid iron

   (i) by melting

At the end of each time interval, an appropriate number of layers is charged to compensate for the change in total volume. The fraction of voids is assumed to be 0·35.

Heat transfer and thermal balances

Three discriminate temperatures are calculated, i.e. the mean temperature of the ores (or temperature of liquid iron and slag, as the case may be), the mean temperature of the coke, and the gas temperature. The solids are assumed to be homogeneous in temperature, the influence of particle size and thermal conductivity of the material being taken into account via the heat-transfer coefficient. Heat transfer by radiation is considered to be unimportant.

The Reynolds–Nusselt relationships obtained by Beer and Krainer may be used to calculate the heat-transfer coefficients to sinter and to coke.[9] The values found in this way are 233 and 51 W/m^2 K (200 and 44 $kcal/m^2$ °C h), respectively. It is felt, however, that these values are valid only in the case of a strictly homogeneous gas distribution which, in practice, does not exist. Moreover, it is not believed that all of the ore surface nor all of the interstitial space is accessible to the gas flow. The results presented in this paper are obtained by using coefficients of 47 W/m^2 K (40 $kcal/m^2$ °C h) for sinter, and 33 W/m^2 K (28 $kcal/m^2$ °C h) for coke.

It is very difficult to describe the heat transfer to the molten materials in the lower part of the furnace because film thickness, path of descent etc. are unknown. There are three possible ways of heat transfer: coke–liquid, gas–coke, and gas–liquid. The heat-transfer coefficient from gas to coke is the only one which also occurs in equations pertaining to other parts of the furnace, the other two being completely free chosen factors. As only a very small fraction of the total surface area of the coke is wetted by the liquids, heat transfer between coke and liquids will hardly influence the coke temperature and is therefore not taken into account.

The heat-transfer coefficient from gas to liquid has been chosen such that in the reference case a pig-iron temperature of 1570°C is obtained at tuyere level. Owing to heat losses in hearth and runners this corresponds approximately to the observed 1 420°C in the torpedo car. Heat of reaction is subtracted from, or added to, the enthalpy of the component, the temperature of which is rate-determining.

The heats of melting are introduced via the enthalpies of the components. Melting is assumed to take place between 1 227 and 1 327°C. A factor f is defined to indicate the fraction of a fusible component that is in the fluid state. Heat losses to cooling water have been measured at various heights in the furnace for several of the furnaces at Hoogovens. In the model these heat losses are assumed to be proportional to the local gas temperature. The proportionality coefficient, which is a function of height, has been chosen such that the heat losses calculated for the reference case are in accordance with the actual observations. The heat losses are subtracted from the gas enthalpy.

Mass transfer

The following reactions are being taken into account:

$$H_2O(l) \rightarrow H_2O \qquad \qquad (1)$$

$$FeO_x + CO \rightleftarrows FeO_{x-1} + CO_2 \qquad (2)$$

$$FeO_x + H_2 \rightleftarrows FeO_{x-1} + H_2O \qquad (3)$$

$$CO_2 + C \rightarrow 2CO \qquad \qquad (4)$$

$$H_2O + C \rightarrow CO + H_2 \qquad \qquad (5)$$

$$(Fe_{0.947}O) + C \rightarrow 0.947Fe + CO \qquad (6)$$

$$(MnO) + C \rightarrow [Mn] + CO \qquad \qquad (7)$$

$$(SiO_2) + 2C \rightarrow [Si] + 2CO \qquad \qquad (8)$$

It will be observed that the watergas shift reaction is not included. It is assumed that this reaction has to be catalyzed either by carbon or by Fe/FeO. In the first case, the rate equations for the reactions (4) and (5) will implicitly describe the rate of the shift reaction. In the second case the reaction is described by rate equations (2) and (3). The rate equations for the chemical reactions will be found in the appendix.

DESCRIPTION OF REFERENCE STATE

Since work on the dynamic model was started several years ago, the reference state that is now to be described may seem slightly old-fashioned. The geometry of the model (Fig. 2) corresponds to that of Hoogovens BF 5 as it was in 1967. Production was about 100 tons per hour. The burden consisted mainly of acid and basic sinter, but in addition small amounts of lump ores, steel slag, and bauxite were charged. Slag weight was 321 kg, and wet coke consumption 450 kg, both per ton of pig iron. The carbon content of the wet coke was 89·6%. Taking the losses into account, 2 163 Nm³/min of hot blast containing 9 g/Nm³ H_2O and having a temperature of 982°C was blown into the furnace. Injection of heavy fuel oil amounted to 5·36 t/h. Top gas pressure

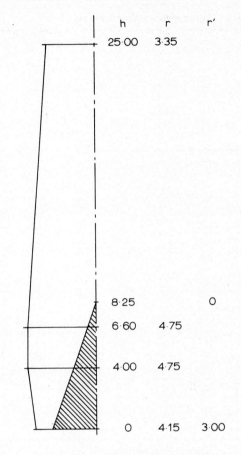

shaded area indicates deadman; h height above tuyeres, m; r furnace radius; r' radius of deadman

2   *Blast-furnace dimensions as used in the model*

was 0·2 atmospheres. Calculations based on these data led to the results given in Table 1.

TABLE 1   Calculations based on experiments on BF5 model

Top gas	BF 5	Model
CO, %	23·5	22·93
CO₂, %	17·6	17·70
H₂, %	3·2	3·05
Temperature, °C	210	223

Pig iron	BF 5	Model
C, %	4·51	4·62
Mn, %	0·84	0·84
Si, %	0·60	0·60

A closer approximation of the measured gas analysis could be realized, but in view of the inaccuracy of the blast-furnace input data this was thought to be unimportant.

Temperature and concentration profiles for the reference state are shown in Figs. 1 and 3. Temperatures for the gas-ore pinchpoint, at 9·5 m above the tuyere plane, are 919 and 911°C, respectively. For the gas-coke

TABLE 2   Characteristics of the steady states

Process characteristics		Experiments*									
		1	2	3	4	5	6	7	8	9	10
Pig iron											
production	t/h	98·45	97·11	98·34	98·88	96·76	95·63	101·66	107·08	97·18	94·55
C	%	4·62	4·66	4·59	4·63	4·62	4·48	4·51	4·52	4·53	4·58
Si	%	0·60	0·60	0·60	0·42	0·60	0·61	0·61	0·60	0·60	0·60
Mn	%	0·84	0·82	0·90	0·72	0·86	1·05	1·00	0·96	0·98	0·91
temperature†	°C	1 568	1591	1 555	1 550	1 569	1 512	1 521	1 529	1 534	1 552
Coke consumption											
kg/t pig iron		444·8	518·0	408·2	409·6	408·2	276·9	264·1	252·3	276·9	277·0
Fuel oil	t/h	5·36	—	8·30	8·30	8·70	19·35	20·17	21·12	19·28	19·32
kg/t pig iron		54·4	—	84·4	83·9	89·9	202·2	198·4	197·2	198·4	200·4
Blast											
rate‡	Nm³/min	2 163	2 163	2 163	1 893	1 893	2 163	2 163	2 163	1 818	1 472
temperature	°C	982	982	982	982	982	982	1 082	1 182	982	982
humidity	g/Nm³	9	9	9	9	9	9	9	9	9	9
oxygen	%	21·0	21·0	21·0	24·0	24·0	21·0	21·0	21·0	26·0	31·0
Flame temperature											
°C		2 117	2 320	2 007	2 147	2 131	1 705	1 756	1 802	1 823	1 946
Melting zone											
upper limit	m	3·65	3·45	4·00	3·10	3·60	5·83	5·42	5·14	4·97	4·20
lower limit	m	2·65	2·45	2·95	2·15	2·70	4·58	4·19	3·93	3·85	3·34
Top gas											
temperature	°C	223	190	248	184	198	349	325	307	271	204
CO ⎫	%	22·93	24·37	22·23	24·74	24·46	20·73	20·52	20·44	22·68	25·61
CO₂ ⎬dry basis	%	17·70	17·87	17·47	18·95	18·89	15·68	16·25	16·64	18·48	20·92
H₂ ⎭	%	3·05	0·75	4·21	4·64	4·83	8·32	8·54	8·80	9·48	11·10
H₂ utilization	%	41.1	39·8	41·9	40·7	40·7	43·6	43·9	44·0	42·5	40·7
Indirect reduction	%	68·4	63·8	71·0	69·4	71·2	80·1	78·7	77·6	80·5	80·9

* Variations applied are underlined
† At tuyere level
‡ Including extra oxygen and humidity

pinchpoint, at 15·7 m above the tuyere plane, temperatures are 776 and 766°C. The hydrogen increase at about 900°C is caused by liberation of the hydrogen content of the coke. It will be observed that there is only the slightest indication of a chemical reserve zone. This is partly due to the fact that, in accordance with observations made in the laboratory, the sinter is supposed not to react with relatively CO_2-rich gas before a temperature of 600 to 700°C has been reached, which leaves a rather short indirect reduction zone. It will be shown later on (Fig. 14) that the chemical reserve zone becomes more pronounced if the furnace stack is hotter.

On the other hand, the burden components have different reducibilities. The position of the FeO level for acid sinter is 1·5 m closer to the tuyere plane than that for basic sinter. Figure 14 demonstrates that an increase in reducibility of the acid sinter has an effect on the CO_2 profile.

INJECTION OF FUEL OIL

Partial replacement of metallurgical coke by auxiliary fuels is now a well-established practice. Therefore, some model experiments were conducted involving the use of various amounts of fuel oil, eventually combined with oxygen enrichment of the blast or increased blast temperature. In these cases, the dynamics were thought to be of minor importance compared to the steady-state characteristics. To save computer time, the paths along

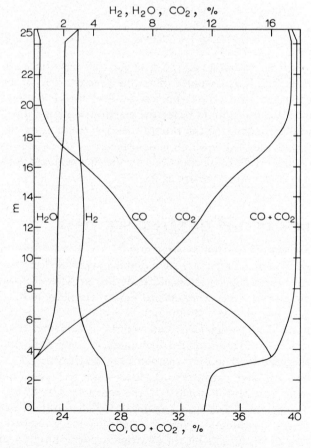

3   Gas concentration profiles for the reference state

which these steady states had to be reached were made as short as possible, using means that are not at the disposal of the blast-furnace operator. As a consequence, only the characteristics of the steady states are presented (Table 2).

Table 3 shows the coke savings obtained by injection of fuel oil without the use of extra oxygen or increased blast temperature. The pig-iron silicon content is 0·6%. It has been assumed that there is no soot formation. One of the consequences of oil injection is a lower pig-iron temperature. This temperature, as well as the silicon content, depends on the time available for heat and mass transfer from gas to liquids, and thus on the distance between tuyere zone and melting zone. Another factor of importance in this respect is the mean temperature difference gas–liquids which, in its turn, depends mainly on the flame temperature.

TABLE 3   Coke saving obtained by injection of fuel oil

Oil, kg/THM	Coke, kg/THM	Integral replacement ratio
—	518	—
50	448	1.40
100	388	1·30
200	281	1·18

A general impression of the relationships between pig-iron temperature, silicon content, flame temperature, and level of melting zone is given in Fig. 4, which was constructed using all available data. Even so, no claims for accuracy are being made. It appears that the silicon content depends mainly on the melting-zone level. Conversely, the flame temperature is the predominant factor in determining the pig-iron temperature. The flame temperature may be raised by way of a higher hot-blast temperature. A comparison of the columns 6, 7 and 8 in Table 2 shows that, although a nice coke saving is obtained, the effect on the pig-iron temperature is rather small. For the rest, most plants will not have much room left for a substantial increase of the hot-blast temperature.

Oxygen enrichment of the blast is another way to increase the flame temperature. Columns 3 and 4 in Table 2 show that oxygen enrichment from 21 to 24% results in a slightly cooler furnace hearth. The pig-iron temperature decreases in spite of a higher flame temperature. This is brought about by a change in the temperature profile in the stack. As a consequence, the indirect reduction zone is shortened. More carbon is consumed for endothermic FeO reduction and less is available for combustion. Besides, less heat is imported with the hot blast because a substantial part of the nitrogen has been removed from it.

If the original silicon content is to be maintained some extra fuel is required (Table 2, column 10). It appears that this brings the indirect reduction back to its original level, so that the pig-iron temperature increases even if the flame temperature decreases. Contrary to the expectations a slight fuel saving was found when oxygen enrichment was used in combination with very high amounts of fuel oil (Table 2, columns 8, 9, 10). It appears that in these cases the indirect reduction actually increases. The data suggest an optimum in fuel economy somewhere around 5% of extra oxygen. More work is needed to confirm this.

DYNAMIC RESPONSES OF THE FURNACE

The dynamic behaviour of the blast-furnace process was studied by applying stepwise increases or decreases in one of the independent variables. To avoid confusion it is pointed out that, for instance, the amount of oil injected per hour is an independent variable, whereas the oil consumption per ton of pig iron is not. Likewise, the amount of coke per ton of iron in ore can be varied independently, whereas the coke consumption per ton of hot metal depends on the pig-iron composition. This means that the end effect of, for instance, a step in blast enthalpy has to be corrected for variations in fuel consumption.

Variations in common blast-furnace practice

The results of calculations in which respectively coke consumption, oil rate, hot-blast temperature, blast moisture, and blast rate were changed stepwise are summarized in Table 4, columns 11 to 15 and Figs. 5 to 9. In these figures a logarithmic time scale has been used. The short horizontal lines at left indicate the levels of the dependent variables at time zero. It appears that, especially in the case of the fuel steps, it takes a very long time before the new steady state is attained. In our opinion, actual blast-furnace trials might easily lead to different conclusions because, owing to the ever-present scatter in silicon, it is very hard to decide at what moment the experiment may be considered as finished.

In the case of the oil step the dynamic behaviour of the furnace is characterized by an initial chilling due to the decomposition of the oil. It takes some hours before the effect of the increased indirect reduction becomes noticeable in the hearth. The calculated increase in pig-iron silicon due to an increase in coke consumption may be somewhat larger than commonly found in the

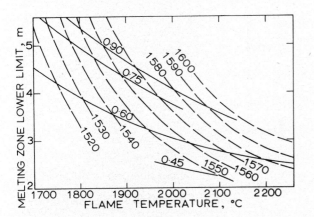

4 Pig-iron temperature and silicon content as a function of melting-zone level and flame temperature

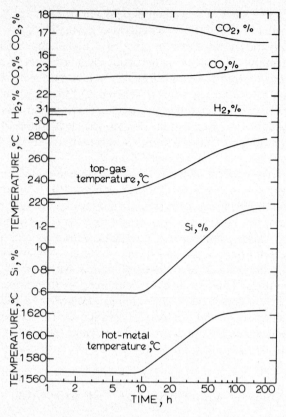

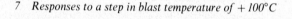

5   Responses to a step in coke charged of +30 kg per ton of pig iron

7   Responses to a step in blast temperature of +100°C

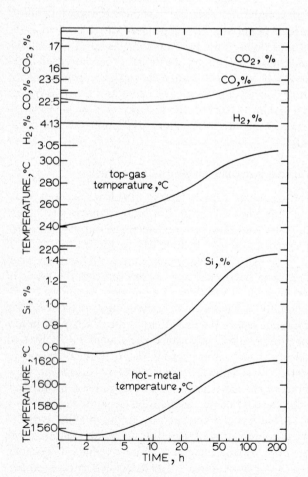

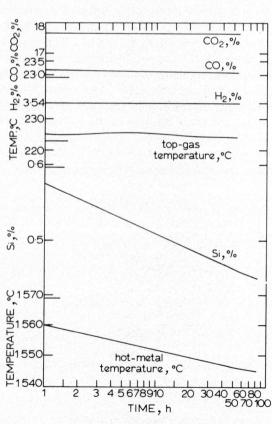

6   Responses to a step in oil rate of 50%; oil consumption increased from 54 to 91 kg/THM

8   Responses to a step in blast moisture of +10 g/Nm³

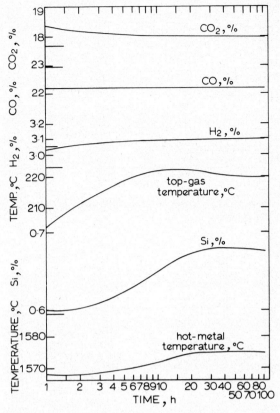

9 *Responses to a step in blast rate of* −20%

literature. We are under the impression, however, that the experimental evidence concerning the Si–coke relationship (60 to 70 kg coke per % Si) has not been renewed for several years. Since then, the value of several items on the furnace heat and mass balances may have changed considerably. For instance, the amount of reducing gas available per ton of pig iron is much smaller, and the CO/CO_2 ratio in top gas decreases steadily. Accordingly, if pig iron with a high silicon content is to be produced, a larger fraction of the additional CO generated by combustion of the extra coke will participate in the ore reduction, thereby lowering the incremental heat requirements.

In the calculations, pig iron with a 0·77% higher silicon content was obtained at the cost of an increment in total fuel consumption of 31·2 kg, expressed as coke with 89·6% C. This means that 40·5 kg of coke was needed per % of silicon. An additional 2 kg of coke would have been required if it had been attempted to maintain a constant slag composition. To obtain the coke equivalent of each step use was made of the coke–silicon relationship calculated above. Coke–oil replacement ratios were derived from Table 3.

The effect of the variation in blast temperature may be compared with that found in the experiments 12 and 13: 16·8 resp. 13·1 kg coke/100°C. Figure 9 shows that the well-known rapid heating of a furnace following a

TABLE 4 Results of variations in common blast-furnace practice

Process characteristics		Experiments* 1	11	12	13	14	15
Pig iron							
production	t/h	98·45	89·93	88·52	100·34	99·90	77·62
C	%	4·62	4·49	4·44	4·61	4·61	4·60
Si	%	0·60	1·37	1·47	0·83	0·45	0·68
Mn	%	0·84	1·16	1·20	0·96	0·75	0·90
temperature†	°C	1 568	1 630	1 622	1 600	1 545	1 575
Coke consumption							
kg/t pig iron		444·8	469·5	439·8	443·2	444·6	444·2
Fuel oil	t/h	5·36	5·36	8·04	5·36	5·36	4·29
kg/t pig iron		54·4	59·6	90·8	53·4	53·7	55·3
Blast							
rate‡	Nm³/min	2 163	2 163	2 163	2 163	2 163	1 730
temperature	°C	982	982	982	1 082	982	982
humidity	g/Nm³	9	9	9	9	19	9
oxygen	%	21·0	21·0	21·0	21·0	21·0	21·0
Flame temperature							
	°C	2 117	2 119	2 028	2 199	2 064	2 102
Melting zone							
upper limit	m	3·65	5·95	6·85	4·10	3·40	3·70
lower limit	m	2·65	4·95	5·85	3·15	2·30	2·90
Top gas							
temperature	°C	223	278	311	219	223	220
CO ⎫	%	22·93	23·44	23·32	23·20	23·05	22·28
CO₂ ⎬ dry basis	%	17·70	16·64	15·96	17·75	17·71	18·00
H₂ ⎭	%	3·05	3·05	4·13	3·04	3·54	3·10
H₂ utilization	%	41·1	41·5	41·8	41·3	41·2	40·5
Indirect reduction	%	68·4	71·0	73·1	67·9	69·2	70·1
Coke equivalent of step							
	kg/t pig iron			+35·2	+12·1	−5·0	+2·7

* Variations applied are underlined
† At tuyere level
‡ Including extra oxygen and humidity

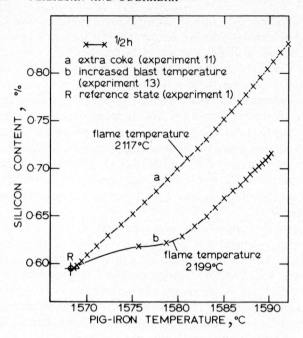

10   Influence of change in flame temperature on model response to extra heat

decrease in blast rate cannot be reproduced by the model. It is concluded that, in addition to the assumptions made in the model, other hypotheses would be necessary to explain this phenomenon. So far, no attempts in this direction have been made.

It remains to be mentioned that the dynamic behaviour of the furnace depends to some degree on the change in flame temperature. In Fig. 10 the relations between pig-iron temperature and silicon content are shown for the experiments 11 and 13. Points on the curves are spaced half an hour apart. In experiment 11 there is virtually no change in flame temperature. As soon as the extra coke arrives at the tuyeres pig-iron temperature and silicon start to increase simultaneously.

Experiment 13, on the other hand, is characterized by a sudden increase of the flame temperature which, as is shown in Fig. 4, has a predominant influence on the pig-iron temperature. Consequently, the rise in pig-iron temperature during the first hour is more important than the increase in silicon content.

Effect of process disturbances

The independent variables mentioned thus far can be measured and controlled. There are others, however, which are much harder to control. One of these is the gas distribution over the furnace cross-section. In the model, which is one-dimensional, simulation of variations in the gas-distribution pattern is rather difficult. It is possible, however, to simulate the resultant changes in the average values of the heat and mass transfer coefficients. It is felt that there must be some similarity between the effects of a change in gas-distribution pattern and a change in burden reducibility, in itself one of the factors which is difficult to control.

Figures 11 to 13 show the effect of a 20% increase in reducibility starting from the steady states 1, 6 and 8

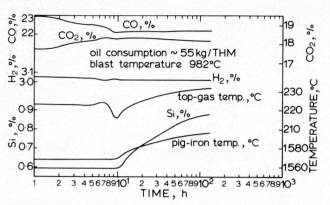

11   Responses to a step in ore reducibility of +20% starting from steady state 1

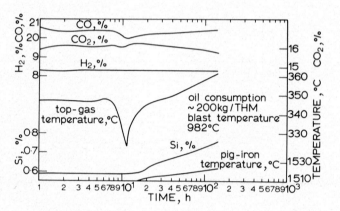

12   Responses to a step in ore reducibility of +20% starting from steady state 6

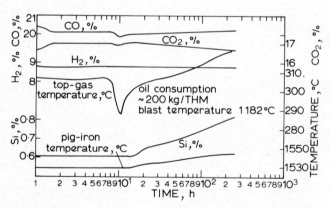

13   Responses to a step in ore reducibility of +20% starting from steady state 8

indicated in Table 2. In these cases one of the old ores was replaced by a new ore having a 56% higher reducibility. It appears that the responses are very slow, especially when the fuel oil rate is high.

The gas curves show an initial increase in indirect reduction. When the new ore approaches the melting zone gas production by direct reduction is diminished. A declining gas volume causes the top-gas temperature to decrease until the old ore has disappeared from the direct reduction zone. Gas production increases again when the coke saved in the direct reduction zone reaches the tuyeres. At the same time, indirect reduction starts to slowly decrease because the rising melting zone

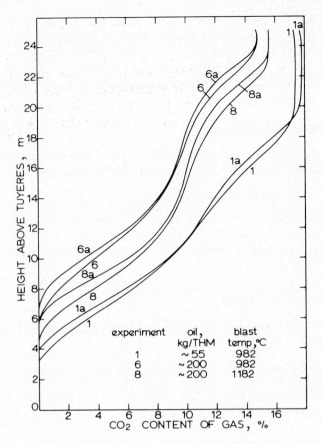

14   *Influence of an increase in reducibility on CO_2 profiles*

after eight hours. The reheating of the furnace is a very slow process. This simulation was performed following an incident at one of the IJmuiden blast furnaces caused by interruption of the oil flow. This led to a chilled furnace in about the same time as indicated by the calculation.

Finally, some calculations were performed concerning cooling water leakage into the lower part of the furnace. The steady states 1, 6 and 8 served again as starting points. The amount of water was 3·25 tons per hour, which led to more than one percent of extra hydrogen in top-gas. As a leakage of this size will certainly not be tolerated for more than a few hours, it did not seem to make much sense to prolong the calculations too far. Consequently, the silicon curves in Fig. 16 are plotted against a linear time scale.

It appears that there is not much difference between the silicon response curves. However, pig-iron temperatures at tuyere level after 12 h were 1 501°, 1 443°, and 1 475°C, respectively. It is concluded that, as far as water leakage is concerned, low flame temperatures do necessarily lead to earlier freezing of the furnace.

Limitations of the model

As follows from the basic assumptions, the use of the model is limited to experiments in which modifications in gas, liquid and solid flow distribution over the furnace cross-section play a minor role. It should be remarked that fundamental knowledge pertaining to gas and liquid dynamics in the lower part of the furnace, including the deadman, is still far from complete. In our opinion, substitution of gaps in knowledge by hypotheses based on intuition should not be carried too far.

Execution of the calculations

Use is made of a Univac 1108 computer. It takes about five minutes of calculation time to simulate one day of blast-furnace practice. The program occupies about 16 K core space (1 K = 1 024 words of 36 bits).

ACKNOWLEDGEMENT

The authors are grateful to Mr H. Veldman for the important part he took in the development of the Fortran program.

diminishes the space available for this reaction. The magnitude of this effect, of course, depends upon the initial level of the melting zone.

CO_2 profiles for the steady states 1, 6, and 8, and for the experiments with increased reducibilities, are shown in Fig. 14. In the experiments 6 and 8 the stack is hotter than in experiment 1, due to the increased amount of reducing gas. Consequently, reduction starts earlier and more room is left for a chemical reserve zone. This zone, of course, is more distinct when the ore has a better reducibility. Figure 15 shows the consequences of an interruption of the fuel oil injection. Nothing seems to happen at first, but after about three hours the furnace starts to chill rapidly. Oil injection was gradually resumed after six hours, and the initial injection rate of 9·4 tons per hour (96 kg per ton of pig iron) was attained

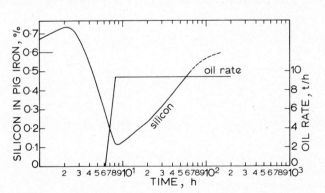

15   *Decline of silicon content in pig iron following an interruption of the oil injection*

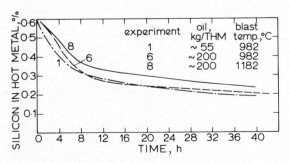

16   *Simulation of chilling caused by a cooling-water leakage of 3·245 tons/h*

REFERENCES

1 H. BEER *et al.*: Internat. Conf. on Iron and Steelmaking, paper B3, 1965, Amsterdam
2 G. A. FLIERMAN AND J. M. VAN LANGEN: *ibid.*, paper B2
3 G. A. FLIERMAN: 'Mathematical models in metallurgical process development', 212–6, 1969, London, The Iron and Steel Institute
4 I. MUCHI: *Trans. ISI Japan*, 1967, **7**, 223–37
5 J. YAGI AND I. MUCHI: *ibid.*, 1970, **10**, 181–7
6 J. YAGI AND I. MUCHI: *ibid.*, 392–405
7 C. J. FIELDEN AND B. I. WOOD: *JISI*, 1968, **206**, 650–8.
8 L. V. BOGDANDY *et al.*: *Trans. ISI Japan*, 1971, **11**, (1), 131–6
9 H. P. BEER AND H. KRAINER: *Techn. Mitt. Krupp. Forschungsber.*, 1966, **24**, 25–47

APPENDIX

Evaporation of coke moisture

The saturation pressure of water vapour can be approximated as follows:

$$p^*H_2O = \exp(-5\,098/TC + 13 \cdot 67)\ \text{atmospheres}$$

The partial water vapour pressure being

$$pH_2O = PTOP \cdot H_2O/GAS$$

the following simple rate equation will suffice:

$$V_1 = g_1 \cdot H_2O(l) \cdot (p^*H_2O - pH_2O)$$

The rate constant g_1 has been chosen such that all of the water evaporates in the top cells. Its value is $0 \cdot 1$.

Gaseous reduction of iron oxides

$$V_2 = g_2 \cdot Fe(pCO - K_2 \cdot pCO_2) \cdot \exp(-E_2/R \cdot TO)$$
$$\times (1 - f)$$
$$V_3 = g_3 \cdot Fe(pH_2 - K_3 \cdot pH_2O) \cdot \exp(-E_3/R \cdot TO)$$
$$\times (1 - f)$$

The rate constants g_2 and g_3 are functions of the actual value of $x = O/Fe$. The equilibrium constants K_2 and K_3 are functions of both temperature and x. The numerical values of g, K and E for different ores have to be derived from laboratory experiments.

Gaseous oxidation of coke carbon

$$V_4 = g_4 \cdot C(pCO_2 - K_4 \cdot p^2CO) \cdot \exp(-E_4/R \cdot TC)$$
$$V_5 = g_5 \cdot C(pH_2O - K_5 \cdot pCO \cdot pH_2)$$
$$\cdot \exp(-E_5/R \cdot TC)$$

The values of the rate constants g_4 and g_5 are determined by the coke reactivity which, in its turn, depends upon the coke size, and on catalytic effects. The values used for the rate constants g_4 and g_5 are $2 \cdot 8 \times 10^6$ and $4 \cdot 2 \times 10^4$. The activation energies are 50 and 40 kcal per mole, respectively.

Reduction of liquid FeO

It is assumed that liquid FeO is reduced by solid carbon only, according to the following simple rate equation:

$$V_6 = g_6O \cdot \exp(-E_6/R \cdot TO) \cdot f/u$$

A value of 30 kcal/mol has been assumed for E_6. The value of g_6 is chosen such that all FeO is reduced before tuyere level is reached. This requirement is satisfied by $g_6 = 10$.

Reduction of MnO

MnO is supposed to be reduced from the slag phase by solid carbon.

$$V_7 = g_7 \cdot MnO \cdot \exp(-E_7/R \cdot TO) \cdot f/u$$

in which g_7 equals $1 \cdot 43 \times 10^5$. A value of 50 kcal/mol was assigned to E_7.

Reduction of silica

It is assumed that silica reduction proceeds to completion above the tuyere zone. Oxygen transport in the metal phase is considered to be the rate-determining step. The following rate equation, which may look somewhat ambitious in view of the simplicity of the preceding ones, was derived:

$$V_8 = g_8 \cdot F\{(aSiO_2/aSi)^{0 \cdot 5} - K_8 \cdot pCO)$$
$$\cdot \exp(-E_8/R \cdot TO)/u$$

where $F = $ (kmol of slag times kmol of iron)$^{0 \cdot 5}$

$$aSiO_2 = 0 \cdot 1(SiO_2/\text{kmol of slag})$$

$$\log aSi = {}^{10}\log(Si/Fe) + 4 \cdot 45 \times 10^{-4}TO - 2 \cdot 67$$

$$K_8 = \exp(42\,850/TO - 22 \cdot 1)$$

$$g_8 = 3 \cdot 5 \times 10^8$$

$$E_8 = 80\ \text{kcal/mol}$$

Discussion on chapter one: Ironmaking

CHAIRMAN: J. M. VAN LANGEN (HOOGOVENS, IJMUIDEN BV)

The following papers were discussed: *Mathematical model for the prediction of the residual lining thickness in the stack and bosh sections of a blast furnace* by T. A. Bandak; *Numerical simulation of the blast furnace process* by G. A. Flierman and H. Oderkerk.

The Chairman in opening the discussion said that he had a number of questions. He said that at KNHS they had been trying to measure the temperatures in the brick lining as a function of time in years. In some instances they had found that the heat conduction through the wall depended very much on the penetration of hot metal into the bricks. It was the depth of penetration of the metal which governed the amount of material which still had the original conductivity and where metal penetration had occurred the thermal conductivity was very high. He asked how Mr Bandak had taken this into account in his calculations.

In reply, **Mr Bandak** said that they had many thermocouples positioned in various parts of the stack wall and the bosh and the average reading had been used. They had assumed that, when the temperature indicated by the thermocouple started to rise rapidly, either hot metal or slag had reached the hot junction.

Dr van Langen thought this a sensible interpretation, but suggested that conversely the effective wall thickness could be greater than that actually present, because the brickwork as well as not eroding could have acquired a lower thermal conductivity. **Mr Bandak** agreed and said that they hoped to have avoided that particular problem by plotting results of temperature measurements and then examining the form of the resulting curves. Points remote from the curves were assumed to be in error.

Dr van Langen also noted that Mr Bandak had reached the conclusion that a plumbago wall would be more advantageous than a semi-graphite wall for reasons of cost. Dr van Langen wondered if there would also be a difference in the heat losses resulting from the different walls. Experience at KNHS showed that a furnace which had walls in plumbago had a coke consumption which was lower by 10–15 kg/t of hot metal than one where the refractory was semi-graphite. Could Mr Bandak have calculated this effect? Would the model predict the amount of heat removal from the furnace by the water cooling and the difference in coke rates to be expected with different wall constructions? **Mr Bandak** said that the method could easily determine the amount of heat which passed through any wall made of any material. This was one of its main features. The semi-graphite would not be practical if used in the same thickness as the plumbago and firebrick, rather, the thickness should be less. The model would predict accurately the furnace cooling losses and changes in the coke rate due to changes in wall construction.

Mr. N. J. Cavaghan (BSC, General Steels Division, Research Organization) asked two questions. First, referring to Fig. 17 of the paper, where the actual wear was compared with the predicted wear on the residual lining, Mr Cavaghan noted that the actual wear was more uniform than the predicted wear. He asked if when the lining was removed from the furnace whether any covering material had to be removed from the bricks. Was there a burden build-up of any sort on the face of the refractories which could have evened out the wear. If build-up occurred, could it be accounted for in the model. In reply, **Mr Bandak** said that the degree of build-up varied with the position in the furnace and he could not accurately predict where it would occur for the purposes of calculation. Plots of the thickness of build-up around the circumference of the blast furnace measured during re-linings showed that sometimes it was thicker than the original wall and sometimes it was far thinner. Accordingly, Mr Bandak had assumed that build-up could occur up to a maximum of the thickness of the original lining.

In introducing his second question, **Mr Cavaghan** said that he could have read the paper wrongly but what seemed to be missing was the time dependency of the rate of wear of the lining. He had noted Fig. 16, where the rate of wear in an actual lining was compared with the predicted final level. Somewhere in the model must be included an optimum thickness for the residual lining. **Mr Cavaghan** could visualize a situation where a very thin residual lining would be acceptable, provided it was going to be reached in ten years' operation. He asked if the model could be made time dependent and therefore used to predict the residual lining thickness and when it would be reached. **Mr Cavaghan** said that he would be very pleased to have a dynamic model which could make this calculation. **Mr Bandak** said that the paper contained a steady-state model of the residual thicknesses obtained when thermal equilibrium was achieved in the furnace. Practical experience indicated roughly the life of certain linings, e.g. a firebrick lining would wear out very quickly, in six months or a year. The plant operators in his case were mainly concerned with knowing what the minimum residual thickness would be with a certain wall construction and he personally did not see the need for the dynamic model.

Mr A. E. Pengelly (BSC, General Steels Division, Research Centre Teesside) said that it was obvious from the formulation in Fig. 17 that the model was very dependent upon the heat transfer coefficients that had to be built into it; their accuracy was also very important. By inserting coolers into the blast-furnace stack one hoped to get a good heat transfer coefficient. Perhaps, more importantly, one hoped to get the same heat transfer coefficient for each set of coolers in each part of the structure. The degree to which one could achieve uniformity was perhaps at least as important as the degree to which one could predict how long it would take to achieve the residual lining thickness and Mr Pengelly asked for comment on the degree of uniformity of the lining thickness when the furnace lining was demolished.

Mr Bandak said it was not uniform at all, and for the purposes of his study he had considered the minimum lining thickness. In some parts there would be say, 10% wear, while in other parts on the same circumference or the same level in the furnace the wear might only be about 8%. There was also no uniformity either in the upper or lower stack, but the plant operators were not interested in the general condition of the furnace, rather they were interested in what was the worst condition at the hottest spot. Thus one had to look at the situation pessimistically and assess whether the worst condition would occur.

Before closing the discussion on this paper, **the Chairman** said that at KNHS they had been trying to do the same calculation and had arrived at a similar result, but because of shortage of time they had done their work in two dimensions only. He asked Mr Bandak to explain again why he thought it necessary to do it in three dimensions. **Mr Bandak** said that if the calculations were made only in two dimensions it was not possible to determine the influence of the number of coolers per row. The three dimensional study, however, enabled one to determine the effect of the number of coolers per row on the residual thickness. He had not presented any information regarding the number of coolers per row in the present paper, but such information had been deduced for the no. 4 blast furnace at Port Talbot.

Prof. J. Szekely (State University of New York at Buffalo, USA) in opening the discussion on the paper by Dr Flierman and Mr Oderkerk said that the model depended critically on the frequency factors g_1 to g_8 that were used, and to some degree on the activation energies. He gathered from the paper that the majority of these frequency factors were fitted parameters rather than quantities that were calculated from more fundamental or general equations. He asked first how, and by what procedure were the parameters fitted. Second, were any difficulties experienced regarding the possible ill-conditioning of the system owing to the inter-connexion of the parameters? Third, how sensitive was the model to the values chosen for the parameters? Fourth, did the authors believe it was truly reasonable to fix numerical values of the rate constants and make them only temperature-dependent, and then use them to predict the behaviour of the system over a range of conditions?

Dr Flierman in reply said that with regard to the reduction of iron ores, the data were based on laboratory experiments where one measured the reduction rate in conditions similar to those pertaining in the blast furnace, with regard to gas composition and temperature. For the gaseous oxidation of the coke carbon, the authors had taken data from coke reactivity measurements and then examined the effects of increasing the reactivity by a factor of 2 or 4. They had found that the coke reactivity did not play a very important role in the complete model, so they had not carried out any further experiments on this point. The reduction of liquid FeO that goes into the slag and is reduced by contact with the coke matrix was estimated. Dr Flierman was of the opinion that this estimation was not a very important possible cause of error. The reduction of iron is completed in a blast furnace. All the oxygen was removed from the ore so that it was only necessary to choose a factor which was such that at a given level in the furnace all the oxygen was gone. Changing the value of the factor had shown them that the rate of removal of oxygen was slightly affected.

With regard to silicon, again a factor had been chosen to arrive at the silicon content of the metal. The value of the heat transferred to the coke was deduced from information reported in the literature. The transfer of heat to the liquid was again described by an arbitrary factor. However, the temperature of the liquids at the furnace taphole was known and by adding an amount to compensate for the heat losses in the hearth one could deduce the heat content at the tuyere level. The values for heat transfer to the liquids were then chosen so that the liquids arriving at the tuyere level had a sensible value of the heat content.

Dr J. A. Brimacombe (University of British Columbia, Department of Metallurgy) commented that he sympathized with the authors in their problem of trying to obtain kinetic parameters for their equations. He himself had worked on a mathematical model of the SLRN direct reduction process and had the same problems in trying to obtain heat transfer coefficients and activation energies by using comparatively crude equations to describe very complex processes. Dr Brimacombe also asked whether the authors had problems with instabilities in calculating temperatures in the heat balances.

Dr van Langen, replying on behalf of Dr Flierman, said that initially there had been problems of instability, but with the present way of tackling the equations which was described in the paper the method was stable.

Prof. F. Oeters (Technical University of Berlin) said that the authors had made the assumption that the furnace worked homogeneously over the section. This was not generally the case in practice and the consequence was that the mean attainment of equilibrium, or the mean distance from equilibrium, in the degree of reduction was less than if a furnace did work homogeneously. The authors had used reducibility values which were obtained from laboratory tests, and Prof. Oeters wondered if they had made any corrections to the reducibility values with respect to the non-homogeneous working. What were the consequences of this non-homogeneous working with regard to the values of the model results? In reply **Dr Flierman** said that they had not applied any correction to the reducibility data. A non-homogeneously working furnace could not be compared with a homogeneous one and the authors had considered the possibility of modifying the model so as to account for non-homogeneity. However, there were problems in that too many assumptions were required. They could have considered three concentric vertical cylinders in the model, corresponding to three regions of working in the shaft, but this really turned the model into three parallel furnaces and it was necessary to assume no interchange between the columns which was unrealistic. For that reason they had abandoned the idea of making a two- or three-dimensional model. The present model had been verified using their own plant data, and with the burden that they used at KNHS they obtained reasonable correspondence between observed and calculated coke rates. The authors were only interested in their own burden and so in this respect the problem was simplified.

Prof. Dr R. Wartmann (Hoesch Hüttenwerke AG, Germany) said that one year previously in Düsseldorf a model developed by his company had been presented. They had now carried out much work with the aid of that model and that raised a particular point in the present paper. Contrary to what had been stated in the paper, Dr Wartmann had concluded that the speed of the coke reaction (coke reactivity) had a very great effect on the results produced by the model. For example, a change in the speed of gas formation from the coke not only influenced the degree of indirect reduction but also the performance of the furnace. The relationship between gas, coke, and temperature would also change as would the melting area. Dr Wartmann thus believed that the speed of the coke reaction was the most important factor in a blast-furnace model. **Dr Flierman** in reply said that if one had a very reducible burden which started to reduce at, say, the 800°C temperature level, a lot of oxygen had already been removed before the coke reaction temperature was attained at about 1 050° or 1 100°C. At that level, for their particular circumstances, the authors believed that the reduction velocity of the pellets and sinter burden had already been very much reduced. Also, the temperature was quite low with only a very slow formation of carbon dioxide and it was implicit that the coke reactivity would have only a small effect. In general terms, Dr Flierman said that the question hinged on whether or not the ore was nearly completely reduced at a temperature when the carbon gasification started.

Mr N. J. Cavaghan asked Dr Flierman to amplify the comment in the paper where it was stated that with operation at high oil injection rates, stopping oil injection cooled a furnace very rapidly. Would the authors like to comment on the future, where it was predicted that injection rates as high as 200 kg of oil per tonne of iron produced would be used. We might also have bosh gas injection and very little coke in the burden at all. Was it a rider from the paper that there must be oxygen injection to go with injected fuel so that there was always a fail safe condition. Certainly at the amount of oil the authors were using, a stoppage led rapidly to a chilled hearth which had been predicted by the model. Mr Cavaghan suggested that the injection of oxygen would not provide the fail safe condition he had described, but rather it was necessary to keep the flame temperature and iron and slag temperatures at a reasonable level in operation. If with very high levels of fuel oil injection one was forced to switch off the oil, he believed that one would be forced to stop the furnace. Oxygen injection would not improve the position. Finally, Mr Cavaghan asked if the model was able to predict future operation at very low coke rates and high hydrocarbon usage. Could it say what was the optimum usage of hydrocarbons?

Dr Flierman in reply said it was certainly necessary at very high oil rates to stop the furnace if the injection must be interrupted, as the furnace could not operate temporarily with a big shortage of fuel. Oxygen injection did not change this situation. It appeared from the calculations that pig iron and slag temperatures depended on the silicon content of hot metal as well as on the flame temperature. Consequently, the injection of oxygen or the application of very high hot blast temperatures was necessary at high injection rates to maintain reasonable pig iron and slag temperatures. With the model it was possible to calculate the coke saving caused by injection of reformed gas and/or oil. Thus, the optimum usage could be calculated as a function of the prices of gas, oil, and coke.

chapter 2: electric steelmaking

Optimization of energy distribution in the operation of an electric melting shop

H. H. Borggrefe, K. Hohendahl, and G. Zingel

Contracts between power stations and industrial consumers of electrical energy depend on a method of power measurement which enables the consumers to make considerable savings in energy costs by efficient utilization of the energy supplied. In steelworks, arc furnaces can be used as correcting elements for power control purposes. If a process computer is used, the possible scope of power control, taking into account limiting factors and the sequence of operations, already covers all the main conditions for controlling the steelmaking procedure. This control regulates voltage steps and desired currents to prescribed levels, depending on the energy used, so that the resulting arcs have the lengths required for economic furnace operation. It is shown that reproducible adjustment of arc lengths and the maintaining of prescribed melting energy levels not only reduces energy costs but also enables appreciable savings to be made in refractory materials.

OBJECTIVES

Maximum control

The connexion to the RWE power station and the energy distribution in the Krefeld melting shop of Deutsche Edelstahlwerke are shown in Fig. 1. The metering points for electrical energy and the way of summation are also shown.

The tariffs against which the power stations provide energy to large consumers differ in value but not in structure. The tariff consists of an energy part and a power part. For the energy price a difference between a day and night tariff exists. The power price takes into account the maximum power drawn. The measurement of power is achieved by adding up the electrical energy drawn over an agreed period (in Germany usually 15 min) and dividing the sum by this period. The calculation of the power price is based on the highest power drawn within an accounting period. Especially important is that only during the so-called tariff period is the maximum power determined. Outside these periods power is not measured. The efficiency of the energy provision of an industrial enterprise is characterized by the capacity-hour number. It is calculated as the quotient between drawn electrical energy and the measured maximum power. It has a direct effect on the power price and on the energy price it acts as a capacity-hour discount.

At the beginning of an accounting period each works estimates its required probable maximum power and takes care that it will not be exceeded. By making the proper choice of this value the energy costs can be influenced a lot. When operating with several furnaces, energy restriction during certain periods in the day means a reduction in overall production. However, this is small compared to the reduction in energy costs. Obviously this presupposes that energy users that can switch off power for a short time without causing adverse metallurgical, process-technological, or constructional effects are available. The arc furnace is ideal in this respect during the melt-down period. Except for extra heat losses there are no undesired side effects. As the furnaces are high energy users, and their power can be altered with step switches, they are especially suited to be control elements.

Arc furnaces

The process periods of arc-furnace operation can be

Dr Borggrefe and Dr Zingel are with Deutsche Edelstahlwerke, Krezdel. Mr Hohendahl is with Siemens AGI

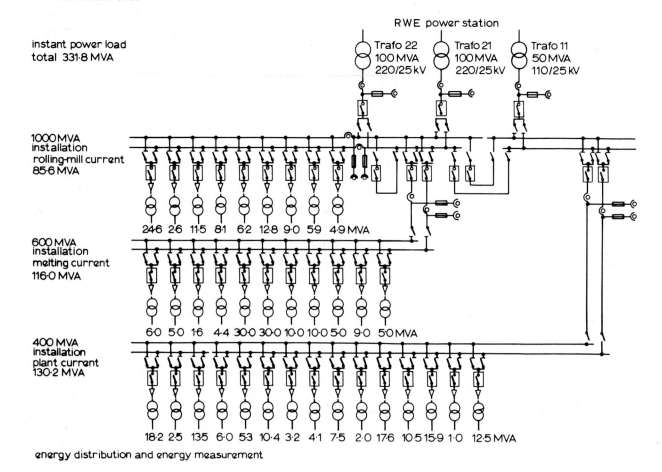

1   Connexion to the RWE power station

clearly distinguished. At Deutsche Edelstahlwerke they are defined as:

(i) melt-down period
(ii) initial metallurgical period
(iii) refining period.

Depending on furnace type, charge weight, and steel quality for each heat, a power diagram can be determined. This diagram reflects the above mentioned process periods. The melt-down period can be clearly determined. The other periods are more uncertain. Energy control, therefore, can at the present stage of knowledge only make use of the melt-down period. The required melt-down energies consist of the physical heat of melting, the empirically determined heat losses and heat gains resulting from chemical reactions. Therefore, the energy is a known characteristic for specific points in the process.

Experience up to now has shown that within the available accuracy, current interruptions necessary for maximum power control have no influence on the required melt-down energy. The furnace productivity over a campaign is characterized by two requirements, i.e. the shortest possible melting time and the lowest and most evenly distributed refractory wear. A workable compromise between these counteracting requirements can only be obtained if the working points are given not as voltage steps but as arc lengths. Currents

and transformer steps that fulfil the required conditions are well known in arc-furnace operation and can be determined precisely during the commissioning of the plant.

Priorities

It has already been mentioned that those furnaces which are in the melt-down period are fit for maximum power control. In general, the furnace operation must not be changed the further the process has progressed. Therefore it is necessary to determine an order of priorities between the furnaces in a shop and to keep this up to date. For the determination of priorities the value of the heat can also be taken into account with respect to delay time, specific price multiplied by specific productivity in

$$\frac{\text{money units}}{\text{tonne}} \times \frac{\text{tonne}}{\text{hour}}$$

Following the steelmaking process is a prerequisite for a workable process control. As a criterion for transition from one period to another cannot be taken directly from the process, it is necessary to indicate this moment manually. This input has to be organized such that the production personnel are not asked to make much effort, but also such that no improper use can be made of the input. This means that the indication of a process

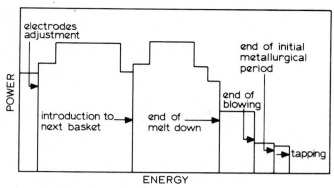

power as current and voltage step *v.* the energy used

2   Power diagram of a heat

transition is only accepted when the computer has checked that the following criteria have reached likely values:

   (i) charge evolution
  (ii) energy consumed
 (iii) time elapsed.

Furnace control

The above arguments lead to an interaction of maximum power control and furnace control. Maximum power control is only possible with accurate priority control, which in turn is only possible if the computer follows the steelmaking process. However, following the process necessitates the introduction into the computer of necessary data to control the furnace directly. These relations are represented in Fig. 4.

CONCEPT OF SOLUTION

Furnace control

Figure 3 shows the control panel of each of the five connected furnaces. It contains a switch for the input of charge data and a process number that has the function of determining the power diagram for the heat from tables stored in the computer memory. In the upper part a time indicator is installed giving the time to the end of the respective process periods. Under the charge

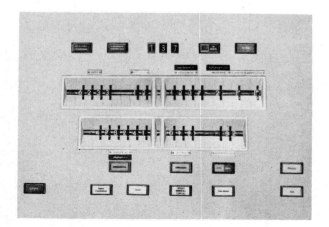

3   Control panel for maximum power and furnace control

data switches are the switches for the single process phases and for data transmission. A prescribed order of switching is realized, in that the switches can only be operated when the computer makes them light up. Therefore, a minimum of operational effort, the greatest possible care in operation, and protection against improper use are obtained. A correction input makes it possible to correct errors in introduced data and also to change charge data during the heat.

The type of coupling between computer system and process enables the installation to operate in two ways:

  (i) the computer executes all passive functions, manual control is possible, and the computer executes no control functions
 (ii) as in (i), but the computer executes the control functions.

A basic principle is that the computer can be switched on during a heat without any disturbance of the process. Also, it is always possible to switch from automatic to manual control without interrupting the heat. This is an advantage, if for example, the first basket of a charge requires a special treatment for which the computer has no data stored, but the known process can be executed from the second basket onwards. Melting of the first basket load is manually controlled. The second can immediately be handled automatically without process interruption. To enable this, it is still necessary to feed all available data into the computer during manual control. The system is built so that all data, including the manual interventions, are treated. At the switchover to automatic operation the computer can immediately execute the control functions, so that a smooth transition is assured.

According to the prescribed power diagram, (Fig. 2) the computer automatically controls the current and voltage setting, and switches off the furnace when the energy setpoint is reached. The energy setpoint for a period of time is calculated as follows:

energy setpoint = actual total charge
           × specific energy

The operator is always able to change the preset values and to alter the settings deduced from the energy setpoint forwards or backwards in time. However, this has no influence on the prescribed total energy as follows from the above mentioned relationship.

Maximum control

The maximum control serves two objects:

  (i) to realize a prescribed constant power–time relationship as accurately as possible
 (ii) in any case to avoid exceeding the maximum.

To solve this problem a strategy can be imagined in which the available energy is exactly planned ahead, distributed over the separate users. For this a system would be required that controls the planned setpoints. This strategy leads to success if the energy users only alter their consumption in a prescribed manner, as for

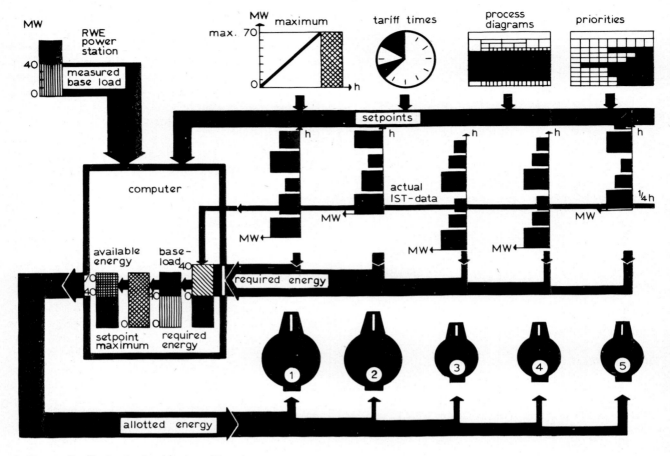

4   *Energy distribution in the electric melting shop*

example, in the case of heating furnaces for electrode manufacture.

For arc furnaces for steelmaking this condition is not sufficiently fulfilled. A power diagram according to Fig. 2 is valid, but in this diagram shifts in the timing that do not influence the relation between power and energy can occur. Such a shift in timing occurs at every deviation from normal operation such as, for example:

(i) deviations from the predicted specific energy
(ii) changed heating times for organizational reasons
(iii) breakdowns.

Each of these deviations will disturb the energy distribution schedule and requires the making of a new schedule. Therefore under these conditions no satisfactory solution can be expected using this strategy. The method chosen here therefore assumes that at a suitable maximum power value for a sufficient number of switchable consumers keeping strictly to the maximum, there will be maximum use of the available energy, at least to the degree described in the method above.

Coarse control

The control of the maximum is performed acyclically. The times, at which a check is calculated, are obtained with the following formula (*see* Figs. 5 and 6)

$$A_R = P_{max} \cdot T_1 + P_{v1}(T_R - T_1)$$

in which

A_R energy still available for the control period
P_{max} maximum possible power at time t
T_1 time interval up to change in power
P_{v1} predicted power after power change
T_R rest in control period.

This calculation is made for the first time when a new control period, e.g. of 15 min, starts. After that the calculations are made only when the predicted time of

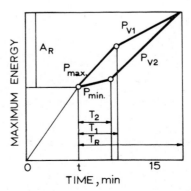

$A_R = P_{max} \cdot T_1 + P_{V1}(T_R - T_1)$ gives switching time $t + T_1$
$A_R = P_{min} \cdot T_2 + P_{V2}(T_R - T_2)$ gives switching time $t + T_2$

5   *Control calculation*

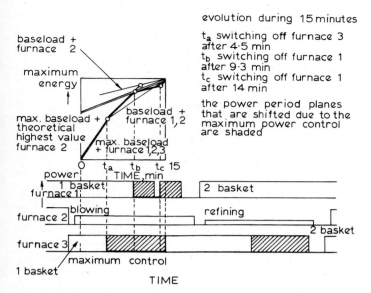

evolution during 15 minutes

t_a switching off furnace 3 after 4·5 min
t_b switching off furnace 1 after 9·3 min
t_c switching off furnace 1 after 14 min

the power period planes that are shifted due to the maximum power control are shaded

6 *Maximum control*

control is reached or when a change takes place in the required power for the furnace.

Additional to these acyclic calculations, calculations are performed periodically, e.g. every 2 min when extreme power conditions prevail. The step in power change that can be taken at time $t + T_1$ is calculated roughly by computer based on the momentary plant conditions and priorities. The power after the step is therefore

$$P_{V1} = P_S + P_G - P_A$$

in which

P_S measured sum of all furnace powers
P_G measured base load
P_A coarse step that can be switched off.

The power setting P_{max} for the interval $t + T_1$ takes account of uncontrollable variations in the base load.

$$P_{max} = P_S + P_{G\,max}$$

in which

$P_{G\,max}$ measured base load including the empirically encountered maximum deviation.

Therefore, T_1 can be calculated. As long as T_1 is not less than zero, there is no danger of exceeding the maximum. $T_1 = 0$ means that the coarse step must be switched off, $T_1 > 0$ means that during the rest of T_1 a further check is not necessary, if the furnace power is not increased.

Along the same lines is calculated T_2, the time interval before increasing the power in order to make full use of the available energy. For this the following relation is valid

$$A_R = P_{min} \cdot T_2 + P_{V2}(T_R - T_2)$$

with

$$P_{min} = P_S + P_{G\,min}$$

$$P_{V2} = P_S + P_G + P_Z$$

$P_{G\,min}$ measured base load minus the empirically determined largest deviation
P_Z the computer calculated coarse step to switch on.

In order to ensure the availability of the required power for furnaces in the refining stages, and to avoid unpredicted power changes during refining necessitating changes to the other furnaces, which would cause increased switching, a certain span of power requirement has been taken into account. For furnaces in the refining stages, energy is reserved corresponding to their momentary transformer setting.

Inquiry

In order to avoid switching on a furnace that has to be switched off again immediately by the maximum control, an inquiry of whether energy is available for this furnace is directed to the computer before switching on. In this case, deviations from the priority prescriptions are allowed for a short period if extra switching can be avoided. Therefore, a higher priority furnace, which will be used for a short time only according to the schedule, stays switched off, if to switch it on, a lower priority furnace would have to be switched off. Equally, switching on can be prohibited shortly before the end of a control period.

Precision control

By the control strategy so far described, maximum efficiency is achieved by switching on or off in large steps, e.g. a complete furnace. To avoid the switching on of large power steps for each control period, a precision control is realized by actuating the step switch of one furnace. For this the furnace with the lowest priority that is in the melt-down period is taken, as this is not yet at the minimum possible power step. The power deviation ΔP, that will have to be corrected by precision control, can be calculated as

$$\Delta P = \frac{A_R}{t_R} - (P_G + P_S)$$

$\Delta P > 0$ requires increase of power
$\Delta P < 0$ requires decrease of power.

To avoid hunting around $\Delta P = 0$, that could cause increased switching on of the step switch, a threshold is built in. Only when the threshold value is exceeded is the switch actuated.

Priority control

The priority control of the furnaces is completely independent of the control proper. It is continuously operated also outside the tariff periods, so that at the start of the tariff periods the priority determination is up to date. The determination of the coarse and precision steps takes place based on the order of priorities. The priorities for switching off depend on the process stages of the heats in the order:

(i) melting down
(ii) blowing
(iii) initial metallurgical stage
(iv) refining.

Within these stages the order is determined according to the starting time of a stage. Also the value of the charge in the furnace has an influence on the priority order. In certain circumstances a furnace can be changed in order, so it is possible to handle with effectively special or test charges.

Boundary conditions

From the review given here it is clear that the mathematical formulation of the control program can be kept simple. However, a good system requires a precise treatment of the boundary conditions together with the mathematical relations. In the case under consideration it is important to seek a solution that minimizes the amount of switching in order to avoid extra wear on the installation. Only by an intelligent choice of the limit values such as the variation of the base load to be expected, the reserved span of power for the furnaces in their refining periods, and the threshold for precision control, can this additional condition be fulfilled. It proves that a good system is most important for the choice of the limit values.

Computer hardware

For the present task a Siemens computer model 301 is installed with a core store of 12 288 words, a tape reader and puncher, a typewriter for communicating with the computer, and one for producing a data sheet. As the computer room is not always manned, an extra writer is installed in the energy control panel, giving data about the system and the installation. The interface contains 168 digital inputs, 96 alarms, and 192 digital outputs. The data of the heat records are processed in a computer centre. For this purpose the data are also produced as punch tape.

Interface

The process data the computer needs are taken, as far as possible, directly from the process. The marking of the process stages has not proved trustworthy. Manual inputs, organized such that they allow unequivocal information about the stage of the heat, are introduced from the control panel (Fig. 3). Signals taken from the process, are:

(i) position of the transformer step switch
(ii) position of the current switch
(iii) number of counts of the energy counter of the furnaces and the total input
(iv) single signals, such as the tariff period, start of the control period (e.g. 15 min), furnace tilted, furnace switch on, off.

The following commands are put out direct to the process:

(i) setpoint of the transformer step switch
(ii) setpoint of the current switch
(iii) furnace switch on, off
(iv) electrodes lift, lower.

The data from all furnaces, except the single inputs are put in via a multiplex input system, that at the computer input takes the width of a computer word of 24 bits. Similarly the output to the process uses a multiplex channel having the same width (Fig. 7).

Computer program

For programming the computer, the assembler language PROSA 300 is used. The computer actions not available in model 301, are simulated. For the accuracy required here, fixed-point arithmetic is sufficient.

The data listed in the computer are partly grouped per furnace (power lists), and partly according to the process (process lists). Based on the specific data per charge put in at the control panel, the computer selects from these lists the required furnace diagram. For producing the record the data assembled during a heat are stored and printed in the record at the end of the heat. The recording takes place in the interval between two heats. Only after finishing the record is the input of new data possible. This does not cause delays, but saves storing capacity. The program is constructed from independent parts, so that its structure is independent of the number of furnaces treated.

Errors in the data inputs that cannot be removed by repeating, as well as disturbances in the program operation lead to error indications on the communication typewriter which are repeated on the typewriter in the control panel. At electrical failure, the computer is stopped in a period given by the flywheel converter. After short interruptions (< 10 min) an unfinished charge

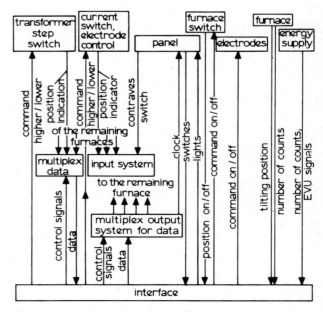

7   *Process connexion, shown for one furnace*

can be continued. After long delays the data of an interrupted charge are put on record, and the system is restarted.

RESULTS

The commissioning of the installation and the development of the computer inputs and outputs were not without difficulties, as the developments had to be made without interrupting production. As the steelmaking cycle repeats itself over several hours, fairly long times are needed for production tests. The only possible approach is passive computer operation, described above.

For the control of the power maximum the precision theoretically possible is obtained. The precision amounts to two counts of the total energy counter as this counting is the result of two sums. The precision could be improved if the counting steps were reduced from 100 kWh per count to 33 kWh. The maximum is not achieved when there is insufficient power demand, or the switching on of a furnace is unpredictably delayed. Here, a greater precision can only be obtained with an undesirable frequency of switching, because there exists a relation between the unpredictable load variations, number of switchings, and obtained precision.

In the present case, the load variations and the count steps allow an approach to the power maximum with a permissible switching frequency. On the average two furnaces are switched off per 15 min and 5–10 transformer step switchings take place. The conditions become somewhat worse if for economical reasons the maximum power value chosen is very low, so that under certain plant conditions the switching off of furnaces outside the melt-down period is necessary. This can be explained as follows. It sometimes happens that a furnace which is the first to be switched off according to its priority, accepts less power during melt-down than a furnace in its blowing period, which is only second priority for switching off. This can cause an undesirable switching frequency, which has to be avoided because of the precision of regulation.

Furnace control by computer has contributed to the rationalization of the production schedule. Notwithstanding the continuously increasing production by ever greater furnace productivity, and ever shorter heat times, the personnel have been relieved of routine jobs. Although now more personnel who are inexperienced have to be used productivity could be improved. It has proved possible to determine the specific energy diagram for the respective qualities with such an accuracy that a standard process schedule was obtained. This resulted in a certain gain in melt-down energy as unnecessary heating can be avoided at the end of a basket or at the end of the melt-down period. Additionally, a certain gain in time was experienced. Further, the lengthening of the lifetime of the refractory walls and roof is significant. Since applicable working points have been obtained for the furnace diagrams, there has been an increase in wall and roof life of about 30% compared to the operation without the computer, combined with a considerable saving in fettling time and spraying materials.

Three-phase electrode position-control system models for electric-arc furnaces

R. Roebuck

Dynamic models of three types of electrode position-control systems used for power input regulation with direct arc three-phase electric furnaces are outlined and the relevant features and dynamic characteristics are compared. The modelling and identification techniques used to derive these models are illustrated and the effectiveness of the techniques is discussed. The use of these models for fault finding, examination of setting-up procedures and control-system design is illustrated and a brief discussion of the economic considerations of using these models is also included.

During the past few years the capacity for producing steel in electric-arc furnaces has steadily increased. Electric-arc-furnace steels include the major part of the world's specialized alloy and stainless steels. With the increase in availability of steel scrap and the advent of prereduced iron manufacturing processes coupled with the substantially increasing market for higher quality steel products, the quantity of steel manufactured in electric-arc furnaces is more than likely to increase. Economic savings resulting from increased yield and improved efficiency can be very substantial, and thus more effective control of the electric-arc furnace process is becoming more important. Consider the example of a furnace with an annual output of 200 000 t with typical operating costs (1972) as shown below:

	£/t
Electrical energy	2·50
Graphite electrodes	1·50
Refractories	1·50
Labour	1·00
Scrap	13·00
Alloys	18·00
Oxygen	0·50
Total	38·00/ingot tonne

Operating costs including depreciation £2·00/min

To illustrate the magnitude of possible savings consider a 1% reduction in electricity, oxygen, electrodes, and refractory consumption and a 1% saving in working time.

1% saving in electricity, oxygen, electrodes, and refractories	£0·06/t
	£12 000 p.a.
1% saving in working time	3 days p.a.
	£8 600 p.a.

Every 1% improvement all round will give savings in excess of £20 000 per furnace, plus any additional profit from the capability to produce more steel. This is equivalent to £0·1/ingot tonne or 0·26%. In addition typically 5% of the graphite cost or £0·07/t can be incurred because of electrode breakages from scrap falls, non-conducting scrap, bad electrode jointing and handling, and poor quality graphite. Some breaks caused by scrap falls and non-conducting scrap can be prevented by good control systems.

This paper discusses the use of electrode position-control system models in order to investigate the design of electrode position servomechanisms to maximize heat transfer from the electric-arc discharge to the steel scrap and minimize electrode wear and refractory erosion. Maximum arc-power input will also minimize the tap to tap time and allow a greater output to be achieved, which could also reduce electrode and refractory

The author is with BSC, Swinden Laboratories

erosion/ingot tonne. The operation of electrode position-control systems for electric power input regulation and process constraints in direct electric-arc furnaces have been discussed in previous work[1,2,3,4] and thus only the process constraints relative to electrode position control will be discussed briefly. Refractory wear from the arc discharge tends to increase with arc length if the refractories are exposed to the arc discharge, and electrode wear tends to increase excessively when operated over extended periods with high arc currents. However, very short arc lengths are undesirable due to the increased possibility of scrap falls and consequent electrode breakages caused when boring into scrap with a very short arc length. Short arcs can also produce undesirable and excessive electrode-slag activity.

Electric-arc furnace transformers are normally designed to have a duty cycle which will allow up to 25% overload during the melting period. This operating point quite often corresponds to the maximum arc power and thus any deviation from this point will reduce arc power. A typical power curve for an electric-arc furnace transformer and secondary system on top voltage tap is illustrated in Fig. 1 together with a typical power input program in Fig. 2. In order to illustrate the possible costs of operating an arc furnace with a set point error consider a mean current unbalance of 5%. This could be caused by a set point drift, excessive control-system dead zone, a slow control system, or bad scrap giving rise to a poor power input profile. Consider an average 5% increase in phase current and MVA. This will give rise to a 10% increase in transformer heating, about 1% increase in circuit power, 1% reduction in arc power, and also a power factor reduction from 0·77 to 0·74.

In view of the increased transformer heating it may well be necessary to reduce the voltage tap in order to limit power dissipation before the end of the melting

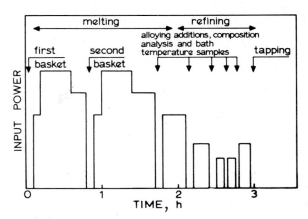

2   Typical production cycle for a three-phase electric-arc furnace

cycle. However, in view of the improved cooling at higher temperatures the period under overload conditions would probably need to be reduced by only 7%. The circuit power would then probably have to be reduced to less than the nominal rating if the duty cycle rating was not to be exceeded. Additional time would then be needed to input the required energy. The required energy input would also have to be increased because of the increased heat loss during the additional melting time. This will result in an additional 3% melting time and 1% extra electrical energy being required, which is in excess of £30 000 p.a. for the typical furnace already considered. This is equivalent to a total additional cost of £0·15/ingot tonne or 0·39%. Any penalty charges for operating at a lower power factor would obviously increase the operational cost of operating with current unbalance.

In order to minimize refractory wear, when melting down, the furnace transformer should be operated with a set point corresponding to maximum arc power where the arc length will be substantially less than when operating with a higher power factor set point. The set point arc currents should not cause excessive electrode ablation and if this occurs larger diameter electrodes should be considered. The electrode position-control system should be fast enough to minimize overheating caused by short circuits and also to minimize long arc lengths caused by the arc stretching to extinction. The sensitivity of the control system should be sufficient to minimize the dead zone in the electrode position servo-mechanism. Electrode velocity and control system sensitivity also determine the average power input during the melting period and this must be taken into account when designing the control system. However the system sensitivity must not be too great in order to minimize electrode mast activity which can give rise to excessive electrode-slag activity, supply system disturbances and electrode breakages.

The modelling and design of electrode position control systems for electric-arc furnaces has received little attention in the past. Brown and Langman[5,6] used transfer function relationships to simulate a non-linear single-phase model in the design of adaptive controllers. Nicholson and Roebuck[7,8] have used linear and non-linear single-phase multivariable models in order to

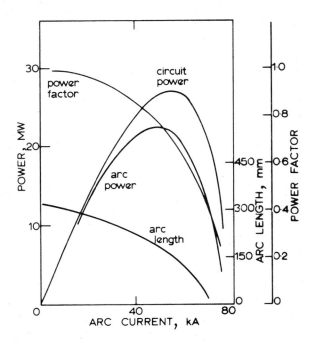

1   Typical arc-furnace power curves

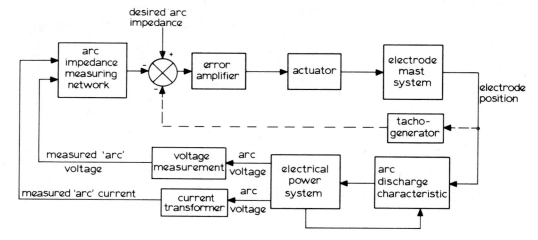

3   *Block diagram of impedance control for one phase of a typical arc-furnace control system*

design optimally controlled electrode-position servo-mechanisms. In previous work[9] the author has described simple linear techniques for the analysis of multivariable interacting three-phase control-system models. However, the derivation and identification of non-linear three-phase models of electrode position-control systems has received little attention. The models outlined in this work are suitable for analog computer simulation and also digital simulation if implicit algebraic equations can be solved. The simulation work illustrated in this paper was mainly carried out on analog/hybrid computers. Various simulation techniques for this particular application have previously been discussed.[7]

All the electrode position-control systems illustrated and described in this paper operate on the same basic principle of maintaining constant 'arc' impedance as shown in Fig. 3. A voltage signal is provided to give a 'lower signal' to the electrode position controller when too little arc current is available. A current signal is provided to give a 'raise signal' when too much arc current is being carried in a particular phase. With the two signals combined, as illustrated in Fig. 3, they produce an effective constant 'arc' impedance regulator. In order to prevent one electrode driving into the scrap, when the other two electrodes are too far away from the scrap to draw an arc, the electrical power-supply system is left floating relative to the control system common potential and hence the voltage of the electrode touching the scrap falls to zero preventing any further downward movement. However, this causes substantial interference between phases under normal operation.

CLASSICAL IDENTIFICATION TECHNIQUES

In order to carry out an investigation into the behaviour of dynamic systems it is necessary to obtain the transfer functions or differential equations describing the system. However, the dynamics of a system are often obtained by measurements in the time or frequency domain. These notes outline the classical identification techniques used to convert from one domain to another within the time, frequency, or complex domain. All the techniques

described assume that the system under investigation can be described by linear differential equations.

Fourier series analysis of periodic signals

Any periodic function can be represented in the form of a Fourier series where

$$f(t) = \frac{a_0}{2} + a_1 \cos(t) + a_2 \cos(2t) + \ldots + a_n \cos(nt)$$
$$+ b_1 \sin(t) + b_2 \sin(2t) + \ldots + b_n \sin(nt)$$

where

$$a_n = \frac{1}{\pi} \int_0^{2\pi} f(t) \cos(nt)\,\mathrm{d}t$$

and

$$b_n = \frac{1}{\pi} \int_0^{2\pi} f(t) \sin(nt)\,\mathrm{d}t$$

If the continuous function is sampled discretely as shown in Fig. 4,

then

$$a_n = \frac{1}{m} \sum_{k=1}^{2m} f_k \cos\frac{nk\pi}{m}$$

and

$$b_n = \frac{1}{m} \sum_{k=1}^{2m} f_k \sin\frac{nk\pi}{m}$$

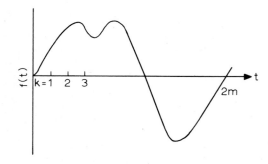

4   *A continuous function sampled discretely*

The above expressions are suitable for use as a digital algorithm for calculating Fourier series coefficients. For graphical analysis a simple vector summation can be used.

$$a_n + jb_n = \frac{1}{\Delta n} \sum_{k=1}^{2m} fk \underline{/nk\pi/m}$$

To faithfully reproduce a signal the sampling period must be at least twice the highest significant frequency component present.

Fourier integral analysis of aperiodic signals

From the Fourier integral

$$f(t) = \frac{1}{2\pi} \int_{-\infty}^{\infty} \left(\int_{-\infty}^{\infty} f(t)\, e^{-wt}\, dt \right) e^{jwt}\, dw$$

a Fourier transform pair can be defined as follows

$$f(t) = \frac{1}{2\pi} \int_{-\infty}^{\infty} g(w)\, e^{jwt}\, dw$$

$$g(w) = \int_{-\infty}^{\infty} f(t)\, e^{-jwt}\, dt$$

where $f(t)$ is an impulse response and $g(w)$ the corresponding frequency response.

TIME TO FREQUENCY CORRELATION

The above equations can be used for translation between the time domain and frequency domain. In order to utilize these equations the known function must be analytic and thus a discrete algorithm is required for use with experimental data as illustrated in Fig. 5.

Using trapezoidal approximations of the impulse transient response gives the discrete time to frequency conversion algorithm shown below.

$$g(w) = \frac{f_0}{jw} + \sum_{n=0}^{k} \left[\left(\frac{f_{n+1} - f_n}{t_{n+1} - t_n} \right) \right.$$

$$- \frac{1}{w^2} (\cos wt_n - j \sin wt_n)$$

$$\left. - \left(\frac{f_{n+1} - f_n}{t_{n+1} - t_n} \right) - \frac{1}{w^2} (\cos wt_{n+1} - j \sin wt_{n+1}) \right]$$

Techniques do exist for fast Fourier transforms when repeated evaluation of large quantities of data exist for deriving high-order models.[16]

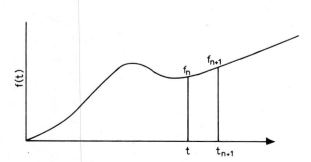

5   Discrete algorithm required for use with experimental data

Decomposition of frequency responses (Appendices 1, 2, and 3)[10]

The transfer function for a time invariant system can be expressed as a ratio of two polynomials in S

$$G(S) = \frac{b_m S^m + \ldots + b_1 S + b_0}{a_n S^n + \ldots + a_1 S + a_0}$$

This can be decomposed into Heavisides form of partial functions for inverse Laplace transformation

$$G(S) = \frac{k_1}{S + \alpha_1} + \ldots + \frac{k_n}{S + \alpha_n}$$

Bode's form of decomposition is to factor both the numerator and the denominator

$$G(s) = \frac{K(S + \beta_1) \ldots (S + \beta_m)}{(S + \alpha_1) \ldots (S + \alpha_n)}$$

Bode's decomposition of a frequency response provides an approximate graphical technique for deriving a transfer function. Bush's form of decomposition can be represented as follows:

$$G(s) = \frac{(\ldots ((b_m S + b_{m-1})S + b_{m-2})S + \ldots)S + b_0}{(\ldots ((a_n S + a_{n-1})S + a_{n-2})S + \ldots)S + a_0}$$

Bush's decomposition of a frequency response provides a more accurate graphical and numerical technique for deriving highly oscillatory transfer functions. Wiener's form of decomposition is given by

$$G(s) = a_0 + a_1 \left(\frac{1-S}{1+S} \right) + \ldots + a_n \left(\frac{1-S}{1+S} \right)^n$$

Wiener Lee's decomposition of a frequency response provides an accurate graphical and numerical technique for deriving heavily damped transfer functions.

Transformation between open- and closed-loop frequency response

The closed-loop transfer function

$$C(s) = \frac{G(s)}{1 + G(s) \cdot H(s)}$$

The open-loop transfer function

$$G(s) = \frac{C(s)}{1 + C(s) \cdot H(s)}$$

Graphical conversion techniques are as follows:

(i) Hall's charts consist of rectangular axes for the open-loop response and contours for closed-loop magnitude and phase. This technique is most useful for converting from open-loop to closed-loop response

(ii) Chen-Shen's chart consists of rectangular axes for the closed-loop response and contours for the open-loop Cartesian form. This technique is most useful for converting from closed-loop to open-loop response

(iii) Nichol's chart consists of rectangular axes for open-loop log magnitude and phase, and closed-loop contours also give the log magnitude and phase. This technique is more suitable for converting from open-loop to closed-loop form.

Complex curve fitting of frequency response[11]

Levy's complex curve fitting technique separates the numerator and denominator of the unknown transfer function $M(jw)$ into real and imaginary parts. If the data points are given by $C(jw)$, then the problem is therefore to minimize the error function:

$$[C(jw) - M(jw)]$$

at each sampling point on the frequency response curve. Using a modified least squares approach, the error^2 is summed up over the sampling frequencies and setting the partial derivatives of this summation with respect to each of the coefficients to zero to give a set of linear simultaneous algebraic equations which can be solved to give the fundamental form of transfer function.

Simple time domain to transfer function transformation

Simple graphical techniques for step time response to transfer function translation. For systems which can be approximated by a first order lag

$$G(s) = \frac{A}{1 + ST} = \frac{\theta_0}{\theta_{in}}$$

where $A = \theta_0/\theta_{in}$ when $t \to \infty$ and $t = T$ when $\theta_0 = 0.632 A\theta_{in}$. For oscillatory systems which can be approximated by a second-order transfer function

$$G(s) = \frac{w_n^2}{S^2 + 2.\xi.w_nS + w_n^2} = \frac{\theta_0}{\theta_{in}}$$

$$\xi = \frac{\delta}{2 + \delta^2}$$

where the logarithmic decrement $\delta = \log_e \theta_i(\theta_{i+1})$ and θ_i is the amplitude of the ith overshoot $w_n = w_0/\sqrt{1 - \xi^2}$ where w_0 is the damped natural frequency.

Non-linear modelling

The classical linear identification techniques discussed have been used together with PRBS techniques to model non-linear electrode position-control servomechanisms. The servomechanism models have been derived as a number of low order transfer functions. In all but one case these transfer functions consist of linear time constants and gain characteristics which may be of linear or non-linear form. The non-linear gain characteristics have been obtained from static characteristic checks on plant and the associated time constants obtained by identifying the transfer function over a linear operating region using the techniques discussed. The only exception to this case consists of a non-linear gain characteristic with a time constant which varies

with input amplitude. This transfer function was estimated from static characteristic checks and step input disturbances carried out on plant.

IDENTIFICATION USING PSEUDO RANDOM BINARY SEQUENCES (Appendix 4)[12]

All the classical identification techniques discussed previously have one major disadvantage which is the requirement that the system to be identified must be off-line. Obviously a transient response can be obtained much more quickly than a frequency response. However it is not always feasible to have a large arc furnace available off-line if maintenance programs have to be carried out during short shut down periods. In addition to this, off-line identification does not allow the effective gain of the arc discharge to be identified as the arc only forms part of the feedback loop of the control system when the furnace is operating. If a maximum length pseudo-random binary sequence is used to identify the impulse response of a system various assumptions have to be checked. For the system shown in Appendix 4 the cross correlation of the system output with a known input disturbance is given by

$$\phi_{wy}(\tau) = \int_{-\infty}^{+\infty} g(\lambda)[\phi_{ww}(t - \lambda) + \phi_{wu}(\tau - \lambda)] \, d\lambda$$

where

$\phi_{wy}(\tau)$ is the cross correlation between input and output

$\phi_{ww}(\tau)$ is the auto-correlation of the input

$\phi_{wu}(\tau)$ is the cross correlation between the known input and the noise input disturbances

$g(t)$ is the system impulse response.

The total length of the sequence must be an order of magnitude greater than the largest system time constant to be identified. The basic sequence interval should be an order of magnitude less than the smallest system time constant to be identified. The cross correlation between the input PRBS and any noise disturbance should be negligible when compared with the auto-correlation function of the PRBS. In order to minimize disturbances within the system under identification the magnitude of the input PRBS sequence should be restricted to give sufficiently sensible results.

$$\text{Given} \quad \phi_{wy}(\tau) = \int_{-\infty}^{\infty} g(\lambda)\delta(\tau - \lambda) \, d\lambda = g(\tau)$$

The impulse response of a system is given by the cross correlation of the system output and input when excited with white noise. Consider the auto-correlation function of a pseudo-random binary sequence as illustrated in Appendix 4. If it is assumed that the PRBS is generated from a maximum length sequence where the basic discrete time interval is taken as λ the complete cycle length for an nth order characteristic polynomial is given by $N\lambda = (2^n - 1)\lambda$ and the auto-correlation function is given by

$$\phi_{ww}(\tau) = \frac{1}{N\lambda} \int_0^{N\lambda} w(t) . w(t + \tau) \, dt$$

i.e.

$$\phi_{ww}(t) = 1 - \frac{N + 1}{N}\left(\frac{\tau}{\lambda}\right) \quad \text{for } (\tau) < \lambda$$

and

$$\phi_{ww}(t) = -\frac{1}{N} \quad \text{for } \lambda < (\tau) < (N - 1)\lambda$$

The cross-correlation function between a maximum length sequence and the output from a system to which a maximum length PRBS has been applied as an input is given by

$$\phi_{wy}(\tau) = \frac{1}{N\lambda} \int_0^{N\lambda} w(t) . y(t + \tau) \, dt$$

i.e.

$$\phi_{wy}(\tau) = g(t) \quad \text{the system impulse response.}$$

If points are required on the impulse response curves $\phi_{wy}(\tau)$ can be evaluated at intervals which are multiples of λ from the equation below

$$\phi_{wy}(\tau) = \frac{1}{N\lambda} \sum w(t) . y(t + \tau)$$

where $t = 0, \lambda, 2\lambda \ldots N\lambda$.

ELECTRODE-POSITION SERVOMECHANISM MODELS

Dynamic non-linear models are developed for three distinct types of electrode-position controllers. These models are derived from theoretical considerations and plant data where the general form of the models were determined from past experience in modelling similar servomechanism control systems. The data obtained from plant trials are used to estimate the parameters in the predefined structure of the models. Mathematical models of the three types of controllers are derived for one phase only since the servomechanisms are virtually identical for all three phases. Phase unbalance is introduced into the control system by the unbalance electrical power system.

Hydraulic actuator

The direct haul hydraulic actuator electrode position-control servomechanism is illustrated in Fig. 6 and the mathematical model being developed is also based upon the block diagram representation of this figure. The error detected by the arc impedance measuring circuit provides the input to the hydraulic regulator valve amplifier. The output position of the two-stage regulator valve is coupled mechanically to the spool of the water flow control valve, which adjusts the volume of liquid in the electrode ram and in turn positions the electrode tip.

ARC IMPEDANCE MEASURING NETWORK

The simplified arc impedance measuring circuit shown in Fig. 6 supplies an error signal as direct current to the input of the hydraulic regulator valve. It has been assumed that the main current transformers and interposing transformers have negligibly small time constants and do not saturate. It is also assumed that the rectifier bridges can produce ideal direct current, because of the extremely large smoothing capacitor, and that each bridge can be replaced by a series resistor and ideal rectifier when considering operation about the operating point. It has been shown that the following linear differential equations can be used to predict accurately

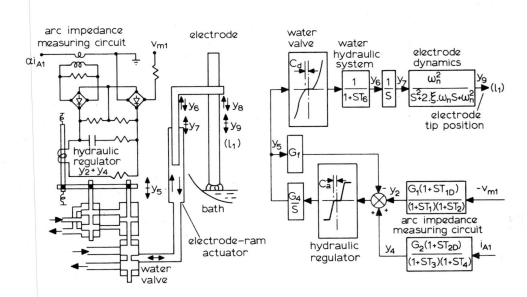

6   *Hydraulic electrode position controller*

the transient behaviour of the arc impedance measuring network about the operating point

$$\dot{y}_1 = \frac{-G_1 . v_{m1} - G_1 . T_{1D} . v_{m1} - y_1}{T_1}$$

$$\dot{y}_2 = \frac{y_1 - y_2}{T_2}$$

$$\dot{y}_3 = \frac{G_2 . i_1 + G_2 . T_{2D} . (i_1) - y_3}{T_3}$$

$$\dot{y}_4 = \frac{y_3 - y_4}{T_4}$$

The coefficients of these equations are calculated from component values accurately measured on site.

HYDRAULIC REGULATOR VALVE

The hydraulic regulator valve is a two-stage hydro-mechanical feedback amplifier and the non-linear characteristics and constraints are illustrated in Figs. 7 and 8. These were obtained on plant from a static characteristic check and a transient response following a step input also illustrated in these figures. The non-linear differential equations governing the performance of the regulator as determined from these plant trials are given by the following:

If

$$(y_4 + y_2 - G_{1f} . y_5) < \pm C_a$$

then

$$\dot{y}_5 = 0$$

If

$$(y_4 + y_2 - G_{1f} . y_5) > C_b$$

then

$$\dot{y}_5 = C_c . G_4$$

If

$$(y_4 + y_2 - G_{1f} . y_5) < -C_b$$

then

$$\dot{y}_5 = -C_c . G_4$$

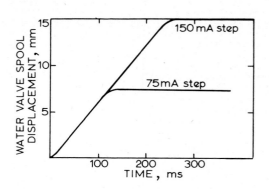

8   *Transient performance of the hydraulic regulator*

If

$$C_b > (y_4 + y_2 - G_{1f} . y_5) > Ca$$

then

$$\dot{y}_5 = G_4 . G_3(y_4 + y_2 - G_{1f} . y_5 - C_a)$$

and if

$$-C_b < (y_4 + y_2 - G_{1f} . y_5) < -C_a$$

then

$$\dot{y}_5 = G_4 . G_3(y_4 + y_2 - G_{1f} . y_5 + C_a)$$

WATER HYDRAULIC SYSTEM

The water hydraulic system is controlled by the flow through a non-linear water flow control valve. This flow control valve is effectively an integrator with a non-linear gain. The experimental static valve characteristic obtained from plant data is illustrated in Fig. 9. The non-linear differential equations governing the behaviour of the hydraulic system are given by the following:

If

$$y_5 < \pm C_d$$

then

$$\dot{y}_6 = 0 \cdot 0$$

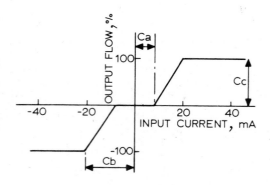

7   *Steady state characteristic of hydraulic regulator*

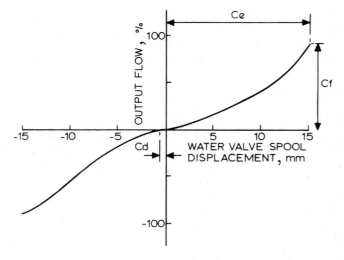

9   *Steady state water flow control-valve characteristic*

If

$$y_5 = C_e$$

then

$$\dot{y}_6 = \frac{C_f - y_6}{T_6}$$

If

$$y_5 = -C_e$$

then

$$\dot{y}_6 = \frac{-C_f - y_6}{T_6}$$

If

$$C_e > y_5 > C_d$$

then

$$\dot{y}_6 = \frac{fn(y_5 - C_d) - y_6}{T_6}$$

If

$$-C_e < y_5 < -C_d$$

then

$$\dot{y}_6 = \frac{fn(y_5 + C_d) - y_6}{T_6}$$

and

$$\dot{y}_7 = y_6$$

where $fn(y_5 + C_d)$ and $fn(y_5 - C_d)$ are the non-linear functions representing the water valve characteristic for downward and upward motion respectively.

In order to obtain a satisfactory mathematical model of these non-linear functions the water valve characteristic is represented by a polynomial approximation of the experimental data. A least squares approximation is used as follows: Given a set of data points (t_k, y_k, e_k),

$$k = 1, M$$

where M is the number of data points, t_k are the abscissa coordinates, y_k are the ordinates, and e_k are the error weightings given to particular points. The approximating polynomial $q_N(t)$ is found such that the expression for P_N is minimized

where $P_N = \sum\limits_{i=1}^{m} e_i[y_i - q_N(t_i)]^2$

A better approximation is required at the threshold of the characteristic because a given error is proportionally larger for small disturbances in water valve spool displacement. In the least squares approximation technique described above, the data points near the threshold of the characteristic were therefore given additional weighting. A sixth order polynomial approximation was finally chosen because the accuracy of this approximation was marginally better than the reliable accuracy

of the original experimental data. The effective time constant of the water hydraulic system has been calculated from the manufacturer's specification of the equipment and hydraulic fluid.

ELECTRODE-MAST STRUCTURE

The electrode-mast structure dynamics were identified using accelerometers on the electrode tip to examine the transient behaviour and frequency response of this mechanical system. The transfer function of this structure could have been identified using Fourier transformers to convert from time to frequency domain and utilizing a decomposition technique to convert from frequency to complex domain. However, the transient response was obviously of a second order form as successive overshoots exhibited almost fixed amplitude ratios. The parameters of the second order model were therefore estimated using the simple expressions in the section on simple time domain to transfer function transformation discussed earlier.

The electrode-mast dynamics can, therefore, be represented as a simple mass-spring damper system without incurring undue inaccuracies and thus the following differential equation can be used to represent the electrode structure behaviour.

$$M \cdot \ddot{y}_9 + F \cdot \dot{y}_9 + K \cdot y_9 = K \cdot y_7$$

or

$$\dot{y}_8 = W_n^2 \cdot y_7 - W_n^2 \cdot y_9 - 2\xi \cdot W_n \cdot y_8$$

and

$$\dot{y}_9 = y_8$$

where

$$W_n^2 = K/M$$

and

$$\xi = \frac{F}{2\sqrt{M \cdot K}}$$

K Stiffness coefficient
F Viscous friction coefficient
M Inertia constant
W_n Undamped natural frequency of oscillation
ξ Damping ratio

Amplidyne, Ward-Leonard, winch actuator

A model of the direct-haul direct-current motor operated electrode-control system illustrated in Fig. 10 is developed on the basis of the block diagram also shown in this figure. The error detected by the arc impedance measuring network is used as the control field input for the amplidyne rotating amplifier. The amplified error available from the amplidyne armature is used to supply the shunt field current for the direct current generator in the Ward-Leonard drive system. The direct-current motor in the drive system positions the electrode via a direct-haul gravity winch system.

Ward-Leonard
controller

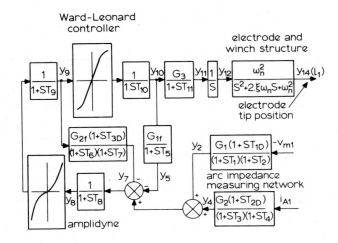

electrode and
winch structure

electrode
tip position

amplidyne

arc impedance
measuring network

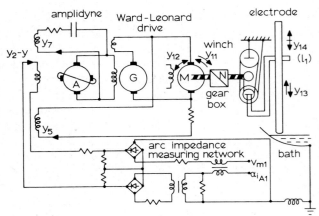

10   *Ward-Leonard drive, winch-operated electrode position controller*

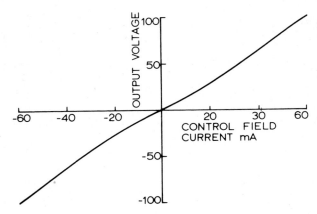

11   *Typical steady state amplidyne characteristics*

ARC-IMPEDANCE MEASURING NETWORK

The greatly simplified arc-impedance measuring circuit shown in Fig. 9 supplies a direct-current error signal to the control field of the amplidyne. Owing to a relatively complicated circuit being employed which included numerous saturating transformers and chokes in addition to the more usual transformers and rectifiers, it was decided to identify the behaviour of this circuit using frequency domain techniques. However, the transient behaviour of the circuit indicates a relatively highly damped response with an apparent high frequency oscillatory mode. It was, therefore, decided that all three classical frequency domain decomposition techniques previously discussed would be used and compared. This exercise clearly illustrated that this arc-impedance measuring network could be represented by linear differential equations identical in structure to those of the hydraulic actuator in equations, but with substantially differing coefficients. The accuracy of the model is not ideal, but higher-order models derived by the decomposition techniques illustrated previously did not increase the accuracy with which the non-linear behaviour of this network could be approximated. This is presumably caused by the non-linearities inherent in the circuit components. Bode's graphical decomposition was the more successful technique in this particular case

because of the inclusion of heavily damped modes and a high-frequency oscillatory mode.

AMPLIDYNE

The amplidyne is a high gain rotating power amplifier used for providing the power to drive the generator shunt field of the Ward-Leonard drive system. The static characteristic of the amplidyne is relatively linear as shown in Fig. 11. This was obtained from data obtained during a static characteristic check on plant. The differential equations governing the behaviour of the amplidyne were obtained from dynamic response checks to a step input disturbance and are given by the following:

$$\dot{y}_8 = (y_2 + y_4 - y_5 - y_7 - y_8)/T_8$$

$$\dot{y}_9 = f_3[(y_8 - y_9)/T_9]$$

where

$$\dot{y}_5 = (G_{1f} \cdot y_{10} - y_5)/T_5$$

$$\dot{y}_6 = (y_9 - y_6)/T_6$$

$$\dot{y}_7 = (G_{2f} \cdot y_6 + G_{2f} \cdot T_{3D} \cdot \dot{y}_6 - y_7)/T_7$$

WARD-LEONARD DRIVE

The Ward-Leonard variable speed drive provides the torque necessary to raise the weight of the electrode-mast structure against gravity. The static characteristics and

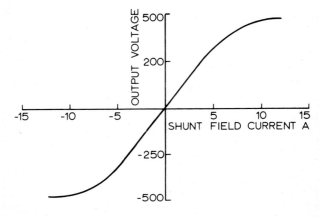

12   *Typical steady state differential compound generator characteristic*

transient response to a step input were again obtained from plant trials and can be described by the following differential equations and non-linear characteristics illustrated in Fig. 12:

$$\dot{y}_{10} = f_4[(y_9 - y_{10})/T_{10}]$$

$$\dot{y}_{11} = (G_3 . y_{10} - y_{11})/T_{11}$$

and

$$\dot{y}_{12} = y_{11}$$

ELECTRODE-MAST DYNAMICS

The dynamic characteristics of the mast structure were again investigated using accelerometer devices on the electrode tip and disturbing the electrode mast with a step input. The equations describing the behaviour of the electrode-mast structure are of the same form as for the hydraulic actuator.

$$\dot{y}_{13} = W_n^2(y_{12} - y_{14}) - 2 . \xi . W_n . y_{13}$$

and

$$\dot{y}_{14} = y_{13}$$

Fourier transform techniques were used to investigate higher order models from the step response data. However, unless unpractical higher order models are used second- or third-order models provide the best compromise between model order and accuracy.

A second amplidyne, Ward-Leonard system has been modelled also where the basic form of the model is very similar to that outlined above. The significant differences occur in the feedback to the stabilizing field of the amplidyne and also the form of the arc-impedance measuring network. The form of the feedback in the stabilizing network is simply given by

$$\dot{y}_7 = G_{2f}(y_9 - y_7)/T_6$$

and the form of the arc-impedance measuring network is given by

$$\dot{y}_2 = (-G_1 . V_{m1} - y_2)/T_4$$

and

$$\dot{y}_4 = (G_2 . i_1 - y_4)/T3$$

Eddy-current coupling–induction motor, winch actuator

The direct haul eddy-current coupling electrode position-control system is illustrated in Fig. 13. The error detected by the arc-impedance measuring network is amplified and used as the eddy-current coupling field current. The field current controls torque transmission between the alternating current induction motor and the winch drum to position the electrode and mast through a direct-haul gravity winch system. The eddy-current control system has been modelled on the basis of the PRBS technique illustrated in the previous section utilizing a commercially produced PRBS generator and correlator. A fourth-order model has been derived from the cross-correlation function approximating to the

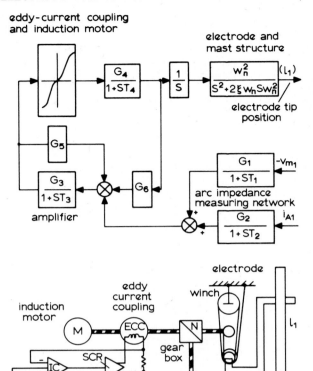

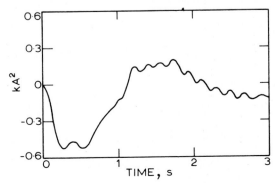

13 *Eddy-current coupling, winch-operated electrode position controller*

system impulse response illustrated in Fig. 14. The impulse response has been converted to a frequency response using the simple Fourier algorithm illustrated earlier. Bush's decomposition was then used to obtain a simple fourth-order transfer function relating electrode position to arc-current error, i.e.

$$\frac{W_m^2 \qquad W_n^2}{(S^2 + 2 . \zeta . W_m S + W_m^2)(S + 2 . \xi W_n S + W_n^2)}$$

where W_n and ξ approximate to the natural undamped frequency of oscillation and damping ratio of the

14 *Impulse response of eddy-current coupling winch system*

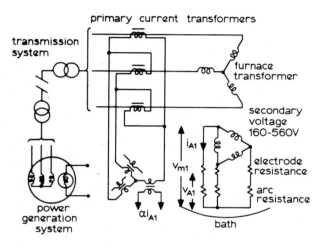

15   *Electrical power-supply system*

electrode-mast structure and W_m and ζ approximate to the overall frequency of oscillation and damping ratio of the control system.

ELECTRICAL POWER-SUPPLY SYSTEM MODEL

A three-phase electrical power-supply system model is developed where the power-generation system is represented as an equivalent synchronous alternator and the power-transmission system is represented as an equivalent three-phase network referred to the secondary of the furnace transformer as shown in Fig. 15.

Electrical power-generation system

The power-generation system will be represented as an equivalent three-phase synchronous machine which will be assumed to be a cylindrical rotor machine consisting of three-phase windings on the rotating armature and one excitation winding on the machine stator. This will enable transient and subtransient effects associated with the national grid system to be included in the generation-system model. The differential equations which are developed to represent the equivalent synchronous machine neglect the armature time constant associated with the direct current components and harmonic components as the fundamental sinusoidal components

are the basic quantities of interest. The equations are developed for electrical transient behaviour only as the effects of load-power changes from one arc furnace are considered to be too small to affect the system frequency and mechanical dynamics. For changes in power-system loading consider the generalized machine representation of the equivalent synchronous alternator shown in Fig. 16. Equating the applied voltages to the short circuit damper windings to zero the equations representing the dynamic performance of the equivalent generalized machine can be expressed in the standard form[13]

if

$$ed = Gd(S) . Sid + ra . id + vd$$

and

$$eq = Gq(S) . Siq + ra . iq + vq$$

then

$$ed = S\theta . Gq(S) . iq + Gf(S) . Sef$$

and

$$eq = -S\theta . Gd(S) . id - S\theta . Gf(S) . ef$$

where

$$Gd(S) = \frac{(1 + S . Td')(1 + S . Td'')Ld}{(1 + S . Tdo')(1 + S . Tdo'')}$$

$$Gq(S) = \frac{(1 + S . Tq'')Lq}{(1 + S . Tqo'')}$$

$$Gf(S) = \frac{(1 + S . Tkd)}{(1 + S . Tdo')(1 + S . Tdo'')} . \frac{Lmd}{rf}$$

ra	armature resistance
rf	field resistance
Ld	direct axis total per unit inductance
Lq	quadrature axis total per unit inductance
Lmd	common per unit mutual or magnetizing inductance on the direct axis
Tdo'	direct axis transient open-circuit time constant
Td'	direct axis transient short-circuit time constant
Tdo''	direct axis subtransient open-circuit time constant
Tdo''	direct axis subtransient open-circuit time constant

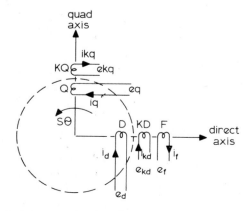

16   *Equivalent generalized machine representation*

Td'' direct axis subtransient short-circuit time constant

Tqo'' quadrature axis subtransient open-circuit time constant

Tq'' quadrature axis subtransient short-circuit time constant

Tkd direct axis damper leakage-time constant

These equations can be used to predict the transient performance of the equivalent three-phase synchronous alternator representing the grid system. For a given range of angular positions θ the transient performance can be investigated over extremely short periods of time on a cycle to cycle basis by observing the instantaneous values of the electrical variables using Park's transformation.[13]

The investigation of transients which extend over longer periods of time, where the actual sinusoidal variations are not of interest, requires rms values of the electrical variables. The excitation and governor of a large alternator set is basically varied to reduce the voltage and frequency errors to a minimum value and to adjust the total output power to meet the demanded load power. It has already been assumed that the mechanical dynamics could be neglected and hence the frequency error is also assumed to be zero. The excitation voltage of the equivalent machine can also be assumed to be constant over the time scale under consideration. In order to obtain a simple analytic solution of the equations representing the dynamic behaviour of the equivalent synchronous alternator it is necessary to consider short-circuit conditions.[13] Consider a line-to-line short circuit of the alternator where θ is again the angle between the direct axis and phase one at the instant of short circuit. For a short circuit between phases it can be shown that the alternating component of current is given by

$$i = \sqrt{3}E\left\{\frac{1}{xd + x2} + \left[\frac{1}{xd' + x2} - \frac{1}{xd + x2}\right]_e\right.$$

$$- t/Tdd'$$

$$+ \left[\frac{1}{xd'' + x2} - \frac{1}{xd' + x2}\right]_e$$

$$\left. - t/Tdd''\right\}\cos(wt + \theta)$$

where

$$Tdd' = \frac{xd' + x2}{xd + x2}\cdot Tdo'$$

$$Tdd'' = \frac{xd'' + x2}{xd' + x2}\cdot Tdo''$$

$$x2 = \sqrt{xd''\cdot xq''}$$

The incremental change in per unit rms current at any given instant is proportional to

$$1 + \left[\frac{xd + x2}{xd' + x2} - 1\right]_e - t/Tdd'$$

$$+ \left[\frac{xd + x2}{xd'' + x2} - \frac{xd + x2}{xd' + x2}\right]_e - t/Tdd''$$

Electrical power-transmission system

The electrical transmission-system model representing the grid system–arc-furnace connexion is illustrated in Fig. 15. An equivalent transmission system referred to the secondary of the furnace transformer, is illustrated in Fig. 17 from which it can be shown that the arc currents are given by

$$\begin{bmatrix} e_{12} \\ e_{23} \\ e_{31} \end{bmatrix} = \begin{bmatrix} r_1 + SL_1 & -(r_2 + SL_2) & \\ & r_2 + SL_2 & -(r_3 + SL_3) \\ -(r + SL_1) & & r_3 + SL_3 \end{bmatrix}$$

The resistance in each phase is the sum of a number of components. The equivalent transmission line resistance is constant but the electrode resistance and the effective resistance of the electric-arc discharge are both variable. However, the electrode resistance varies relatively slowly as wear takes place and the electrode tip profile changes and thus the dynamic effect of this variation can be neglected. The inductance in each phase is also the sum of a number of components. The effective transmission line leakage inductance of the intermediate and furnace transformers have been found to vary with load current and saturation effects. However, this effect is small when compared to the total phase inductance if perturbations about the operating point are being considered and has therefore been neglected. The effects of mutual inductance have been neglected because of insufficient detailed information. From the above equation it can be shown that the transmission system

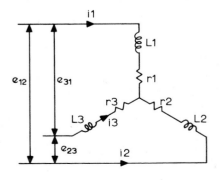

17   Equivalent circuit diagram of the three-phase transmission system

can be represented by the following non-linear vector-matrix differential equation.

$$\sum r \begin{bmatrix} i1 \\ i2 \\ i3 \end{bmatrix} + \sum r \cdot L \begin{bmatrix} Si1 \\ Si2 \\ Si3 \end{bmatrix} + \sum L \begin{bmatrix} S^2i1 \\ S^2i2 \\ S^2i3 \end{bmatrix}$$

$$= \begin{bmatrix} r3 & 0 & -r2 \\ -r3 & r1 & 0 \\ 0 & -r1 & r2 \end{bmatrix} \begin{bmatrix} e12 \\ e23 \\ e31 \end{bmatrix}$$

$$+ \begin{bmatrix} L3 & 0 & -L2 \\ L3 & L1 & 0 \\ 0 & -L1 & L2 \end{bmatrix} \begin{bmatrix} Se12 \\ Se23 \\ Se31 \end{bmatrix}$$

This vector-matrix equation can be linearized by taking a first-order Taylor series expansion to give

$$\sum L \begin{bmatrix} S^2i1 \\ S^2i2 \\ S^2i3 \end{bmatrix} = -\sum R \begin{bmatrix} i1 \\ i2 \\ i3 \end{bmatrix} + \begin{bmatrix} R3 & 0 & R2 \\ -R3 & R1 & 0 \\ 0 & -R1 & R2 \end{bmatrix}$$

$$\times \begin{bmatrix} e12 \\ e23 \\ e31 \end{bmatrix} + \begin{bmatrix} L3 & 0 & -L2 \\ -L3 & L1 & 0 \\ 0 & -L1 & L2 \end{bmatrix} \begin{bmatrix} Se12 \\ Se23 \\ Se31 \end{bmatrix}$$

$$\begin{bmatrix} -(R2 + R3)I1 - (I1 \cdot R1 + I1 \cdot R3 + E31) \\ \quad - (I1 \cdot R1 + I1 \cdot R2 - E12) \\ -(I2 \cdot R2 \cdot I2 \cdot R3 - E23) - I2(R1 + R3) \\ \quad - (I2 \cdot R1 + I2 \cdot R2 + E12) \\ -(I3 \cdot R2 + I3 \cdot R3 + E23) \\ \quad - (I3 \cdot R1 + I3 \cdot R3 - E31) - I3(R1 + R2) \end{bmatrix} \begin{bmatrix} r1 \\ r2 \\ r3 \end{bmatrix}$$

where

$$\sum r \quad = r1 \cdot r2 + r2 \cdot r3 + r3 \cdot r1$$

$$\sum r \cdot L = r1 \cdot L2 + r1 \cdot L3 + r2 \cdot L1 + r2 \cdot L3$$
$$\quad + r3 \cdot L1 + r3 \cdot L2$$

$$\sum L \quad = L1 \cdot L2 + L2 \cdot L3 + L3 \cdot L1$$

$$\sum R \quad = R1 \cdot R2 + R2 \cdot R3 + R3 \cdot R1$$

The steady-state characteristics of a typical three-phase transmission system including the furnace transformer and secondary system are illustrated earlier in Fig. 1.

Electric-arc discharge

Experimental studies by Nottingham[14] have produced a generally applicable empirical equation which can be used to explain the instantaneous characteristics of electric-arc discharges when using similar materials for the electrodes. Thus

$$va = D_1 + D_2 la + \frac{D_3 + D_4 \cdot la}{ia^n}$$

where

va is the arc voltage drop

ia is the arc current
la is the arc length
Dj are the arc discharge coefficients

For discharges in air $n = 2 \cdot 62 \, 10^{-4} \cdot T$ where T is the absolute boiling temperature of the electrode materials in degrees Rankine. For arc discharges in air, the exponent n is about unity for carbon electrodes and slightly less than unity for steels. The electrodes at either end of the arc discharge are graphite and steel, obviously dissimilar materials and hence the exponent n in Nottingham's equation cannot take into account the two differing exponents. The atmosphere in an industrial arc furnace is often far from a normal atmospheric air condition and thus the exponent n could vary substantially. Rectification effects will be apparent when using dissimilar materials to support the arc discharge as the graphite and steel scrap each form the anode and cathode on alternative positive and negative half cycles. This gives rise to differing magnitudes of current in each half cycle. The effects have been neglected due to insufficient detailed information on these topics.

Considering work by Browne[14] and other work by Bowman et al.[15] it can be observed that the term including $ia^{(-n)}$ will be orders of magnitude less than the other terms. When considering deviations from the steady state operating point then

$$va = D_2 \cdot ia$$

The dynamic characteristics of electric-arc discharges can be explained simply by Cassie's or Mayr's equation.[14] The two equations consider heat radiation from the two basic regions of an electric-arc discharge, the arc column and the electrode-arc interface, which have different dynamic characteristics. The heat radiated from high-current high-power arc discharges experienced in a typical electric-arc furnace is assumed to be emitted from the arc column. It is also assumed that the arc column conductance can be described as a function of the stored energy within the column, i.e.

$$\frac{1}{rc} = f(qc) = f\left[\int (wc - nc) \, dt \right]$$

or

$$\frac{d}{dt}\left[\frac{1}{rc} \right] = (wc - nc)\frac{\partial f}{\partial qc}(qc)$$

where

rc is the column resistance per unit length
qc is the excess energy per unit length
wc is the electrical power input per unit length
nc is the rate of energy loss per unit length.

The basic assumptions required to derive Cassie's equation are that column conductance is proportional to the excess energy stored in the column.
Let

$$\theta_c = \frac{Qc}{Nc}$$

where

θ_c is the thermal time constant of the arc column

Qc is the constant energy stored per unit length

Nc is the constant rate of energy loss per unit length

If the arc column conductance is proportional to the excess energy in the arc column then

$$\frac{1}{rc} = \frac{qc}{\theta c \cdot Ec^2}$$

where Ec is the characteristic voltage gradient of the arc column. If it is also assumed that the power loss is proportional to the excess energy in the arc column then

$$nc = \frac{qc}{\theta c}$$

Substituting the above equations in the original differential equation describing the dynamic behaviour of the arc column gives Cassie's differential equation

$$rc \cdot \frac{d}{dt}\left[\frac{1}{rc}\right] = \frac{1}{\theta c}\left\{\left[\frac{e_c}{Ec}\right]^2 - 1\right\}$$

where e_c is the column voltage gradient

Cassie's equation can be used with the other power system equations to predict very short term dynamic arc-furnace behaviour in the order of milliseconds duration. The dynamic characteristics of high-current high-power electric-arc discharges have been studied by Bowman et al.[15] and this work has shown that the transient behaviour of the arc discharge is of sufficiently high frequency to have negligible effect upon the electrode position-control system. It has also been shown by Bowman et al.[15] that Nottingham's equation can also be used to determine time average behaviour of the arc if rms values of voltage and length are considered over periods in excess of one cycle. This will give an effective arc discharge coefficient which will be less susceptible to high frequency variations caused by the stochastic behaviour of the arc discharge. The steady-state solution of Cassie's equation is given by $ec = Ec$. The static characteristic voltage gradient of the arc column is equivalent to the arc discharge coefficient of the approximation to Nottingham's equation illustrated previously. It can, therefore, be seen that the approximation of Nottingham's equation which is being used in this work is the steady-state solution of Cassie's equation.

CONVENTIONAL CONTROL SIMULATION

In order to investigate the dynamic behaviour of the electrode position-control system, it is necessary to simulate the transient performance of the system when subjected to variations in arc discharge characteristics. Digital simulation can be divided into two basic fields; linear multivariable techniques and numerical techniques for non-linear integration. Multivariable techniques can be used to solve linear differential equations and linear algebraic equations whereas numerical integration techniques can also be utilized to solve non-linear equations which are explicit. Analog simulation techniques can easily be used to solve simultaneously either linear or non-linear differential equations and also explicit and implicit algebraic equations which can be of either linear or non-linear form. Hybrid simulation techniques are normally applied to eliminate the inherent practical disadvantages of analog and digital techniques by utilizing the more advantageous aspects of both.

The execution times of all the simulation techniques are vastly different. The quickest execution time is obtained by analog computer simulation techniques but because of recording limitations this advantage is somewhat reduced. However, the extensive programming requirements of analog computers reduce the problem solution time substantially. Non-linear numerical integration techniques require the longest execution time which is substantially increased if automatic plotting of the results is required. However, with the increasing availability of standard scientific subroutines the programming required is relatively small. The major part of the investigations carried out involved non-linear simulation with a reasonably large number of runs and thus analog computer simulation techniques have been utilized for a substantial part of the work. Non-linear digital simulation languages would have been seriously considered if an effective on-line conversational facility was available.

In practice, disturbances in furnace operation are caused by scrap movements and changing bath conditions. Disturbances of this nature have been incorporated into the analysis with errors in set point or alternatively with initial conditions on the electrode-tip and electrode-mast displacements. There are two basic forms of disturbance which are of major importance. When a scrap fall occurs this is equivalent to a step input disturbance to the set point or an initial condition upon the electrode tip and mast displacements. Alternatively when a scrap fall takes place the scrap often strikes the electrode imparting an impulse to the electrode structure which is equivalent to an initial condition on the electrode-tip displacement. Other variations such as changes in arc discharge characteristics simply modify the closed-loop control system gain which is easily incorporated into the analysis.

The two extremes which occur in transient behaviour are caused by equal disturbances to all three phases or disturbances to one particular phase. Normal operating conditions usually lie between these two extremes which very rarely occur. A disturbance to all three phases produces the worst situation in terms of set point error, integrated set point error and maximum electrode-tip acceleration. A disturbance to one phase is more likely to produce a small integrated set point error and reduced electrode-tip acceleration. To investigate these effects a three-phase model obviously has to be utilized. The accuracy of the models derived is of utmost importance when investigating the effects of modified controllers which are to be installed on plant. A brief summary of the accuracy of the models derived in section is given in Table 1. It is interesting to note that reasonable

TABLE 1   Comparison of non-linear model responses with the transient behaviour of the plant

		Hydraulic actuator		Amplidyne-winch	
		Model	Plant	Model	Plant
Initial condition on electrode	Electrode-tip overshoot, %	40	40	13	15
and mast position, 0·05 m	Maximum acceleration, m/s²	0·9	0·5/1·25	0.36	0·3/0·6
arc-discharge coefficient,	Time to first crossover, s	0·56	0·55	0·9	0·9
13 kV/m	Oscillation frequency, Hz	0·6	0·55	0·4	0·45
Limit of stability	Arc-discharge coefficient, kV/m	26	25/30	40	40/45
	Critical oscillation frequency, Hz	0·7	0·7	0·65	0·7

TABLE 2   Comparison of dominant characteristics for four electrode position-control systems

		Electrode structure		Subtransient effects	
	Dominant time constant, s	Damping ratio	Natural frequency of oscillation, Hz	Time constant, s	Oscillation frequency, Hz
Hydraulic actuator	0·58	0·18	3·5	—	—
Amplidyne, Ward-Leonard winch no. 1	1·0	1·0	7·0	—	—
Amplidyne, Ward-Leonard winch no. 2	0·3	0·2	3·5	—	—
Eddy-current coupling, induction motor winch	—	0·5	2·0	—	—
Electrical-power system	1/3·0	—	—	0·035/0·125	2/7·5

approximations to the limit of stability can also be obtained from the classical stability analysis of Bode or Nyquist using single-phase linearized models.

A comparison of the main features of each type of electrode position-control system is summarized in Table 2. The major features of importance are the dominant time constant and electrode-mast characteristic and these are compared with the subtransient time constant of the power-generation system. In all four electrode position-control systems the natural frequencies of oscillation of the electrode structures coincide with the range of effective subtransient frequencies of the electrical power generation system. The damping ratios of the four electrode structures are substantially different. The hydraulic electrode ram structure and the heavier electrode-mast structures used with winch systems all have low damping whereas the lightest electrode-mast structure used with the amplidyne-winch system no. 1 is dead beat or critically damped.

Hydraulic actuator

A three-phase transient response to a common step input disturbance is illustrated in Fig. 18. The effective arc discharge gain for each phase is 13 kV/m or half the value required to achieve critical stability. Figure 18 illustrates the differing transient responses of the three phases where phase one exhibits an increased electrode-tip overshoot, acceleration, and velocity magnitude fall and phase three has a reduced electrode-tip acceleration. Electrode-tip overshoots of 40–50% are experienced with acceleration levels exceeding 1·25 m/s². A three-phase transient response to a single step input disturbance is illustrated in Fig. 19 where the phase which has

been disturbed exhibits surprisingly small electrode-tip overshoot and acceleration. The initial conditions on phase one have given rise to a maximum electrode-tip overshoot of 20% with a maximum acceleration of 0·5 m/s², whereas the other two phases exhibit 35% overshoot with a maximum acceleration of 0·25 m/s². Normal operating conditions will be given by initial conditions which fall between these two extremes, and

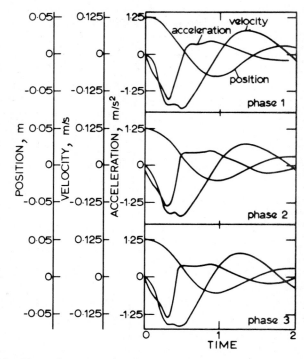

18   Three-phase transient response to a common input disturbance

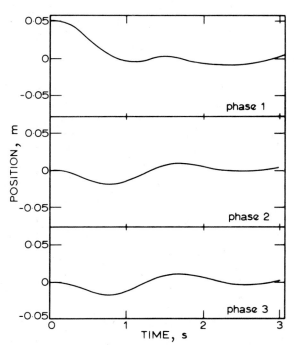

19 *Three-phase transient response to a single step input disturbance of one phase*

thus the maximum levels of overshoot and acceleration will vary accordingly.

A typical disturbance where a given phase is disturbed more severely than the other two is illustrated in Fig. 20. The transient response for one phase only is included as this is the only phase of interest. Here the electrode-tip overshoot, acceleration and velocity magnitude fall between the two extreme cases.

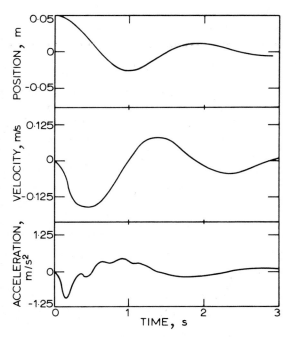

20 *Typical disturbance with hydraulic actuator (only the phase of interest is illustrated)*

Ward-Leonard drive

A typical disturbance in the set point of an amplidyne winch is illustrated in Fig. 21. The overshoot in this controller has virtually been eliminated by correct adjustment of the circuit variables. This rotating winch form of actuator also reduces the levels of acceleration produced by the control system when compared to the hydraulic ram actuator. The winch, winch rope, and electrode-mast type of structure also appear to increase the damping of the structure and thus, the effects of oscillations corresponding to the natural frequency of the mast structure are substantially reduced.

CONTROL-SYSTEM DESIGN

The three types of models described in this paper have been utilized to provide the basis for three different types of investigation. Two of the models which are illustrated were originally formulated to enable a thorough investigation of electrode control-system performance to be carried out after periods of unsatisfactory dynamic behaviour.[4] These models have more recently been used to investigate techniques for improved control-system behaviour.[7,8,9] The third and final model was originally derived during an investigation into the effectiveness of PRBS techniques for modelling non-linear electrode position-control systems.[4]

Hydraulic actuator

The model outlined earlier has previously been utilized to modify the design of the water-flow control valve and to define a precise setting up procedure for the arc impedance measuring network. Simulation work has illustrated that little more can be done to improve the dynamic behaviour of this control system unless the electrode-mast structure is redesigned. If the mast structure could be redesigned to give critical damping, then the standard compensation techniques of reducing dominant time constants and employing lead lag networks can be used to improve stability as shown in Fig. 22. The existing hydraulic electrode position-control system incorporates a number of important design features. A hard limit exists on the maximum velocity

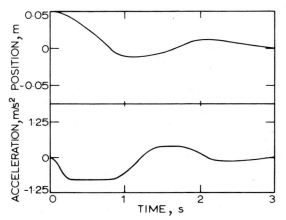

21 *Typical disturbance with amplidyne winch actuator*

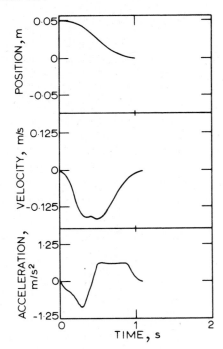

22   *Transient response of modified control system*

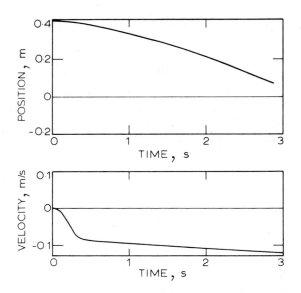

23   *Transient response of modified amplidyne winch actuator*

which can be achieved by the mast structure under open- or closed-loop operation. Also, the closed-loop gain for small input disturbances is considerably less than the gain for large disturbances. These features will assist the reduction of electrode breakages, excessive carbon pick-up and slag activity which causes refractory erosion.

Amplidyne–Ward-Leonard winch

This model was originally derived for examining modified control schemes using existing equipment. Simulation work has since been used to check setting up procedures and to recommend modifications to obtain the required transient behaviour. The amplidyne is a very versatile machine with a substantial number of feedback windings. Modelling and simulation work has indicated that standard stabilization techniques could successfully be utilized. Motor-current feedback and lead-lag error compensation are particularly effective and to a lesser extent, velocity feedback can be used to improve the dynamic performance. In order to maintain closed loop stability when melting commences, it is often necessary to reduce the electrode velocity resulting from an open- or short-circuit condition unless the condition persists. If the condition persists, the electrode mast should be allowed to attain maximum velocity. Motor-current feedback and lead-lag compensation can be utilized to obtain this form of transient response as illustrated in Fig. 23. This situation can occur if a scrap fall occurs after boring down through the scrap charge.

Eddy-current coupling winch

This model was originally derived from data obtained during an investigation into the effectiveness of PRBS techniques for modelling electrode position-control systems. The impulse responses obtained during this

investigation, together with simple models can be used to check the dynamic performance of this particular control system at regular intervals. This type of control system is ideal from a maintenance point of view as the coupling and AC drive motor do not have any rotating commutation devices and all the power amplification is provided by operational amplifiers and silicon controlled rectifiers which should require negligible maintenance. This type of solid state error amplification is also extremely suitable for adding any compensation networks, ranging from lead-lag networks to three-term controllers.

Electrode-mast structures

Unfortunately, the natural frequencies of oscillation of electrode-mast structures coincide with the subtransient time constants of the electrical power generation system. The natural frequencies of oscillation of the power system corresponding to the subtransient time constant vary between 2 and 7·5 Hz depending on many factors, such as power-system loading. This also lies within the flicker frequency range of interest. In order to avoid problems with coincident roots electrode mast structures should be designed to have at least critical damping and if possible, a natural frequency of oscillation outside the range 2·0–7·5 Hz. The winch type of electrode-mast construction lends itself more easily to modified designs than does the hydraulic actuator, because of the inherent stiffness and damping of the steel winch rope assembly. However, Fig. 22 also illustrates the gains to be obtained by redesigning the hydraulic actuator electrode-mast structure.

Setting-up procedures

The extensive use of electrode position-control system models and the associated application on plant has provided a firm basis for defining setting-up procedures with typical control parameter requirements. The broad requirements and starting point for control-system adjustments are outlined below.

The control system should obviously be set up so that it is stable on the highest voltage tap during melting. Some instability is inevitable with the high rate of change of arc current with electrode-tip displacement when the steel scrap is cold. The natural frequency of oscillation of the electrode-mast structure should not be excited by the control system and in order to achieve this, one dominant time constant of about 0·25 to 0·75s should be included. Longer time constants should be used with electrode masts which have low natural frequencies of oscillation, and/or are lightly damped. Dead zones in excess of 5% of the set point should be avoided as the lack of balanced control may prove detrimental to the process performance. To reduce hunting, dead zones of the order of 2% are normally required during melting. Limits should be imposed to constrain maximum electrode velocity to reasonable limits. Maximum velocities should not exceed 0·1 m/s but should be greater than 0·05 m/s. In order to protect the electrical system, withdrawal velocities may be required to exceed penetration velocities which in turn must be restricted to minimize electrode breakages. Acceleration levels should be less than 1 m/s² in order to protect the graphite electrodes.

Fault finding

If an accurate detailed model of a particular electrode position-control system is available, this can be used to assess the dynamic performance of the control system. This can be achieved by comparing the transient behaviour of the plant and the predicted behaviour obtained from the model with identical arc discharge behaviour. After recording the transient performance of the plant, the relationship between 'arc voltage', arc current, and electrode-tip displacement must be obtained. The control-system model can then be used to predict the control-system performance with specified arc discharge parameters. This procedure can be used to check the dynamic behaviour of the electrode position-control system for any arc discharge behaviour. A complete set of transient performance information can be obtained from simulation using the dynamic model to enable comparisons to be carried out on plant. Alternatively, a complete set of transient performance information could also be obtained from the plant itself and used for comparison purposes. However, all these techniques involve detailed examination of chart recordings and/or extensive simulation. The problems are further increased by the sinusoidal nature of the 'arc voltage' and arc current signals which substantially increases the complexity of extracting arc discharge information from the chart recordings. A large proportion of the identification has also to be carried out off line during short shut-down periods.

These problems can be overcome using PRBS techniques with commercial correlation equipment. If a set of impulse responses are obtained from the electrode

position-control system on plant, they can be used for simple graphical comparisons to check dynamic behaviour at regular intervals. Simple models typically second, third or fourth order, can be derived from these impulse responses in order to obtain a measure of control-system transient performance. The techniques illustrated in this paper can easily be utilized for obtaining low order models from impulse responses. In order to facilitate easy comparison between a standard response and a fault finding check response, the check response should be photographed and compared against a transparency of the standard responses. Non-linearities can also be checked to a given degree.

Performance criteria

In order to assess how effective any particular modification to the electrode position-control system has been, or is likely to be, some form of performance criterion must be established. The most obvious performance criterion is one of cost saving. However, this is perhaps the most difficult function to estimate and even more difficult to evaluate on plant.

Cost savings of £0·15/t or 0·4% can be achieved with typical set point or out of balance errors of 5%. It is somewhat more difficult to estimate the cost savings to be gained from ensuring that a position-control system is dynamically set up correctly. As a rough approximation, an increase of 30% in electrode velocity and system sensitivity could reduce the transformer heating by as much as 10% during the first 5 or 10 min melting after charging a basket of cold scrap. However, this will only amount to a 2 or 3% reduction for the whole of the melting cycle and hence, the likely savings are of the order of £0·05/t or 0·1%. This is equivalent to about £7 000–£8 000 p.a. for the typical furnace previously considered. Academic performance criteria based on system stability, maximum electrode velocity and acceleration, and minimum electrode-tip overshoot are typically considered. Dead time or time delay, rise time and effective time constant are also of some importance. The range of values for these criteria recommended by the author from experience on plant and from simulation and modelling investigations are listed in Table 3.

CONCLUSIONS

Three electrode position-control system models have been derived, together with a simple representation of

TABLE 3 Recommended performance criteria for electrode position-control systems

Maximum electrode velocity under open or short circuit	0·05/0·1 m/s
Maximum electrode acceleration	0·9 m/s²
Electrode-tip overshoot on melting taps with a flat bath	0%
Recommended dead zone	2%
Maximum dead zone on melting taps	5%
Effective time constant	0·4 s
Dominant time constant	0·25–0·75 s
Maximum dead time	0·1 s
Electrode-mast structure damping ratio	1·0

the electrical power system and arc discharges. It has clearly been illustrated that accurate three-phase models are a necessity if detailed analysis is to be carried out. The magnitude of possible savings from the use of these models has been illustrated and the substantial cost of operating a furnace under unbalanced operation, or with an incorrect set point, or incorrectly set up has also been outlined. Improved design and control of arc furnace power input regulators is substantially simplified if accurate dynamic models are available for simulation of any plant modifications. Performance criteria for estimating the static and dynamic performance of electric-arc furnace electrode position-control systems are recommended. If substantially improved control schemes are to be implemented, then accurate three-phase models of the control and power systems must be utilized.

The classical modelling techniques used in this work have provided relatively satisfactory models. However, it is felt that more sophisticated statistical techniques could substantially improve the accuracy of the models, especially the representation of the electrical power system and arc discharges. However, commercial PRBS generators and correlators can successfully be utilized in checking the dynamic performance of non-linear electrode position-control systems at regular intervals during normal operation.

REFERENCES

1 H. DRILLER: *Stahl Eisen*, 1954, **74**, 82–95
2 L. KOLKIEWIEZ: *AEI Eng.* (*suppl.*), 1967, 30–3
3 J. D. GIFFORD AND R. ROEBUCK: Fifth Industrial Process Heating Conf., Birmingham, 1972
4 J. D. GIFFORD: Institute of Measurement and Control Conf., Sheffield, 1972
5 P. BROWN AND R. D. LANGMEN: *JISI*,1967, **205**, 837–47
6 P. BROWN: *IEE Conf.*, 1969, **57**, 150–8
7 H. NICHOLSON AND R. ROEBUCK: *Automatica*, 1972, **8**, 683–93
8 H. NICHOLSON AND R. ROEBUCK: *Proc. IEE*, 1973, **120 (3)**, 365–70
9 R. ROEBUCK: Institute of Measurement and Control Conf., Sheffield, 1972
10 C. F. CHEN AND I. J. HASS: 'Elements of control system analysis', 1968, 170–236, Prentice Hall
11 E.C. LEVY: *IRE Trans. Automatic Control*, 1959, **AC-4**, 37–43
12 W. D. T. DAVIES: 'Generation and properties of maximum length sequences', *Control*, June/July/Aug., 1969
13 B. ADKINS: 'The general theory of electrical machines', 1957, Chapman and Hall
14 T. E. BROWNE JNR.: *J. Electrochem. Soc.*, 1955, **102**, 27–37
15 B. BOWMAN et al.: *JISI*, 1969, **207**, 798–805
16 REFERENCES FOR FAST FOURIER TRANSFORMS: IEE Trans. on Audio and electroacoustics, 1967, **AU-15 (2)**

APPENDIX 1

Bode's decomposition

Bode's form of decomposition is used to obtain a transfer function from frequency response data where both the numerator and denominator are factored, i.e.

$$(G/s) = \frac{K(S + \beta_1)(S + \beta_2)\ldots(S + \beta_m)}{(S + \alpha_1)(S + \alpha_2)\ldots(S + \alpha_n)}$$

where β_i are zeros and α_i are poles. Re-arranging the above equation gives the magnitude and phase responses individually i.e.

$$\log|g(\omega)| = \log Q + \log\left|\frac{j\omega}{\beta_1} + 1\right| + \log\left|\frac{j\omega}{\beta_2} + 1\right|$$
$$+ \ldots + \log\left|\frac{jw}{\beta_m} + 1\right| - \log\left|\frac{j\omega}{\alpha_1} + 1\right|$$
$$- \log\left|\frac{j\omega}{\alpha_2} + 1\right| - \ldots - \log\left|\frac{j\omega}{\alpha_m} + 1\right|$$

and

$$\phi(\omega) = \tan^{-1}\frac{\omega}{\beta_1} + \tan^{-1}\frac{\omega}{\beta_2} + \ldots + \tan^{-1}\frac{\omega}{\beta_m}$$
$$- \tan^{-1}\frac{\omega}{\alpha_1} - \tan^{-1}\frac{\omega}{\alpha_2} - \ldots - \tan^{-1}\frac{\omega}{\alpha_n}$$

where

$$Q = \frac{K \cdot \beta_1 \cdot \beta_2 \ldots \beta_m}{\alpha_1 \cdot \alpha_2 \ldots \alpha_n}$$

Bode's technique is based upon the above equations which give rise to three distinct advantages. Initially this technique provides an extremely simple graphical method for fitting a complex curve to frequency response data. Once a transfer function has been obtained then Bode's technique provides a simple straight line approximation to the frequency response. Bode's form of transfer function is also compatible with standard tables of inverse Laplace transforms. However, this technique is difficult, if not impossible, with frequency responses of complicated system transfer functions. From an experimentally determined frequency response the process of identification using Bode's technique is described as follows:

(i) approximate the magnitude-frequency response curve by a series of piece-wise straight lines which are chosen such that they have slopes which are integer multiples of 20 db/decade

(ii) the straight line approximation is then decomposed into single components

(iii) recognize the corner frequencies and deduce the corresponding poles and zeros of Bode's form

(iv) determine any dc gain if the frequency response has zero slope at zero frequency.

APPENDIX 2

Bush's decomposition

Bush's form of decomposition results in a transfer function of the form

$$G(s) = \frac{G(s)}{1 + G(s) \cdot H(s)} = \frac{1}{H(s) + 1/G(s)}$$

Alternatively a closed-loop transfer function $G(s)$ can be

decomposed into an open-loop transfer function $G(s)$ if the feedback transfer function $H(s)$ is known, i.e.

$$(G/s) = \frac{G(s)}{1 + G(s).H(s)}$$

If the open-loop frequency response $g(\omega)$ is expressed in rectangular form

$$g(\omega) = x(\omega) + jy(\omega)$$

and the closed-loop frequency response $c(\omega)$ is also expressed in rectangular form

$$c(\omega) = u(\omega) + jv(\omega)$$

then for conversion from open- to closed-loop frequency response

$$u(\omega) = \frac{x(\omega)(1 + x(\omega)H(\omega)) + y(\omega)^2 H}{(1 + x(\omega)H(\omega))^2 + (y(\omega)H(\omega))^2}$$

and

$$v(\omega) = \frac{b}{(1 + x(\omega)H(\omega))^2 + (y(\omega)H(\omega))^2}$$

or alternatively from closed- to open-loop frequency response

$$x(\omega) = \frac{u(\omega)(1 - H(\omega)u(\omega)) - H(\omega)^2 v(\omega)^2}{(1 - H(\omega)u(\omega))^2 + (Hv(\omega))^2}$$

$$y(\omega) = \frac{v(\omega)}{(1 - H(\omega)u(\omega))^2 + (H(\omega)v(\omega))^2}$$

Consider a typical transfer function

$$G_1(s) = \frac{1}{(a_2 + a_1 s + s^2)s} = \frac{1}{(a_2 + (a_1 + s)S)S}$$

Now

$$G_1(s) = \frac{1}{s} . C_1(s)$$

This is equivalent to a closed-loop transfer function where

$$H_2 = a_2 \quad \text{and} \quad 1/G_2(s) = S(S + a_1)$$

If $G_2(s)$ is now considered as a second closed-loop transfer function then

$$G_2(s) = \frac{1}{s} . C_2(s) = \frac{1}{a_1 + s}$$

i.e.

$$H_3 = a_1 \quad \text{and} \quad 1/G_3(s) = S$$

When continued Bush's technique leads to a continuous fraction expansion

$$G_1(s) = \frac{1}{s} . \cfrac{1}{a_2 + \cfrac{1}{1/s . \cfrac{1}{a_1 + \cfrac{1}{1/s}}}}$$

$C(s)$ has been decomposed into $G(s)$ and H and similarly it is possible to decompose $c(\omega)$ into $g(\omega)$ and H. From an experimentally determined frequency response the process of identification using Bush's technique is described as follows:

(i) using a Bode diagram representation of the frequency response $g_1(\omega)$ determine the class of the transfer function by examining the slope of the frequency response as the frequency tends to zero, i.e.:

class = (zero frequency slope in db/dec)/20

(ii) modify the given frequency response $g_1(\omega)$ by multiplying by $(j\omega)$ to the power of the class of the unknown transfer function to give $c_1(\omega)$. If the class is zero then $g_1(\omega) = c_1(\omega)$

(iii) estimate the value of h_2. From the Bode diagram of $c_1(\omega)$ determine the approximate gain of the modified frequency response as frequency tends to zero

$$h_2 \simeq \log^{-1} \frac{\text{gain in dbs}}{20}$$

(iv) use this value of h_2 with the expressions for $x(\omega)$ and $y(\omega)$ as an initial starting point for calculating $g_2(\omega)$. When the positive feedback applied by the estimated value of h_2 is equal to the desired negative feedback value of h_2 then the slope of $g_2(\omega)$ as frequency tends to zero will be 20 db/dec. Only when the estimated value of h_2 is correct will the zero frequency slope be 20 db/dec. Other values of h_2 will result in zero slope as frequency tends to zero

(v) the frequency response $g_2(\omega)$ is now multiplied by $j\omega$ to give $C_2(\omega)$

(vi) stages 3, 4 and 5 are then repeated until the frequency response $g_i(\omega) = j\omega$. The frequency response has then been decomposed into Bush's form.

The decomposition process of Bush as described above has one distinct advantage over Bode's decomposition. It is inherently accurate with complicated transfer functions and corresponding frequency responses. Bush's technique is also more suitable for highly oscillatory systems with resonant peaks. The main disadvantage of this technique is the extensive requirement to convert between polar and cartesian coordinates in stage 4 above. However, the inherent sensitivity of this technique allows the use of approximate polar to cartesian charts without any loss of accuracy.

APPENDIX 3

Wiener Lee's decomposition

Wiener's form of decomposition gives a transfer function of the form

$$G(s) = a_0 + a_1\left(\frac{1-S}{1+S}\right) + a_2\left(\frac{1-S}{1+S}\right)^2$$
$$+ \ldots + a_n\left(\frac{1-S}{1+S}\right)^n$$

when used to identify any given frequency response. Consider the bilinear transformation

$$S = \frac{(1 - e^{-j\phi})/(1 + e^{-j\phi})}{S \to jw}$$

or

$$e^{-j\phi} = \frac{(1 - S)/(1 + S)}{S \to j\omega}$$

$g(w)$ can be transformed from the ω domain to the ϕ domain by substituting for the expression for $e^{-j\phi}$ in Wiener's form. Equating the real parts of the resulting equation gives

$$P(\phi) = a_0 + a_1 \cos \phi + a_2 \cos 2\phi + \ldots a_n \cos n\phi$$

Once the $p(\phi)$ response is obtained numerically the value of the a_i's can be determined by a corresponding Fourier series analysis, i.e.

$$a_k + \frac{1}{m} \sum_{k=1}^{2m} P_k \cos \frac{nk\pi}{m}$$

BILINEAR TRANSFORMATION

Consider the transformation

$$e^{-j\phi} = \frac{(1 - S)/(1 + S)}{S \to j\omega}$$

Expressing in polar form and rationalizing the right-hand side

$$\cos \phi - j \sin \phi = \frac{1 - \omega^2}{1 + \omega^2} - \frac{2j\omega}{1 + \omega^2}$$

$$= 1 \bigg/ \tan^{-1} - \frac{2\omega}{1 - \omega^2}$$

or

$$\tan \phi = \frac{2\omega}{1 - \omega^2}$$

and hence

$$\omega = \tan \phi/2 \quad \text{or} \quad \phi = 2 \tan^{-1} \omega$$

It is apparent that the interval $(-\infty, \infty)$ in the ω domain corresponds to $(-\pi, \pi)$ in the ϕ domain. This translation can be accomplished numerically or graphically.

LAGUERRE POLYNOMIALS

Wiener Lee's form of decomposition is not directly compatible with inverse Laplace transformation which would limit the usefulness of this technique. However, if the Laplace transform pair associated with Laguerre polynomials is considered the problem is substantially reduced. Laguerre polynomials can be defined as

$$L_n(t) = \frac{e^t}{n!} \frac{d^n}{dt^n}(t^n e^{-t})$$

The Laplace transform pair related to this function is given by

$$\mathscr{L}(e^{-at}L_n[(a - b)t]) = \frac{(S + b)^n}{(S + a)^{n+1}}$$

Utilizing this transform pair the inverse Laplace transformation of Wiener Lee's decomposition is given by

$$F(t) = e^{-t}\left(\sum_{k=0}^{k=n} (-1)^k a_k \frac{d}{dt} L_k(2t)\right)$$
$$+ \delta(t) \sum (-1)^k a_k L_k(0)$$

Wiener Lee's decomposition is therefore compatible with inverse Laplace transforms. The bilinear transformation required renders this technique very useful for non-oscillatory systems where the accuracy is far superior to Bode's technique. From a frequency response which has been obtained experimentally Wiener Lee's technique of decomposition to identify a system transfer function is as follows:

(i) obtain the real part of the system frequency response $R[g(\omega)]$ as a function of ω
(ii) using the expression $\phi = 2 \tan^{-1} \omega$ calculate values of ϕ corresponding to $R[g(\omega)]$ and plot $R[g(\omega)]$ now $P(\phi)$ against ϕ
(iii) change the independent variable from ω to ϕ and by graphical interpolation derive the $P(\phi)$ function with an even number of equally spaced increments in ϕ
(iv) calculate the coefficients of the corresponding Fourier series using graphical techniques for vector addition.

If it is intended to use Wiener's technique then it is possible to derive $R[g(\omega)]$ as a function of equal increments of ϕ when the frequency response data is initially collected. This substantially simplifies the decomposition process as the graphical interpolation for changing the independent variable is no longer required.

APPENDIX 4

Pseudo-random binary sequences

Before defining the procedure for identifying systems or process using pseudo-random binary sequences (PRBS) it is necessary to define one or two functions. The auto-correlation function of $w(t)$ is given by

$$\phi_{ww}(\tau) = \lim_{T \to \infty} \frac{1}{2T} \int_{-T}^{T} w(t)w(t + \tau)\,dt$$

The cross-correlation function of $w(t)$ and $y(t)$ is given by

$$\phi_{wy}(\tau) = \lim_{T \to \infty} \frac{1}{2T} \int_{-T}^{T} w(t)y(t + \tau)\,dt$$

The spectral density of $\phi_{ww}(\tau)$ is

$$\Phi_{ww}(\omega) = \int_{-\infty}^{\infty} \phi_{ww}(\tau)\,e^{-j w\tau}\,d\tau$$

i.e.

$$\Phi_{ww}(\omega) = 2 \int_{0}^{\infty} \phi_{ww}(\tau) \cos w\tau\,d\tau$$

or

$$\phi_{ww}(\tau) = \frac{1}{2\pi} \int_{-\infty}^{\infty} \Phi_{ww}(\omega)\,e^{-j w\tau}\,d\omega$$

The cross spectral density of $\phi_{wy}(\tau)$ is

$$\Phi_{wy}(w) = \int_{-\infty}^{\infty} \phi_{wy}(\tau) \, e^{-jw\tau} \, d\tau$$

and thus

$$\phi_{wy}(\tau) = \frac{1}{2\pi} \int_{-\infty}^{\infty} \Phi_{wy}(\omega) \, e^{-jw\tau} \, d\omega$$

The spectral density of white noise is a constant and thus

$$\Phi_{ww}(\omega) = \angle\,\text{a constant}$$

White noise is by definition totally random and thus the auto-correlation function only exists at zero time, i.e.

$$\phi_{ww}(\tau) = \frac{1}{2\pi} \int_{-\infty}^{\infty} \angle e^{jw\tau} \, d\omega = \delta(t)$$

A binomially distributed square wave sequence has an auto-correlation function which approximates to the unit impulse, i.e.

$$\phi_{ww}(\tau) = 1 - \frac{(\tau)}{T} \quad \text{for } \tau \leqslant T$$

$$= 0 \quad \text{for } (\tau) > T$$

where

$$\Phi_{ww}(\omega) = 4T\left[\frac{\sin wT/2}{wT}\right]^2$$

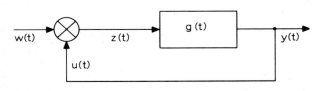

AI   A process using a pseudo-random binary system

A cyclic-pseudo-random binary sequence has a symmetric periodic auto-correlation which is similar to the auto-correlation function for a binomial distributed square wave. Consider a system represented by Fig. A1, The cross-correlation function between the input and output of the system is given by:

$$\phi_{wy}(\tau) = \lim_{T \to \infty} \frac{1}{2T} \int_{-T}^{T} w(t)y(t - \tau) \, dt$$

The convolution integral is given by

$$y(t) = \int_{-\infty}^{\infty} g(\lambda)z(t - \lambda) \, d\lambda$$

therefore

$$\phi_{wy}(\tau) = \lim_{T \to \infty} \frac{1}{2T} \int_{-T}^{T} w(t)$$

$$\times \int_{-\infty}^{\infty} g(\lambda)[w(t + \tau - \lambda) - u(t + \tau - \lambda)] \, d\lambda \, dt$$

i.e.

$$\phi_{wy}(\tau) = \int_{-\infty}^{\infty} g(\lambda)[\phi_{ww}(t - \lambda) + \phi_{wu}(\tau - \lambda)] \, d\lambda$$

If the correlation between the input signal $w(t)$ and the noise $u(t)$ is negligibly small compared with $\phi_{uw}(\tau)$ then

$$\phi_{wy}(\tau) = \int_{-\infty}^{\infty} g(\lambda)\phi_{ww}(\tau - \lambda) \, d\lambda$$

If the known input signal is white noise then the auto-correlation function

$$\phi_{ww}(\tau) = \delta(\tau)$$

and thus the impulse response of the system is given by

$$\phi_{wy}(\tau) = \int_{-\infty}^{\infty} g(\lambda) \, \delta(r - \lambda) \, d\lambda$$

Mathematical model of a humidification chamber for the treatment of waste gases from a large arc furnace

A. T. Sheridan

In an arc-furnace extraction system, using wet precipitators, it is necessary to saturate the gases to avoid build up of dirt on the precipitator plates with subsequent failure. The paper discusses a mathematical model of a humidification system which has been constructed in order to study the effects of alteration of process variables of water temperature, spray atomization, etc. on the humidification achieved. In the model the heat and mass transfer involved have been considered in a simple manner and a set of first-order ordinary differential equations obtained. Rate constants, which have been lumped together in the analysis were calibrated by plant observation and the equations were solved on an analog computer. Possible modifications giving a beneficial effect have been separated from those that would prove ineffectual and their improvements predicted. The three most worthwhile changes were implemented on the six 120/180 ton arc furnaces of the Templeborough melting shop at the Rotherham Works of the BSC, resulting in elimination of the problem of precipitator failure by the baking of dust on the elements. Plant trial results are given.

LIST OF SYMBOLS

L	Latent heat of vaporization of water
$\dot{m}'_G$	Rate of mixing of gas with water
$\dot{m}_G$	Mass flow of gas
$\dot{m}_w$	Mass flow of water
c_G	Specific heat of gas
c_V	Specific heat of water vapour
c_w	Specific heat of water
t	Non-dimensional time/mixing rate
$p(\theta)$	Vapour pressure of water at temperature θ (mass ratio)
α	Ratio of mass of water to mass of gas
θ_D	Dewpoint of gas
θ_G	Temperature of gas
θ_w	Temperature of water

On computer diagram

$A = \theta_G - \theta_w$

$B = c_G + c_V p(\theta_D)$

$C = (\theta_G - \theta_w)[c_G + c_V p(\theta_D)]$

$D = p(\theta_D) - p(\theta_w)$

$E = L - c_V \theta_w$

$F = (L - c_V \theta_w)[p(\theta_D) - p(\theta_w)]$

$G = (\theta_G - \theta_w)[c_G + c_V p(\theta_D)]$
$\qquad + (L - c_V \theta_w)[p(\theta_D) - p(\theta_w)]$

$H = G/\alpha$

$I = c_G + c_V p(\theta_w)$

$J = (\theta_G - \theta_w)[c_G + c_V p(\theta_w)]$

$$\beta = \frac{\text{computer time}}{\text{non-dimensional problem time}}$$

TEMPLEBOROUGH ARC-FURNACE EXTRACTION SYSTEMS

At the Templeborough electric melting shop of Rotherham Works of the BSC there are six* 120/180 ton arc

---

The author is with BSC, Special Steels Division, Rotherham

* Now five

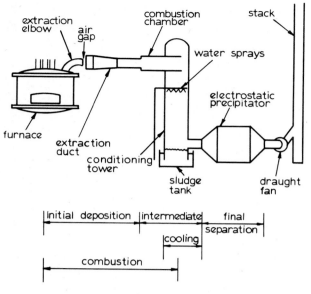

1   Diagram of arc-furnace extraction system

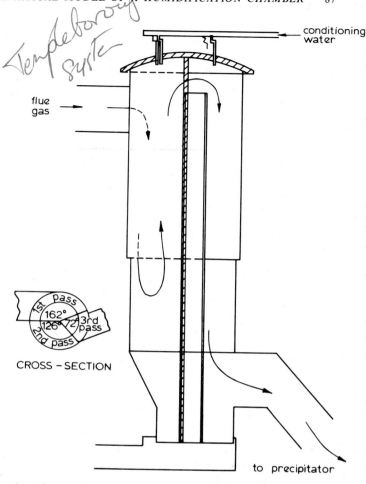

CROSS – SECTION

2   Schematic drawing of conditioning chamber

furnaces with similar waste gas extraction systems. The basic elements of these are:

(i) a horizontal combustion chamber to burn the waste gases from the furnace ensuring a condition of excess air to prevent subsequent explosion
(ii) a multipass cooling and humidification chamber
(iii) wet electrostatic precipitators, leading to a fan and stack
(iv) the extraction volume is 16·5 normal m³/s
(v) the combustion chamber was designed using isothermal modelling[1] and a diagram of the extraction system is shown in Fig. 1.

The object of the conditioning chambers on the TEMS arc-furnace extraction systems was to cool the effluent gases from the furnaces to below 100°C and to saturate them with water vapour. Although the gases were cooled sufficiently, they were often unsaturated, which caused caking of the damp fume on the precipitator electrodes so that it could not be removed by the regular flushing of the precipitator and subsequently resulted in failure. Various alterations to the plant were suggested, but it was first necessary to know the effects of possible alteration of the process variables, i.e.

(i) altering the temperature of the water, e.g. introducing cold or boiling water
(ii) increasing the height of the chamber
(iii) improving the atomization of the water sprays
(iv) increasing the total water flow
(v) introducing steam before, during, or after the conditioning chamber.

A mathematical model was derived which was used to calculate the relative effects of these changes.

FIRST PASS OF THE CONDITIONING CHAMBER

Plant trials had shown that gases entered the conditioning chamber (shown schematically in Fig. 2) at temperatures of up to 1 600°C. They were cooled in the first pass to about 100°C by 11 l/s of effluent plant water at 60°C introduced as sprays and up to 27 l/s as streams to protect the walls of the chamber.

In the first pass, droplets of water boil in the hot gases and the gas temperature/humidity curve follows approximately the equation:

$$c_G \dot{m}_G \frac{d\theta_G}{d\dot{m}_w} = c_w(100 - \theta_w) + L + [c_v(\theta_G - 100)] \quad (1)$$

where c_G, c_w, and c_v are the specific heats of the gas, water, and water vapour respectively, all of which vary with temperature. θ_G and θ_w are the inlet temperatures of the gas and the water. L is the latent heat of vaporization of water, $\dot{m}_G$ is the mass flow of gas and $\dot{m}_w$ the mass flow of water vaporized.

The above equation was integrated in steps to produce the family of curves in Fig. 3. The minimum mass of water necessary to achieve a temperature below boiling point at the end of the first pass is plotted in Fig. 4 against initial gas temperature. Assuming that the gas temperature does not exceed 1 800°C, a minimum water

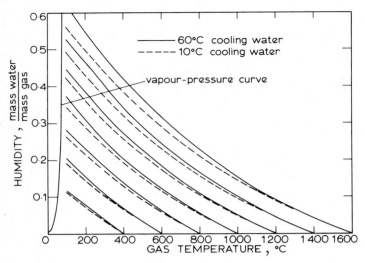

3   *Adiabatic cooling curves for water/effluent gas system*

flow of 15 l/s, in the form of sprays to ensure adequate mixing, is needed. Little advantage would be gained by changing to cold water in this pass.

SECOND AND THIRD PASSES

Equations of mixing

In these passes it is assumed that a mass flow $\dot{m}_G$ of gas at temp. $\theta_G(<100°C)$ and dewpoint θ_D is sprayed with a mass flow $\dot{m}_W$ of water at temperature θ_W. The mixing process is considered to occur in two stages.

FIRST STAGE

An elemental mass flow of gas $\delta\dot{m}'_G$ at temperature θ_G and of dewpoint θ_D mixes with the water at the edge of the boundary layer. The gas takes up (or loses) water $\delta\dot{m}_W$ and approaches its dewpoint at the water temperature θ_W which is increased by an infinitesimal amount of $\delta\theta_W$. Mass balance first stage:

$$\delta\dot{m}_W + \delta\dot{m}'_G[p(\theta_W) - p(\theta_D)] = 0$$

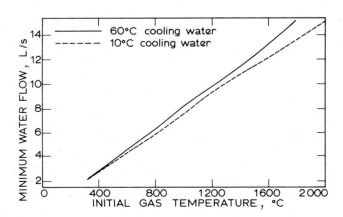

4   *Minimum water requirement for the cooling of 16·5 normal m^3/s of effluent gas to below 100°C*

where $p(\theta)$ is the vapour pressure of water at temperature θ, i.e.

$$\frac{d\dot{m}_W}{d\dot{m}_G} = p(\theta_D) - p(\theta_W) \qquad . \qquad . \qquad . \qquad . \qquad . \quad (2)$$

The total energy change in each stage is zero, which in the first stage is the sum of energy changes due to evaporation and sensible heat. Neglecting second order infinitesimals:

$$(\dot{m}_W + \delta\dot{m}_W)c_W(\theta_W + \delta\theta_W) - \dot{m}_W c_W\theta_W$$
$$+ \delta\dot{m}'_G(\theta_W - \theta_G)[c_G + c_V p(\theta_D)]$$
$$+ \delta\dot{m}'_G L[p(\theta_W) - p(\theta_D)] = 0$$

i.e.

$$c_W\theta_W\frac{d\dot{m}_W}{d\dot{m}_G} + \dot{m}_W c_W\frac{d\theta_W}{d\dot{m}_G}$$
$$= (\theta_G - \theta_W)[c_G + c_V p(\theta_D)] + L[p(\theta_D) - p(\theta_W)] \quad (3)$$

SECOND STAGE

The elemental mass of gas returns to the main gas flow and mixes with it. The mass and heat balances are calculated as before. Mass balance second stage:

$$\dot{m}_G p(\theta_D + \delta\theta_D) = (\dot{m}_G - \delta\dot{m}'_G)p(\theta_D) + \delta\dot{m}'_G p(\theta_W)$$

$$\therefore$$

$$\dot{m}_G \,\delta p(\theta_D) = \delta\dot{m}'_G[p(\theta_W) - p(\theta_D)]$$

i.e.

$$\dot{m}_G\frac{dp(\theta_D)}{d\dot{m}'_G} = p(\theta_W) - p(\theta_D) \qquad . \qquad . \qquad . \quad (4)$$

Heat balance second stage:

$$\delta\dot{m}'_G\theta_W[c_G + c_V p(\theta_W)] + (\dot{m}_G - \dot{m}'_G)\theta_G[c_G + c_V p(\theta_D)]$$
$$+ \delta\dot{m}'_G L[p(\theta_W)] + (\dot{m}_G - \delta\dot{m}'_G)L[p(\theta_D)]$$
$$= \dot{m}_G(\theta_G + \delta\theta_G)[c_G + c_V\{p(\theta_D + \delta\theta_D)\}]$$
$$+ \dot{m}_G L[p(\theta_D + \delta\theta_D)]$$

$$\therefore$$

$$\theta_W[c_G + c_V p(\theta_W)] - \theta_G[c_G + c_V p(\theta_D)]$$
$$- \dot{m}_G c_G\frac{d\theta_G}{d\dot{m}'_G} - \dot{m}_G\theta_G c_V\frac{dp(\theta_D)}{d\dot{m}'_G}$$
$$- \dot{m}_G L\frac{dp(\theta_D)}{d\dot{m}'_G} + L[p(\theta_W) - p(\theta_D)] = 0 \quad . \qquad . \quad (5)$$

By introducing the water to gas mass ratio α and the dimensionless time/mixing rate t such that

$$\dot{m}_W = \dot{m}_G\alpha, \quad \dot{m}'_G = \dot{m}_G t \quad \text{and} \quad \frac{d\dot{m}_W}{d\alpha} = \dot{m}_G = \frac{d\dot{m}'_G}{dt}$$

Equations (2) to (5) can be rewritten as Eqs. (6) to (9): From Eq. (2):

$$\frac{d\alpha}{dt} = p(\theta_D) - p(\theta_W) \qquad . \qquad . \qquad . \qquad . \quad (6)$$

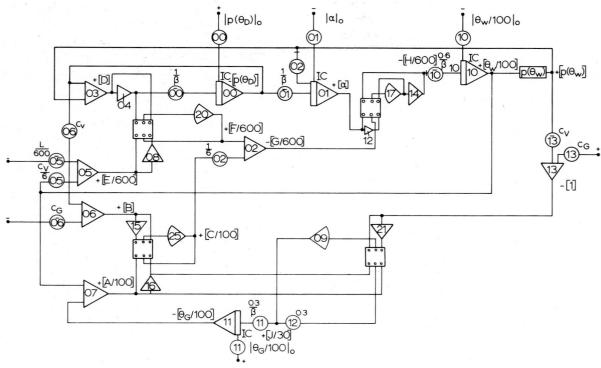

5   Analog circuit

From Eq. (3):

$$c_{\mathrm{w}}\theta_{\mathrm{w}}\frac{\mathrm{d}\alpha}{\mathrm{d}t} + \alpha c_{\mathrm{w}}\frac{\mathrm{d}\theta_{\mathrm{w}}}{\mathrm{d}t} = (\theta_{\mathrm{G}} - \theta_{\mathrm{w}})[c_{\mathrm{G}} + c_{\mathrm{v}}p(\theta_{\mathrm{D}})]$$

$$+ L[p(\theta_{\mathrm{D}} - p(\theta_{\mathrm{w}})]$$

$$\therefore$$

$$\frac{\mathrm{d}\theta_{\mathrm{w}}}{\mathrm{d}t}$$

$$= \frac{\begin{array}{c}(\theta_{\mathrm{G}} - \theta_{\mathrm{w}})[c_{\mathrm{G}} + c_{\mathrm{v}}p(\theta_{\mathrm{D}})]\\ + (L - c_{\mathrm{v}}\theta_{\mathrm{w}})[p(\theta_{\mathrm{D}}) - p(\theta_{\mathrm{w}})]\end{array}}{\alpha c_{\mathrm{w}}} \quad (7)$$

From Eq. (4):

$$\frac{\mathrm{d}p(\theta_{\mathrm{D}})}{\mathrm{d}t} = p(\theta_{\mathrm{w}}) - p(\theta_{\mathrm{D}}) \quad . \qquad . \qquad . \qquad . \quad (8)$$

From Eq. (5):

$$\theta_{\mathrm{w}}[c_{\mathrm{G}} + c_{\mathrm{v}}p(\theta_{\mathrm{w}})] - \theta_{\mathrm{G}}[c_{\mathrm{G}} + c_{\mathrm{v}}p(\theta_{\mathrm{D}})]$$

$$- c_{\mathrm{G}}\frac{\mathrm{d}\theta_{\mathrm{G}}}{\mathrm{d}t} - \theta_{\mathrm{G}}c_{\mathrm{v}}\frac{\mathrm{d}p(\theta_{\mathrm{D}})}{\mathrm{d}t} - L\frac{\mathrm{d}p(\theta_{\mathrm{D}})}{\mathrm{d}t}$$

$$+ L[p(\theta_{\mathrm{w}}) - p(\theta_{\mathrm{D}})] = 0$$

and using Eq. (8):

$$c_{\mathrm{G}}\frac{\mathrm{d}\theta_{\mathrm{G}}}{\mathrm{d}t} = \theta_{\mathrm{w}}[c_{\mathrm{G}} + c_{\mathrm{v}}p(\theta_{\mathrm{w}})] - \theta_{\mathrm{G}}[c_{\mathrm{G}} + c_{\mathrm{v}}p(\theta_{\mathrm{D}})]$$

$$+ c_{\mathrm{v}}\theta_{\mathrm{G}}[p(\theta_{\mathrm{D}}) - p(\theta_{\mathrm{w}})]$$

$$= \theta_{\mathrm{w}}[c_{\mathrm{G}} + c_{\mathrm{v}}p(\theta_{\mathrm{w}})] - \theta_{\mathrm{G}}c_{\mathrm{G}} - c_{\mathrm{v}}\theta_{\mathrm{G}}p(\theta_{\mathrm{w}})$$

$$\therefore$$

$$\frac{\mathrm{d}\theta_{\mathrm{G}}}{\mathrm{d}t} = \frac{(\theta_{\mathrm{w}} - \theta_{\mathrm{G}})[c_{\mathrm{G}} + c_{\mathrm{v}}p(\theta_{\mathrm{w}})]}{c_{\mathrm{G}}} \qquad . \qquad . \qquad . \quad (9)$$

Solution of the equations

The simultaneous differential Eqs. (6) to (9) were solved on an analog computer. There are four dependent variables $\theta_{\mathrm{w}}, \theta_{\mathrm{D}}, \theta_{\mathrm{G}}$, and α and one independent variable t. α and θ_{G} occur as themselves, θ_{D} as $p(\theta_{\mathrm{D}})$ and θ_{w} as itself or $p(\theta_{\mathrm{w}})$. One function generator only was therefore required to convert θ_{w} to $p(\theta_{\mathrm{w}})$.

The analog computer circuit diagram for the solution of the equations is shown in Fig. 5.

Calibration of the dimensionless transit time

The dimensionless transit time incorporates both time and mixing rate. It was calibrated from a knowledge of a value of the gas temperature at the end of the first and third passes and the final dewpoint, coupled with the gas flow rate and the water temperature and flow rate in the system. As an example it was assumed that the following conditions existed, which were typical of conditions obtained from plant trials:

Gas temperature at end of 1st pass	90°C
Gas temperature at end of 3rd pass	80°C
Dewpoint at end of 3rd pass	76°C
Combined water flow in 2nd and 3rd passes	13·6 l/s
Gas flow (dry)	21·2 kg/s
Water temperature	60°C

An estimated value of the dewpoint at the end of the first pass (about 81°C) was fed into the initial conditions of the analog computer. The computer was then operated till the gas temperature had fallen to 80°C and the dewpoint read. The initial estimated dewpoint was then altered and the computer operated again until the final dewpoint was 76°C at a gas temperature of 80°C. The operation time for the computer in time units was then expressed in terms of the distance of travel of the gases in the conditioning chamber. The above conditions were found to be equivalent to an operation of 31 time units on the computer.

Effect of the process variables

Each process parameter was varied independently.

WATER TEMPERATURE

The computer was operated for 31 time units from its initial conditions, with the initial water temperature reduced to 10°C. At the end of the run the gas was found to be 5·1°C above saturation, a deterioration of 1·1°C. It was, therefore, concluded that cold water was slightly detrimental to the system. A run was also performed with the initial water temperature raised to 100°C. The final dewpoint was then 3·6°C showing a slight improvement, but unlikely to offset the installation and running costs of a water heater.

CHAMBER HEIGHT

The height of the chamber was assumed to have been increased by 3·66 m (12 ft) adding 7·32 m to the second and third pass length of 15·2 m (50 ft). This was represented on the computer by increasing the dimensionless transit time from 31 to 46 time units. The final gas temperature was reduced to 2·9°C above the dewpoint, showing a significant improvement.

IMPROVING THE ATOMIZATION OF THE WATER

It was assumed that all droplets in the system were produced at half the previous diameter, which doubles the surface area. The mixing rate and thus the non-dimensional time is increased to 62 units giving a final gas temperature 2·0°C above its dewpoint, showing an improvement which almost dominates other effects.

INCREASING THE TOTAL WATER FLOW

The water flow was increased from 13·61 l/s to 21·2 l/s without alteration of the spray size distribution. The initial conditions were altered by increasing α and the non-dimensional time by a factor of 1·55, (α from 0·643 to 1 and t from 31 to 48). The resultant gas temperature was 3·8°C above the dewpoint giving almost no change.

INTRODUCTION OF STEAM

The introduction of 90 kg/h of steam after the conditioning chamber gave a gas temperature 3·96°C above the dewpoint. Introduction after the first pass changed this figure to 3·98°C, again with negligible effect.

RECOMMENDATIONS BASED ON THE MATHEMATICAL MODEL

Although a specific calibration was chosen in order to produce the results in the previous section, other calibrations gave similar trends. It was deduced from the equations discussed earlier that complete equilibrium is mathematically impossible. In practice, however, effective equilibrium would be achieved if a sufficient number of water droplets were carried by the gas stream into the precipitator. Thus, under the conditions quoted a discrepancy of 4°C between the gas temperature and its dewpoint could be neutralized by introducing by fine sprays, 3 l/s of water into the gas stream at the entrance to the precipitator.

Coupling better atomization in the chamber and an increased chamber height with the above sprays was expected to overcome the problem of unsaturated gases entering the precipitator. The effects of the dust burden on the rate of saturation of the gases was not considered. An average dust burden of 500 kg/h of Fe_2O_3 contributes only 0·4 % to the specific heat of the gas and therefore little effect should be apparent from changes in dust burden concentration.

PLANT TRIALS

Typical conditions in the existing system at the exit of the humidification tower are shown in Fig. 6. Worst conditions were obtained during periods of high waste-gas temperature. Modifications were carried out to the system which consisted of:

(i) passing more water through the sprays, and less through the water curtain protecting the plates in the tower. As effluent plant water was used, conventional sprays could not be employed; those installed consisted of jets impinging on splash plates and it was considered that the higher jet momentum would improve the atomization

(ii) increasing the height of the tower by 3·66 m (12 ft)

(iii) 3 l/s of towns water was used to supply sprays half way down the third pass.

The first results obtained with this new arrangement are shown in Fig. 7 and indicate a high degree of unsaturation and cooled waste-gas temperatures above 100°C. Average temperature differences of over 10°C between waste gas and dewpoint were obtained compared to an average of 5°C on previous trials.

It was subsequently discovered that the cooling water sprays had been installed without splash plates so there was no effective atomization. Obliquely this substantiated the findings of the mathematical model in that efficient atomization was the most important parameter in the process. The defect was remedied and the trials recommenced, producing results which are typified by those in Fig. 8. The waste-gas temperature was usually within 1°C of saturation although occasional small peaks were still evident.

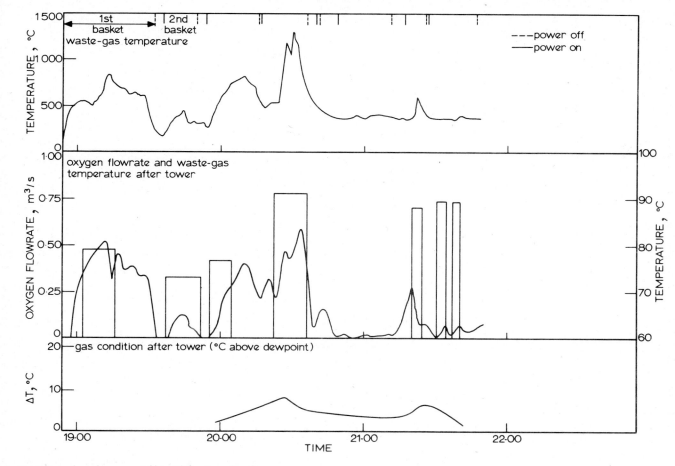

6 *Original performance of humidification chamber*

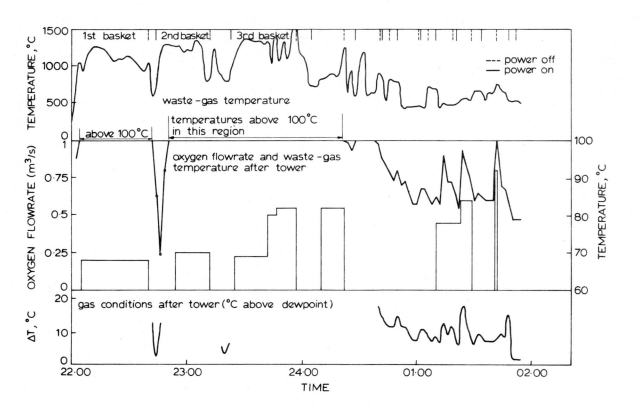

7 *Performance of the humidification chamber after modification with spray plates omitted*

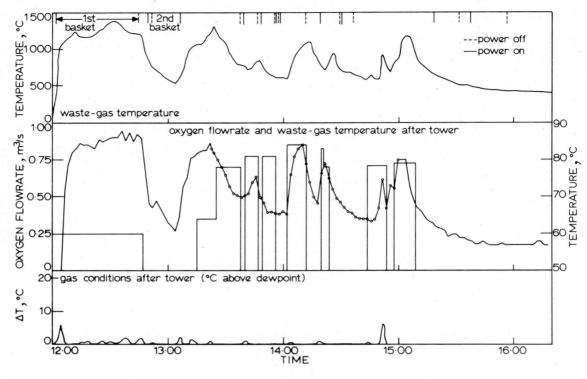

8   *Performance of the humidification chamber after modification with the spray plates included*

The towns water sprays were subsequently repositioned after the conditioning tower and these produced completely saturated conditions throughout the cast. It was later attempted to avoid the cost of towns water by the use of effluent water for the final sprays. These trials proved ineffective as with fine sprays the nozzles became blocked whereas coarser sprays produced droplets which were not sufficiently small to follow the path of the gas in the precipitator, resulting merely in washing of the first plates. Maintaining saturated conditions was found to eliminate the problem of baking of dust on the precipitator electrodes and this appears a necessary condition for the efficient operation of wet electrostatic precipitators on arc-furnace extraction systems.

ACKNOWLEDGMENTS

The author wishes to thank members of the Works Trials Section at Swinden Laboratories for making available the plant data on gas temperature and humidification. The author is grateful to Dr K. J. Irvine, Head of Research, BSC Special Steels Division for permission to publish this paper.

REFERENCE

1 F. FITZGERALD AND A. D. ROBERTSON: *J. Inst. Fuel*, 1967, **7**

Discussion on chapter two:
Electric steelmaking

CHAIRMAN: C. OVER (BSC, GENERAL STEELS DIVISION, TEESIDE)

The following papers were discussed: *Optimization of energy distribution in the operation of an electric melting shop* by H. H. Borggrefe, K. Hohendahl, and G. Zingel; *Three-phase electrode position-control system models for electric-arc furnaces* by R. Roebuck.

Dr F. Fitzgerald (BSC, Corporate Advanced Process Laboratory, Teesside) asked how different in principle was the system described from that which operated at the Rotherham Works (Templeborough melting shop) of the BSC, and which controlled the maximum demand for six furnaces and had been in existence for some ten years. It seemed to Dr Fitzgerald that the principles of the system outlined in the paper and that at Rotherham Works were exactly the same. He said that he had also been interested to hear that there was a 30% improvement in refractory wall life achieved by using the computer control system. It was true that refractory wall life was a function of arc parameters which could be controlled by a computer system, but refractory wall life was also a function of imbalance in the circuit and was very greatly affected by the furnace pressure control. He asked if all these things had been kept constant when the authors evaluated their system. Had they operated and assessed a base practice, introduced the control system for a period, and then reverted to the base practice to ensure that no inadvertent changes had occurred?

Dr Borggrefe said that in principle, compared with the system at the Rotherham Works, there was no basic difference. But the system described in the paper was much smaller. The authors had wanted to have optimization of electrical demand and to program and control the furnaces at the various stages in the melt, but they did nothing new compared to British systems. They had programmed the furnace arc and in that way had achieved better performance during operation, but Dr Borggrefe believed that that had also been achieved in the UK.

Dr Zingel said that compared to the Rotherham Works, the question of optimization of the wear of the refractory walls had been studied more thoroughly in developing the system described in the paper than had been done previously. Regarding control of arc parameters, while there were many methods described, the systems always failed unless one assumed geometrical and electrical symmetry. However, the symmetry of furnaces could not be realized completely in their construction, so the authors had accepted that fact and tried to have a symmetrical approximation in power supply to the furnaces. They had also said that they should try to keep the arc as short as possible. When there is constant voltage, a short arc permits a corresponding increase of the current so that decrease of the arc length gives a better power input to the furnace. Finally, the shorter the arc length, the less the wear of the refractory walls.

In reply to Dr Fitzgerald's question regarding furnace pressure Dr Zingel said that in normal operation they tried never to reach negative values in the furnace. As a final comment on the system at Rotherham Works he emphasized that they had not wanted to copy what had been done there or to install a similar installation, they had merely sought economic optimization of their operations. Deutsche Edelstahlwerke produced both unalloyed and high-grade alloy steels. Chrome–nickel steel has a long refining time, and there is a considerable deposit on the furnace walls which makes it necessary to deal with the problem of refractory wear, and that was as important for them as the problem of distribution of power between the various furnaces.

Mr Roebuck observed that control of the refining period had also been carried out at Rotherham Works, but as the control system, in terms of cost saving in the process, was only marginally better than the operator's performance its use had been discontinued. So far as Mr Roebuck knew, Rotherham Works was the only place where that had been done previously.

Dr L. Willner (Betriebsforschungsinstitut VDEh, Düsseldorf) said that Mr Roebuck claimed that he would have implemented non-linear control if methods had been available for computer implementation. On the other hand, he had said that he had checked the stability of the system using conventional methods. Dr Willner therefore imagined that Mr Roebuck was dealing with a 'multi-input multi-output' system, and he asked if the model would in practice have been very much simplified.

Mr Roebuck in reply said that by using the simple techniques on just one phase of the furnace, for instance, he could achieve a stability evaluation which turned out to be just as good as when he considered three phases. He did not suggest that a simple model behaved in the same manner as a three-phase model, but it did provide a simple way of analysing the stability in the first instance. Although important, the cost savings resulting from the work were not very big and hence the techniques used must be short and speedy so as to keep down the cost of implementing any design changes.

chapter 3: oxygen steelmaking

Review of mathematical modelling for steelmaking and solidification

F. Oeters

MODELS OF BASIC OXYGEN PROCESS

The early models consisted of mass and heat balances for control of the end-point temperature and carbon content of the steel.[1,2,3] Balances were made between the initial and final stage of the process and the extent of oxidation of carbon and the other elements dissolved in the pig iron was calculated from the amount of oxygen blown into the melt. For computing the end-point temperature the oxidation heats of the elements and the melting heat of the scrap were balanced. In a later stage of development the carbon loss was determined by measuring the amount and composition of the waste gas. Thus the oxygen bound to the carbon was also measured. Thus, the difference between this oxygen and the total oxygen blown in, is the oxygen bound to the slag. Models of this kind including waste-gas measurement have been developed and proved at several places.[1-21] In the case of refining pig iron rich in phosphorus by the LDAC process, one can additionally weigh the slag withdrawn after the first blowing period. This gives better accuracy in meeting the end-point carbon and phosphorus content as well as the end-point temperature.[19,20] A further improvement is possible by using sinker thermocouples.[17]

The balance model can be developed in several directions. One possibility is by using statistical models. A second possibility is to use physico-chemical models including kinetic factors. By this type of model the thermal as well as the material development can be integrated. Examples of this kind of model have been developed at several places. Bearing in mind that the percentage distribution to the carbon and the slag forming elements of the oxygen which has been blown in depends on the lance height, J. Maatsch et al.[21] defined a blowing number

$$B = K \cdot \frac{O_B}{h^2} \qquad . \qquad . \qquad . \qquad . \qquad . \qquad (1)$$

where K is an empirical constant, O_B is the rate of oxygen flow in $Nm^3 \, min^{-1}$, and h is the lance height. The blowing number B, which expresses the metallurgical blowing effect, is nearly proportional to that part $\dot{O}_C$ of the oxygen flow rate which will be bound to the carbon. $\dot{O}_C$ may be greater than one if the dissolved carbon reduces the slag. Using the cited Eq. (1), a relation is given between the measurable value $\dot{O}_C$ and the regulating values, i.e. the lance height and the oxygen flow rate.

H. W. Meyer and co-workers[17,18] evaluated the typical form of the carbon evolution curve. Figure 1 shows the specific decarburization rate, which is the quotient of the decrease of carbon content to the oxygen flow rate

$$\Phi = -\frac{d[\%C]/dt}{\dot{O}_B} \qquad . \qquad . \qquad . \qquad . \qquad . \qquad (2)$$

as a function of the bath carbon content $[\%C]$. The curves may be expressed by the expression

$$\Phi = \alpha - \beta \cdot e^{-\gamma[\%C]} \qquad . \qquad . \qquad . \qquad . \qquad (3a)$$

where α, β, and γ are kinetic process constants, varying from melt to melt. The constant β is defined in a way that $\Phi = 0$ when $[\%C] = 0.03\%$. As $0.03 \approx 0$ the function may be approximately expressed by

$$\Phi = \alpha(1 - e^{-\gamma[\%C]}) \qquad . \qquad . \qquad . \qquad . \qquad (3b)$$

With this expression, Φ becomes constant $= \alpha$ at higher carbon contents. Now, if a continuous waste-gas measurement has been installed, the value of α is immediately given by the constant specific decarburization rate at high carbon contents (see Fig. 1). To determine γ, the decarburization rate at two different carbon contents is measured. Given these values, a computer calculates the value of γ. Then the total decarburization curve is given. This enables the prediction of the carbon content and determination of the end-point. In a similar way also the temperature can be predicted. In a comparable way P. Nilles and E. M. Denis[6] proposed a model in which kinetic process constants are introduced

The author is with the Technical University of Berlin

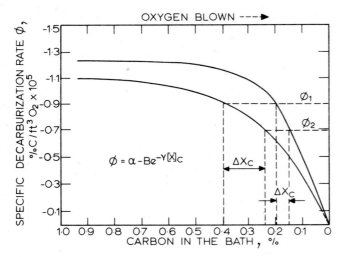

1   Typical end-point refining curves

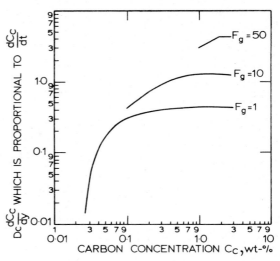

2   Calculated carbon oxidation rate against the carbon concentration for various values of F_g

for the slag forming reactions too. The total oxygen flow D_T^O is distributed to the single reactions. Here D_C^O is the oxygen going directly to the carbon, whereas D_{Fe}^O is the oxygen remaining at the iron. Q^O are the enthalpies belonging to the respective reactions. The single oxidation rates are characterized by a kinetic formula which for silica takes the form

$$D_{Si}^O = f \cdot A_{Si} \cdot \beta_{Si}[\%Si] \quad . \quad . \quad . \quad . \quad (4)$$

D_{Si}^O is the part of the total oxygen flow rate which is to be linked to the silicon, f is a stoichiometric factor, A the reaction surface and β the mass transfer coefficient. Since the reaction surface area depends on how far the slag is emulsified, an emulsion factor is introduced. This factor is characterized by the position of the slag in the system $CaO–FeO–SiO_2$ relative to the dicalcium silicate saturation line. The result is a set of several equations. The parameters contained in this set are determined by adapting them to the real course of the process.

As the concepts of these models show, as yet one is forced to get the kinetic process parameters from plant data. Until now, no general model of the LD process has been developed in which the kinetic parameters are found by applying general physico-chemical laws. However, partial models exist which are able to describe certain parts of this process. A short review about these models will now be given.

Models of emulsification

After W. Löscher[34] had proved experimentally that the high decarburization rates in the basic oxygen process cannot be explained by the simple reaction of the blown oxygen with the smooth bath surface, the formation of an emulsion containing iron oxide drops and carbon monoxide bubbles in the iron mother phase[23,35] is rather probable. J. Szekely and U. Todd[23] quantified this model. Figure 2 gives some curves of the decarburization rate as a function of the carbon content calculated by means of the model. The parameter $F_g = r(L^2/a^2)$ ascribed to the curves is a geometric one with $r = 12/16$, L = diameter of the FeO drops and of the carbon

monoxide bubbles, and a = distance between drops and bubbles. As well as depending on F_g, the plot of the curves depends on the diffusion coefficient of the participating substances. As can be seen, the course of the decarburization shown in Fig. 1 is correctly represented by the model. According to the model, the decarburization rate is determined by the transport of oxygen where it is independent of carbon content, whereas it is determined by the transport of carbon where it is dependent on carbon content.

Models of interaction between the free jet and the melt

The form of the bath depression when a free jet impinges on a liquid surface has been often investigated for single hole as well as for multiple hold lances. During the blow the free jet extends a force on the liquid phase. Thus, the liquid is made to circulate. As the blowing force increases, liquid drops are torn from the surface and are carried out into the gas stream. H. Chatterjee and A. V. Bradshaw[32] developed a model relationship for the beginning of drop formation which in dimensionless representation takes the form

$$\left(\frac{g \cdot \rho_L}{\sigma}\right)^{\frac{1}{2}} \cdot n_C = 0.53 \cdot \log\left(\frac{g \cdot \mu_L^4}{\rho_L \cdot \sigma^3}\right) + 11.33 \quad . \quad . \quad (5)$$

Here, n_C is the critical bath depression, g is gravitational acceleration, ρ_L is the liquid density, σ is the surface tension, and μ_L is the liquid viscosity. The parameter $[(g \cdot \rho_L)/\sigma]^{\frac{1}{2}}$ is the critical radius for the fall of a liquid drop from the end of a capillary. The parameter $(g \cdot \mu_L^4)/(\rho_L \cdot \sigma^3)$ is called the M number. Application of Eq. (5) on LD melts[32] shows that the bath depressions are much higher than the critical ones. So, drop formation occurs.

MODEL OF DECARBURIZATION IN THE OPEN-HEARTH FURNACE

Contrary to the case for the basic oxygen process, a complete model of the decarburizing reaction in the basic open-hearth furnace exists. To get a differential equation for the growth of a single carbon monoxide bubble, T. Kraus[36] starts at the fact that the bubble growth during its ascent is caused by the decrease of the ferrostatic pressure as well as by taking up carbon monoxide which is dissolved in the melt. The mass transfer coefficient for the growth of spherical cap bubbles has to be taken into account. The differential equation takes, for the case of carbon excess in the bath, the form

$$\frac{dN}{dh} = -([O] - [O]^*) \cdot 0{\cdot}85 \left(\frac{D^6 N^5 (RT)^6}{(P_{\text{ext}} + g \cdot \rho \cdot h)^5} \right)^{\frac{1}{12}} \quad (6)$$

Here $[O] - [O]^*$ is the driving concentration difference, D is the diffusion coefficient, P_{ext} is the external pressure, and $g \cdot \rho \cdot h$ is the ferrostatic pressure. Equation (6) represents a relation between the number N of moles in a bubble and the bubble height h between the surface and bottom of the melt. It must be integrated between $h = 0$ (at the surface) and $h = H$ (at the bottom). The lower integration limit for N is the radius of the nucleus, which can be taken as to be about zero. An equation comparable to Eq. (6) has been developed by W. G. Davenport, D. H. Wakelin, and A. V. Bradshaw.[30] The overall decarburization rate is given as the product of the single bubble rate and the number of nucleation centres. The last one can only be determined empirically. B. M. Larsen and U. Sordahl[53] developed an overall model which contains all partial steps being important for the decarburization. Equation (6) may be introduced into this model.

MODELS FOR DISSOLUTION AND MELTING OF SCRAP

Recently, several authors [37–39] developed models for the dissolution and melting of scrap. In spite of the fact that these models have not as yet been applied to plant practice they will be referred to here, for they are, in the author's opinion, rather important. Practical application will be expected in the near future. H. A. Friedrichs, H. Jauer, and O. Knacke[37] developed a model for the dissolution of a solid body in its own melt and proved it experimentally by the dissolution of ice in water. The change of mass m of the body is given by

$$\left(\frac{m}{m_0} \right)^{1/n} = 1 - \tau + 2\sqrt{\tau_{\text{w}} \cdot \tau} \quad (7)$$

Here

m_0 is the mass before melting begins
τ is the dimensionless time t/t_0 with $t_0 =$ time for complete dissolution
τ_{w} is the so-called growing time

The exponent $1/n$ is 1 for the plate, 2 for the cylinder, and 3 for the sphere. As Eq. (7) shows, the solid body initially grows into the liquid, if $\tau < 2\sqrt{\tau_{\text{w}} \cdot \tau}$. The heat of solidification liberated at this process heats the inner part of the solid body to the melting temperature. The results are in good agreement with qualitative observations of

the dissolution of alloying elements in liquid steel. When steel scrap is to be dissolved in iron melts containing carbon, the decrease of the melting point of iron by carbon has to be considered. This case was treated by J. Szekely.[38] For the melting temperature one gets the expression

$$T_{\text{mp}} = 1\,536 - 8\,830 \frac{\beta \cdot C_1(t)}{\beta + dx/dt} [°C] \quad . \qquad . \qquad . \quad (8)$$

$C_1(t)$ is the carbon content of the melt, which is time dependent, if the melt is refined at the same time. β is the mass transfer coefficient of carbon, and dx/dt is the melting velocity.

Equation (8) must be combined with the heat conduction equation in order to get a solution for dx/dt. The model allows the calculation of the dissolution rate of scrap in a melt which is refined at the same time. The decrease of carbon $C_1(t)$ with time must be given as an appropriate function. R. Jeschar and E. Millies[39] developed a model for the melting of scrap. The mathematical onset is similar to that of Knacke and co-workers. However, the initial growth of the solid body does not take place here. Instead of the growing time, a preheating time is introduced. This is the time between the beginning of heating and the beginning of melting, where the latter is given by the condition that the surface of the body must assume the melting temperature. In the model it is further assumed that the liquid metal formed immediately flows off the surface. Calculations have been made for plates. As the results of Jeschar and Millies show, the time necessary for complete melting grows with the square of the plate thickness. Furthermore, the influence of the surrounding temperature and the heat transfer coefficient (Biot number) on the melting velocity is demonstrated by the model. With the models described here it is principally possible to calculate the dissolution and melting of scrap. Appropriate statements must be made for the heat transfer coefficients.

SOLIDIFICATION MODELS

Exact solutions to the solidification of metal melts in moulds were established by Neumann in the 19th century. These are based on certain simple conditions, the most important of them including temperature independent material properties, a constant ingot surface temperature, and a one-dimensional heat flow. These conditions often do not hold. Recently, mathematical models have been developed, which are partly independent of these hypotheses. But in general, the condition of a one-dimensional heat flow remains. G. Horvay and R. H. Edsall[40] found an exact solution to the heat flow in sand or iron moulds, which assumes that there is a heat resistance with a constant heat exchange coefficient between the inner surface of the mould and the surface of the ingot. In this case the temperature of the two surfaces differ, but they approximate while time passes. This model can particularly be used to describe correctly the heat flow at the beginning of the solidification, when the heat resistance in the interface matters very much. One has to have in mind that the $\sqrt{t}$ law does not hold in this case.

For continuous casting one needs models in which the heat flow is non-stationary in the solidified shell, but nearly stationary between the ingot surface and the cooling water. Two problems arise here. One has to know firstly the temperature development at the ingot surface, and secondly the change of the heat exchange coefficient between ingot and mould due to gap formation. Instead of the ingot surface temperature one can also assume the heat flow rate into the mould. The mean heat flow rate integrated over the bath height can be found by measuring the heat reception of the cooling water. Different kinds of models have been developed and tested. A. W. D. Hills et al.[41–43] have applied the so-called integral profile method. In this method the temperature development in the solidified skin is given by a power series. Its parameters result from the boundary conditions. It is also given how the heat exchange coefficient between mould and ingot surface depends on time and on the distance from the upper level of the melt. By means of this model Hills et al. could correctly interpret heat flow measurements in continuous casting machines. A similar model has been developed by A. Tien.[44] Also, J. J. Gauthier, Y. Morrilon, and J. Dumont-Fillon developed a heat transfer model for the continuous-casting process.[45]

SEGREGATION MODELS

The starting point for the development of segregation models is the diffusion equation. It must be solved for the case of a moving phase boundary. Models have been established for macrosegregation as well as for microsegregation. They differ in the boundary conditions assumed for the solution of the diffusion equation. In macrosegregation, diffusion is neglected in the solid, whereas in the liquid, diffusion or complete mixing is assumed, depending on the intensity of convection. In microsegregation, complete mixing is assumed in the liquid and diffusion is considered in the solid.

Macrosegregation models

In macrosegregation, the effective segregation coefficient, i.e. the ratio of the concentrations in the solid and in the liquid is given by the formula of Burton, Prim, and Slichter:[46]

$$L_{\text{eff}} = \frac{L}{L + (1 - L) \cdot e^{-\text{v}/\beta}} \qquad . \qquad . \qquad . \qquad (9)$$

In this formula, L is the real segregation coefficient which results from the phase diagram, v is the solidification velocity, and β is the mass transfer coefficient, which characterizes the material exchange in the liquid. By means of Eq. (9) the segregation can be calculated in principle if β is known. β depends on the flow in the melt. In Figure 3 the concentration is plotted in the solid and in the liquid close to the solidification front for the

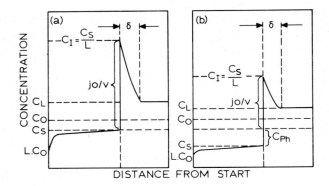

a Without chemical reaction at the interface
b With chemical reaction at the interface

3   *Solidification with imperfect stirring*

macrosegregation case. Starting from this concentration function, P. Nilles[47] developed a model for the segregation of rimming steel, in which he determined β making certain assumptions on the oxygen balance. This model gives good predictions for sulphur, phosphorus, and oxygen segregation in steel ingots.

F. Oeters, K. Rüttiger, A. Diener, and G. Zahs[48] expanded this model to the case when, in front of the solidification interface, new phases, e.g. oxides, are precipitated. Precipitation is possible because, as Fig. 3 shows, the concentrations are enriched in front of the solidification interface so that the values of the oxide equilibria can be exceeded. According to Oeters et al. the amount of new phase precipitated is given by

$$C_{\text{Ph}} = \frac{L}{1 - e^{-\text{v}/\beta} + (v \cdot L)/(\beta' \cdot L_{\text{eff}})}$$

$$\times \left(C_1 - \frac{L}{L_{\text{eff}}} \cdot c^* \right) \qquad . \qquad . \qquad . \qquad (10)$$

Here

L_{eff} = segregation coefficient defined by Eq. (9).
c^* = equilibrium concentration of the precipitation reaction $[\text{mol/cm}^{-3}]$
C_1 = concentration in the bulk melt $[\text{mol/cm}^{-3}]$
β' = mass transfer coefficient of the precipitation reaction $[\text{cm/s}^{-1}]$.

The other signs are as in Eq. (9).

With the model the precipitation of oxygen in rimmed steel ingots and the blowhole formation in vacuum decarburized ingots could be predicted. G. Ebneth[49] developed a method for determining the mass transfer coefficient β in a way which was more generally applicable than the method of Nilles. Using the concept of the bubbled wall streaming, Ebneth could give a differential equation for the velocity of the liquid steel, flowing parallel to the solid–liquid interface. From this velocity, the mass transfer coefficient can be calculated by a generally known dimensionless expression between the Nusselt number, the Reynolds number, and the Schmidt number. The model agrees excellently with practical results of sulphur and phosphorus segregation in ingots.

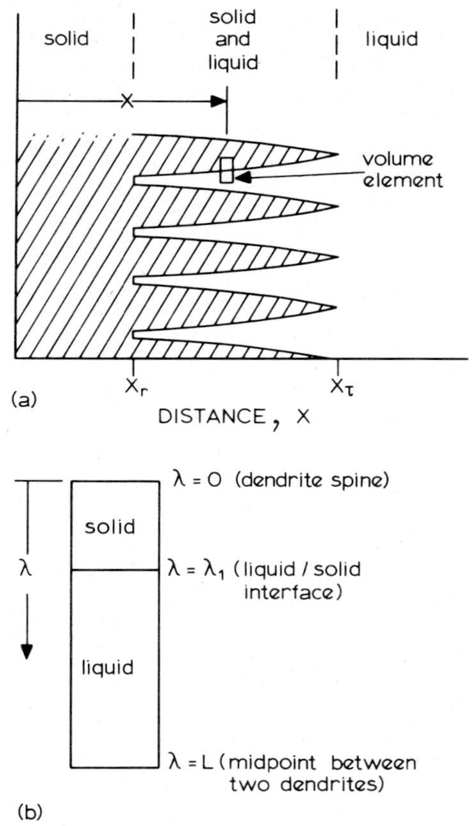

4 Scheme of microsegregation model

Models of microsegregation

A microsegregation model has been developed by H. D. Brody and M. C. Flemings.[50] Figure 4 shows the scheme. The dendrites are considered as plates growing into the melt. During the time t_f, the so-called local solidification time, the solidification front migrates in a volume element vertical to the general direction of heat flow from the point $\lambda = 0$ at $t = 0$ to the point $\lambda = 1$ at t_f. The distance 1 is half the mean distance of the dendrites. In the same time the heterogeneous zone passes the volume element. In order to calculate the segregation, complete mixing is assumed for the liquid whereas partial mass equalization by diffusion is assumed for the solid. Being given a linear solidification law, the concentration C_S^* in the solid at the solid–liquid interface is

$$C_S^* = L \,.\, C_0\left[1 - \frac{f_s}{1 + \alpha L}\right]^{L-1} \quad . \quad . \quad . \quad (11)$$

For a parabolic solidification law the concentration is given by

$$C_S^* = L \,.\, C_0[1 - (1 - 2\alpha L) \,.\, f_s]^{(L-1)/(1-2\alpha L)} \quad . \quad (12)$$

Here

L = the true segregation coefficient

C_0 = the concentration in the liquid at the beginning of solidification [mol/cm^{-3}]

f_s = the solidified part

α = a dimensionless expression: $= \dfrac{4 \,.\, D_s \,.\, t_f}{1^2}$

D_s = diffusion coefficient in the solid [cm^2/s^{-1}].

The product $\alpha \,.\, L$ controls the amount of segregation. For $\alpha \,.\, L \gg 1$ no microsegregation occurs. For $\alpha \,.\, L \ll 1$ the segregation is a maximum. The model of Flemings *et al.* has been proved to be correct by experiments on aluminium copper melts[50] and on alloyed iron melts.[51,52]

REFERENCES

1 W. J. SLATOSKY: *J. Met.*, 1960, **12**, 226–30

2 CONF. REPORT: International Conf. on Iron and Steelmaking, 1965, Amsterdam

3 H. W. MEYER AND J. A. GLASGOW: *Iron Steel Eng.*, 1966, **43**, 116–22

4 P. CESSLIN *et al.*: 'Congress Automation', 1965, 279–85, Congressbook, Liège

5 PH. CESSELIN AND C. STAIB: *Neue Hütte 11*, 1966, 583–91

6 P. NILLES AND E. M. DENIS: *J. Met.*, 1969, **21**, 74–9

7 C. HOLDEN AND A. HOGG: *JISI*, 1960, **196**, 318–32

8 R. A. FLINN *et al.*: *Trans. Met. Soc. AIME*, 1967, **239**, 1 776–91

9 TH. KOOTZ: *JISI*, 1960, **196**, 253–9

10 J. M. VAN LANGEN: *JISI*, 1960, **196**, 262–4

11 J. MAATSCH: *Techn. Mitt. Krupp*, 1963, **21**, 1–4

12 R. HAMMER *et al.*: *Stahl Eisen*, 1957, **77**, 1 303–8

13 Commission des Aciéries à l'oxygène, CIT, 1963, **5**, 1 283–6

14 Congrès International sur les Aciéries à l'oxygène, 1963, 371–425, Congressbook

15 K. BOROWSKI *et al.*: *Arch. Eisenh.*, 1967, **38**, 501–7

16 *Automation*, 1970, Düsseldorf

17 H. W. MEYER *et al.*: 'Heat and mass transfer in process metallurgy', 1967, 173–200, A. W. D. Hills

18 H. W. MEYER AND J. A. GLASGOW: *Iron Steel Eng.*, 1966, 116–22

19 W. DÖRR AND W. RECKNAGEL: *Stahl Eisen*, 1965, **85**, 1 686–91

20 F. J. HUFNAGEL *et al.*: *Stahl Eisen*, 1968, **88**, 1–5

21 J. MAATSCH *et al.*: *Stahl Eisen*, 1966, **86**, 1 205–21

22 F. OETERS: *Arch. Eisenh.*, 1966, **33**, 209–19

23 J. SZEKELY AND M. R. TODD: *Trans. Met. Soc. AIME*, 1967, **239**, 1 664–6

24 P. KOZAKEVITCH *et al.*: Congrès International du Touquet, 1964, 248–63, Conferencebook

25 H. V. ENDE AND W. D. LIESTMANN: *Stahl Eisen*, 1966, **86**, 1 189–205

26 H. W. MEYER *et al.*: *J. Met.*, 1968, **20**, 35–42

27 B. TRENTINI: *Trans. Met. Soc. AIME*, 1968, **242**, 2 377–88

28 P. KOZAKEVITCH: *J. Met.*, 1969, **21**, 57–68

29 K. W. LANGE: *Arch. Eisenh.*, 1972, **43**, 93–101

30 W. G. DAVENPORT *et al.*: 'Heat and mass transfer in process metallurgy', 1967, 207–40, A. W. D. Hills, London

31 H. LOHE: *Fortsch. Ber. VDIZ.*, 1967, **3**, 59

32 H. CHATTERJEE AND A. V. BRADSHAW: *JISI*, 1972, **210**, 179–87

33 H. KRAINER *et al.*: *Techn. Mitt. Krupp*, 1965, **23**, 53–66

34 W. LÖSCHER: *Hoesch Ber.*, 1970, **4**, 43–52

35 O. KNACKE: *Stahl Eisen*, 1965, **85**, 938–9

36 T. KRAUS: *Schweiz. Arch. Ange. Wiss. Techn.*, 1962, **28**, 452–68

37 H. A. FRIEDRICHS *et al.*: *Z. Metallk.*, 1972, **63**, 169–72

38 J. SZEKELY: 'Kinetik metallurgischer Vorgänge bei der Stahlherstellung', (Ed. W. Dahl *et al.*), 71–90, 1972, Düsseldorf

39 R. JESCHAR AND E. MILLIES: *Arch. Eisenh.* 1966, **37**, 283

40 G. HORVAY AND R. H. EDSALL: *Trans. Met. Soc. AIME*, 1960, **218**, 927–33

41 A. W. D. HILLS: *JISI*, 1965, **203**, 18–26

42 A. W. D. HILLS AND M. R. MOORE: 'Heat and mass transfer in process metallurgy', (Ed. by A. W. D. Hills), 1967, 141–66, London

43 A. W. D. HILLS: *Trans. Met. Soc. AIME*, 1969, **245**, 1 471–9

44 R. H. TIEN: *Trans. Met. Soc. AIME*, 1965, **233**, 1 887–91

45 J. J. GAUTHIER *et al.*: 'Mathematical models in metallurgical process development', 178–85, 1970, London, The Iron and Steel Institute

46 A. BURTON *et al.*: *J. Chem. Phys.*, 1953, **21**, 1 987–91

47 P. NILLES: *JISI*. 1964, July, 601–9 and 'Mathematical models in metallurgical process development', 162–77, 1970, London, The Iron and Steel Institute

48 F. OETERS *et al.*: *Arch. Eisenh.*, 1969, **40**, 603–13 and 'Mathe-matical models in metallurgical process development', 162–77, 1970, London, The Iron and Steel Institute

49 G. EBNETH: Dissertation Techn. Univ. Berlin, 1971

50 H. D. BRODY AND M. C. FLEMINGS: *Trans. Met. Soc. AIME*, 1966, **236**, 615–24

51 M. C. FLEMINGS *et al.*: *JISI*, 1970, **208**, 371–81

52 K. SCHWERDTFEGER, *Arch. Eisenh.*, 1970, **41**, 923–37

53 B. M. LARSEN AND U. SORDAHL: 'Physical Chemistry of Process Metallurgy', (2), 1961, 1 141–79, New York

Dynamic model of the BOS process

R. Weeks

A mathematical model of the BOS process has been developed to simulate the entire process. This paper gives a resumé of the major areas of the model, oxidation of the various impurities, slag formation, heat balance, and mass balances together with some details of the computer facilities and technique employed in the model development.

The benefits and applications of mathematical models of complex processes occurring in iron and steelmaking are well known within the Strip Mills Division of BSC, whose steelmaking capacity is almost entirely dependent on the BOS process; a detailed mathematical model of this process would prove an extremely valuable tool. A model describing the basic mechanisms involved in the BOS process and taking account of their thermodynamic limitations, was therefore formulated. The model was intended to simulate each instantaneous change occurring within the process and as such can be termed a truly dynamic model.

In the absence of sufficient detailed information in certain areas, initial hypotheses are required for completeness. These were originally described using information available from our operating experience and literature surveys. The uncertainties inherent in these hypotheses, particularly as the reactions rarely reach equilibrium,[1] limit the value of this dynamic model as a process control tool, but it has proved particularly useful in our feasibility studies and in off-line evaluation of the results of changes in operating practices. These studies help minimize, or even alleviate, abortive or uneconomic plant or process modifications. It should also be mentioned that this model has only been used, to date, to simulate the refining of low-phosphorus hot metal into a low-carbon deep-drawing steel.

BATH REFINING

To describe the various time paths involved in the refining of the metal bath in any steelmaking process,

the limiting factors governing the rates of reaction must be determined. Heterogeneous reactions such as these can be divided into sequential steps; mass transfer of reactants to the phase boundary, interfacial chemical reaction, and mass transfer of reaction products away from the phase boundary. It is generally agreed[2] that, in high-temperature processes, the chemical reaction step is much faster than the others and that the refining reactions are effectively limited by mass transfer. If the concept of Nernst boundary layers between the reacting species is assumed to apply to low-phosphorus hot metal and slag, then Fick's laws of diffusion can be used[3] to determine the reaction rate equations. Detailed derivations of these equations are given in Appendix 1. At the time of writing, insufficient dynamic information was available to fully quantify these limiting factors. However, a plausible set of mechanisms, which agrees with much of the published literature,[1,2,3] has been taken to limit the reactions involved. These mechanisms are briefly outlined next.

Carbon removal

The kinetics of this principal refining reaction have recently been very capably reviewed.[1] Oxygen is initially delivered to the bath via the jet impingement zone. This oxygen-enriched material is then swept away from the interaction zone by the combined effect of rising CO bubbles, natural convection and the absorption of energy from the oxygen jet, thus exposing a further layer of metal to the oxygen jet, and the pattern is repeated. This material then effectively reacts with the carbon dissolved in the metal at a suitable nucleation site.[3] Metal droplets dispersed in the slag provide an extended slag/metal

The author is with BSC, Strip Mills Division, Newport

interface which acts as another major site for carbon removal. Representations of these emulsions are discussed later in the paper. As the oxygen delivery rate is increased, decarburization is accelerated and towards the end of the process, as the carbon content is appreciably reduced, the rate-limiting step becomes the mass transfer of carbon.[4] Several change-over points for the limiting factor, from oxygen transfer to carbon transfer, were examined and the exact position was found to have little effect, providing it was in the approximate range 0·35–0·1 % carbon.[4,5,6]

Removal of other impurities

It has been suggested[2] that the main rate-limiting factor for the silicon and phosphorus reactions is mass transfer through the metal towards the interface. However, while this seems reasonable for the silicon reaction, lumpy heterogeneous slags markedly inhibit dephosphorization[3] and therefore the rate limiting step for phosphorus removal has been taken as similar to that assumed for manganese, removal of the oxidation product from the slag/metal interface. These oxidation products have been taken to exist at the interface in equilibrium with the bulk concentrations of the impurities.[7]

Sulphur is a slightly different proposition since no definite mechanism has yet been accepted for the removal of sulphur.[1] With this in mind, the model removes 10 % of the input sulphur[8] via a gas-phase reaction and assumes that the remainder is distributed between bath and slag according to an equilibrium distribution ratio, approximated from experimental results.[9] Since it is transferred to the slag via the slag/metal interface, the rate-controlling step is taken as the diffusion across the slag boundary layer and the reaction rate equation can be derived in a similar fashion to the other impurities.

Fume formation

The amount of fume formed in the BOS process would appear to be best quantified by practical measurements. Currently a reasonable approximation is about 1 % of the charged metallic weight.[10] The rate of generation of this fume, however, is uncertain. The major cause of fume formation has been shown[11] to be explosive oxidation of iron droplets in an exothermic atmosphere. More fume would therefore be produced under light slag cover, especially at the beginning and end of the blow. Yet as the decarburization reaction increases in intensity, more CO bubbles form and burst, thereby creating a higher incidence rate of the explosive mechanism, which to a certain extent counteracts the effect of increased slag bulk. In view of these considerations the rate of generation of the fume has been taken to be constant which is approximately true for a consistent operational procedure.

Heat balance

The rate of change of temperature of the molten bath is predicted from the rates of removal of the bath impurities and from a knowledge of the various mechanisms involved in scrap melting, lime dissolution, etc., which are discussed later. Standard heats of reaction, heat capacities, etc. were taken from the literature.[12] The heat balance was subsequently modified to correct high-temperature predictions and all the reactions taking place outside the bath itself, fume oxidation, carbon dioxide formation, and heat transfer to the oxygen jet were treated as a single source. This source was then taken to radiate a certain proportion of its heat back to the bath and in this manner, more realistic temperature predictions were obtained. This is an important area of the model since the reaction rates themselves are temperature dependent.

Materials balances

The rates of change of both hot-metal weight and slag weight are continually updated by the incremental changes in the various impurities, the inblow additions and the creation of the reaction products. Here again, the mechanisms governing scrap melting, lime dissolution, etc. play an important role.

OXYGEN DISTRIBUTION

As mentioned earlier, oxygen is delivered to the bath via the jet impingement zone. The actual distribution of oxygen between slag and metal is difficult to determine but the oxygen is delivered via two main mechanisms. The first and probably the most important is oxygen transfer through the slag where ferrous oxide (FeO) is oxidized to ferric oxide (Fe_2O_3) which travels to the slag/metal interface of the bath or emulsion where it is reduced back to ferrous (FeO) yielding oxygen. The second mechanism is oxygen transfer by direct impingement of the jet on the exposed metal at the impact zone. Here the oxygen combines with iron to form ferrous oxide (FeO) which is swept through the bath, effectively increasing the bulk oxygen concentration.

The model determines the amounts of oxygen involved in each of these mechanisms by direct proportion to the respective areas of slag and steel exposed to the oxygen jet. The areas exposed are determined from energy considerations between the oxygen jet and the molten bath, where the shape of the cavity formed at the impact zone is known.[13] The oxygen distribution is calculated in detail in Appendix 2. The actual amount of iron oxide formed in the slag is determined from a detailed oxygen balance after suitable allowance has been made for the carbon monoxide oxidized by entrainment within the oxygen jet.

SLAG DEVELOPMENT

The oxidation products formed during the refining of the bath have been documented elsewhere.[14,15] This section briefly describes the mechanisms that are assumed to govern the solution rates of the additional materials added during the process to ensure the development of a suitable basic slag.

Lime dissolution

The rate of solution of lime is an extremely complex subject to predict satisfactorily. The major factors involved are slag composition, slag temperature, and lime quality.[16,17] The two main limitations on early lime dissolution are physical constraints, such as slopping, and the formation of complex dicalcium silicate shells around the lime particles. In general, however, the rate of solution increases with the addition of fluxes, such as fluorspar and iron oxides.[18] Also, the relatively high slag temperatures encountered early in the blow are mainly due to the formation of FeO,[19] and therefore the rate of lime dissolution was taken to be a function of the weight percentage of the sum of manganese oxide and iron oxides (expressed as ferrous oxide) in the slag.

Other additions

Although the effect of fluxes, such as fluorspar, can vary with the time of addition,[20] they usually become part of the active slag in a fairly short time. The dissociation of scale and ore also probably proceeds very rapidly and consequently in the absence of definite information the rates of solution of these materials were taken to be constant. The amount of refractory lining erosion was derived from practical experience and the rate of wear was taken as linear throughout the blow.

Emulsion formation

The rates of evolution and destruction of the emulsions common to the BOS process depend mainly on the amount of energy absorbed from the oxygen jet, the rate of formation of CO bubbles and the surface properties of the various media involved.[21] These emulsions have extremely large interfacial areas and, therefore, contribute significantly to the speed of refining. Normally, with a fairly constant operating practice, the rate of emulsion formation can be taken as dependent on the rate of generation of CO bubbles, as a first approximation. The additional agitation provided by this carbon boil should theoretically increase the rates of removal of the other impurities.[2,22] Therefore, the relevant reaction rate equations are modified by an emulsion factor which was defined to be a function of the decarburization rate.

SCRAP MELTING

Basically the melting of scrap can be represented by simultaneous heat and mass transfer. Initial melting can occur below the scrap liquidus temperature due to preliminary carburization of the surface of the scrap. The rate of melting is extremely difficult to model accurately since practical data are very limited. A simple mechanism is currently employed in the model which treats the scrap as one piece of material of uniform temperature. This is heated up gradually as the bath temperature increases until an average melting temperature (normally taken to be below the liquidus) is attained. Melting of the outer layer of the scrap then begins and

the scrap gradually melts until complete solution is obtained. The rate of melting is taken as a direct function of the temperature gradient between the scrap and the metal bath. This hypothesis provides results which are in approximate agreement with much more detailed treatments.[23,24] Suitable allowance is also made for the introduction of the scrap impurities into the metal bath.

MODEL STRUCTURE

The model is not designed to compute the requisite amount of materials to be input to the vessel. This can be done via any adequate static model. Rather it is designed to accept given input conditions, weights and analyses of scrap, hot metal, and associated blast-furnace slag carryover, and to refine these materials with a given operational procedure of lance height, oxygen flow rate and materials addition. To date, the input conditions and the operational procedure used have been those of the particular plant under study, enabling the effects of any major changes in practice to be predicted without incorporating the discrepancies associated with plant-to-plant variations.

MODEL SOLUTION

The complex system of differential equations was solved by simulating the use of an analog machine on a digital, using an IBM computer package known as CSMP.[25] This package is fairly efficient, simulating an entire blow in less than a tenth of real time. The only serious difficulties were encountered during optimization due to extreme sensitivity in certain areas, when using earlier versions of the package.

The model was initially developed on an IBM 360/40 computer. This machine was subsequently replaced by a 360/50 providing even faster operation. The entire simulation, including CSMP modules, at present uses about 70K bytes of core storage. The uncertainties present in each of the reaction rate equations (*see* Appendix 1) were gathered together into a single parameter, termed a reaction rate constant. The values of these constants were updated to match the predictions of the model with the real world. This was done by minimizing an error function consisting of suitably weighted sums of squares of the differences between actual and predicted values. Initially, this optimization was attempted by trial and error, or to use its mathematical title 'manual hill climbing', but this proved too frustrating. After trials with various methods of hill climbing, the Simplex method utilizing a simple binary search, is now used. This is claimed[26] to be an adequate method for an approximate solution and also performs well under noisy conditions.

MODEL CALIBRATION

The model was initially developed solely from data known before and after the blowing period. No dynamic information was available and therefore the selection of process paths was governed by the end-point predictions. This state of affairs was alleviated by a comprehensive investigation of waste gas analyses and flow rates within the BSC.[27,28]

A second stage was therefore reached in the process of model calibration. Not only were the turndown conditions to be predicted satisfactorily, but a measured decarburization profile was also to be simulated. The procedure adopted to date has been to modify the rate constants until the desired turndown conditions are obtained simultaneously with an approximate decarburization profile. The model was calibrated in this fashion for two different works and also for different data sets for a single works. Small pilot vessels have subsequently become available. In-blow sampling and temperature measurement permit the determination of the reaction rate profiles throughout the entire blow. These data provide a comprehensive check of model predictions and highlight aspects of the model requiring further development.

RESULTS

Initially the model was used to examine data from two different plants. One set of data from each plant was used to determine the rate constants for that plant, in terms of attainment of the actual steel analysis and a realistic decarburization profile. The model predictions for the two works are shown in Figs. 1 and 2, and the values of the rate constants derived for both plants are given in Table 1. Further sets of data from one plant were also calibrated in terms of end-point attainment to

TABLE 1   Comparison of rate constants for different works

Rate constant	Works 'A'	Works 'B'
RCCARB1	1·33	6·15
RCCARB2	0·3	1·6
RCOXY	0·07	0·08
RCDIR	0·07	0·06
RCSIL	0·065	0·15
RCSUL	0·02	0·17
RCPHOS	0·00016	0·0003
RCMANG	0·008	0·10

compare derived rate constant values between casts and, as examples, two sets of rate constants are shown in Table 2.

The sensitivity of the model to errors in the initial calibration of the rate constants was also examined by using the initially derived rate constants to predict the resulting end-points for other data sets. Some typical results of this procedure are shown in Figs. 3 and 4.

TABLE 2   Comparison of rate constants after calibration of different data sets for works 'A'

Rate constant	Set 1	Set 2
RCCARB1	1·33	1·70
RCCARB2	0·3	0·2
RCOXY	0·07	0·07
RCDIR	0·07	0·07
RCSIL	0·065	0·065
RCSUL	0·02	0·08
RCPHOS	0·00016	0·00005
RCMANG	0·008	0·004

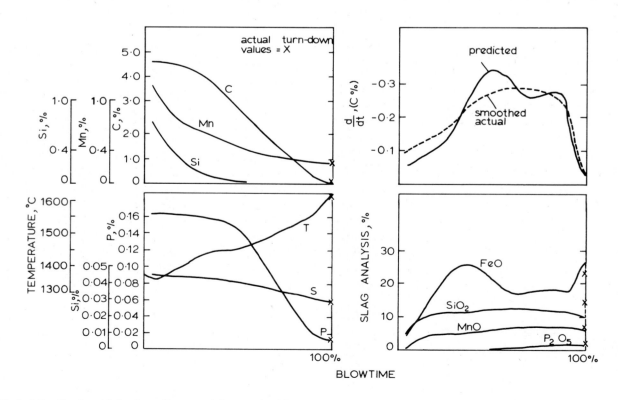

1   Works 'A'   *Predicted behaviour of cast used for initial calibration*

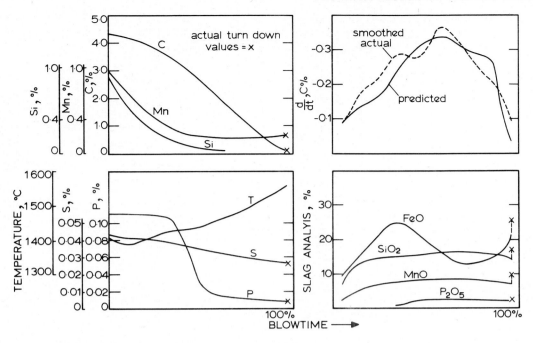

2   Works 'B'   *Predicted behaviour of cast used for initial calibration*

The rate constants themselves were also varied individually by $\pm 10\%$ and the effects on end-point prediction are shown in Table 3. The data input to the model was varied by $\pm 5\%$ to investigate the effect on the turn-down predictions. Table 4 shows these effects in terms of actual changes in end-point prediction and as percentage variations.

Examples of one of the current uses of the model are shown in Figs. 5 and 6 by the comparison of the predicted effect on the sulphur profile of increasing the amount of blast-furnace slag from 1% to 2% of the initial hot-metal weight without modifying the operational procedure in any way. Finally, information from a small pilot vessel was also simulated by the model and the predictions are shown in Fig. 7.

DISCUSSION OF RESULTS

During model development major difficulties have been experienced with satisfactory predictions of end-point phosphorus content and turn-down temperature. In the BOS process, phosphorus removal depends on complex

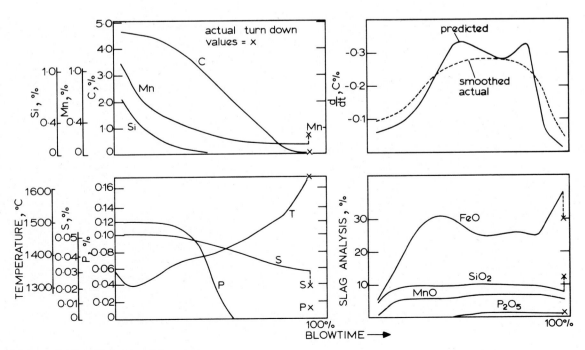

3   Works 'A'   *Predicted behaviour of a subsequent cast*

TABLE 3 Effect of variations in rate constants

Rate constant	Amount of change, %	Changes in turn-down predictions Actual predictions (and percentage change)							
		C		Mn		P		S	
RCSUL	−10	0.047	(0)	0.19	(0)	0.008	(0)	0.022	(1)
	+10	0.047	(0)	0.19	(0)	0.008	(0)	0.022	(−1)
RCSIL	−10	0.048	(3)	0.186	(−2)	0.006	(−25)	0.022	(−1)
	+10	0.046	(−2)	0.195	(3)	0.010	(25)	0.022	(1)
RCPHOS	−10	0.047	(0)	0.19	(0)	0.010	(25)	0.022	(0)
	+10	0.047	(0)	0.19	(0)	0.007	(−13)	0.022	(0)
RCMANG	−10	0.047	(−1)	0.208	(9)	0.008	(0)	0.022	(1)
	+10	0.047	(0)	0.178	(−6)	0.008	(0)	0.022	(−1)
RCCARB	−10	0.054	(15)	0.178	(−6)	0.003	(−63)	0.021	(−3)
	+10	0.042	(−11)	0.205	(8)	0.022	(175)	0.023	(3)

Percentage change is expressed as: $\dfrac{\text{(New prediction − Original prediction)}}{\text{Original prediction}} \times 100$

TABLE 4 Effect of variations in input data

Input data	Amount of change, %	Changes in turn-down predictions Actual predictions (and percentage change)									
		C		Mn		P		S		T	
Initial hot metal weight	−5	0.029	(−38)	0.158	(−17)	0.0005	(−42)	0.020	(−8)	1 640	(1)
	+5	0.084	(79)	0.228	(19)	0.0137	(63)	0.023	(5)	1 600	(−1)
Hot metal carbon content	−5	0.032	(−32)	0.178	(−7)	0.009	(8)	0.022	(0)	1 640	(1)
	+5	0.075	(58)	0.206	(8)	0.008	(−2)	0.022	(0)	1 600	(−1)
Oxygen flow rate	−5	0.091	(92)	0.197	(3)	0.007	(−15)	0.022	(1)	1 570	(−3)
	+5	0.028	(−41)	0.185	(−3)	0.011	(28)	0.022	(−1)	1 670	(3)
Initial hot metal temperature	−5	0.062	(31)	0.127	(−33)	0	(−100)	0.020	(−7)	1 585	(−2)
	+5	0.032	(−32)	0.287	(50)	0.084	(900)	0.024	(11)	1 650	(2)
Duration of blow	−5	0.087	(84)	0.197	(3)	0.010	(22)	0.023	(4)	1 575	(−3)
	+5	0.029	(−39)	0.185	(−3)	0.006	(−27)	0.021	(−4)	1 665	(3)
Assumed heat loss	−5	0.046	(−3)	0.194	(1)	0.010	(17)	0.022	(0)	1 620	(0)
	+5	0.048	(2)	0.188	(−1)	0.007	(−14)	0.022	(0)	1 615	(0)

Percentage change is expressed as $\dfrac{\text{(New prediction − Original prediction)}}{\text{Original prediction}} \times 100$

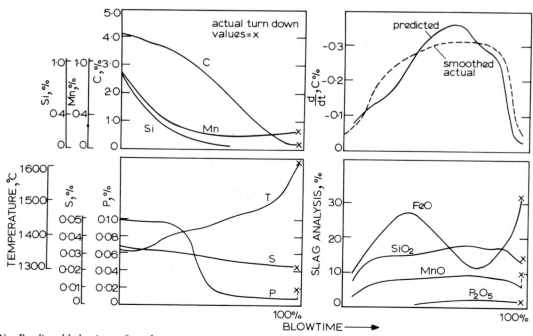

4 Works 'B' *Predicted behaviour of a subsequent cast*

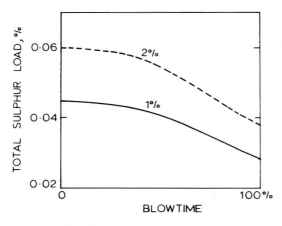

5 Works 'A' *Effect of BF slag conveyor on sulphur profile*

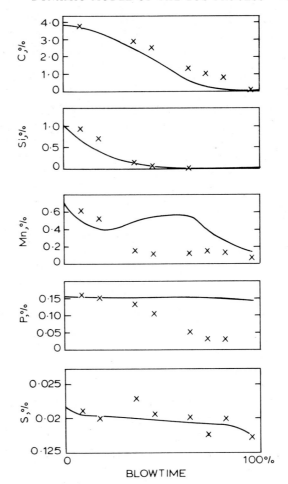

7 *Predictions for a small pilot plant*

reactions which are usually far from equilibrium. This phosphorus problem was partially resolved by utilizing more recent investigations[32] and reasonable predictions of turn-down temperature were obtained by performing a dynamic heat balance around the metal bath itself, rather than around the vessel, as mentioned previously. Figures 1 and 2 also show that after calibration, good predictions of turn-down conditions can be obtained with the present form of model. Simultaneous attainment of turn-down carbon content and an accurate decarburization rate profile is more difficult. The predicted decarburization rate is shown and compared with a decarburization rate calculated from actual plant measurements and smoothed by averaging. A large part of the discrepancies could possibly be explained by inaccuracies in the measured waste-gas flow rate which tended to pulsate and occasionally oscillate across the stack ducting.

Table 1 shows two sets of calibrated rate constants for different works. Vessel capacity at Works B is about twice that at Works A, while blowing times are similar. Yet, no simple scaling factor emerges between the two sets of rate constants for the different vessels. Not only can the rate constants vary from vessel to vessel as shown in Table 1, but they can also vary for different sets of data from the same vessel as shown in Table 2. However, variations in certain of the constants, notably the oxygen

constants, produced very small changes in end-point predictions and were therefore kept constant. It can be seen that in some cases relatively large changes are required to obtain the desired end-point conditions. These variations indicate further development of the model is required.

A large part of the deviation of the predictions from the actual values could be due to errors in the input data and the effect of data errors can be estimated from the figures shown in Table 4. This table shows the difference between the new prediction and the old prediction as a percentage of the old prediction when the data input is in error by as much as 5%. It can be seen that the major inaccuracy occurs in the prediction of final carbon and phosphorus contents. It is difficult to obtain accurate data from a production vessel and therefore the main use of the model to date has been to investigate the effects of variations in the input data or in the inherent assumptions. As an example, the amount of blast-furnace slag, input to the BOS process, was allowed to vary and the results are shown in Figs. 5 and 6. If the amount of the slag, which is carried over with the hot metal, is not adequately controlled, severe problems can occur, particularly with the attainment of sulphur specifications.

Figures 3 and 4 show detailed model predictions as examples of using initially calibrated rate constants to

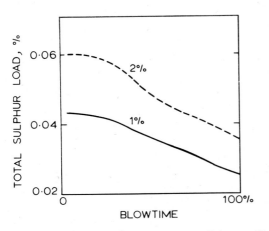

6 Works 'B' *Effect of BF slag conveyor on sulphur profile*

predict the end-points for other data sets. As a first approximation, the predictions are all of the desired order of magnitude with the notable exception of phosphorus, which is extremely sensitive. Schemes aimed at controlling the process would find these results far from satisfactory and this suggests the value of reliable dynamic information before the end of the blow to enable the process paths to arrive at the desired objective. The effects of variations ($\pm 10\%$) of the more important rate constants are shown in Table 3, again in terms of the changes in predicted values, the major fact of consequence here being the comparatively large changes in phosphorus predictions for variations in the rate constant governing the removal of carbon. This is mainly because slag/metal emulsification plays a major role in phosphorus removal and, as mentioned earlier, the model currently takes the degree of emulsification to be dependent on the decarburization rate. This series of investigations highlighted one of the weaker areas of the model, i.e. the mathematical representation of emulsions, and further studies in this area are being pursued within the Corporation. The results of predictions for a small pilot vessel are shown in Fig. 7. The predicted values of phosphorus content could indicate either a completely false value for the rate constant governing carbon removal or that scaling effects become important in the mathematical representation of slag–metal emulsions.

CONCLUSIONS

The following conclusions were derived:

(i) the model can be calibrated to provide a reasonable representation of full-scale production vessels but needs certain modifications to enable simulation of small pilot vessels

(ii) the data input to models of this type should be subject to stringent validity checks, since starting at the wrong position ensures the prediction of a false trajectory

(iii) the model is a useful tool for off-line evaluation of changes in operating procedures or additions etc., but needs considerable development, particularly in the field of emulsion representation and material dissolution, before it can be considered an accurate picture of the BOS process.

ACKNOWLEDGMENTS

The author wishes to thank the Director, Technical Services, of the Strip Mills Division, BSC, for permission to present this paper.

REFERENCES

1 R. D. WALKER AND D. ANDERSON: *Iron Steel*, 1972, Jun., 271–6
2 F. OETERS: *Arch. Eisenh*, 1966, **37**, 209–19
3 T. KOOTZ AND A. ALTGELD: *Thyssenforschung*, 1970, **2** (4), 121–6
4 J. SZEKELY AND M. R. TODD: *Trans. Met. Soc. AIME*, 1967, **239**, 1 664–6
5 G. BREUER *et al.*: *Arch. Eisenh.*, 1968, **39**, 553–7
6 H. MEYER *et al.*: *J. Met.*, 1968, Jul., 35–42
7 T. J. HANRATTY: *J.A.I. Chem. Eng.*, 1956, **2** (3), 359–62
8 M. YOSHII AND M. ICHINOHE: *Tetsu-to-Hagané*, 1970, **56**, 34–41
9 J. CHIPMAN *et al.*: *Trans. Met. Soc. AIME*, 1956, **206**, 862–8
10 M. P. KVITKO: *Stal in English*, 1970, **11**, 860–2
11 A. F. ELLIS AND J. GLOVER: *JISI*, 1971, **209**, 593–9
12 J. PEARSON: BISRA Report no. SM/AF/12/65
13 A. CHATTERJEE AND A. V. BRADSHAW: *JISI*, 1972, **210**, 179–87
14 A. V. RUDNEVA AND V. V. SMOKTIN: *Izv. A. N. SSSR*, 1963, May–Jun., **3**, 58–66
15 F. BARDENHEUER *et al.*: *Blast Furn. and Steel plant*, 1970, Jun., 401–7
16 F. BARDENHEUER *et al.*: *Stahl Eisen*, 1968, **88**, 1 285–90
17 R. D. WALKER AND D. ANDERSON: *Iron Steel*, 1972, Aug., 403–7
18 P. NILLES *et al.*: Joint Conf. UK and Continental Oxygen Converter Working Group, May, 1970
19 F. BARDENHEUER *et al.*: *Stahl Eisen*, 1968, **88**, 613–21
20 P. NILLES *et al.*: *CRM Met. Rep.*, Jun., **27**, 1971, 27–32
21 P. KOZAKOVITCH: *J. Met.*, 1969, Jul., 57–68
22 P. NILLES AND E. M. DENIS: *J. Met.*, 1969, Jul., 74–9
23 I. MUCHI: *Proc. ICSTIS*: (suppl.) *Trans. ISI Japan*, 1971, **11**, 360–6
24 K. MORI AND H. NOMURA: *Tetsu-to-Hagané*, 1969, **55**, 347–54
25 IBM, Application Program, CSMP, 360A/CX/16X
26 J. A. NELDER AND R. MEAD: *Computer Journal*, 1965, **7** (4), 308
27 C. J. KEARTON: Private communication, April 1968
28 T. H. HAMMOND: Private communication, April 1968
29 F. D. RICHARDSON: *Met. Trans.*, 1971, Oct. **2** (10), 2 747–56
30 J. CHIPMAN: 'Basic Open Hearth Steelmaking', 1951, Chapter 16, AIME
31 J. F. ELLIOTT *et al.*: 'Thermochemistry for Steelmaking', 1963, Addison-Wesley
32 G. W. HEALY: *JISI*, 1970, **208**, 664–8
33 J. MAATSCH: *Techn. Mitt. Krupp.*, *Forschungsber.*, 1962, **20**, 1–9
34 K. G. SPIETH *et al.*: 'Iron and Coal Trades Review', 1960, 679–82
35 C. HOLDEN AND A. HOGG: *JISI*, 1960, **196**, 318–32
36 A. R. ANDERSON AND F. R. JOHNS: *Jet Propulsion*, 1955, **25**, 13–5
37 J. D. KAPNER AND K. LI: Research Report to AISI, Carnegie Inst. of Tech., 1967

APPENDIX 1

Model equations

SYMBOLS

a_i	activity of ith species
A	area of gas/metal or slag/metal interface
b_i	activity coefficient for ith species when concentration of the ith species is expressed as mole fraction
$C\%$	weight percent of carbon in metal
CaO	calcium oxide content of the slag, $\%$
C_i	concentration in mol/v of the ith species
Cp_i'	average specific heat capacity of the ith species
D_i	diffusion constant for ith species
DT	temperature difference between bath and base temperature
F	ratio of W_{HM_0}/W_{HM}
FeO_T	total slag iron oxides expressed as weight of FeO

f_i activity coefficient for ith species when concentration of the ith species is expressed as weight percent

ΔH_i heat of reaction of ith species

K_i equilibrium constant for the ith species

M_i molecular weight of ith species

n_i number of moles of the ith species

O2DIR   fraction of oxygen delivered direct to metal

$\underline{O}_s^\%$ weight percentage of oxygen in metal at saturation

P_i pressure of ith species

R radiation factor

S cross-sectional area of bath

t time

T temperature, °C

W_i weight of ith species

$X_i^\%$ weight percent of ith species removed from metal

Z total number of moles of slag

$\Delta\delta$ boundary layer thickness

ρ_i density of ith species

σ Stefan–Boltzmann constant

underlined quantities   composition in metal

bracketed quantities   composition in slag

Superscripts

*   equilibrium value

%   weight percent of initial hot-metal weight (underlined) or of actual slag weight (bracketed)

Subscripts

FUM   fume

HM   hot metal

i   various elements and compounds

LIN   dissolved refractory lining

0   initial value

RB   ore

SCR   scrap

SL   slag

Mass balance

To determine the metal weight, a dynamic materials balance is used

$$\frac{d}{dt}(W_{HM}) = \frac{W_{HM_0}}{100} * \left(\frac{d}{dt}(C^\%) - \frac{d}{dt}(X_{Si}^\%) - \frac{d}{dt}(X_{Mn}^\%)\right.$$

$$\left. - \frac{d}{dt}(X_P^\%) - \frac{d}{dt}(X_s^\%)\right) - \frac{d}{dt}(W_{SCR})$$

$$- L_1 * \frac{d}{dt}(W_{FUM}) - L_2 * \frac{d}{dt}(W_{FeO})$$

where L_1, L_2 are constants depending on the analysis of the relevant materials.

Slag balance

A further dynamic materials balance is formulated to evaluate the slag weight

$$\frac{d}{dt}(W_{SL}) = \frac{W_{HM_0}}{100} * \left(2{\cdot}14 * \frac{d}{dt}(X_{Si}^\%) + 1{\cdot}29 * \frac{d}{dt}(X_{Mn}^\%)\right.$$

$$\left. + 2{\cdot}29 * \frac{d}{dt}(X_P^\%) + \frac{d}{dt}(X_s^\%)\right) + \frac{d}{dt}(W_{CaO})$$

$$+ \frac{d}{dt}(W_{FeO}) + \frac{d}{dt}(W_{LIN})$$

Slag components

The number of moles of each of the slag components are also dynamically calculated in the normal manner.

Emulsion factor

The model represents the increased rates of impurity removal due to emulsion formation by modifying the reaction rate constants by a factor

$$TURB = \left(KEMA + KEMB * \frac{d}{dt}(C^\%)\right)^{KEMC}$$

where KEMA, KEMB, and KEMC are constants. This factor is an attempt to simulate the stirring effect within the bath due to interfacial turbulence between slag and metal in addition to the continuous formation of gas bubbles.[29] Studies were also attempted to enable this factor to represent the effects of slag composition and thus surface properties. No significant improvements were made in the impurity removal profiles and therefore the factor described above is still used in the model, until further information becomes available.

Slag density

In the reaction rate equations, derived later in this Appendix, the effective slag density is required to enable the concentrations within the slag to be redefined in terms of weight percent. In view of the volume of gas contained within the slag, dispersed as bubbles of varying sizes, it is felt that the apparent density provides a more useful estimate than the actual, in a similar fashion to the stabilization of emulsions due to the apparent viscosity of the slag.[17] The model uses a typical slag height profile for a given works, derived from a series of audiometer traces, to give an approximate slag volume which, in conjunction with the calculated slag weight, determines the apparent slag density.

Fraction of CO oxidized to CO$_2$ by entrainment within the oxygen jet

This fraction is determined from a relationship involving the size and shape of the oxygen jet, developed from data collected within BSC. Fraction of CO burnt to

$$CO_2 = L_3 + L_4 * \frac{\text{Lance height}}{\text{Jet velocity}}$$

where

L_3 and L_4 are constants.

This relationship provides an average value throughout the blow rather than an instantaneous absolute value.

Oxygen balance

The rate of deformation of slag iron oxides expressed as ferrous oxide (FeO) is determined by performing an oxygen balance.

$$\frac{1}{71 \cdot 85} \frac{\mathrm{d}}{\mathrm{d}t}(\mathrm{FeO_T}) = \text{number of moles of oxygen supplied from the lance}$$

moles of oxygen consumed by impurity oxidation

moles of oxygen dissolved in the bath

moles of oxygen to oxidize CO to CO_2 in the jet

moles of oxygen from dissociation of ore and scale

Heat balance

The bath temperature is obtained by performing a dynamic heat balance with respect to the metal bath. The rate of change of heat content of the bath in a given period is determined from the amount of heat generated by the relevant reactions within the bath at 25°C less the heat required to raise the reaction products to the bath temperature. Reactions taking place above the slag/metal bath raise the temperature of the waste gases and therefore a certain amount of heat is provided at the surface of the melt due to radiation. The full heat balance can be written as follows

$$\frac{\mathrm{d}}{\mathrm{d}t}(C'_{p_{HM}} W_{HM} T_{HM}) = -\left(\Delta H_{CO} + \frac{N_{CO}}{12 \cdot 01} C'_{P_{CO}} DT \right)$$

$$\times * \frac{W_{HM_0}}{100} \cdot \frac{P_{CO}}{P_T} \cdot \left(-\frac{\mathrm{d}}{\mathrm{d}t}(C\%) \right)$$

$$-\left(\Delta H_{CO_2} + \frac{M_{CO_2}}{12 \cdot 01} C'_{pCO_2} DT \right)$$

$$\times * \frac{W_{HM_0}}{100} \cdot \frac{P_{CO_2}}{P_T} \left(-\frac{\mathrm{d}}{\mathrm{d}t}(C\%) \right)$$

$$-\left(\Delta H_{Ca_2SiO_4} + \frac{M_{Ca_2SiO_4}}{28 \cdot 09} C'_{pCa_2SiO_4} \cdot DT \right)$$

$$\times * \frac{W_{HM_0}}{100} \cdot \frac{\mathrm{d}}{\mathrm{d}t}(X_{Si}^\%)$$

$$-\left(\Delta H_{MnO} + \frac{M_{MnO}}{54 \cdot 94} C'_{P_{MnO}} DT \right) * \frac{W_{HM_0}}{100} \frac{\mathrm{d}}{\mathrm{d}t}(X_{Mn}^\%)$$

$$-\left(\Delta H_{Ca_4P_2O_9} + \frac{M_{Ca_4P_2O_9}}{61 \cdot 94} C'_{pCa_4P_2O_9} DT \right)$$

$$\times * \frac{W_{HM_0}}{100} \frac{\mathrm{d}}{\mathrm{d}t}(X_P^\%)$$

$$-\left(\Delta H_{Fe-FeO} \cdot \frac{55 \cdot 85}{M_{FeO}} + C'_{P_{FeO}} DT \right) * \frac{\mathrm{d}}{\mathrm{d}t}(W_{FeO_T})$$

$$-\left(\Delta H_{FeO-Fe} \frac{\%FeO}{100} \frac{55 \cdot 85}{M_{FeO}} + \Delta H_{Fe_2O_3-Fe} \frac{\%Fe_2O_3}{100} \right.$$

$$\left. \cdot \frac{111 \cdot 7}{M_{Fe_2O_3}} \right) \frac{\mathrm{d}}{\mathrm{d}t}(W_{RB})$$

$$+ \sigma S.R.((T_{FLAME} + 273 \cdot 2)^4 - (T_{HM} + 273 \cdot 2)^4)$$

$$-\frac{\mathrm{d}}{\mathrm{d}t}(\text{Heat losses})$$

$$-\frac{\mathrm{d}}{\mathrm{d}t}(C'_{p_{SCR}} W_{SCR} T_{SCR}) - C'_{p_{CaO}} \cdot DT \cdot \frac{\mathrm{d}}{\mathrm{d}t}$$

(Weight of unreacted lime)

Derivation of reaction rate equations

CARBON

As stated in the text, carbon removal is limited initially by oxygen transfer changing ultimately to carbon transfer. Both these mechanisms can be represented mathematically in a similar fashion and therefore the reaction rate equation for the removal of carbon will only be derived in terms of oxygen transfer as the limiting step. According to Fick's first law, the rate of oxygen transfer across the gas/metal interface can be expressed as:

$$\frac{\mathrm{d}}{\mathrm{d}t}(n_O) = -\frac{D_0 A}{\Delta \delta}(C_O - C_O^*) \quad . \quad . \quad . \quad . \quad (A1)$$

Since oxygen transfer has been taken as the rate-limiting step

$$\frac{\mathrm{d}}{\mathrm{d}t}(n_O) = \frac{\mathrm{d}}{\mathrm{d}t}(n_O^*)$$

Transforming to percentages, gives

$$\frac{\mathrm{d}}{\mathrm{d}t}(n_O^*) = \frac{W_{HM_0}}{1\,600} \frac{\mathrm{d}}{\mathrm{d}t}(O^* \%) \quad . \quad . \quad . \quad (A2)$$

$$C_O = \frac{\rho_{HM} O \% F}{1\,600} \quad . \quad . \quad . \quad . \quad . \quad (A3)$$

and

$$C_{O^*} = \frac{\rho_{HM} O^* \% F}{1\,600} \quad . \quad . \quad . \quad . \quad (A4)$$

Note that expressing the amount of oxygen as weight percent of the initial hot metal weight avoids the necessity of a second term in the differential of Eq. (A2). This necessitates the introduction of the ratio $W_{HM_0}/W_{HM} = F$ elsewhere. Substituting (A2), (A3), and (A4) in (A1),

$$\frac{W_{HM_0}}{1\,600} \frac{\mathrm{d}}{\mathrm{d}t}(O^* \%) = -\frac{D_0 A F \rho_{HM}}{1\,600 \Delta \delta}(O\% - O^* \%) \quad (A5)$$

Now the equilibrium constant for the carbon monoxide reaction is

$$K_{CO} = \frac{a_{CO}}{a_{C^*} a_{O^*}} \quad . \quad . \quad . \quad . \quad . \quad (A6)$$

But between 1 400–1 630°C, carbon monoxide can be approximated to an ideal gas.[31] Therefore the activity can be represented by the partial pressure P_{CO} of carbon monoxide expressed in atmospheres. Now the carbon at the interface can, for all practical purposes, be set equal to the carbon level in the bulk metal phase since it is the oxygen gradient rather than the carbon gradient across the boundary layer that controls the rate of reaction. Therefore

$$K_{CO} = \frac{P_{CO}}{(f_C \underline{C}\%F)(f_O \underline{O}*\%F)} \qquad . \qquad . \qquad . \qquad (A7)$$

Substituting for $\underline{O}*\%$ from (A7) in (A5) gives

$$\frac{W_{HM_0}}{1\,600} \frac{d}{dt}(\underline{O}*\%) = -\frac{D_0 A F \rho_{HM}}{1\,600\,\Delta\delta}$$
$$\times \left(\underline{O}\% - \frac{P_{CO}}{f_C \cdot \underline{C}\% f_O \cdot K_{CO} \cdot F^2}\right) \qquad . \qquad . \qquad (A8)$$

Now the number of moles consumed in the decarburization reactions

$$C + O \rightarrow CO$$

and

$$C + 2O* \rightarrow CO_2$$

can be expressed as

$$n_{\underline{O}*} = n_{CO} + 2n_{CO_2} \qquad . \qquad . \qquad . \qquad . \qquad (A9)$$

and

$$n_{\underline{C}} = n_{CO} + n_{CO_2} \qquad . \qquad . \qquad . \qquad . \qquad (A10)$$

Dividing (A10) by (A9).

$$\frac{n_{\underline{C}}}{n_{\underline{O}*}} = \frac{n_{CO} + n_{CO_2}}{n_{CO} + 2n_{CO_2}} \qquad . \qquad . \qquad . \qquad (A11)$$

Now if n_T represents the total number of moles of gas

$$\frac{n_{\underline{C}}}{n_{\underline{O}*}} = \frac{(n_{CO} + n_{CO_2})/n_T}{(n_{CO} + 2n_{CO_2})/n_T} \qquad . \qquad . \qquad (A12)$$

But

$$n_{CO}/n_T = P_{CO}/P_T \quad \text{and} \quad n_{CO_2}/n_T = P_{CO_2}/P_T$$

where P_T is the total pressure. Therefore, since $P_T = P_{CO} + P_{CO_2}$

$$n_{\underline{C}} = \left(\frac{P_T}{P_{CO} + 2P_{CO_2}}\right) n_{\underline{O}*} \qquad . \qquad . \qquad (A13)$$

Differentiating (A13)

$$\frac{d}{dt}(n_{\underline{C}}) = \left(\frac{P_T}{P_{CO} + 2P_{CO_2}}\right) \frac{d}{dt}(n_{\underline{O}*})$$
$$+ n_{\underline{O}*} \frac{d}{dt}\left(\frac{P_T}{P_{CO} + 2P_{CO_2}}\right) \qquad . \qquad (A14)$$

Since the equilibrium ratio of CO and CO_2 does not change appreciably with changes in carbon (and therefore with time) until below about 0·1% carbon,[30] as a first approximation we may write

$$\frac{d}{dt}\left(\frac{P_T}{P_{CO} + 2P_{CO_2}}\right) = 0 \qquad . \qquad . \qquad . \qquad (A15)$$

and then (A14) reduces to

$$\frac{d}{dt}(n_{\underline{C}}) = \left(\frac{P_T}{P_{CO} + 2P_{CO_2}}\right) \frac{d}{dt}(n_{\underline{O}*}) \qquad . \qquad . \qquad (A16)$$

Converting to percentages

$$\frac{W_{HM_0}}{1\,201} \frac{d}{dt}(\underline{C}\%) = \left(\frac{P_T}{P_{CO} + 2P_{CO_2}}\right) \frac{W_{HM_0}}{1\,600} \frac{d}{dt}(\underline{O}*\%). \quad (A17)$$

Substituting for $d/dt(\underline{O}*\%)$ in (A8)

$$\frac{d}{dt}(\underline{C}\%) = -\frac{1\,201}{W_{HM}}\left(\frac{P_T}{P_{CO} + 2P_{CO_2}}\right)\frac{D_0 A \rho_{HM}}{1\,600\,\Delta\delta}$$
$$\times \left(\underline{O}\% - \frac{P_{CO}}{f_C \cdot \underline{C}\% \cdot f_O \cdot K_{CO}F^2}\right) \qquad . \qquad (A18)$$

We now define a 'reaction-rate constant' as

$$RCCARB = \frac{D_0 A}{\Delta\delta} \qquad . \qquad . \qquad . \qquad . \qquad (A19)$$

and assume that this remains constant for a given vessel and operating procedure. The final equation for carbon elimination then becomes

$$\frac{d}{dt}(\underline{C}\%) = -\frac{RCCARB}{W_{HM}} \cdot \rho_{HM} \frac{1\,201}{1\,600}\left(\frac{P_T}{P_{CO} + 2P_{CO_2}}\right)$$
$$\times \left(\underline{O}\% - \frac{P_{CO}}{f_C \cdot \underline{C}\% \cdot f_O \cdot K_{CO}F^2}\right) \qquad . \qquad (A20)$$

where P_{CO} can be calculated from the expressions for the equilibrium constants. The equilibrium constants themselves, together with the interaction coefficients can be obtained from the literature.[31]

MANGANESE

The rate-limiting step for this reaction has been taken as the diffusion of the oxidation product across the boundary layer and therefore

$$\frac{d}{dt}(n_{Mn}) = \frac{d}{dt}(n_{(MnO)})$$
$$= -\frac{D_{MnO} \cdot A}{\Delta\delta}(C_{(MnO*)} - C_{(MnO)}) \qquad . \qquad (A21)$$

Converting to percentages

$$\frac{d}{dt}(n_{Mn}) = \frac{d}{dt}\left(\frac{W_{HM_0}}{5\,493}(Mn_0\% - X_{Mn}\%)\right)$$
$$= -\frac{W_{HM_0}}{5\,493}\frac{d}{dt}(X_{Mn}\%) \qquad . \qquad . \qquad (A22)$$

$$C_{(MnO*)} = \rho_{SL}\frac{(MnO*)\%}{7\,093} \qquad . \qquad . \qquad . \qquad (A23)$$

$$C_{(MnO)} = \rho_{SL}\frac{(MnO*)\%}{7\,093} = \frac{\rho_{SL}}{5\,493}\frac{W_{HM_0}}{W_{SL}}X_{Mn}\% \qquad . \qquad (A24)$$

Substituting back in (A21)

$$\frac{W_{HM_0}}{5\,493}\frac{d}{dt}(X_{Mn}^{\%}) = -\frac{D_{MnO}\cdot A\cdot\rho_{SL}}{\Delta\delta\,7\,093}$$

$$\times\left((MnO^*)^{\%} - \frac{7\,093}{5\,493}\frac{W_{HM_0}}{W_{SL}}X_{Mn}^{\%}\right)$$

$$. \quad . \quad . \quad . \quad (A25)$$

Now from the equilibrium equation

$$K_{MnO} = \frac{a_{MnO}}{a_{Mn}a_0} = \frac{b_{MnO}\left(\dfrac{W_{SL}(MnO^*)^{\%}}{7\,093\,Z}\right)}{f_{Mn}(Mn_0^{\%} - X_{Mn}^{\%})F\cdot f_0Q^{\%}\cdot F} \quad (A26)$$

Eliminating $(MnO^*)^{\%}$ from equations (A25) and (A26) and writing as before

$$RCMANG = \frac{D_{MnO}\cdot A}{\Delta\delta} \quad . \quad . \quad . \quad (A27)$$

we obtain the reaction rate equation for manganese

$$\frac{d}{dt}(X_{Mn}^{\%}) = \frac{RCMANG\,\rho_{SL}}{W_{HM_0}\,W_{SL}}\left(\frac{5\,493K_{MnO}ZF^2}{b_{MnO}}\right.$$

$$\left.\times f_{Mn}(Mn^{\%} - X_{Mn}^{\%})f_0Q^{\%} - W_{HM_0}X_{Mn}^{\%}\right)$$

$$. \quad . \quad . \quad . \quad (A28)$$

where as before the equilibrium constants and the interaction coefficients can be obtained from the relevant literature.[31]

PHOSPHORUS

In a similar fashion to manganese, the diffusion of phosphorus can be expressed as

$$\frac{d}{dt}(n_P) = 2\frac{d}{dt}(n_{P_2O_5})$$

$$= -\frac{2A\cdot D_{P_2O_5}}{\Delta\delta}(C_{(P_2O_5)^*} - C_{(P_2O_5)}) \quad . \quad (A29)$$

Transforming to percentages

$$\frac{d}{dt}(n_{\underline{P}}) = \frac{d}{dt}\left(\frac{W_{HM_0}}{3\,098}(P_0^{\%} - X_P^{\%})\right) = -\frac{W_{HM_0}}{3\,098}\frac{d}{dt}(X_P^{\%})$$

$$. \quad . \quad . \quad . \quad (A30)$$

$$C_{(P_2O_5)^*} = \rho_{SL}\frac{(P_2O_5^*)}{14\,196} \quad . \quad . \quad . \quad (A31)$$

$$C_{(P_2O_5)} = \rho_{SL}\frac{(P_2O_5)^{\%}}{14\,196} = \rho_{SL}\frac{W_{HM_0}\cdot X_P^{\%}}{6\,196W_{SL}} \quad . \quad (A32)$$

Therefore

$$\frac{W_{HM_0}}{3\,098}\frac{d}{dt}(X_P^{\%}) = \frac{2\cdot D_{P_2O_5}A\cdot\rho_{SL}}{14\,196\,\Delta\delta}$$

$$\times\left((P_2O_5^*)^{\%} - \frac{14\,196}{6\,196}\frac{W_{HM_0}}{W_{SL}}X_P^{\%}\right)$$

$$. \quad . \quad . \quad . \quad (A33)$$

Now further studies of the phosphorus distribution[32] have shown that, when excess lime is present,

$$\log\left(\frac{(P)}{\underline{P}}\right) = \frac{22\,350}{T} + 7\log(CaO)^{\%}$$

$$+ 2\cdot5\log(FeO_T^{\%} - 24\cdot0 \quad . \quad . \quad (A34)$$

Using this expression to determine the equilibrium phosphorus pentoxide values, we may write

$$\frac{(P^*)}{\underline{P}} = (10)^Y$$

where

$$Y = \frac{22\,350}{T} + 7\log(CaO)^{\%} + 2\cdot5\log(FeO_T)^{\%} - 24\cdot0$$

and therefore

$$\frac{(P_2O_5^*)^{\%}}{T} = \frac{141\cdot96}{30\cdot98}\frac{(P^*)^{\%}}{\underline{P}} = \frac{141\cdot96}{30\cdot98}(10)^Y$$

so that

$$(P_2O_5^*)^{\%} = \frac{141\cdot96}{30\cdot98}(10)^Y\underline{P}^{\%}F$$

Substituting for $(P_2O_5^*)^{\%}$ in equation (A33) gives

$$\frac{d}{dt}(X_P^{\%}) = 2\,RCPHOS\,\rho_{SL}\left(\left(\frac{(10)^Y}{W_{HM}}\right)(P_0^{\%} - X^{\%})\right.$$

$$\left. - \frac{1}{2}\frac{X_P^{\%}}{W_{SL}}\right) \quad . \quad . \quad . \quad (A35)$$

where as before Y is the right-hand side of equation (A34) and

$$RCPHOS = \frac{D_{P_2O_5}A}{\Delta\delta}$$

SILICON

The rate-limiting step for the removal of silicon has been taken as the transfer of silicon through the metal bath.

$$\frac{d}{dt}(n_{Si}) = -\frac{D_{Si}}{\Delta\delta}A(C_{Si} - C_{Si}^*) \quad . \quad . \quad (A36)$$

Converting to percentages

$$\frac{d}{dt}(n_{Si}) = -\frac{W_{HM_0}}{2\,806}\frac{d}{dt}(X_{Si}^{\%}) \quad . \quad . \quad (A37)$$

$$C_{Si} = \frac{W_{Si}}{28\cdot06}\frac{\rho_{HM}}{W_{HM}} = SI^{\%}\cdot\frac{\rho_{HM}}{2\,806}F \quad . \quad . \quad (A38)$$

$$C_{Si}^* = SI^{*\%}\frac{\rho_{HM}}{2\,806}F \quad . \quad . \quad . \quad (A39)$$

Therefore (A36) can be rewritten

$$\frac{W_{HM_0}}{2\,806}\frac{d}{dt}(X_{Si}^{\%}) = \frac{D_{Si}\cdot A}{\Delta\delta}\frac{\rho_{HM}}{2\,806}F\cdot(SI^{\%} - SI^{*\%}) \quad (A40)$$

Writing the activity of silicon in terms of weight percent

$$a_{Si} = W_{Si}^{\%}f_{Si} = SI^{\%}\cdot f_{Si}\cdot F \quad . \quad . \quad (A41)$$

or

$$SI^{*\%} = \frac{a_{Si}^{*}}{f_{Si} \cdot F} \qquad \qquad (A42)$$

But

$$a_{Si}^{*} = \frac{a_{SiO_2}}{a_0^2 K_{SiO_2}} \qquad \qquad (A43)$$

The activity of SiO_2 in basic slags is extremely low and therefore a_{Si}^{*} is negligible in comparison with the activity of silicon in the bulk, after the first few minutes of the blow. Then (A40) becomes

$$\frac{HM_0}{2\,806} \frac{d}{dt}(X_{Si}^{\%}) = \frac{D_{Si}A}{\Delta\delta} \frac{\rho_{HM}}{2\,806} F \cdot SI^{\%} \qquad (A44)$$

also

$$SI^{\%} = SI_0^{\%} - X_{Si}^{\%} \qquad \qquad (A45)$$

Therefore

$$\frac{d}{dt}(X_{Si}^{\%}) = \frac{RCSIL}{W_{HM}} \rho_{HM}(SI_0^{\%} - X_{Si}^{\%}) \qquad (A46)$$

where

$$RCSIL = \frac{D_{Si} \cdot A}{\Delta\delta}$$

SULPHUR

The diffusion mechanism for sulphur is expressed as

$$\frac{d}{dt}(n_s) = -\frac{D_s A}{\Delta\delta}(C_{(s^*)} - C_{(s)}) \qquad (A47)$$

Transforming to percentages

$$\frac{d}{dt}(n_s) = \frac{d}{dt}\left(\frac{W_{HM_0}}{3\,206}(S_0^{\%} - X_s^{\%})\right) = -\frac{W_{HM_0}}{3\,206}\frac{d}{dt}(X_s^{\%})$$

$$\qquad (A48)$$

$$C_{(s^*)} = \rho_{SL}\frac{(S^*)^{\%}}{3\,206} \qquad \qquad (A49)$$

$$C_{(s)} = \rho_{SL}\frac{(S)^{\%}}{3\,206} = \rho_{SL}\frac{W_{HM_0}}{W_{SL}}\frac{X_s^{\%}}{3\,206} \qquad (A50)$$

Substituting back in (A47)

$$\frac{W_{HM_0}}{3\,206}\frac{d}{dt}(X_s^{\%}) = \frac{D_s A \cdot \rho_{SL}}{3\,206\,\Delta\delta}\left((S^*)^{\%} - \frac{W_{HM_0}}{W_{SL}}X_s^{\%}\right) \qquad (A51)$$

Now based on experimental observations the equilibrium sulphur distribution ratio between slag and metal can be taken as[9]

$$\frac{(S^{\%})}{\underline{S}^{\%}} = \left(\frac{n_{CaO} + n_{MnO} + n_{MgO}}{n_{SiO_2} + n_{P_2O_5} + n_{Al_2O_3}}\right)$$

$$* \left(3{\cdot}47 - 6{\cdot}1 * \frac{FeO_T}{W_{SL}}\right)$$

$$+ 14{\cdot}9 * \frac{FeO_T}{W_{SL}} - 5{\cdot}8 \cdot \qquad (A52)$$

Using this expression to determine the equilibrium sulphur values, we may write

$$\frac{d}{dt}(X_s^{\%}) = RCSUL\rho_{SL}\left(\frac{(\underline{S}_0^{\%} - X_s^{\%})^* DR}{W_{HM}} - \frac{X_s^{\%}}{W_{SL}}\right) \quad (A53)$$

where $RCSUL = D_s A/\Delta\delta$ and DR is the right-hand side of (A52).

OXYGEN

Oxygen supplied to the bath via the slag can be expressed as

$$\frac{d}{dt}(n_O) = \frac{D_0 A}{\Delta\delta}(C_{(FeO)} - C_{FeO^*}) \qquad (A54)$$

Transforming to percentages

$$\frac{d}{dt}(n_O) = \frac{W_{HM_0}}{1\,600}\frac{d}{dt}(O^{\%}) \qquad (A55)$$

$$C_{FeO^*} = \rho_{SL} \cdot \frac{FeO_T^{*\%}}{7\,185} = \frac{\rho_{SL} \cdot FeO_T^{*}}{71{\cdot}85 W_{SL}} \qquad (A56)$$

$$C_{(FeO)} = \frac{\rho_{SL} \cdot FeO_T}{71{\cdot}85 W_{SL}} \qquad (A57)$$

Giving

$$\frac{W_{HM_0}}{1\,600}\frac{d}{dt}(O^{\%}) = \frac{D_0 A \rho_{SL}}{71{\cdot}85 W_{SL} \Delta\delta}(FeO_T - FeO_T^*) \quad (A58)$$

At equilibrium, we may write

$$a_{FeO_T} = \frac{O^{\%} \cdot F}{\underline{O}_s^{\%}} \qquad \qquad (A59)$$

where[28]

$$\underline{O}_s^{\%} = \exp\left(\frac{-14\,555}{T^{\circ}K} + 6{\cdot}296\right) \qquad (A60)$$

Also

$$a_{FeO_T} = b_{FeO_T}N_{FeO_T} = b_{FeO_T}\frac{FeO_T}{71{\cdot}85 * Z} \qquad (A61)$$

Therefore combining equations (A59) and (A61) we have

$$FeO_T^* = \frac{71{\cdot}85 Z O^{\%} F}{b_{FeO_T}\underline{O}_s^{\%}} \qquad \qquad (A62)$$

Substituting into Eq. (A58)

$$\frac{d}{dt}(O^{\%}) = RCOXY\frac{1\,600}{W_{HM_0}W_{SL}}\rho_{SL}$$

$$\times \left(\frac{FeO_T}{71{\cdot}85} - \frac{Z \cdot \underline{O}^{\%} F}{b_{FeO_T}\underline{O}_s^{\%}}\right) \cdot \qquad (A63)$$

where

$$RCOXY = \frac{D_0 A}{\Delta\delta}$$

The oxygen supplied directly to the bath is taken to be a proportion of the oxygen supplied from the lance (*see* Appendix 2). This fraction depends on the area of metal exposed to the jet expressed as a function of the total contact area between jet and bath.

$$O2DIR = RCDIR \frac{A_{ST}}{(A_{ST} + A_{SL})}$$

$$* (O_2 \text{ mass flow rate}) \quad . \quad . \quad . \quad (A64)$$

where RCDIR is a scaling constant. Then the total oxygen supplied to the bath is

$$\frac{d}{dt}(Q^\%) = RCOXY \frac{1\,600}{W_{HM_0} W_{SL}} \rho_{SL}$$

$$\times \left(\frac{FeO_T}{71 \cdot 85} - \frac{Z \cdot Q^\% \cdot F}{b_{FeO_T} Q_s^\%} \right) + O2DIR \quad (A65)$$

APPENDIX 2

Oxygen distribution

The model currently considers the cavity formed at the oxygen jet–metal bath impact zone to be approximately conical in shape[33] (*see* Fig. A1). This shape gives the maximum penetration for given operational conditions. Other cavity shapes were considered but the difference in the relative areas of slag and steel exposed is small. For simplification, the following relationships are derived for a single hole nozzle acting in the vertical plane. The results are applicable for multi-hole nozzles if interactions between the separate jets do not occur. In our experience, this is true if the separate apertures are inclined by more than 8° to the vertical. Note that the cavities formed by dual circuit lances[34] would have to be treated separately. If only slag were present, the oxygen jet would displace a cone of radius RSL and depth HSL of slag; nomenclature is explained in Fig. A1. From Newton's second law, the force required to maintain this cavity is:

$$F = (\tfrac{1}{3} * \pi * RSL^2 * HSL * \rho_{SL}) * g \quad . \quad . \quad (A66)$$

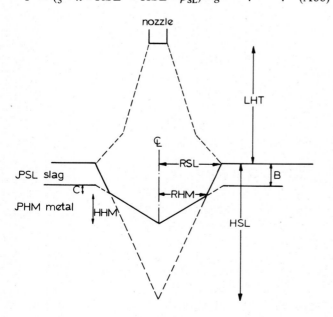

A1   Theoretical jet–bath interaction zone

where g is acceleration due to gravity and ρ_{SL} is the density of the slag. Now the weight of steel in the actual cone (RHM, HHM) must equal the weight of slag in the theoretical cone (RHM, HSL − C − B).

$$\rho_{HM} * HHM = \rho_{SL} * (HSL - C - B) \quad . \quad . \quad (A67)$$

Where ρ_{HM} is the density of the metal. Also, if we can neglect the effect of jet dispersion through the slag layer, then by similar triangles:

$$\frac{RSL}{(HHM + C)} = \frac{RHM}{HHM} \quad . \quad . \quad . \quad . \quad (A68)$$

and

$$\frac{RSL}{HSL} = \frac{RHM}{(HSL - C - B)} \quad . \quad . \quad . \quad (A69)$$

Solving Eqs. (A2), (A3), and (A4):

$$HHM = \frac{\rho_{SL}}{\rho_{HM}} \left(HSL - \frac{B\rho_{HM}}{\rho_{HM} - \rho_{SL}} \right) \quad . \quad . \quad (A70)$$

$$RHM = \frac{RSL}{HSL} \left(HSL - \frac{B\rho_{HM}}{\rho_{HM} - \rho_{SL}} \right) \quad . \quad . \quad (A71)$$

$$C = \frac{B\rho_{SL}}{\rho_{HM} - \rho_{SL}} . \quad . \quad . \quad . \quad . \quad (A72)$$

Now the area of steel exposed to the oxygen jet is:

$$AHM = \pi * RHM * (RHM^2 + HHM^2)^{\frac{1}{2}} \quad . \quad (A73)$$

The area of slag exposed to the oxygen jet is:

$$ASL = \pi \times (RSL * (RSL^2 + HSL^2)^{\frac{1}{2}} - RHM *$$
$$\times (RHM^2 + (HSL - B - C)^2)^{\frac{1}{2}}) \quad (A74)$$

Substituting in (A72) and (A73) for HSL, HHM, RHM, and C from Eqs. (A66), (A70), (A71), and (A72) gives the areas of slag ASL and steel AHM exposed to the jet in terms of the applied force F and the radius of the impact zone RSL. This applied force is provided by a certain amount of the momentum flux of the oxygen jet:

$$F = K * (M * V) \quad . \quad . \quad . \quad . \quad (A75)$$

where M is oxygen flow rate per nozzle aperture * density of oxygen and V is jet velocity at nozzle exit resolved in the vertical direction.

It can be shown[35] that the weight of material displaced from the cavity must lie somewhere between one and two times the vertical component of the jet momentum. The actual situation lies somewhere between these two extremes and from analysis of the operational practices at various plants the value of K was taken as 1·25. The radius of the impact zone RSL can be determined[36,37] from the oxygen flow rate, lance height, nozzle details, and a knowledge of the behaviour of supersonic jets under the conditions encountered within the vessel. Therefore for a given nozzle, the oxygen distribution between slag and metal, in terms of the relative areas exposed, can be expressed as a function of the two main control parameters of the process, oxygen flow rate and lance height.

Dynamic mathematical model of the LD steelmaking process

J. R. Middleton and R. Rolls

A dynamic mathematical model of the LD process which closely simulates the behaviour of a full-scale plant vessel has been developed. This development arose from a need to improve upon the performance of established static models. The essential structure of the dynamic model incorporates thermal and mass balance equations that have been derived from an examination of the process reaction kinetics, which express the rates of change of process variables. Estimation of unknown parameters in the equations has been expedited by the use of hill-climbing techniques. It has been possible to test and fit the model with data obtained by an 'in-blow' bomb sampling procedure from many heats which have represented a wide range of steelmaking conditions. The simulation shows greater accuracy than that of an earlier model which was recently reported.[7] An indication will be given of the closeness of fit of the end-point conditions predicted by the model with actual plant data to show that an application of the model to on-line control of plant operation is not only feasible, but economically desirable. The model to be described is capable of being periodically up-dated with 'in-blow' measurements of carbon content of the metal and bath temperature. This is an essential requirement to maintaining the accuracy of forward predictions of the appropriate corrective actions to meet the specified end-point conditions, particularly when transient changes in process variables are occurring, such as vessel-lining wear.

The extensive use of automatic-control techniques for steelmaking processes has expanded considerably in recent years. This has been made possible because of improved sampling techniques for data measurement and consequently, there has been an added stimulus to develop more accurate mathematical models to simulate process stages. There is now a large amount of published work concerned in particular with basic oxygen steelmaking.[1-3] Current developments in control techniques as applied to oxygen steelmaking have been highlighted in the recent international conferences in Luxembourg[4] and Tokyo.[5]

At present, there are two basic types of model that are applied to LD and BOF processes. These are typically described as 'static' and 'dynamic' mathematical models simulating process behaviour. The so-called 'static'

models comprise sets of heat and mass balance equations that enable the process requirements (oxygen blown, scrap weight, limestone etc.) to be calculated from known initial conditions of charge composition, weight, and temperature to give the required end-point specification of steel carbon content, temperature, and weight.

In contrast, 'dynamic' models comprise differential equations which describe the rate of change of bath and/or slag composition throughout the blowing stage and are especially constructed to take into account variations in blowing conditions and additions sequences as continuous sensors feed back data to the control system throughout the process. Thus, it is within the capability of the dynamic model to prescribe the appropriate corrective action to ensure that the 'trajectory' of the process path achieves the required end-point 'target' for steel temperature and carbon content in particular. Furthermore, the unique trajectory for an individual heat may be controlled to follow the most

Dr J. R. Middleton is with the Whitehead Consulting Group and Dr R. Rolls is in the Department of Metallurgy, University of Manchester

economic path, but only when the accuracy of the model and the process data are assured. Clearly, this claim deserves further amplification, and it is the purpose of this paper to describe current work, which has been in progress in Manchester since 1966, to develop a true dynamic model that will provide a reliable and reproducible simulation of both LD and BOF processes. One of the principal objectives of our work has been that the dynamic mathematical model should be capable of incorporating the effects of variations of charging, blowing, and additions practices within each blow, thereby overcoming the basic deficiencies of static models. Furthermore the model should be able to accept in-blow information from process sensors (such as waste-gas composition and flow-rate measurements or auxiliary lance carbon and temperature data) which will enable its use in conjunction with a suitable control algorithm to ensure the simultaneous attainment of the specified end-point conditions of bath carbon content and bath temperature.

DEVELOPMENT OF MATHEMATICAL MODEL

In the earlier stages of our work, a static model developed from statistical regression analyses was modified by Cambridge[6] because of the principal limitation of all static models that they are not able to incorporate changes in the process kinetics of a particular heat (e.g. blowing history) in formulating end-point requirements. Thus, the essential modifications to be incorporated in the improved simulation program were:

(i) the selection of a set of chemical reactions, for which data were available, which characterized the process
(ii) the development of mathematical relationships describing the kinetics of steelmaking reactions
(iii) the development of mathematical relationships describing the effects of variations in blowing and additions practices on the process kinetics
(iv) the estimation of a scrap-melting profile based on theoretical considerations and plant observations
(v) the estimation of a bath temperature profile based on temperature measurements from 'bomb' thermocouples dropped into a vessel during the refining stage.

This preliminary work was confined to the second blow of an LD–AC heat for which limited data were available and which also constituted a critical period for process control. The dynamic model of the second blow of the LD–AC process evolved in this early work deliberately circumvented the major problems of:

(i) the derivation of a scrap-melting mechanism
(ii) the simulation of the initial transient behaviour of the bath and slag formation
(iii) the estimation of unknown parameters over the whole period of normal operation in order to simplify and shorten the computational procedure.

In spite of limited plant data being available, it was possible to test and improve this initial dynamic model to represent LD process behaviour as well as that of LD–AC. A report of part of this work was presented at Tokyo.[7] This further improvement involved establishing an alternative mechanism for the decarburization reaction, incorporating the concept of slag/metal emulsification into the model and finally, we attempted to derive an accurate model of the thermal characteristics of the process. Some aspects of the structure of the current UMIST dynamic model will be discussed later in this paper.

CURRENT IDEAS ON DYNAMIC MODELLING

Many of the earlier developments in dynamic control were designed to facilitate control for the production of low carbon steels of a generally consistent specification.[8] A particularly desirable control requirement was, and still will be, to minimize slag ejections (foaming and slopping) from the vessel by controlling the principal blowing parameters, i.e. lance height and oxygen flow rate. However, a more detailed understanding of the physics and physical chemistry of slag emulsion formation is awaited before precise control of this phenomenon can be achieved through digital computation.

The important work at CNRM[9] has established some of the advantages of controlled blowing to a specific course for the decarburization rate, provided that an optimum course for slag formation is followed conjointly. By measuring the fume temperature and regulating oxygen flow it is considered that the trajectory for the desired decarburization rate can be followed. Audiometric measurements would also permit lance height adjustments to be made to produce the required slag composition for controlled reactions. The implementation of control actions has been discussed by West,[10] as being dependent upon the tolerances allowed for the end-point conditions. He raises the important question as to whether the measurement systems and predictive techniques are capable of working to such tolerances. The use of error analysis and the establishment of calibration techniques is clearly a vital activity in the development of a soundly based, automatic control system.

Auxiliary lances have been successfully developed by which a consumable type sensor is capable of rapidly and simultaneously measuring the bath temperature and carbon content during blowing.[10] This development has made possible the addition of a dynamic control system to an existing static control system, to improve end-point control. Nagano et al.[11] have considered the merits of three types of dynamic control which they describe as:

(i) dynamic stop method in which blowing is stopped at the most desirable point without altering the carbon and temperature trajectories
(ii) route-adjustment method in which the carbon and temperature trajectories (routes) are altered at the final stage of blowing

(iii) reaction-control method in which a continuous control of reactions throughout blowing is attempted.

Their experiences with the dynamic stop method indicate that with the aid of a sublance as an effective sensor both process analysis and process control can be satisfactorily improved.

There is evidence [8,9,10] that each of these control methods can be applied to specific steelmaking practices with a reasonable likelihood of success. The margins of error in measurement and control, however, may alter randomly with uncertainties in detecting and defining clearly such process states as, for example, the amount of melted scrap, or the homogeneity of mixing in the vessel, or the degree of completion of chemical reactions in the slag/metal emulsification stage. Until our understanding of these and other process variables has reached a higher level, it is unlikely that the prediction and attainment of the required end-point conditions will ever be completely successful, no matter how accurate the sensors or the mathematical model may be.

PHYSICO-CHEMICAL CONSIDERATIONS

Basic oxygen steelmaking has as its prime objectives the selective oxidation from liquid iron of carbon, silicon, manganese, and phosphorus together with a transfer of sulphur from the bath to the slag. It is vital to ensure that these reactions can be stimulated and completed with minimal loss of iron as oxides to the slag and to the waste gases as oxide fume. Control of the oxidation reactions, and therefore of both temperature and composition, is based upon a judicious use of scrap, ore, and limestone additions and a careful choice of oxygen-blowing rate and lance-height positions to ensure scrap melting and adequate mixing of the vessel contents without losses from foaming and slopping of the slag/metal emulsion.

In constructing a mathematical model of the process of refining, descriptions of the oxidation reactions are usually based upon the most recent information available which reports characteristic equilibrium constants and other thermochemical data for the known operating temperature range. Philbrook[11] has already drawn attention to the limitations of existing data, frequently obtained under idealized, thermodynamically isolated, laboratory conditions, and therefore not completely representative of complex solution behaviour. Further difficulties are encountered when the kinetics of refining reactions are considered. Many of the rate-limiting steps in the overall rates of reactions are known to be transport phenomena.[12] Clearly bath turbulence may influence both transport rates and reaction-interface areas. Both of these parameters are difficult to detect and to quantify accurately in dynamic conditions. It has been necessary in the present work, therefore, to adopt a conventional approach in describing the kinetics of the oxidation reactions. We have used as the basic form of

rate equation, the expression:

$$\dot{x}_i = \frac{-A_i D_i}{\delta_i}(a_i - a_i^*) \qquad . \qquad . \qquad . \qquad (1)$$

where

$\dot{x}_i$ = rate of transport of component i to the reaction interface

D_i = diffusion coefficient for component i

δ_i = thickness of the boundary layer for component i,

a_i = activity of component i in the bulk phase (X)

a_i^* = activity of component i at the reaction interface

A = area of the reaction interface.

We can define the mass transfer coefficient k_i, as

$$k_i = \frac{A_i D_i}{\delta_i} \qquad . \qquad . \qquad . \qquad . \qquad . \qquad (2)$$

since the individual values of A and δ are unknown. Thus, Eq. (1) becomes:

$$\dot{x}_i = k_i(a_i - a_i^*) \qquad . \qquad . \qquad . \qquad . \qquad (3)$$

If it is assumed that at the high temperatures attained in steelmaking, chemical equilibrium is reached at the reaction interface, then a_i^* can be determined from a knowledge of the composition of phase Y and the appropriate equilibrium constants, since a_i is known from the composition of phase X. The variation of D_i over the steelmaking temperature range is not significant. Parameters A_i and δ_i, however, will be strongly influenced by turbulence in the vessel. Reaction rates are increased when turbulence produces a large increase in the interfacial area between phases. The work of Oeters,[13] has shown that the mass transfer coefficient can be expressed as a function of the decarburization rate and the blowing conditions. Cambridge[6] simplified the complex expression derived by Oeters to the form:

$$k_i = \frac{kk_i BR^{0.554} \dot{x}_{CO}^{0.15}}{L^{0.680}} = kk_i . ADJ \qquad . \qquad . \qquad . \qquad (4)$$

where kk_i is a constant for the reactions concerning the removal of element i, BR is the oxygen blowing rate, $\dot{x}_{CO}$ is the rate of CO evolution from the bath, L is the lance height, ADJ is a function designated the 'turbulence factor'. Middleton[14] has derived an empirical relationship to describe the effects of slag/metal emulsification during the latter two-thirds of a typical LD blow. Experimental data indicate that the rate of carbon monoxide evolution is the predominant controlling factor. The following simple linear relationship was found to describe the change in interfacial area during blowing:

$$EMULF = 1 + M\dot{x}_{CO} \qquad . \qquad . \qquad . \qquad . \qquad (5)$$

where

$EMULF$ = ratio of actual interfacial area to still bath interfacial area

M = constant

$\dot{x}_{CO}$ = rate of carbon monoxide evolution.

$EMULF$ as an 'emulsification factor' has been used in

the present work to determine the mass transfer coefficient k_i of Eq. (2).

Scrap melting

It was convenient in our earlier studies[6] to assume that all the scrap had melted before the second blow of LD–AC practice or in the latter two-thirds of LD practice. However, a model of the complete process should include a scrap melting mechanism. It is apparent from the work of Mori and Nomura,[15] that the effect of carbon diffusion between the melt and the scrap and its consequent influence on the effective melting point of the scrap must be taken into account in addition to heat transfer phenomena.

When the interactions between the diffusion and the thermal effects are expressed, mathematically, the resultant equation set to describe scrap melting becomes very complex. A simplified mathematical treatment of the melting process has been discussed by Szekely *et al.*[16,17] The shape and dimensions of the scrap and heterogeneity of the stages of melting should be included, where measurable, in the model. Because of the inherent practical difficulties of measurement (unless a regular size of scrap is adopted), the use of simple empirical relationships to describe scrap melting are justifiable as a first approximation.

Lime, limestone, and ore additions

Additions which are made to the vessel are not absorbed into the slag instantaneously. It is necessary, therefore, to introduce an absorption delay into the equations that describe the rate of entry of CaO and FeO into the slag from the additions. Extensive studies[3] have confirmed the many factors that can govern the dissolution rates of lime additions and in the light of limited experimental data, it has been assumed in the present work that the dissolution rate was proportional to the quantity of undissolved material present and that solution occurred over a finite period. Hematite ore additions were assumed to dissociate such that the resulting FeO was incorporated in the slag:

$$Fe_2O_{3(ore)} \rightarrow 2(FeO)_{slag} + \tfrac{1}{2}(O_2)_{gas}$$

The overall rate of change of the FeO content of the slag $\dot{x}_{FeO}$ can then be represented by the mass balance equation:

$$\dot{x}_{FeO} = \dot{x}'_{FeO} + \dot{x}''_{FeO} - \dot{x}'''_{FeO} \qquad . \qquad . \qquad . \qquad . \quad (6)$$

where

$\dot{x}'_{FeO}$ is the rate of formation of FeO by reaction between the oxygen jet and the bath

$\dot{x}''_{FeO}$ is the rate of absorption of FeO into the slag from ore additions

$\dot{x}'''_{FeO}$ is the rate of transfer of oxygen as FeO from the slag to the metal.

Thermal considerations

The derivation of a heat balance for the process is based upon a knowledge of thermochemical data for the chemical reactions, which include heats of reactions and heats of transformations, and an assessment of heat losses from the system, which is difficult because of uncertainties in the estimated contribution of several factors that cannot be measured accurately. For example, heat absorption by lime, limestone, and ore additions is not an instantaneous event. The rate of heat absorption, therefore, has been assumed to be linearly proportional to the quantity of undissolved material in the slag. Heat transferred by evolved carbon monoxide is readily calculable, but values for heat losses from the bath and slag by radiation, conduction and convection are uncertain. Variations in the free surface area of the slag, for example, which will affect radiation losses will vary with the degree of emulsification, with vessel wear and with compositional and constitutional changes for individual heats. There is some justification, therefore, for adopting the use of a constant average heat loss term in the absence of reliable experimental data.

In modelling the heat balance, it has been assumed that the volume of the high-temperature reaction zone (i.e. the oxygen jet impact area) is small compared with the bulk bath, which itself is considered to be of uniform temperature (as a consequence of convection currents and stirring in the bath during blowing). It has also been assumed that the rate of heat transfer from the reaction zone is proportional to the amount of heat generated by the reactions. The time required for this heat to be uniformly distributed throughout the bath by convection and stirring is an unknown parameter which must be determined by the hill-climbing procedure. The increase in bath temperature during blowing has been calculated from an expression for the specific heat of the bath, which incorporates data for the specific heats of the bath components, such that the effects of changes in bath composition can be readily determined.

THE STRUCTURE OF THE UMIST DYNAMIC MODEL

The UMIST dynamic model consists of a set of 40 first order, non-linear differential equations and a similar number of algebraic equations. The differential equations represent simple molecular models for metal, slag and gas reactions and energy changes which occur during steelmaking. They express the rates of change of the process states with time, e.g. the bath and slag composition changes, as a function of the present process state, the current values of the process variables and eight unknown parameters. The equations are highly interactive. The general form of the differential equations is:

$$\dot{\underline{x}} = f(\underline{x}, \underline{u}, t)$$

$$\underline{x}(0) = \underline{c}$$

The equation set is numerically integrated using a modified Euler technique. Using this method it is possible to increase the integration step length to its maximum consistent with maintaining the stability of the model. The inputs to the model are:

    (i) hot metal composition
    (ii) hot metal temperature
    (iii) hot metal weight
    (iv) scrap weight
    (v) lance heights throughout the blow
    (vi) blowing rates throughout the blow
    (vii) ore, lime, and limestone additions throughout the blow.

The outputs of the model are:

    (i) the bath carbon, manganese, silicon, phosphorus, and oxygen contents
    (ii) the slag CaO, P_2O_5, SiO_2, MnO, Fe_TO contents
    (iii) the bath temperature
    (iv) the bath weight
    (v) the slag weight.

These outputs are available quasi-continuously throughout the blow. The model is capable of accepting update information on bath composition or temperature at any point during the blow. In its FORTRAN form the current version of the model occupies about 7K of core store.

Parameter optimization

The optimum values of the unknown parameters are established by using the Rosenbrock[18] hill-climbing technique. In this method the parameter values are systematically varied until the minimum value of a cost function is achieved. The cost function is the sum of the squares of the differences between the measured and the predicted values of bath and slag compositions and temperatures.

Sensitivity analysis

When a model is to be used in a control environment it is important to know the sensitivity of the model to perturbations in the input data. In practice such perturbations could arise as errors in analysis or measurement. If a model is strongly sensitive to such errors then its value is clearly reduced since in practice, inaccurate predictions could carry heavy penalties. Against this background an initial sensitivity analysis of the part blow model was performed. The initial conditions data were varied from their true values by up to 10%. In the case of the bath components a discrepancy of about 10% remained throughout the blow. In terms of weight percentages this meant that the discrepancy at the end of the blow was within the accuracy of chemical analysis. In the case of bath temperature it was considered that an error of more than 1% (i.e. about 15–16°C) was unlikely and at this level the simulation was affected only slightly. Perturbations of 50°C resulted in an increased decarburization rate and a reduced phosphorus removal such as characterize the process but there were no indications of instability. Experience with the model has shown that only gross perturbations cause instability and that the measurement errors likely to arise in practice would not have disastrous results when input to the model. Further studies are in progress at UMIST to examine the effects of initial and intermediate perturbations on the model output.

Model solution time

Early in the development of the dynamic model it became apparent that the time required for the simulation of a blow would be unacceptable in a control environment. Using an IBM 1130 computer the simulation of a 20 min blow was taking 15 min. When used in a control system it would be necessary for the simulation to be run, for example, upon the receipt of update information, such as a bath temperature at 12 min from the commencement of the blow. In order that the simulation should be completed, together with the calculation of the necessary control actions in time for those actions to be effected, it was clear that it was necessary to reduce the simulation time to an order of less than one minute. The principal reason for the excessive time required for the digital simulation was the numerical integration using relatively small time steps. While it was recognized that the solution time of the model could be reduced by improving the efficiency of the program and the integration method or by writing the programs in machine code, it was considered that the improvement time by these methods would be insufficient and that hybrid computation offered a solution of higher potential. By virtue of its parallel operation, the integration of a set of differential equations patched on the analog section of a hybrid configuration can be very rapid. Thus, the model was set up on a hybrid configuration comprising a PDP-10 digital computer and two Redifon Astrodata Ci 175 computers. Initially a reduced version of the model was used. This version did not contain the scrap melting mechanism or the heat balance.

Owing to limitations of component availability it remained necessary to calculate some of the more highly non-linear terms in the digital section of the configuration. However, the digital calculations were kept to a minimum since they substantially extended the time required for a hybrid solution. After very considerable effort the time required for the solution of the model began to approach the desired speed. However, in the intervening period the digital model had been transferred to the PDP-10 computer and now had a solution time of 7 s which was faster than the currently obtainable solution time on the hybrid computer. Since digital computers suitable for process control and exhibiting a similar execution speed to the PDP-10 computer have become generally available, much of the incentive to use hybrid computation with its inherent difficulties has been removed. However, with further development it may remain advantageous, where many repeated solutions are required such as in parameter optimization or the design of control systems, to re-exploit hybrid techniques.

SAMPLING AND DATA COLLECTION

In the development of a dynamic model of the basic oxygen process it is necessary to obtain information on the process states at intermediate stages of the blow to ensure that the model is an accurate representation of the process throughout the blow. Unfortunately, this type of data is not generally available. It was considered to be unsatisfactory to obtain samples and temperatures by stopping the blow at intermediate times and turning down the vessel. This was for several reasons:

(i) during the period between the cessation of blowing and the obtaining of samples the bath and slag reactions would move towards equilibrium states and any sample would probably not correspond to the state being represented in the model

(ii) owing to the interruptions in blowing the temperature and reaction profiles would become nontypical which would lead to the establishment of non-typical parameter values

(iii) such trials would interfere with the normal melting-shop operation.

The installation of an auxiliary lance for sampling and temperature measurements was not feasible in the circumstances obtaining at the time. Therefore, a 'bomb' sampling technique was developed and used to obtain bath and slag samples at intermediate points in the blow thereby overcoming the objections listed above. A portable bomb chute was constructed and inserted through an inspection door in the elbow of a lime chute. The portable chute was required for the delivery and retrieval of the bomb. The bomb itself comprised a standard cylindrical sample mould with its upper aperture sealed by an aluminium cap which prevented the ingress of slag until the mould was submerged in the steel bath. The sampler is shown diagrammatically in Fig. 1. The sampler was connected to a length of $\frac{3}{8}$in steel chain for recovery purposes. This method provided satisfactory samples without interruption to the blow.

Intermediate temperatures were obtained by use of bomb thermocouples. The bomb samples, together with slag removed from the support chain, have also been utilized in a study of slag/metal emulsification.[19] It is anticipated that the results of these studies will become embodied in the future development of the dynamic model. The other process data required for simulations and parameter estimation have been obtained from computer logged data.

RESULTS

Thirty basic oxygen blows for which in-blow bomb sample data are available have been simulated. Parameter optimization which has been carried out on a number of blows has shown that even over large time intervals all but one of the optimum parameter values remain relatively constant. The exception is the parameter accounting for heat losses from the vessel. This is not unexpected since the parameter is clearly affected by such factors as vessel wear and delays between heats. Conversely a standard set of parameter values were established by hill climbing for the first of a trial series of heats which were extensively sampled. This standard set of values was then used in simulations of the remaining 19 heats of the trial. Typical simulation results are shown in Figs. 2–6. For that trial the standard deviations

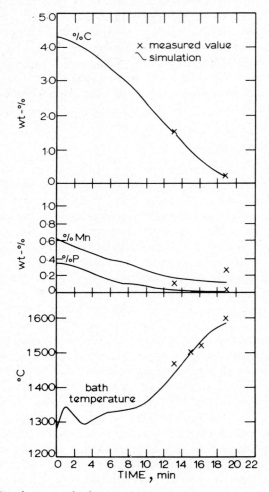

2   *Simulation results for cast A*

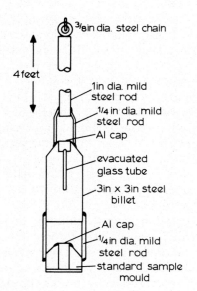

1   *Bomb sampling device*

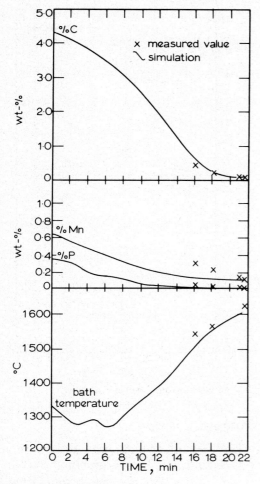

3   Simulation results for cast B

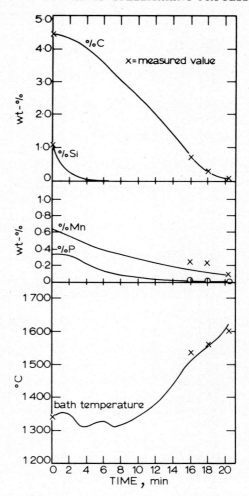

4   Simulation results for cast C

of the errors in the predicted end-point bath temperature and bath carbon content were 10·46°C and 0·036%. The tapping carbon values ranged from 0·04% to 0·24%.

It should be noted, however, that for these simulations the model was not supplied with updating information on composition or temperature at any point during the blow. It has always been, and remains, the intention to update the model during the blow in order to improve the accuracy of end-point prediction upon which the relevant control actions will be taken. It is anticipated that in-blow updating information will arise from auxiliary lance measurements of bath carbon and temperature. The effect of updating the model during the blow can be seen in Fig. 6. It is apparent that in the case where the simulation has become inaccurate a considerable improvement in the end-point prediction results from in-blow updating. It is further planned to develop an adaptive mechanism for the heat losses parameter and it is anticipated that this should yield a useful improvement in temperature predictions.

APPLICATION OF THE MODEL IN A CONTROL SYSTEM

At the present time the associated control algorithms for use in conjunction with the model have not been

developed. However, an initial investigation has yielded a possible useful approach to the development of a total control scheme. It has shown that the most useful relationships to be incorporated into a control algorithm are those shown in Table 1.

Simple linear empirical relationships were determined for the effect of the various control variables on the end-point carbon and temperature values. The model is first updated with a bath carbon and bath temperature reading at about mid-blow to give most reliable prediction of the end-point states, assuming a pre-determined blowing strategy to the end of the blow. The predicted end-point states are compared with the specified values. It is then determined which of nine possible error conditions (including one no-error condition) exists. Using the empirically determined control relationships an appropriate control action is taken to correct the error condition. The simulation is then rerun incorporating

TABLE 1   Factors used in control relationships

End-point state	Control variable utilized
Carbon	Oxygen-blowing rate Lance height
Temperature	Oxygen-blowing rate Limestone additions

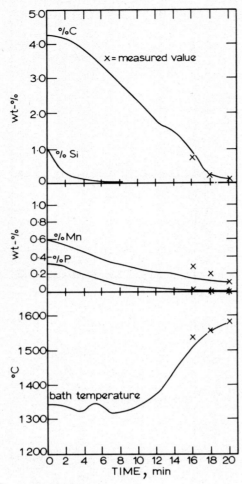

5   *Simulation results for cast D*

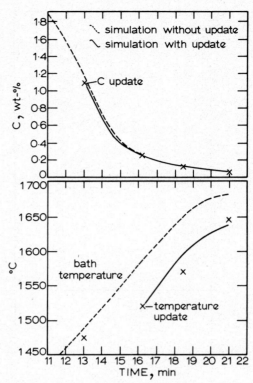

6   *Effect of in-blow updating on simulation for cast E*

the recommended control action to determine whether the new predicted end-point states are satisfactory or whether further control action is required. The cycle is then repeated if necessary until the predicted end-point states comply with those specified. Further the whole control process may be repeated at a later stage of the blow if further updating information becomes available.

CONCLUSION

A dynamic mathematical model of the LD process which closely simulates the behaviour of the full-scale plant has been developed. The model is capable of being periodically updated 'in-blow' with measurements of bath carbon content and bath temperature as they become available from sensors such as auxiliary lances or waste gas analyses. The accuracy of the model in predicting bath composition and temperature approaches that of the measurements themselves. It is considered that because the basic model has reached a sufficiently advanced state of development, future emphasis should be on the development of suitable associated control algorithms to evolve a control system which should offer advantages over the existing systems.

ACKNOWLEDGMENTS

The authors are grateful to Prof. H. H. Rosenbrock for helpful discussions and for the provision of computing facilities and to the BSC for their encouragement and material support for the work.

REFERENCES

1 H. W. MEYER: *JISI*, 1969, **207**, 781
2 D. G. BRINN: *BSC Res. and Development Rep.*, 1970, SW/156/1
3 D. G. BRINN AND R. L. DAVIES: *BSC Res. Rep.*, 1971, SM/TN/I/8
4 J. Inter. de Siderurgie, Luxembourg, 1970
5 Proc. Int. Conf. on Sci. and Tech. of Iron and Steel, 1971 (I), Tokyo
6 E. L. CAMBRIDGE: PhD Thesis, Univ. of Manchester, 1969
7 E. L. CAMBRIDGE et al.: Proc. Int. Conf. on Sci. and Tech. of Iron and Steel, 1971, (I), Tokyo
8 W. E. DENNIS et al.: *J Met.*, 1969, Jul., 80
9 P. NILLES et al.: CNRM, 1971, **27**, 3
10 N. NAGAOKA et al.: Proc. Int. Conf. Sci. and Tech. of Iron and Steel, 1971, (I), 351, Tokyo
11 W. O. PHILBROOK: Proc. 1st Conf. Thermodynamic Props. of Materials, 1967, 367, Pittsburgh
12 L. S. DARKEN: 'Basic open hearth steelmaking', 1964, AIME
13 F. OËTERS: *Arch. Eisenh.*, 1966, **37**, 209
14 J. R. MIDDLETON: PhD Thesis, Univ. of Manchester, 1971
15 K. MORI AND H. NOMURA: *Tetsu-to-Hagané*, 1969, **55**, 347
16 J. SZEKELY AND N. J. THEMELIS: 'Rate phenomena in process metallurgy', 467, 1971, Wiley-Interscience
17 Y. K. CHUANG AND J. SZEKELY: *Int. J. Heat Mass Transfer*, 1971, **14**, 1 285
18 H. H. ROSENBROCK AND C. STOREY: 'Computational techniques for chemical engineers', 1966, Pergamon
19 D. J. PRICE: 'Chemical metallurgy of iron and steel', 1972, London, The Iron and Steel Institute

Statistical approach to oxygen steelmaking

A. A. Greenfield

The general philosophy underlying the paper is to pursue optimal controls in terms of only those process variables that can be observed easily and reliably, using whatever techniques are currently available or can be invented and applied quickly. Although process models developed from consideration of more fundamental mechanisms have some merit, the prospect of direct application to production within the next few years is unlikely. The approach proposed in the paper is progressing well and nearing maturity with relatively less effort than is applied elsewhere by other groups using conventional mechanistic modelling and process theoretical methods.

This paper describes a statistical approach to process control using a digital computer, the description being illustrated throughout by reference to the basic oxygen steelmaking process which is currently being studied at the BSC Corporate Laboratories in Sheffield. The present UK capacity for production of steel in oxygen converters is of the order of 15 Mtons and this may double during this decade. Present world capacity is about 350 Mtons. The case for studying the process with the aim of improving its control is indisputable. The paper also describes the process, the research environment, and the control objectives.

There are many research groups in the UK, and presumably more throughout the world, studying the problem. Every group has its own evolved model that seems to differ widely from all the others. They do, however, reduce to two basic types which are thought of as the purely theoretical model and the empirical or statistical model. Such a clear-cut distinction is mistaken and another section of the paper debates this issue.

Whatever the model, it will contain parameters or coefficients whose values have to be deduced or estimated from real observed data. An important technique that is used is that of multivariate regression analysis. This is described in terms of both its mathematical development and of some of the data acquired from pilot-plant trials. The predictive ability of the regression equations is demonstrated using a further set of acquired data.

A feature of batch processes is that plant conditions vary and no batch is like any other. Refractories degrade, slags deposit, moving parts wear, sensor characteristics change, power supplies fluctuate, and calibrations drift. Any of these physical variations should be represented by changes in the model parameters, but usually the full data set from one production batch is needed to estimate the new parameters, and by the time this has been done it is too late to use the adjusted model in the control of the batch to which it was uniquely applicable and from which it was derived. The paper also describes a rapid method of recognizing and adjusting model parameters so that they can still be used during the course of the same production batch that is generating the data. A slight diversion is needed to describe a concept in optimization that may not be familiar to all who are interested in controlling steelmaking processes. This is the concept of dynamic programming and a further section discusses how it is being used to specify a good refining path. Two handicaps to the use of dynamic programming and multivariate regression analysis, or at least the related parameter adjustment routines, are that they are time consuming and that they occupy large areas of computer core (rapid-access memory). In both respects these routines compete with the essential routines for data acquisition, conversion, storage, and control output. A final section of this paper describes how the computer is being used outside production time to estimate what the optimum controls, evaluated by dynamic programming, would be under widely varied conditions, how relationships are established between

---

The author is with the BSC Corporate Laboratories, Sheffield

these simulated controls and conditions, and how the relationships can be applied directly to the control of oxygen steelmaking, minimizing competition with other routines.

THE CONTROL PROBLEM

The oxygen steelmaking process, in the simplest terms, starts with liquid hot metal, usually between 1 250° and 1 350°C, which contains about four percent of carbon. The process ends when the carbon content has been reduced to a specified level and the temperature has been raised to a suitable level for pouring into ingot moulds. The situation is illustrated in Fig. 1. Here, the square on the upper left represents the starting area and the square on the lower right the desired end-point specification. The centre line represents the relationship between carbon and temperature for a refining path that goes ideally through the centre of the finishing box. Whether or not the path shown is the best depends upon the criteria by which it is judged. If it is judged by only its ends then it is the best; but equally with an infinity of other paths. The path is influenced by hot metal composition, scrap consumption, scrap melting rate, lime, flux, and ore additions, and by blowing practice. The upper and lower lines are not so good as the middle one because they do not reach the centre of the end-point box, if that is the only criterion but on other criteria either of the outer lines could be the best. Although an infinity of paths could exist between the start and end points, the path shape shown must be similar to that occurring in practice. At first most of the oxygen is used to oxidize silicon, manganese, and some iron so that although the metal temperature rises sharply the carbon removal rate is low. Towards the end, when little carbon remains, more iron oxidation occurs and the temperature rises sharply. During the major part of the blow, the rates are fairly steady.

In fact, the process is much more complicated than described since there are many more elements involved than have been mentioned and the reactions between them in a single homogeneous phase would be difficult enough to describe. But instead there are three phases present (liquid metal, slag, and gas) and the distributions of elements and of temperatures are far from homogeneous. If the process could be represented as a trajectory as in Fig. 1 but in terms of all variables within the system, the result would be a multidimensional graph that would give nightmares to any human being. The first part of the control problem then is to represent the process in terms of manageable equations. The second part is to decide how to manage the equations so as to determine the best control action at any time. The problem is made even more difficult by the speed of the process. On occasions the end point has been reached in 12 min and often takes no more than 20 min. Another problem is the process temperature which itself is difficult enough to measure, but which also makes almost impossible the direct determination of metal and slag compositions. There are major researches into temperature sensing and composition analysing devices.

However, the problem may be thought of as being made easier because the number of possible controls is small. The oxygen blowing rate may be controlled, as can the height at which it is directed at the molten surface by varying the lance position. The slag composition, bulk, and physical properties can be modified by adding lime and fluxes. Temperature rises can be moderated by adding a solid coolant such as iron ore. Most of the trials so far have been done with a constant oxygen rate so it is fairly close to the truth and valuable for its simplicity to represent the control process in terms of only three variables:

(i) lance height
(ii) lime additions
(iii) ore additions.

ALTERNATIVE MODELS

The first part of the control problem is the process modelling: its representation in terms of manageable equations. Much of the literature and contemporary discussion is devoted to so-called theoretical models with scant references to 'statistical' models which are dismissed with the implication that they contribute nothing to an understanding of fundamental mechanisms. It is an aim of this paper to promote a better respect for the statistical approach.

'Theoretical' models are generated by consideration of mechanisms such as reaction rates, diffusion rates, turbulence, materials balances, and energy balances. This type of model would be better described as an 'explicit mechanistic' model because expressions have been stated for each of the recognized or assumed mechanisms. It should be understood, however, that such expressions are based on chemistry's fundamental assumptions of linearity and from this viewpoint the approach is the same as the statistical, even though the models may have departed far from linearity by the time they have been developed. Furthermore, the fundamental linear relationships involve unknown parameters, such as reaction rates, which have to be estimated from observed data. It is strange that builders of 'theoretical' models justify their models by the invocation of physico-chemical so-called 'laws' which in fact are only algebraic descriptions based on statistical evidence and estimation.

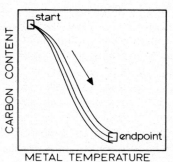

1   Oxygen steelmaking process

This argument is not to deny the value of such models in exploring fundamental mechanisms. Rather it is to warn against over-endowing them with the reputation for being explanatory rather than merely descriptive, which is all they are. Their disadvantages are that they are generally computationally tortuous and they involve variables which are neither observable nor deducible in available real time, such as phosphorus, manganese, and iron oxide contents of the slag. Furthermore, the solution of the control optimization problem is often intractible if the process equations are non-linear. Another common fault is that such models are predictively inaccurate and have to be adjusted by fiddle factors. There were graphical examples in several papers presented at the 1969 Mathematical Models ISI conference in which close agreements were claimed between observed and predicted variable profiles, but the best that could honestly be said of them was that there were topological similarities. The discrepancies were nevertheless recognized and adjusted! Thus departure from 'theoretical' prediction had to be compensated by statistical estimation!

The first practical value of explicit mechanistic models is that they will help to identify the more significant process state and control variables. This will show at least where effort should be expended in the development of sensors and control equipment. The second practical value of these models is that parts of them may show exactly how to derive say one or two usable variables from many more observed variables thus simplifying whatever process equations are used for control. The type of model usually dubbed 'statistical' would be better described as simply a 'linear' model: not because it is not statistical but because any other model type is also statistical in that it has parameters (including fiddle factors) that need to be established from observed data. A linear model does not deny the existence of internal physico-chemical mechanisms. These are implicit in the model but are admitted to be unquantified before data generation and are represented by the regression coefficients which await estimation.

One of the great advantages of the proposed linear model is that it can be represented only in terms of those variables which can be observed or easily deduced. There is no point, for practical control purposes, in having a model that is strongly dependent on unobservable internal compositional or physical variables, nor even upon external variables which are difficult or unreliable to measure. An example of the latter is slag height which has been shown to be correlated with carbon removal rate and temperature gradient. It is difficult to measure continuously with present equipment so it has been dropped from the model.

It may also be necessary eventually to exclude metal temperature since this is difficult to record automatically and continuously. It has, however, been kept in the model for the present with the hope that suitable continuous sensors will soon be available. Meanwhile the necessary data for model development and testing have to be captured by spot devices such as bomb thermocouples,

insertion lances, and other sensors being developed. Waste-gas temperature is a relatively easy state variable to measure that is clearly related to both bath temperature and chemical activity so it is included in the model, but it may have to be excluded in suppressed combustion extraction systems. The audible noise generated by the plant is also related to general physical and chemical activity so it has been included.

Two other variables which are not directly measurable must be included because they provide the criterion by which the process is judged. They are carbon composition and rate of carbon removal. These are deduced with good precision from other variables observed. Waste-gas analysis by a mass spectrometer and waste-gas mass flow measurements can be used to deduce carbon removal rate which, when integrated and subtracted from the initial metal carbon analysis, will give a residual carbon figure. Thus, these are two variables which, although not observed directly, simplify the model by being included instead of the many directly observed variables from which they are derived. At present the state variables included in the model are:

(i) bath temperature, °C
(ii) waste-gas temperature, °C
(iii) audiometer, % scale
(iv) carbon, %
(v) carbon removal rate, % per min.

Another advantage of the linear model is that it is easily expressible as a set of different equations in terms of discrete time intervals. For example, if there was only one state variable (x) and one control variable (v) the model may be expressed as:

$$x(k + 1) = c + ax(k) + bv(k) \qquad . \qquad . \qquad . \qquad (1)$$

where $x(k)$ refers to the value of x at the kth time, $x(k + 1)$ refers to its value at the $(k + 1)$th time, and $v(k)$ is the value of the control at the kth time. c, a, and b are coefficients of the equations. For completeness, an error term should be added to the equation or an E should be put before the left hand x to indicate prediction or expectation.

$$Ex(k + 1) = c + ax(k) + bv(k) \qquad . \qquad . \qquad . \qquad (2)$$

In the present study there are five independent or state variables and three control variables so the full set of equations is better represented in matrix form:

$$Ex(k + 1) = \mathbf{A}x(k) + \mathbf{B}v(k) \qquad . \qquad . \qquad . \qquad (3)$$

The necessary constant term in Eqs. (1) and (2) has been absorbed into (3) by the creation of a dummy state variable x_0 which always has the value of unity. The model has been identified. The next problem is to decide what time increments should be used and then to estimate the coefficients, matrices $\mathbf{A}$ and $\mathbf{B}$. The methods are described next.

MULTIVARIATE REGRESSION

Mathematical development

The model (3) can, for the sake of statistical development, be expressed more generally in terms of the observed data as:

$$\mathbf{Y} = [\mathbf{1}|\mathbf{X}]\mathbf{C} + \mathbf{e} \qquad . \qquad . \qquad . \qquad . \qquad . \qquad (4)$$

where

Y is an n by q matrix where n is the number of observations, q is the number of dependent variables

X is an n by p matrix where p is the number of independent variables, both state and control

1 is a unit vector, n by **1** representing the dummy variable x_0 (*see* section on alternative models)

C is a $(p + 1)$ by q coefficients matrix equivalent to the transpose of $[\mathbf{A}:\mathbf{B}]$ where A and B correspond to the coefficients matrices in Eq. (3)

e is an n by q matrix of errors on the n by q observations of the dependent variables.

The least squares estimator of C is

$$\hat{\mathbf{C}} = \left[\begin{pmatrix} \mathbf{1}' \\ \mathbf{X}' \end{pmatrix}(\mathbf{1}|\mathbf{X}) \right]^{-1} \begin{pmatrix} \mathbf{1}' \\ \mathbf{X}' \end{pmatrix}\mathbf{Y} = \begin{pmatrix} \mathbf{1}'\mathbf{1} & \mathbf{1}'\mathbf{X} \\ \mathbf{X}'\mathbf{1} & \mathbf{X}'\mathbf{X} \end{pmatrix}^{-1}\begin{pmatrix} \mathbf{1}'\mathbf{Y} \\ \mathbf{X}'\mathbf{Y} \end{pmatrix} \quad (5)$$

Recognizing that

$$\mathbf{1}'\mathbf{1} = n \qquad . \qquad . \qquad . \qquad . \qquad . \qquad . \qquad (6)$$

creating a new idempotent matrix

$$\mathbf{J} = \left(\mathbf{I} - \frac{1}{n}\mathbf{1}\mathbf{1}' \right) \qquad . \qquad . \qquad . \qquad . \qquad (7)$$

where **I** is a unit n by n matrix, and using a well established theorem on the inversion of a partitioned matrix, Eq. (5) can be written as:

$$\hat{\mathbf{C}} = \begin{bmatrix} \dfrac{1}{n} + \dfrac{1}{n^2}\mathbf{1}'\mathbf{X}(\mathbf{X}'\mathbf{J}\mathbf{X})^{-1}\mathbf{X}'\mathbf{1} & \vline & -\dfrac{1}{n}\mathbf{1}'\mathbf{X}(\mathbf{X}'\mathbf{J}\mathbf{X})^{-1} \\ \hdashline -\dfrac{1}{n}(\mathbf{X}'\mathbf{J}\mathbf{X})^{-1}\mathbf{X}'\mathbf{1} & \vline & (\mathbf{X}'\mathbf{J}\mathbf{X})^{-1} \end{bmatrix}$$

$$\times \begin{bmatrix} \mathbf{1}'\mathbf{Y} \\ \mathbf{X}'\mathbf{Y} \end{bmatrix}$$

$$= \begin{bmatrix} \dfrac{1}{n} + \dfrac{1}{n^2}\mathbf{1}'\mathbf{X}(\mathbf{X}'\mathbf{J}\mathbf{X})^{-1}\mathbf{X}' \quad \mathbf{1}'\mathbf{Y} \\[2mm] -\dfrac{1}{n}\mathbf{1}'\mathbf{X}(\mathbf{X}'\mathbf{J}\mathbf{X})^{-1}\mathbf{X}'\mathbf{Y} \\[2mm] -\dfrac{1}{n}(\mathbf{X}'\mathbf{J}\mathbf{X})^{-1}\mathbf{X}'\mathbf{1}\mathbf{1}'\mathbf{Y} + (\mathbf{X}'\mathbf{J}\mathbf{X})^{-1}\mathbf{X}'\mathbf{Y} \end{bmatrix} \quad (8)$$

This is standard multivariate regression analysis using raw data, but for the sake of minimizing computational errors it was decided at the Corporate Laboratories to develop a technique that used the correlation matrix instead of the raw data. A computer program already existed to generate a correlation matrix from raw data. The following matrices were defined:

$$\mathbf{D} = \text{diag}(S(x_i))^{-1} \qquad . \qquad . \qquad . \qquad . \qquad (9)$$

where

x_i is the ith independent variable and $S(x_i)$ is the sample standard deviation of x_i.

$$\mathbf{E} = \text{diag}(S(y_j))^{-1} \qquad . \qquad . \qquad . \qquad . \qquad (10)$$

where y_j is the jth dependent variable and $S(y_j)$ is the sample standard deviation of y_j.

$$\mathbf{Z} = \mathbf{JXD} \qquad . \qquad . \qquad . \qquad . \qquad . \qquad . \qquad (11)$$

$$\mathbf{V} = \mathbf{JYE} \qquad . \qquad . \qquad . \qquad . \qquad . \qquad . \qquad (12)$$

Equations (11) and (12) represent standardizing transformations on the raw data. The cross products matrix (**M**) is:

$$\mathbf{M} = \begin{pmatrix} \mathbf{Z}' \\ \mathbf{V}' \end{pmatrix}(\mathbf{ZV}) = \begin{bmatrix} \mathbf{Z}'\mathbf{Z} & \mathbf{Z}'\mathbf{V} \\ \mathbf{V}'\mathbf{Z} & \mathbf{V}'\mathbf{V} \end{bmatrix}$$

$$= \begin{bmatrix} \mathbf{D}'\mathbf{X}'\mathbf{J}\mathbf{J}\mathbf{X}\mathbf{D} & \mathbf{D}'\mathbf{X}'\mathbf{J}\mathbf{J}\mathbf{Y}\mathbf{E} \\ \mathbf{E}'\mathbf{Y}'\mathbf{J}\mathbf{J}\mathbf{X}\mathbf{D} & \mathbf{E}'\mathbf{Y}'\mathbf{J}\mathbf{J}\mathbf{Y}\mathbf{E} \end{bmatrix} \qquad . \qquad . \qquad . \qquad (13)$$

If **M** is pivoted about the first partition submatrix $\mathbf{D}'\mathbf{X}'\mathbf{J}\mathbf{J}\mathbf{X}\mathbf{D}$, to give **M**(pivoted), then

M(pivoted)

$$= \begin{bmatrix} -(\mathbf{D}'\mathbf{X}'\mathbf{J}\mathbf{J}\mathbf{X}\mathbf{D})^{-1} & -(\mathbf{E}'\mathbf{X}'\mathbf{J}\mathbf{J}\mathbf{X}\mathbf{D})^{-1}\mathbf{D}'\mathbf{X}'\mathbf{J}\mathbf{J}\mathbf{Y}\mathbf{E} \\[2mm] -\mathbf{E}'\mathbf{Y}'\mathbf{J}\mathbf{J}\mathbf{X}\mathbf{D}(\mathbf{E}'\mathbf{X}'\mathbf{J}\mathbf{J}\mathbf{X}\mathbf{D})^{-1} & \mathbf{E}'\mathbf{Y}'\mathbf{J}\mathbf{J}\mathbf{Y}\mathbf{E} - \mathbf{E}'\mathbf{Y}'\mathbf{J}\mathbf{J}\mathbf{Y}\mathbf{D}(\mathbf{D}'\mathbf{X}'\mathbf{J}\mathbf{J}\mathbf{X}\mathbf{D})^{-1}\mathbf{D}'\mathbf{X}'\mathbf{J}\mathbf{J}\mathbf{Y}\mathbf{E} \end{bmatrix}$$

The partition $(\mathbf{D}'\mathbf{X}'\mathbf{J}\mathbf{J}\mathbf{X}\mathbf{D})^{-1}$ is the correlation matrix of the independent variables. Thus if **M**(pivoted) in Eq. (14) is compared with $\hat{\mathbf{C}}$ in Eq. (8) it is clear that the correlation matrix can be used to calculate $\hat{\mathbf{C}}$ provided a transformation T can be found such that:

$$T\{-(\mathbf{D}'\mathbf{X}'\mathbf{J}\mathbf{J}\mathbf{X}\mathbf{D})^{-1}\mathbf{D}'\mathbf{X}'\mathbf{J}\mathbf{J}\mathbf{Y}\mathbf{E}\}$$

$$= -\frac{1}{n}(\mathbf{X}'\mathbf{J}\mathbf{X})^{-1}\mathbf{X}'\mathbf{1}\mathbf{1}'\mathbf{Y} + (\mathbf{X}'\mathbf{J}\mathbf{X})^{-1}\mathbf{X}'\mathbf{Y} \quad . \quad (15)$$

Since **J** is idempotent and **D** is diagonal the expression in braces on the left side of Eq. (15) is equal to

$$-\mathbf{D}^{-1}(\mathbf{X}'\mathbf{J}\mathbf{X})^{-1}\mathbf{X}'\mathbf{J}\mathbf{Y}\mathbf{E} \qquad . \qquad . \qquad . \qquad . \qquad (16)$$

and the expression on the right side of Eq. (15) is equal to

$$-(\mathbf{X}'\mathbf{J}\mathbf{X})^{-1}\mathbf{X}'\mathbf{J}\mathbf{Y} \qquad . \qquad . \qquad . \qquad . \qquad (17)$$

Thus the required transformation is premultiply by **D** and postmultiply by **E**. This gives all the coefficients in $\hat{\mathbf{C}}$ except for the first row shown in Eq. (8). If it is noted that:

$$\mathbf{1}'\mathbf{X} = n\bar{\mathbf{x}}' \quad \text{and} \quad \mathbf{1}'\mathbf{Y} = n\bar{\mathbf{y}}' \qquad . \qquad . \qquad (18)$$

where $\bar{\mathbf{x}}$ and $\bar{\mathbf{y}}$ are the mean vectors of the data sets **X** and **Y**, then the first row of Eq. (8) reduces to:

$$\bar{\mathbf{y}}' - \bar{\mathbf{x}}'\hat{\mathbf{C}} \qquad . \qquad . \qquad . \qquad . \qquad . \qquad (19)$$

The model and data

Data were chosen from two experimental heats which were suitable from two viewpoints. One was that these two heats were considered by the steelmaking department to represent good process performance within their range of experience. The other was that all the variables listed in the two previous sections were measured. A difficulty was that all the observations were not made at equal time intervals. The only way that this could be overcome was by interpolation. Another difficulty was that audiometer readings were widely varying so that a smoothed average value had to be used.

A time interval of half a minute was chosen. This may seem too big but examination of graphs of carbon/time and temperature/time marked with the control actions of varying lance height and adding lime and ore suggested that the process had sufficient inertia for such a long time interval to be adequate. The subsequent statistical analysis supported this decision. For the two heats the five state variables and three control variables were tabulated with values at half minute intervals. The data were entered into the laboratory's IBM 1800 computer and with a program called LAG, the state variables were shifted through one time increment so as to create observations on the state dependent variables $\mathbf{x}(k + 1)$ as in Eq. (3). A correlation matrix was generated and then the multivariate regression analysis described earlier was done, leading to the following set of equations (E indicates expected or predicted value):

$$Ex_1(k + 1) = 231.4 + 0.851x_1(k) + 0.04975x_2(k)$$
$$- 0.2241x_3(k) + 3.3704x_4(k)$$
$$- 64.47x_5(k) - 0.01906v_1(k)$$
$$- 27.175v_2(k) - 23.32v_3(k) \qquad (20)$$

$$Ex_2(k + 1) = 373.55 - 0.078x_1(k) + 0.9362x_2(k)$$
$$- 0.280x_3(k) - 3.0622x_4(k)$$
$$- 65.121x_5(k) - 0.34641v_1(k)$$
$$- 13.908v_2(k) + 154.89v_3(k) \qquad (21)$$

$$Ex_3(k + 1) = -7.5704 - 0.01511x_1(k)$$
$$+ 0.000444x_2(k) + 0.7848x_3(k)$$
$$- 2.503x_4(k) + 3.105x_5(k)$$
$$+ 0.075v_1(k) - 3.0013v_2(k)$$
$$+ 2.8795v_3(k) \qquad . \qquad . \qquad . \qquad (22)$$

$$Ex_4(k + 1) = 0.1004 - 0.000057x_1(k)$$
$$- 0.000029x_2(k) + 0.000085x_3(k)$$
$$+ 0.990x_4(k) - 0.4577x_5(k)$$
$$+ 0.0000135v_1(k) - 0.00323v_2(k)$$
$$- 0.0374v_3(k) \qquad . \qquad . \qquad . \qquad (23)$$

$$Ex_5(k + 1) = -0.1549 + 0.000108x_1(k)$$
$$+ 0.000310x_2(k) + 0.000170x_3(k)$$
$$+ 0.0783x_4(k) + 0.5358x_5(k)$$
$$- 0.0005432v_1(k) - 0.00901v_2(k)$$
$$+ 0.0746v_3(k) \qquad . \qquad . \qquad . \qquad (24)$$

x_1 = HM temp., °C
x_2 = WG temp., °C
x_3 = audiometer, % scale
x_4 = carbon, %
x_5 = carbon rate, % per min
v_1 = lance height,

$$v_2 = \text{lime addition}\left[\frac{\text{wt CaO}}{\text{wt SiO}_2 \text{ in hot metal}}\right]$$

$$v_3 = \text{ore addition}\left[\frac{\text{wt ore} \times 100}{\text{wt (hot metal + scrap)}}\right]$$

As indications of the closeness of fit the five equations respectively described the following amounts of variation in the predicted values:

metal temperature, 98%
waste-gas temperature, 97%
audiometer, 76%
carbon, 99.7%
carbon rate, 77%

The predictive abilities are illustrated in Figs. 2 and 3 which show the predicted and observed values of metal temperatures and carbon percentages against time. Each prediction was made using Eqs. (21) and (23) at the previous time state, half a minute in advance, using the current observed values of all state and control variables. The same original data set was also used to generate equations predicting the controls that would be decided by the human operators, given a set of state variable values within the original ranges. A program was then written to use these equations together with some practical constraints and starting values to predict the course of a complete heat without reference to any

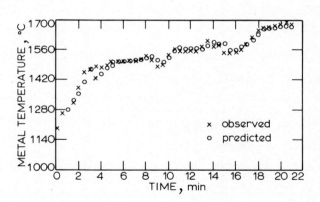

2 *Predicted and observed values of metal temperature against time*

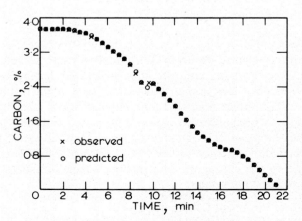

3 *Predicted and observed values of carbon percentage against time*

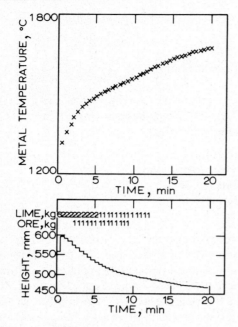

4   *Prediction with associated control, metal temperature*

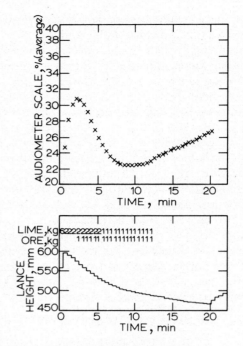

6   *Prediction with associated control, audiometer*

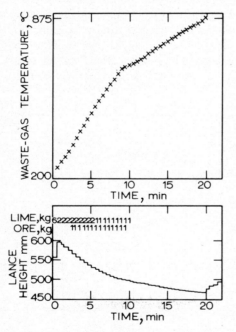

5   *Prediction with associated control, waste-gas temperature*

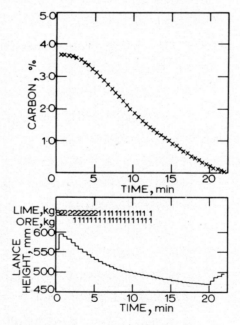

7   *Prediction with associated control, carbon*

observed in blow data. Figures 4 to 8 show the predictions with associated controls. Without knowing the actual responses to the controls, that is without having any observed values, it was assumed at each point in time that the values predicted for that point were what had actually been observed and these were used for predicting the next point. It is a small programming modification to use actual observed values when these are available on-line to the computer. The starting conditions for this simulated blow were:

(i) hot metal weight, 990 kg
(ii) scrap weight, 75 kg
(iii) silicon in metal, 0·71 %

(iv) carbon in metal, 3·67 %
(v) hot metal temp., 1 285°C
(vi) waste-gas temp., 200°C.

It is not claimed that this method of calculating a control decision will yield an optimal control strategy, only that it is a useful check on the multivariate predictivity. However, parts of the program will be useful in applying the optimization method.

PLANT VARIATIONS

The estimated coefficients discussed in the previous section are applicable only to conditions similar to those

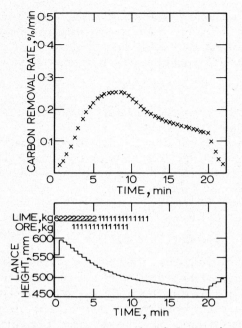

8   Prediction with associated control, carbon removal rate

from which the data were obtained, to estimate the coefficients. Although they do reflect the fundamental mechanisms of the process, as argued previously, and these are invariant, the coefficients also reflect the plant conditions, such as the vessel geometry, the refractory conditions, oxygen lance nozzle wear, and sensor calibration drifts. It is important to change the coefficients as soon as condition changes are sensed. The safest thing to do is to assume that the conditions are changing all the time, not only that they are different from previous blows at the beginning of a new blow, but that at any time during a blow there may be gradual changes or an occasional internal minor disruption that will require coefficient modifications.

Use can be made of a technique which is an extension to regression analysis for updating coefficients estimated from n observations by the data from one further observation without doing a complete re-analysis with the augmented data. If the original n observations $(\mathbf{X}, \mathbf{Y})$ have provided the cross products matrix $\mathbf{XX'}$ whose inverse is $(\mathbf{XX'})^{-1}$, and there are further observations represented by the data row $(\mathbf{x'}, \mathbf{y'})$ the new cross products matrix is $(\mathbf{XX'} + \mathbf{xx'})$. The complete inversion is avoided by an easily derived relationship:

$$(\mathbf{XX'} + \mathbf{xx'})^{-1} = (\mathbf{XX'})^{-1} - \frac{(\mathbf{XX'})^{-1}\mathbf{xx'}(\mathbf{XX'})^{-1}}{1 + \mathbf{x'}(\mathbf{XX'})^{-1}\mathbf{x}} \quad (25)$$

This can now be substituted into the original least squares multivariate regression solution to give coefficients modified by the extra data. That assumes, however, that the population coefficients are constant and the new data have been used merely to improve the estimates. In the steelmaking process control situation, the assumption is different. It is that the population coefficients have changed. This can be satisfied by introducing a weighting factor which diminishes the importance of the original n observations relative to the new single

observation. Such an expedient is used by commercial departments for estimating trends and predicting future sales from past demand data. If, for example, $\mathbf{C_0}$ is the matrix of coefficients estimated from the original n observations and these are weighted by a factor α when the new row $(\mathbf{x'}, \mathbf{y'})$ is introduced, the new estimates of $\mathbf{C}$ are

$$\mathbf{C_1} = \mathbf{C_0} + \mathbf{G} - (\alpha^2 + \mathbf{x'}(\mathbf{XX'})^{-1}\mathbf{x})^{-1}$$
$$\times ((\mathbf{XX'})^{-1}\mathbf{xx'}(\mathbf{C_0} + \mathbf{G})) \quad . \quad . \quad . \quad (26)$$

where

$$\mathbf{G} = \alpha^{-2}(\mathbf{XX'})^{-1}\mathbf{xy'} \quad . \quad . \quad . \quad . \quad (27)$$

The procedure adopted is to assume always that variations in the coefficients are about the original coefficients derived from historical data and the variation is estimated afresh with the introduction of every new observation. What is not done, however, is that the coefficients modified by one observation are carried forward to be re-modified by the next observation. The adopted procedure not only provides a neat standard computation but also makes it easier to cope with fluctuating conditions. Thus the only values that need to be stored at the start of a run are the coefficients matrix $\mathbf{C_0}$, the inverted original cross-products matrix $(\mathbf{XX'})^{-1}$, and a value for α. The computation of Eq. (26) involves nothing more than matrix multiplication and addition. The only inversion required is $(\alpha^2 + \mathbf{x'}(\mathbf{XX'})^{-1}\mathbf{x})^{-1}$ and this is only a scalar. Thus, the computation time is brief. Simulated blows are being examined to derive the best value of α to satisfy rapidly changing conditions. This study has not been concluded but a value of about 0·5 seems to support the model predictions.

DYNAMIC PROGRAMMING

The oxygen steelmaking converter process may be viewed as constituting a multi-stage decision process with the following sequence of operations:

   (i) at time k, the state of the system is observed in terms of the elements of the state variable vector $\mathbf{x}(k)$

  (ii) a decision is made, a value of the control vector $\mathbf{v}(k)$ is chosen on the basis of $\mathbf{x}(k)$ and according to some prespecified decision rule

 (iii) the state of the system changes as a result of the decision

 (iv) the sequence a, b, c is repeated until some stopping condition is reached.

The input vector $\mathbf{v}(k)$ which minimizes an appropriate performance index is called an optimal policy and a mathematical method devised by Bellman[1] to determine the optimal policy is called dynamic programming. The method is based on Bellman's principle of optimality which may be described by reconsideration of Fig. 1. As mentioned earlier, the central path may be considered as the best if the only criterion by which it is judged is that it ends in the centre of the end-point box. In practice, there are other criteria such as constraining the slag production to be between certain minimum and maximum levels, restricting over and under activity of the process, efficiently using the oxygen supply so that there is neither too much lost by poor absorption in the liquid nor too much oxidation of iron, minimizing the ore additions and refractory wear, and keeping the total processing time reasonably short. It may be possible to build all these and other criteria into a single performance index and if possible this should be describable entirely in terms of those variables included in the process model. In the discrete time case the performance index would be the summation of a function of the process variables from present time (0) to the end of the process (T):

$$J = \sum_{k=0}^{T} f(\mathbf{x}(k), \mathbf{v}(k)) \qquad . \qquad . \qquad . \qquad (28)$$

J can be called the cost of control. The aim is to find an optimal policy $\tilde{\mathbf{v}}(k)$ which minimizes J and thereby defines the unique best path to the centre of the end box. A new version of Fig. 1 is shown in Fig. 9 in which two alternative paths are drawn, both ending in the centre of the end box.

Supposing that ABC is the optimal path from A to C then the principle of optimality states, and it can be proved mathematically, that BC is the optimal path from the mid-point B to C. Thus given C the required end point, the two-stage process requires the finding of a mid-point B such that BC is optimal. If, on the other hand, a mid-point B' had been found such that the first stage of the process, AB', was optimal, then it would not necessarily follow that $AB'C$ was optimal. This is a simplified illustration of dynamic programming as an iterative method starting with the end point and working backwards to the starting point. In general it is difficult to solve but its solution is much easier if the process equations are linear and the performance index is a quadratic form. In this case, the problem can be stated succinctly as:

Given that the process is represented by the equations:

$$\mathbf{x}(k+1) = \mathbf{A}\mathbf{x}(k) + \mathbf{B}\mathbf{v}(k) \qquad . \qquad . \qquad . \qquad (29)$$

and the optimal path is to be judged according to a performance index

$$J = \sum_{k=0}^{T} (\mathbf{x}'(k)\mathbf{Q}\mathbf{x}(k) + \mathbf{v}'(k)\mathbf{S}\mathbf{v}(k)) \qquad . \qquad . \qquad (30)$$

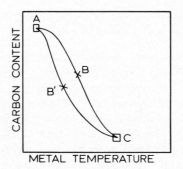

9   *New version of oxygen steelmaking process*

where $\mathbf{x}(k)$ and $\mathbf{v}(k)$ are the state and control vectors at time k, and $\mathbf{Q}$ and $\mathbf{S}$ are positive definite matrices, then the problem is to determine a feedback matrix $\mathbf{F}$ such that the following decision can be made about $\mathbf{v}$:

$$\text{optimal } \mathbf{v}(k) = \tilde{\mathbf{v}}(k) = \mathbf{F}\mathbf{x}(k) \qquad . \qquad . \qquad . \qquad (31)$$

The solution to this problem is by the following recursive procedure:

A new matrix $\mathbf{P}$ is introduced for computational expediency and this is initially set equal to $\mathbf{Q}$. Then the following two calculations are repeated alternately until convergence is reached for $\mathbf{F}$:

$$\mathbf{F} = -(\mathbf{B}'\mathbf{P}\mathbf{B} + \mathbf{S})^{-1}\mathbf{B}'\mathbf{P}\mathbf{A} \qquad . \qquad . \qquad . \qquad (32)$$

$$\mathbf{P}_1 = (\mathbf{A} + \mathbf{B}\mathbf{F})'\mathbf{P}(\mathbf{A} + \mathbf{B}\mathbf{F}) + \mathbf{F}'\mathbf{S}\mathbf{F} + \mathbf{Q} . \qquad . \qquad (33)$$

The work described in the early sections of this paper indicates that the process may be described adequately as in Eq. (29) ignoring random variations and changes in process conditions for the present. The outstanding question is: can a performance index J be constructed as a quadratic form (Eq. 30) in terms of only, but all, the variables included in the model (Eq. 29)? Neither the literature consulted on dynamic programming nor the literature on steelmaking is helpful. The former (Ref. 1 and others) makes the assumption that a suitable index has been defined, and the latter relates only to end-point carbon and temperature variations and is admitted to use hypothetical costs only.

Rather than making a choice entirely by guessing, a rational, but perhaps still questionable, procedure was adopted to select the matrices $\mathbf{Q}$ and $\mathbf{S}$. The first stage was to say that the relative costs of variations from accepted values of variables were inversely proportional to the orders of magnitude of permitted variation of the variables. For example, in the pilot plant the lance height may range over a hundred or more millimetres on either side of roughly 600 mm. It is hoped to control carbon to within at most 0·1 % of whatever value may be needed at any stage of the process. Thus the relative costs of variation would be in the ratios:

$$\text{(carbon costs)/(lance height costs)} = (100)^2/(0·1)^2$$

Thus if the diagonal entry in $\mathbf{S}$ for lance height was specified as 1, the relative entry in $\mathbf{Q}$ for carbon would be 10^6. This idea was considered until $\mathbf{S}$ and $\mathbf{Q}$ were fully constructed and they were then tried in the application of Eqs. (32) and (33) using the coefficients expressed in Eqs. (20) to (24) together with starting values and aim end points from a typical heat. The result was a feedback matrix which gave initial controls fairly close to the controls adopted by human operators within that band of operating conditions. (Lance height 570 mm, lime addition 1 unit, no ore addition.)

The second stage was to use a randomization procedure to vary the elements of $\mathbf{Q}$ and $\mathbf{S}$ about the values in the first stage until values were reached which led to recommended controls equal to those of the human operators. The two matrices were then believed to represent adequately the relative costs of variations in all the process state and control variables. Computer trials are now continuing to simulate the performance of the pilot plant and generate optimal controls according to different starting and end requirements. There are, however, two major difficulties. One of these is the variability of the plant and the corresponding coefficients discussed earlier. The other is the lengthy computation required by dynamic programming and the unacceptable competition it would give to other routines if run in real time. A proposed solution to these problems is being developed by further off-line simulation. The method adopted is:

(i) start with the initial values of **Q** and **S** as above and of the coefficients **C** of the section on multivariate regression

(ii) use randomization to obtain consecutive values of the state variable vectors

(iii) according to the differences in the state variable vectors of (ii) modify the coefficients **C** using the method described in the section on plant variation

(iv) use randomization to vary end-point requirements, silicon composition, and other process parameters

(v) apply the dynamic programming method to the situation described by the results of (iii) and (iv) to obtain optimal controls

(vi) store the values generated by (ii), (iv), and (v)

(vii) repeat (ii) and (vi) several hundred times

(viii) use multivariate regression analysis on the data stored in (vi) to obtain predictive equations for optimal controls according to different consecutive values of state variables and various required end points and other process parameters.

Finally, the predictive equations for optimal controls will be tested by using real-time computer logged data and printing on a typewriter the recommended controls for use by the plant operators.

CONCLUSION

The general philosophy behind this paper is to pursue optimal controls in terms of only those process variables which can be observed easily and reliably using whatever techniques are currently available or can be invented and applied quickly. Although process models developed from consideration of more fundamental mechanisms have some merit, the prospect of direct application to production within the next two years is uncertain. The methods proposed in this paper are proceeding well and already nearing maturation with relatively far less effort than is being applied elsewhere by other groups using conventional mechanistic modelling and process theoretic methods.

REFERENCE

1 R. BELLMAN: 'Dynamic programming', 1957, Princeton University Press

Unified modelling of various steelmaking processes

S. Asai and I. Muchi

Oxidation reactions taking place in molten steel in the various refining processes have correlation with each other through a medium of the reactions, and the transitional variations in each concentration of the reaction components in molten steel may be determined on the basis of the balances of the following two kinds of driving forces. Namely, one force has an essential tendency allowing the system to approach to the equilibrium, and another force caused by oxygen supplied into a bath acts in the opposite direction and has a tendency to keep the system away from the equilibrium. On the basis of the two driving forces mentioned above, a simplified model is proposed in this paper, and the important dimensionless factors, A and B, determining the effects of the feed rate of available oxygen, the degree of mixing of molten steel and the temperature of molten steel and the partial pressure of the carbon monoxide gas on the transitional variations of process variables are involved in the model. By the use of this model, the experimental data of oxidation reactions obtained by the other investigators have been quantitatively analysed, and the differences in the proceeding sequence of the oxidation of silicon and the decarburization which are widely known from the comparison between the experimental data obtained in LD converter and those in the crucible have been clarified quantitatively in this work.

SYMBOLS

A dimensionless number $= I\Theta_t = U_j\Theta_t/W$ (−)

a_j activity of j-component   (−)

B dimensionless number $= S\Theta_t/WC_{i,c}$ (−)

C_j concentration of j-component (%), kg(j)/kg(Fe)

c_j dimensionless concentration of j-component $= C_j/C_{i,c}$ (−)

F_j function shown in Eq. (5)   (kg(O)/kg(Fe))

f_j function shown in Eq. (15)

I mass-transport factor   (l/s)

$K(T)$ equilibrium constant   (atm . kg(Fe)²/kg(O)kg(C))

M_j molecular mass of j-component   (kg/kgmol)

N_j overall rate of mass transfer   (kg(j)/s)

$n_{j,k}$ rate of mass transfer of j-component in kth step (kg(j)/s)

p_j partial pressure of j-component   (atm)

$R_{j,k}$ resistance for the transfer of j-component in kth step   (s/kg(Fe))

S feed rate of available oxygen   (kg(O)/s)

T temperature of molten steel   (K)

t dimensionless temperature $= T/T_i$ (−)

U_j rate constant of overall reaction   (kg(Fe)/s)

W mass of molten steel   (kg(Fe))

α_j stoichiometric coefficient   (−)

Θ_t total blowing time   (min)

Θ elapsed time   (s)

θ dimensionless elapsed time   (s)

Suffix

1   oxygen

i   initial value

*   equilibrium state

For the case of various refining processes, oxidation reactions taking place in molten steel have been investigated actively. However, the following differences have not been sufficiently analysed; the differences in the proceeding sequence of the oxidation of silicon and the decarburization which are widely known from the comparison between the results observed in LD converter

The authors are with the Nagoya University, Japan

and those in crucible, the differences in the oxygen level in molten steel among the experimental data obtained by the other investigators in open hearth, LD converter and crucible, and the differences in the oxygen level produced by the feed rate of oxygen in LD converter. Oxygen reactions taking place in molten steel have correlation with each other through oxygen in a steel bath as a medium of reactions, and the transitional variations in each concentration of the reactant in molten steel may be determined on the basis of the balances of the following two kinds of driving forces. One force has an essential tendency allowing the system to approach to the equilibrium, and another force caused by the oxygen supplied into a bath acts in the opposite direction and has a tendency to keep the system away from the equilibrium.

In this paper, on the basis of the two driving forces mentioned above, a simplified model is proposed by taking account of the effects of the feed rate of the available oxygen, the degree of mixing and the temperature of molten steel, and the partial pressure of the carbon monoxide gas on the transitional variations of process variables. The experimental data obtained by the other investigators concerning the differences in the proceeding sequence of oxidation and those in the oxygen level mentioned above are explained theoretically by the use of this model.

CONCEPT OF MODEL

From the experimental data obtained by the other investigators in LD converter, crucible, and open hearth, it can be found that the relation between the concentrations of carbon and oxygen in molten steel is distributed above the C–O equilibrium line. This relation is illustrated in Fig. 1(a). The solid line (1) represents the C–O equilibrium line and the dotted line (2) represents the actual trajectory which moves from the high carbon concentrations to low ones. In the decarburization, the absorbed oxygen is almost consumed for the decarburization reaction and the rest of it is accumulated in molten steel. Taking the material balance for oxygen at the time elapsed, Θ, Eq. (1) is described as follows:

$$\int_0^\Theta (S/W)\,\mathrm{d}\Theta = (C_O - C_{i,O}) + (M_O/M_C)$$

$$\times (C_{i,C} - C_C). \qquad . \qquad . \qquad . \qquad (1)$$

As shown in Fig. 1, Eq. (1) is presented by a group of lines (operating line) which move in the direction of the arrow as blowing time proceeds. Then, if feeding of oxygen is cut at the time when the concentrations of carbon and oxygen are shown by a point J, the point J would move to the point M along the path of operating line, and finally the system would reach its equilibrium state at the point M. Since the equilibrium relation between the concentrations of carbon and oxygen is given by Eq. (2), the intersection of the operating line and the equilibrium line, a point (C_C^*, C_O^*), can be determined from Eqs. (1) and (2) as a function of time elapsed, the

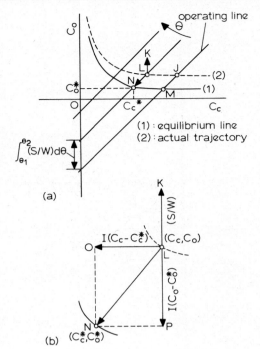

1 *Relation between the concentration of carbon and oxygen in molten steel and operating line*

temperature of molten steel and the partial pressure of the carbon monoxide. If the concentrations of carbon and oxygen are shown by a point L and the intersection of the operating line and the equilibrium line is given

$$C_O \cdot C_C = p_{CO}/K(T) \qquad . \qquad . \qquad . \qquad . \qquad (2)$$

by a point N, then the system would move from the point L to the point N by the action of the driving force, $\overrightarrow{LN}$. Figure 1(b) is the magnified figure of Fig. 1(a). As is shown in Fig. 1(b), the driving force, $\overrightarrow{LN}$, can be resolved into the driving forces, $\overrightarrow{LO}$ and $\overrightarrow{LP}$. The smaller the resistances of reaction and mass transfer taking place during the movement from the point, L, to the point, N, are, the more rapidly the system arrives at the point, N.

When the oxygen gas is absorbed into molten steel, the driving force corresponding to the amount of (S/W) in the direction of $\overrightarrow{LK}$ against LP acts upon the system at the point, L. As shown by the dotted line in Fig. (1), the concentration relation of C–O obtained from the practical operations can be determined on the basis of the balance of two kinds of the driving force mentioned above. On the basis of the idea mentioned above, the differences of the oxygen level among the experimental data obtained in open hearth, LD converter and crucible can be explained as inferring the experimental data[1,2] reported already; the largest gap between the experimental data and the equilibrium line can be seen in open hearth, and larger one in LD converter, and the data in crucible almost coincide with the equilibrium line. In open hearth the value of the feed rate of oxygen is so small that the driving force, $\overrightarrow{LK}$, becomes small. On the other hand, as the mixing of molten steel may be very weak, the driving force, $\overrightarrow{LN}$, becomes smaller. Thus, it can be deduced from the balance of two driving forces mentioned above that the largest deviation from the equilibrium line takes

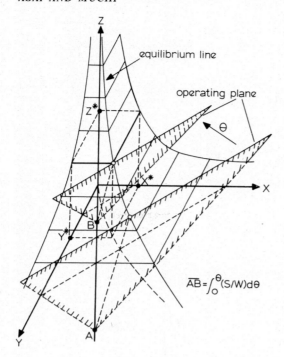

2   Schematic diagram of equilibrium line and operating planes in rectangular coordinates

place in open hearth. The feed rate of oxygen in LD converter is so large that the driving force, $\overrightarrow{LK}$, becomes large. On the other hand, as the mixing of molten steel caused by the oxygen jet is violent, the driving force, $\overrightarrow{LN}$, becomes larger. From the balance of two driving forces mentioned above, it can be inferred that the data observed in LD converter may be nearer to the equilibrium line than those in open hearth.

In the case of the crucible, the weak oxidizing gas used is so small that the driving force, LK, becomes very small. On the other hand, as the high-frequency induction equipment is adopted, the mixing of molten steel becomes violent in crucible. Thereby, it may be estimated qualitatively that the concentration relation of C–O in crucible approaches to or almost exists on the equilibrium line. From a survey of the experimental data[3,4] obtained by changing the feed rate of oxygen gas in LD converter, it was found that the deviation of the concentration relation of C–O from the equilibrium line was enlarged by an increase in the feed rate of oxygen gas. Furthermore, by applying a similar view concerning the concentration relations of C–O to those of C–Si–O or C–Mn–O systems, it has been explained qualitatively that the oxidations of silicon or manganese take precedence in LD converter and that the decarburization proceeds preferentially in crucible.

The concentration relation of C–Si–O or C–Mn–O systems is illustrated in Fig. 2 by the rectangular coordinate, X–Y–Z, where each axis of X, Y, and Z represents the concentrations of C, Si, or Mn, and O, respectively. In Fig. 2, the equilibrium lines of X–Z and Y–Z are illustrated on the planes of X–Z and Y–Z, respectively. Each equilibrium line mentioned above forms the curved surface parallel to Y-axis and X-axis, respectively.

The intersection of these curved surfaces becomes the equilibrium line in three-dimensional system. If the system was in the equilibrium state, the concentration relation of each component of the system would be represented by the equilibrium line. Now, Eq. (1) represents the operating line for the case of binary system. From the mass balance concerning oxygen, Eq. (3) can be described for the case of ternary system.

$$\int_0^\Theta (S/W)\,\mathrm{d}\Theta = (C_O - C_{i,o}) + (M_O/M_C)(C_{i,c} - C_C)$$
$$+ 2(M_O/M_{Si})(C_{i,Si} - C_{Si}). \qquad . \quad (3)$$

As is shown in Fig. 2, Eq. (3) expresses the operating plane which moves in the direction given by the arrow during the progress of blowing. In the same manner as for the case of the binary system, the two kinds of driving forces may be considered for the case of the ternary system. That is, one force moves the system to the point of intersection of the operating plane and the equilibrium line and another force shifts the system in the positive direction of Z-axis, and the balance of these driving forces determines the transitional path of the system. Usually, the experimental results in the crucible are obtained under comparatively high temperatures, so that the equilibrium relation of Y–Z(Si–O or Mn–O) may exist far from Z-axis and Y-axis. On the other hand, since the equilibrium relation of Z–X(O–C) is scarcely affected by the temperature, the intersection of the curved surface formed by the equilibrium relation of O–Si or O–Mn and one formed by the equilibrium relation of O–C may be projected near Y-axis on X–Y plane (C–Si or C–Mn). Thus, the point of intersection of the operating plane and the equilibrium line may exist near Z–Y plane. Since the system may be drawn toward the point of interjection, the system may be attracted at first from the point shown by initial concentrations to the direction of Y-axis on the X–Y plane and then to the direction of an origin. That is, for the case of the experiments in crucible the proceeding sequence of the decarburization becomes earlier than that of the oxidation of silicon or manganese.

Since the temperature of molten steel in LD converter during the initial blowing time is comparatively low, the equilibrium relation of Z–Y may exist nearer both Z- and Y-axes, and it may be projected in the neighbourhood of X-axis on X–Y plane. For this reason, at first the system may be attracted to the direction of Y-axis on X–Y plane and then to the direction of an origin. That is, for the case of the blowing process in LD converter the oxidation of silicon or manganese takes place earlier than the decarburization. Further, since the temperature of molten steel in LD converter rises during the progress of blowing time, the equilibrium line projected on X–Y plane moves from the side of X-axis to that of Y-axis. Since the more violent the mixing of the molten steel in LD converter becomes, the more rapidly the system approaches to the equilibrium state and the equilibrium line exists in the neighbourhood of X-axis on the X–Y plane during the initial blowing time, it may be considered that the oxidation of silicon takes place more rapidly than the decarburization reaction in the case of violent mixing. From the experiments conducted by Watanabe et al.,[5] it was reported that in the case of a deep cavity in the bath the oxidation of silicon took place more rapidly than the decarburization.

Extension to multicomponent system

In the preceding paragraph binary and ternary systems have been taken into consideration, and in this paragraph the previous analysis is extended to the case of multicomponent system. Corresponding to Eq. (1) for the case of binary system and Eq. (3) for the case of ternary system, Eq. (4) can be obtained from the mass balance of oxygen for the case of multicomponent system.

$$\int_0^\Theta (S/W)\mathrm{d}\Theta = (C_O - C_{i,o})$$
$$+ \alpha_j(M_O/M_j)(C_{i,j} - C_j) \quad . \quad . \quad (4)$$

where $j = 1, 2 \ldots n$ represents such components as O, C, Si, Mn, P, $\ldots$, respectively, and α_j is a stoichiometric coefficient representing the number of moles of j-component which reacts with a mole of oxygen, O. The concentration of each component in equilibrium state can be described as a function of the oxygen concentration and the temperature of molten steel by the use of the equilibrium concentration relation, as follows:

$$C_j = F_j(C_1, T), \quad j = 2 \sim n \quad . \quad . \quad . \quad (5)$$

Polynomial relating to C_1 can be obtained by substituting Eq. (5) into Eq. (4). The equilibrium concentration of the oxygen, C_1^* can be determined from the polynomial mentioned above by giving the initial concentrations of each component, $C_{i,j}$. And so, the equilibrium concentration of each component, C_j^* ($j = 2, \ldots n$), can be obtained by substituting C_1^* into Eq. (5).

Considering that the rate of the change in the concentrations of each component may be determined on the balance of the driving forces, Eq. (6) relating to the concentrations of oxygen and Eq. (7) relevant to the other j-components can be described as follows

$$\mathrm{d}C_1/\mathrm{d}\Theta = I(C_1^* - C_1) + S/W \quad . \quad . \quad . \quad (6)$$
$$\mathrm{d}C_j/\mathrm{d}\Theta = I(C_j^* - C_j), \quad j = 2 \sim n \quad . \quad . \quad . \quad (7)$$

Oxidations of molten steel in the refining process consist of each elementary process and of the mass transfer, but each elementary process may be considered as a rapid reaction, since the refining process proceeds usually at high temperature. Thus, the mass transfer in the refining process can be assumed to be the rate-controlling step. In Eq. (6) and Eq. (7), C_j^* ($j = 1 \sim n$), means the equilibrium concentration of j-component. Here, the process where j-component approaches to the equilibrium state may be imagined, and it may be assumed that there exist m steps of mass transfer during the process. The rate of mass transfer and the resistance for the transfer of j-component in kth step on the way to the equilibrium are signified by $n_{j,k}$

and $R_{j,k}$, respectively. Now, $n_{j,k}$ may be described by Eq. (8), and then, the overall rate of mass transfer, N_j, can be represented by Eq. (9) under the assumption of the quasi steady-state conditions for each step.

$$n_{j,k} = (1/R_{j,k})(C_{j,k} - C_{j,k-1}), \quad k = 1 \sim m,$$
$$j = 2 \sim n \quad (8)$$
$$N_j = W \cdot \mathrm{d}C_j/\mathrm{d}\Theta = U_j(C_{j,m} - C_{j,o})$$
$$= U_j(C_j^* - C_j), \quad j = 2 \sim n \quad (9)$$

where U_j in Eq. (9) is a function of $R_{j,k}$ ($k = 1 \sim n$), and for the case where all resistances can be assumed to be in series, U_j becomes equal to $(\sum_{k=1}^n R_{j,k})^{-1}$. In Eq. (9), $C_{j,o}$ means the concentration of j-component supplied from the bulk of molten steel to the first step, and so $C_{j,o}$ may be expressed by C_j. Further, $C_{j,m}$ means the concentration of the j-component supplied from the mth step to the $(m + 1)$th step, and from the assumption that the system reaches its equilibrium state at the mth step, $C_{j,m}$ can be replaced by C_j^*. Since the elementary processes and the mass transfer steps may be included in the refining process, a coefficient, U_j, in Eq. (9) may be considered as the rate constant of overall reaction. Now, the consideration concerning the relation between U_j and I may be expressed as the following. Dividing both sides of Eq. (9) by the mass of the molten steel, W, Eq. (9') is obtained.

$$\mathrm{d}C_j/\mathrm{d}\Theta = (U_j/W)(C_j^* - C_j) \quad . \quad . \quad . \quad (9')$$

From the comparison of Eq. (9') with Eq. (7), $U_j = I \cdot W$ can be described as the relation between U_j and I. Thus it may be considered that the value of I depends on the type of the components, but the results calculated in terms of the same value of I on the transitional variations of the concentration of each component are in good agreement with the experimental data. For this reason, it is deduced that U_j may be scarcely affected by the kind of components. For the case of the equilibrium state, Eq. (4) can be represented by Eq. (10).

$$\int_0^\Theta (S/W)\,\mathrm{d}\Theta = (C_1^* - C_{i,1})$$
$$+ \sum_{j=2}^n \alpha_j(M_O/M_j)(C_{i,j} - C_j^*) \quad . \quad (10)$$

Eq. (11) is obtained from Eqs. (4) and (10).

$$(C_1 - C_1^*) - \sum_{j=2}^n \alpha_j(M_O/M_j)(C_j - C_j^*) = 0 \quad . \quad (11)$$

Furthermore, Eq. (12) can be described by differentiating Eq. (4) with respect to Θ.

$$S/W = \mathrm{d}C_1/\mathrm{d}\Theta + \sum_{j=2}^n \alpha_j(M_O/M_j)(-\mathrm{d}C_j/\mathrm{d}\Theta) \quad . \quad (12)$$

Substituting Eq. (9) into Eq. (12), and applying the relation $U_j = I \cdot W$, Eq. (13) is obtained.

$$S/W = \mathrm{d}C_1/\mathrm{d}\Theta + I \sum_{j=2}^n \alpha_j(M_O/M_j)(C_j - C_j^*) \quad . \quad (13)$$

Equation (6) can now be expressed by substituting Eq. (11) into Eq. (13). It may be found that Eqs. (6) and (7) based on the concept of the balance of driving forces can also be derived from Eq. (4) representing the mass balance for oxygen and Eq. (9) concerning the rate of mass transfer. In the analysis of the vacuum degassing process, Nemoto et al.[6] reported that the relation between the operating time and the difference of the carbon concentration in a ladle and its equilibrium concentration was shown by the straight line on the semilogarithmic graph paper. This means that I defined by Eq. (7) may be constant actually. The dimensionless equation of Eqs. (4)–(7) can now be given by Eqs. (14)–(17), respectively.

$$\int_0^\theta B\,d\theta = (c_1 - c_{i,1}) + \sum_{j=2}^n \alpha_j(M_O/M_j)(c_{i,j} - c_j) \quad (14)$$

$$c_j^* = f_j(c_1^*, t), \quad j = 2 \sim n \quad . \quad . \quad . \quad . \quad (15)$$

$$dc_1/d\theta = A(c_1^* - c_1) + B \quad . \quad . \quad . \quad . \quad (16)$$

$$dc_j/d\theta = A(c_j^* - c_j), \quad j = 2 \sim n \quad . \quad . \quad . \quad (17)$$

where $A \equiv I\Theta_t$, $B \equiv S\Theta_t/WC_{i,C}$, $c_j \equiv C_j/C_{i,C}$, $t \equiv T/T_i$, $\theta = \Theta/\Theta_*$, and f_j in Eq. (15) corresponds to F_j in Eq. (5). The value of c_1^* can be obtained by solving Eq. (14) and Eq. (15) simultaneously. The values of c_j^* $(j = 2 \sim n)$ can be obtained by substituting the value of c_1^* into Eq. (15). The transitional variations of the concentrations of each component in molten steel during the process of blowing can be calculated by substituting the values of c_j^* $(j = 1 \sim n)$ into Eq. (16) and Eq. (17).

Consideration of A and B

Dimensionless term, A, is defined by the relation of $A \equiv I\Theta_t = U_j\Theta_t/W$, and it means the mass transferred per unit mass of molten steel. When the value of A is large, the mixing of molten steel becomes violent for a given refining time. The difference between the concentrations of each component in molten steel and those in equilibrium state can be determined by the value of A. From Eqs. (16) and (17), c_j becomes equal to c_j^* $(j = 1 \sim n)$ for the case of $A = \infty$, and the relations of $c_1 = \int_0^\Theta B\,d\theta + c_{i,1}$ and $c_j = c_{i,j}$ $(j = 2 \sim n)$ can be obtained for $A = 0$. For the case of very large values of A, it can be seen from Eqs. (14) and (15) that the concentrations of each component in molten steel, c_j $(j = 1 \sim n)$, approach to the equilibrium concentrations, c_j^* $(j = 1 \sim n)$, which changes during the process of blowing. As the concentration, c_1^*, means the lowest concentration of oxygen, oxygen concentration becomes very low in cases such as mentioned above. On the other hand, the value of A becomes small in the case where the mixing of molten steel is mild. Since the progress of oxidation is retarded in the case where the value of A is very low, the concentrations of each component except oxygen would become nearly equal to the value of the initial concentrations, $c_{i,j}$, and the oxygen concentration shows very

high values. Further, the dimensionless term B is defined by the relation $B \equiv S\Theta_t/WC_{i,C}$, and it means the ratio of the effective mass of oxygen supplied into molten steel to the initial mass of carbon in molten steel.

It is well known that the quality of a steel depends largely on the level of the concentration of oxygen in molten steel, and the level in the various refining processes can be determined by the two dimensionless terms of A and B defined in this work. For instance, the level in a degassing process may be determined by only A, since the desorption and the absorption of O_2 gas do not take place in the process. The increases in the value of B and also in the oxygen concentration in molten steel are caused by the increase in the flow rate of oxygen during the given blowing time, but A acts to diminish the increase in the oxygen concentration. The value of B can now be obtained on the basis of the operating conditions, but the value of A cannot be evaluated unless the overall reaction coefficient, U_j, is represented as a function of the operating conditions. The information concerning the possibility to reduce the oxygen concentration may be obtained by evaluating such the value of A that the results calculated from the oxidation model mentioned above coincide closely with the observed data.

Various components have been taken into account in this work, but the change in the values of U_j owing to the kind of components has not been found. And so, it may be allowed to take the same value of A for each case of various components under consideration. From the reason mentioned above the transitional variations of each component in molten steel may be evaluated by the use of the dimensionless terms A and B.

ANALYSIS OF THE DATA OBTAINED BY THE REFINING EXPERIMENTS IN CRUCIBLES

System of Fe–Si

Experiments refining the system of Fe–Si by the gaseous mixture of Ar, H_2, and H_2O in the MgO crucible were conducted by Kawai et al.[7] under the conditions of constant partial pressures of steam and constant temperatures of molten steel. For these experiments, Eqs. (14) and (15) can be expressed by Eqs. (14a) and (15a).

$$\int_0^\theta B\,d\theta = (c_O - c_{i,O}) + 2(M_O/M_{Si})(c_{i,Si} - c_{Si}) \quad (14a)$$

$$c_O^2 \cdot c_{Si} = a_{SiO_2} \exp\{2\cdot303(-30\,720/T + 11\cdot76)\}$$
$$/(C_{i,C} \times 10^2)^3 \quad . \quad . \quad . \quad (15a)[8]$$

Since it was inferred from the data of the chemical analysis of the slag sampled by a quartz pipe that the slag of FeO–SiO_2 was saturated by SiO_2, the value of a_{SiO_2} was assumed to be equal to 1. For the calculations of the concentrations of silicon and oxygen, the values of the temperature of molten steel and the initial concentration of silicon in molten steel have been taken as equal to the data adopted in their experiments, and the values

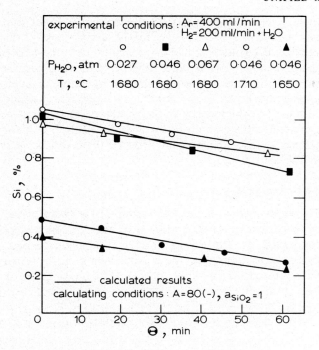

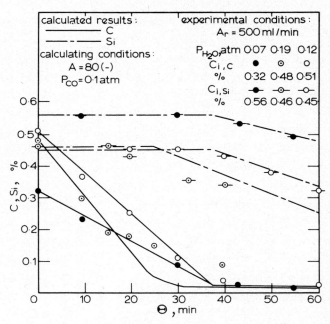

3   *Comparison of calculated results with data observed by Kawai et al.[7] above the concentration of silicon in Fe–Si alloys*

4   *Comparison of calculated results with data observed by Kawai et al.[7] above the concentrations of carbon and silicon in Fe–C–Si alloys at 1 650°C*

of the flow rate of oxygen used in the calculations have been estimated from the numerical analysis of the experimental data. The initial concentration of oxygen has been estimated from the assumption that the system in their experiments was in the equilibrium state at starting point. The value of A has been adopted to be equal to 80, and also the same value of A has been used for the calculations on the other systems.

In Fig. 3 the calculated results concerning the transitional variations of the concentration of silicon in the case of Fe–Si system have been compared with the experimental data obtained by them, and the close agreements between the observed data and the calculated results can be seen regardless of the various experimental conditions such as temperature, concentration, and partial pressures of steam.

System of Fe–C–Si

The experiments refining the system of Fe–C–Si by the gaseous mixture of Ar and H_2O in the MgO crucible were conducted by Kawai et al.[7] under various experimental conditions. Similar experiments conducted in a gaseous mixture of Ar and CO_2 in MgO crucible were reported by Niiri et al.[9] For these cases mentioned above, Eq. (14) can be expressed by Eq. (14b), and Eq. (15) can be given by Eqs. (15b) and (15a).

$$\int_0^\theta B \, d\theta = (c_O - c_{i,O}) + (M_O/M_C)(c_{i,C} - c_C)$$

$$+ 2(M_O/M_{Si})(c_{i,Si} - c_{Si}) \quad . \quad . \quad . \quad (14b)$$

$$c_O \cdot c_C = p_{CO} \cdot \exp\{2\cdot303(-1\,160/T - 2\cdot003)\}$$

$$/(c_{i,C} \times 10^2)^2 \quad . \quad . \quad . \quad (15b)[8]$$

The value of a_{SiO_2} has been assumed to be equal to 1 as with the case of Fe–Si system. Further, $p_{CO} = 0\cdot1$ atm has been adopted for the case of the experiments conducted by Kawai et al. where the rate of decarburization was comparatively slow, and $p_{CO} = 0\cdot5$ atm for the case of the experiments by Niiri et al.[9] where the rate of decarburization was comparatively fast. Considering the rate

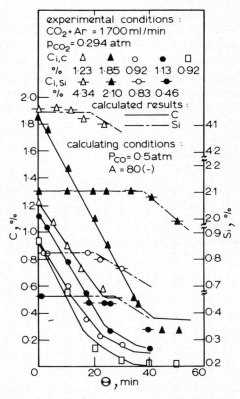

5   *Comparison of calculated results with data observed by Niiri et al.[9] above the concentrations of carbon and silicon in Fe–C–Si alloys at 1 600°C*

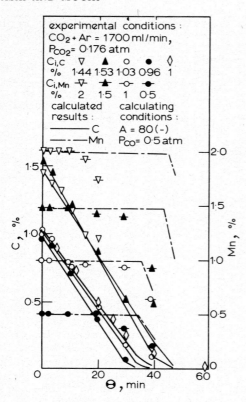

experimental conditions :
$CO_2 + Ar = 1700$ ml/min,
$P_{CO_2} = 0.176$ atm

$C_{i,C}$	$\triangledown$	$\blacktriangle$	$\circ$	$\bullet$	$\diamondsuit$
%	1·44	1·53	1·03	0·96	1
$C_{i,Mn}$	$\triangledown\!\!-$	$\blacktriangle\!\!-$	$-\circ-$	$-\bullet-$	
%	2	1·5	1	0·5	

calculated   calculating
results :   conditions :
———— C   A = 80 (-)
—·—·— Mn $p_{CO} = 0.5$ atm

6   *Comparison of calculated results with data observed by Niiri et al.[9] above the concentrations of carbon and manganese in Fe–C–Mn alloys at 1 600°C*

of decarburization, the values of the partial pressure of CO, $p_{CO} = 0.5$ atm or 0·1 atm have been used for the other systems in this work.

The comparisons of the calculated results with the experimental data relevant to the concentration of carbon and silicon in Fe–C–Si system have been illustrated in Figs. 4 and 5, and the close agreement between them has been obtained in spite of the differences in the experimental conditions, such as the temperatures or the initial concentrations of molten steel adopted by each investigator.

System of Fe–C–Mn

The experiments refining the system of Fe–C–Mn by the gaseous mixture of Ar and CO_2 in the MgO crucible were conducted by Niiri et al.[9] under the various experimental conditions. For these experiments, Eq. (14) can be expressed by Eq. (14c) and Eq. (15) can be given by Eqs. (15c) and (15b).

$$\int_0^\theta B \, d\theta = (c_O - c_{i,O}) + (M_O/M_C)(c_{i,C} - c_C)$$

$$+ (M_O/M_{Mn})(c_{i,Mn} - c_{Mn}) \quad . \quad . \quad (14c)$$

$$c_O \cdot c_{Mn} = a_{MnO} \cdot \exp\{2·303(-15\,050/T + 6·81)\}$$

$$/(C_{i,C} \times 10^2)^2 \quad . \quad . \quad . \quad (15c)^8$$

Basing the phase diagram of manganese–oxygen–iron system, the value of the activity of MnO has been assumed as $a_{MnO} = 1$. The other data given in the experimental conditions have been also adopted in the calcula-

tions. Concerning the concentrations of carbon and manganese in Fe–C–Mn system, the comparisons of the calculated results with the experimental data have been shown in Fig. 6. Some differences between them may be seen in the case of the higher concentration of manganese and it may be guessed that such differences would be caused by the increase in the vapour pressure of manganese. For the case of the lower concentration of manganese, the close agreement between them can be seen in Fig. 6.

System of Fe–C–Cr

The experiments refining the system of Fe–C–Cr by the gaseous mixture of Ar and CO_2 in MgO crucible were conducted by Niiri et al.[9] under the various experimental conditions. For these experiments, Eq. (14) can be expressed by Eq. (14d) and Eq. (15) can be given by Eqs. (15d) and (15b).

$$\int_0^\theta B \, d\theta = (c_O - c_{i,O}) + (M_O/M_C)(c_{i,C} - c_C)$$

$$+ 2(M_O/M_{Cr})(c_{i,Cr} - c_{Cr}) \quad . \quad . \quad (14d)$$

$$c_O^2 \cdot c_{Cr} = [a_{FeCr_2O_4} \cdot \exp\{2·303(-54\,300/T$$

$$+ 23·44\}]^{\frac{1}{3}}/(C_{i,C} \times 10^2)^3 \quad . \quad . \quad (15d)^8$$

The value of the activity of $FeCr_2O_4$ has been assumed as $a_{FeCr_2O_4} = 1$. Numerical calculations have been made by using the same data as with the experimental conditions. Concerning the concentrations of carbon and chromium in Fe–C–Cr system, the comparison of the calculated results with the experimental data has been illustrated in Fig. 7. The transitional variations in the

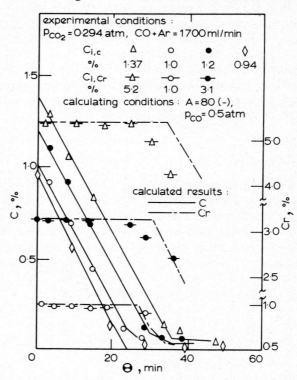

experimental conditions :
$P_{CO_2} = 0.294$ atm,   CO + Ar = 1700 ml/min

$C_{i,c}$	$\triangle$	$\circ$	$\bullet$	$\diamondsuit$
%	1·37	1·0	1·2	0·94
$C_{i,Cr}$	$-\triangle-$	$-\circ-$	$-\bullet-$	
%	5·2	1·0	3·1	

calculating conditions : A = 80 (-),
                          $p_{CO} = 0.5$ atm

calculated results :
———— C
—·—·— Cr

7   *Comparison of calculated results and data observed by Niiri et al.[9] above the concentrations of carbon and chromium in Fe–C–Cr alloys at 1 600°C*

concentrations of carbon and chromium have been in good agreement between both results.

System of Fe–Si–Mn

The experiments refining the system of Fe–Si–Mn by the gaseous mixture of Ar and CO_2 in MgO crucible were conducted by Kawai et al.[7] under the various experimental conditions. For these experiments Eq. (14) can be expressed by Eq. (14e) and Eq. (15) can be given by Eqs. (15a) and (15c).

$$\int_0^\theta B\,d\theta = (c_O - c_{i,O}) + 2(M_O/M_{Si})(c_{i,Si} - c_{Si})$$
$$+ (M_O/M_{Mn})(c_{i,Mn} - c_{Mn}) \qquad . \qquad . \quad (14e)$$

The values of a_{SiO_2} and a_{MnO} have been expressed as a function of the concentrations of manganese and silicon in molten steel on the basis of the figure obtained by Richardson et al.[11] Figure 8 represents the comparison between the calculated results and the observed data.

QUANTITATIVE ANALYSIS ON THE DIFFERENCES IN THE PROCEEDING SEQUENCE OF OXIDATIONS

As is well known in the refining processes in LD converter and crucible, the differences in the proceeding sequence between the oxidations of silicon and manganese and the decarburization can be observed, and the considerations regarding such differences have been expressed qualitatively earlier in this paper. In order to explain quan-

titatively the differences, the effects of the temperature of molten steel on the transitional variations of the concentration of carbon and silicon have been evaluated from Eqs. (14b), (15a), and (15b) while keeping the other conditions except the temperature constant, and the calculated results are shown in Fig. 9. Supposing the refining progress in crucible, the results calculated under the conditions keeping the temperature at 1 600°C during the blowing time is illustrated by a dot-and-dash line in Fig. 9. Further, supposing the blowing process in LD converter, the results calculated under the conditions increasing the temperature from 1 200 to 1 600°C linearly are illustrated by a solid line in Fig. 9.

In the case represented by the dot-and-dash line, first of all the decarburization takes place and then the oxidation of silicon proceeds in the region of the low concentration of carbon. On the other hand, in the case represented by the solid line, first of all the oxidation of silicon takes place and then the decarburization occurs. Characteristics of each 1st, 2nd, and 3rd period of the decarburization pattern in LD converter are shown clearly by the solid line.

CONCLUSION

Concerning the oxidation of molten steel taking place in the various refining processes, a simplified mathematical model has been developed by taking account of the two types of driving forces. The experimental results obtained by the other investigators for the various oxidations have been quantitatively explained on the basis of the model proposed in this paper. The effects of the feed rate of oxygen and the degree of mixing of molten steel on the transitional variations of process variables have been investigated theoretically. It is well known from the comparison between the results observed in LD converter and those in crucible that there are differences in the proceeding sequence of the oxidation of silicon and the decarburization. Such differences and also the differences of oxygen level existing among the experimental results obtained by the other investigators

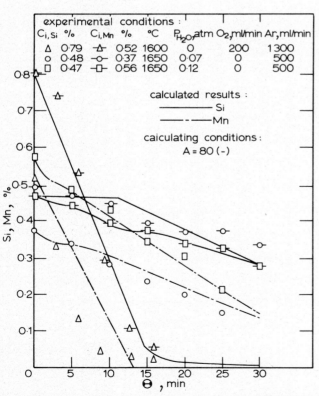

8   *Comparison of calculated results and data observed by Kawai et al.[7] above the concentrations of silicon and manganese in Fe–Si–Mn alloys at 1 600 and 1 650°C*

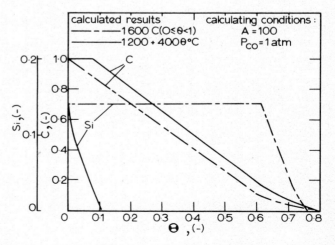

9   *Effects of the temperature of molten steel on the transitional variations of the concentrations of carbon and silicon*

in open hearth, LD converter and crucible have been explained theoretically. Further, it may be considered that the model can be applied extensively to the analysis concerning the other reactions than oxidation.

REFERENCES

1 S. TAMAMOTO *et al.*: *Tetsu-to-Hagané*, 1968, **54**, (2), 381
2 K. MORI AND H. NOMURA: *Tetsu-to-Hagané*, 1970, **55**, (11), S460
3 F. I. BASHLIY *et al.*: *Izvest. VUZ Cher. Met.*, 1970, **3**, 32
4 M. P. KVITKO *et al.*: *Stal in English*, 1970, **6**, 428
5 S. WATANABE *et al.*: *Tetsu-to-Hagané*, 1971, **57**, (4), S259
6 H. NEMOTO *et al.*: *Nippon Kokan Techn. Rep.*, 1970, **50**, 21
7 Y. KAWAI AND K. MORI: *Tetsu-to-Hagané*, 1970, **56**, (6), 695
8 Japan SPS 19th Comm., 1968, 40, 2, 73, 112, Nikkan Kogyo Shinbun
9 Y. NIIRI *et al.*: *Tetsu-to-Hagané*, 1969, **55**, (6), 437
10 J. F. ELLIOTT *et al.*: 'Thermochemistry for steelmaking', 466, 1963, Addison-Wesley Pub. Co.
11 K. P. ABRAHAM *et al.*: *JISI*, 1960, **194**, (9), 82

Discussion on chapter three:
Oxygen steelmaking

CHAIRMAN: C. OVER (BSC, GENERAL STEELS DIVISION, TEESSIDE)

The following papers were discussed: *Dynamic model of the BOS process* by R. Weeks; *Dynamic mathematical model of the LD steelmaking process* by J. R. Middleton and R. Rolls.

Prof. J. Szekely (State University of New York at Buffalo, USA) said that in the mass-transfer coefficients that Mr Weeks had used, he had considered that the boundary layer or stagnant layer thickness was the same for each component, so that the transfer coefficients for individual components would be in the linear ratio of the diffusion coefficients. This was to some degree contrary to the mass-transfer theory and Prof. Szekely asked Mr Weeks for his comments. Regarding the emulsion factor which was used, Prof. Szekely asked if Mr Weeks could give some idea as to its numerical magnitude. It is known that in BOS practice the presence of the emulsion produces a fantastic increase in the interfacial area, so that an error in the emulsion factor could lead to considerable errors in the results of the calculations. Further, if the emulsion factor was related to CO evolution overall, there may perhaps be only poor indication of possible imbalances or slopping in operation. Again Mr Weeks' comments would be helpful. Finally, with regard to scrap melting kinetics, Prof. Szekely said that he was interested to read in the paper acknowledgment of some more recent ideas on scrap melting, namely, that carbon diffusion might play an important role. Therefore, if scrap melting kinetics were to be considered one would have to take into account the temperature and the carbon trajectories during the blow. However, was it not true that in the paper these factors were not considered in assessing scrap melting rates in the first instance?

Mr Weeks in reply said that the rate constant defined interaction area, diffusion coefficient, and boundary layer thickness, and was an initial approximation and that both the interaction area and the boundary layer thickness were in direct proportion to the diffusion coefficients. With regard to Prof. Szekely's comment on the significance of the numerical value of the emulsion factor, Mr Weeks agreed, but he had stressed throughout the paper that it was not adequately represented. Mr Weeks also said that the recent ideas on scrap melting had not been incorporated in the paper, mainly because at the plant they had no idea of the carbon content, size of the scrap, and the temperature at which various components melted. Because of the lack of definite plant data an approximation had been used which gave good results.

Prof. F. Oeters (Technical University of Berlin) questioned the values of the velocity constants. The ratio of velocity constants for sulphur and phosphorus removal was 200:1, sulphur to phosphorus. Mr Weeks had also said that this ratio would not be observed throughout the blow and Prof. Oeters wondered if he could explain the discrepancy. Prof. Oeters said that in the BOS process, when one blew with lime, it took some time to form a sufficiently basic slag to absorb the phosphorus. Thus, in the first part of the blow the phosphorus was not removed because the slag was too acid and could not absorb it. Only towards the end of the process, when the slag was sufficiently basic, was there a removal of phosphorus. Prof. Oeters therefore asked if the explanation of the ratio was due to the use of a mean value of velocity constant throughout the process.

Mr Weeks agreed that constant values had been used throughout the blow and he observed that there was insufficient data to indicate the variation of the rate constants throughout the blow.

Dr J. R. Leigh (BSC, Corporate Engineering Laboratory) said that he imagined that Mr Weeks was interested in looking at a plant which had not yet been built and where the fitting of the rate constants could not be done in advance. He therefore asked how works *A* would look if one used the rate constants determined at works *B* and *vice versa*. Would a useful result be obtained by using some sort of average rate constant and could Mr Weeks say whether the differences in rate constants were due to inherent differences between plants or whether they were affected by the numerical method of solution which was used? **Mr Weeks** replied that he had tried to use several versions of the rate constants for different vessels to reproduce the operating data of other vessels. In all cases the results were poor and so he concluded that the rate constants may well be works dependent. Certainly, in predicting the characteristics of a new plant, one would be theorizing.

Dr P. J. Kreyger (Hoogovens, IJmuiden) referred to Figs. 2, 3, and 4 of Mr Weeks' paper, where the decarburization rate was plotted as a function of blowing time and 'predicted' and 'actual' values were compared. In Figs. 3 and 4 the actual line was smoother than the predicted one and since the decarburization rate was strictly connected to the removal of oxygen as carbon oxides from the vessel, it represented the oxygen stream. On the same figures were plotted the iron oxide contents of the slags, showing a pronounced peak at about one quarter of the blow. Dr Kreyger said that the two things were related. When the decarburization rate is smooth there is a smooth change in the iron oxide content in the slag. He asked if Mr Weeks had experimental values of the iron oxide content in the slag. From the basis of measurements made at Hoogovens, Dr Kreyger would prefer to have a decarburization rate similar to the 'actual' one in the graphs since a reasonably flat decarburization rate during the boil leads to only minor changes in the iron oxide content of the slag.

In reply, **Mr Weeks** said that he had little information regarding what happened during the blow. The problem of instability had already been mentioned at the conference and he had found his model to be extremely sensitive, particularly during the first minute of the blow, especially with regard to carburization and FeO values. The peak in the FeO values in the figures might be due to misallocation of oxide between slag and metal.

In opening the discussion on the paper by J. R. Middleton and R. Rolls, **Dr Kreyger** said that Dr Middleton had described end-point control using the dynamic model in terms of a standard deviation of 10° in temperature and of 0·03% of carbon. However, Dr Kreyger had doubts about the precision in carbon control. How was the accuracy related to the initial carbon content of the hot metal? He suggested that the accuracy of the initial carbon concentration must be appreciably greater than the accuracy of the end point.

In reply **Dr Middleton** said that the initial carbon content was one of the important inputs to the model.

In that part of the paper dealing with the initial appraisal of sensitivity analysis, it was noted that disturbances of up to 10% in the initial conditions led to a discrepancy which remained at about 10% throughout the blow. In other words, if one started with perhaps a 0·35% discrepancy at the start of the blow, by the end of the blow the model had reduced that discrepancy, supposing a 0·2% carbon end point, to the order of 0·02%. Dr Middleton emphasized that the tests were done on a 'post mortem' basis, and that the samples were analysed very carefully, so the standard of chemical analysis might perhaps have been higher than would have been obtained in normal day-to-day practice.

Mr A. E. Pengelly (BSC, General Steels Division) commented upon the discussion which had followed Mr Weeks' and Dr Middleton's papers. While the former was concerned at the inadequacy of data, the latter seemed quite confident that detailed results from a modest number of blows was sufficient for his purpose. Mr Pengelly suggested that good data could be obtained, albeit with difficulty, but it was essential that the range of conditions explored was wide enough to cover the large field of variation which was inevitable even in the single general form of steelmaking practice. Dr Middleton had chosen what was probably the most consistent and tightly scheduled LD plant in the UK for his work and, with such a modest number of blows, it seemed unlikely that the spread of data would have been adequately wide. Illustrating his point, Mr Pengelly showed two decarburization curves (Fig. 1) for two quite typical blows at the plant where Dr Middleton had

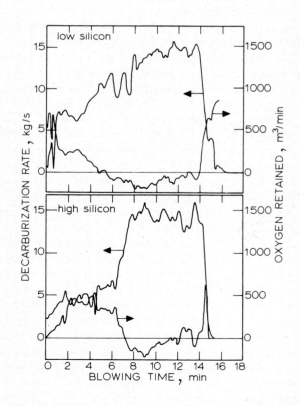

1 Decarburization curves for two typical blows at Normanby Park Works

worked. With low-silicon iron, the shape of the decarburization curve was radically different from that with high-silicon iron, although virtually all other variables in the process were similar. There was nothing exhaustive about this simple example, but it did serve to illustrate one of the many differences which occurred in the character of typical LD blows. Before reasonable confidence could be placed in the predictive ability of a model, it would be essential to explore at least a representative range of such things. In addition to the decarburization rate curves given in the figure, a parameter called 'oxygen retained' was given. This is the difference between the oxygen lancing rate and the oxygen content of the waste gases which originally came from the lance. During slag making, this had a positive value but it was interesting to note that it could be considerably negative half way through the heat. The implication of this was that oxygen was in some way being released from the slag, probably in the form of CO. This was obviously likely to be related to lance operating practice and was also a major variable which must be accounted for in a model.

Dr Middleton took up Mr Pengelly's point on consistency of operation at Normanby Park and said that he accepted that the operation by and large was probably very consistent, but during the initial development work on the model the works was operating an LDAC practice and at that stage the model only simulated the second part of the blow. The works then went over to the use of foreign ore and a straight LD practice, and the model, without changing any of the parameter values or other alterations, gave surprisingly good results. There was a further development when the works increased their blowing rates substantially and the model without modification gave respectable results again. Thus, although there was a very consistent practice at Normanby Park Works, the model had been successfully tested in a variety of operating conditions.

Mr N. A. Townsend (BSC, Corporate Engineering Laboratories) said that Dr Middleton had pointed out, quite rightly, the difficulty of accounting for scrap-melting mechanisms when scrap was very variable and in practice this was generally the case. Dr Middleton had implied, though, that if there were a regular, consistent form of scrap, it could be possible by some means or other to account for melting analytically. Was this the case? Second, had Dr Middleton simulated the effect of different types of consistent batches of scrap? **Dr Middleton** replied that the scrap-melting mechanisms in a model of the kind he had presented, while an important part of the model, which must be described with a reasonable accuracy because it accounted for a considerable drop in the carbon content by dilution, did not introduce a large error so long as the scrap was being melted in a time scale that was reasonably consistent with that which obtained in reality. Dr Middleton had not simulated the effects of different types of scrap.

Dr P. J. Kreyger disagreed with Mr Weeks about the role of the scrap-melting mechanism and presented the following contribution:

DYNAMIC MODEL OF THE DISSOLUTION OF SCRAP IN THE BOS PROCESS

B. Snoeijer, H. W. den Hartog, and P. J. Kreyger
(Hoogovens, IJmuiden BV)

Undissolved heavy scrap at BOF turndown is a disadvantage since it disturbs the end-point control, lowers the steel output, and creates a hazard for operating personnel in front of the tilted converter. The rate of dissolution of the scrap depends heavily on the distribution of the scrap size and is one of the major variables determining the temperature evolution of the liquid phase. Since a number of metallurgical reactions occur in the liquid phase and are influenced considerably by temperature, scrap dissolution rate has a direct effect on the steelmaking process and BOF end-point control.[1]

Scrap-dissolution rates have been studied making use of a computer to solve the theoretical equations of the physico-chemical reactions and heat transfer in a BOF during the blow.[2] At Hoogovens a mathematical model has been made in which the chemistry of the steelmaking process as a function of time is described by relationships determined experimentally from bath sampling and measurement of the off-gas composition during the blow. Scrap dissolution is incorporated by taking due account of the non-steady-state heat transfer to the scrap metal and carbon transfer across the scrap/liquid metal interface.[3,4] The special feature of this model is its capacity to calculate the simultaneous dissolution of scrap of different sizes. Two fractions of scrap differing in thickness are totally exposed to the bath, while a third fraction, the heavy scrap, is only exposed on one side. This represents scrap which remains fixed on the bottom of the converter during the blow and is often observed at first turndown.

RESULTS

In Figs. 2–7 computed results are presented pertaining to blow M9222 of the BOF no. 2 at Hoogovens. At first turndown undissolved scrap was observed. These results demonstrate the potential of the present model. The converter is charged with 223·4 tons of hot metal, 35 tons of heavy scrap from the slabbing mill (this scrap is taken to be 20 cm in thickness), and 59 tons of light scrap (for the computation a thickness of 0·5 cm is assumed). Figure 2 shows the size of totally exposed scrap as a function of the blown oxygen quantity for the cases where:

(i) the total amount of the charged scrap is heavy
(ii) 35 tons of heavy scrap and 59 tons of light scrap are charged.

The calculation is carried out with a value of heat transfer coefficient between bath and scrap $\alpha = 2\ \text{W/cm}^2$ °C. It is shown that for the case where only heavy scrap is present, the scrap is dissolved in a time appreciably shorter than for the case where heavy scrap is combined with light scrap.

The temperature for conditions similar to those of Fig. 2 is given in Fig. 3. The presence of light scrap

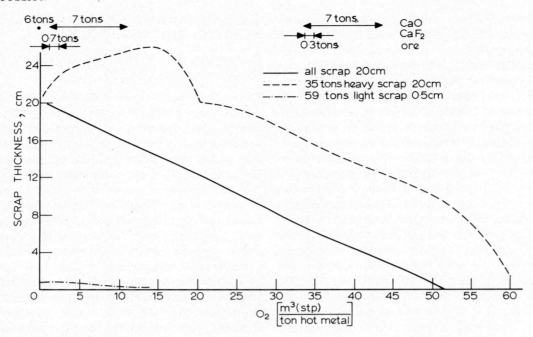

2   Dissolution of scrap during blowing

results in a temperature of the liquid metal which is lower on the average during the blow. This phenomenon is also of importance for the total heat balance of the charge since the heat content of carbon oxides leaving the bath is related to the liquid phase temperature. Hence, the heat losses from the bath will depend on the scrap size.

Figure 4 demonstrates the delay in the dissolution of scrap which is only exposed on one side to the metal in the bath. From this result it is concluded that scrap

sticking to the vessel bottom should be avoided. Observations have shown that the possibility of undissolved scrap at the end of the blow is greatly reduced by blowing at low lance positions. Presumably it is the higher degree of bath turbulence at a small distance between bath and lance which prevents scrap from sticking to the vessel wall. Bath turbulence will also increase the transfer rates between the solid and liquid phase of the metal.

In Fig. 5 the time for melting as a fraction of the blowing time is plotted against the heat transfer coefficient, α.

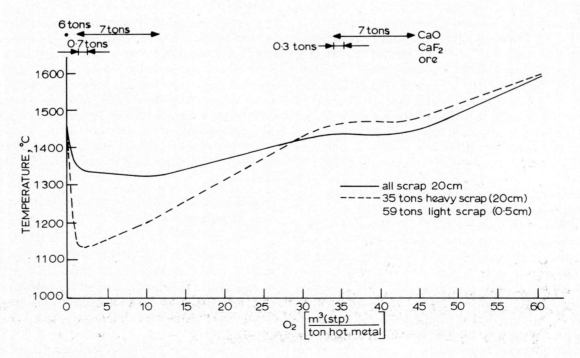

3   Temperature of molten metal during blowing

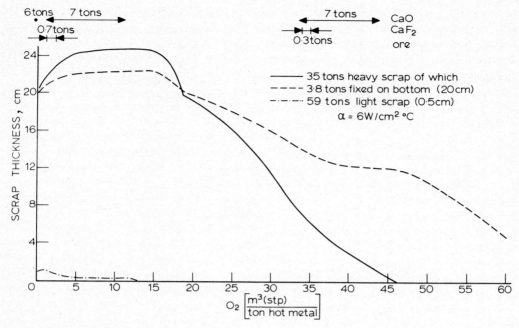

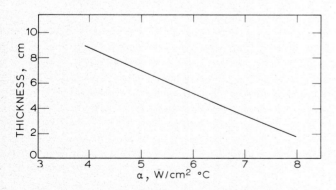

4   *Dissolution of scrap during blowing*

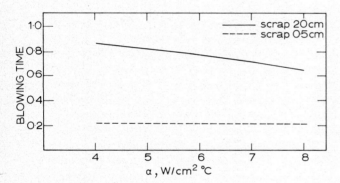

5   *Moment of complete dissolution of scrap; 3·8 tons heavy scrap on bottom*

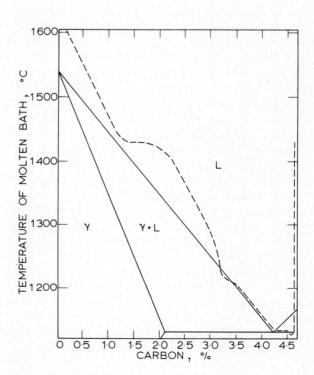

6   *Thickness of scrap stuck on the bottom at the end of blowing*

The time of melting of both heavy and light scrap exposed on all sides is not very dependent on values of α between 4–8 W/cm² °C. The dependency of the fraction of undissolved scrap exposed on one side only on the heat transfer coefficient is also of importance (Fig. 6) as it gives the possibility of estimating the numerical value of α on the basis of the number and size of undissolved pieces of heavy scrap. Finally, in Fig. 7 the temperature

is plotted *v.* carbon contents of the liquid metal together with the carbon–iron phase diagram.

FUTURE APPLICATION

This dynamic model of scrap dissolution in the BOF process will be used for further optimization of scrap charging. Another interesting application of the model is in conjunction with an off-gas analysis system. Process control on the basis of gas analysis involves a rapidly repeated calculation of mass and heat balances by an

7   *Temperature of bath* v. *carbon concentration*

on-line computer. The present mathematical model makes it possible to include the effects of scrap size when calculating the required amount of oxygen and cooling materials for termination of the blow at the required end-point conditions.

REFERENCES

1 V. P. BONDARENKO AND S. G. AFANAS'EV: *Steel in the USSR*, 1971, **1**, 785–8
2 S. ASAI AND J. MUCHI: *Trans. ISI Japan*, 1971, **11**, 107–15
3 K. MORI AND H. NOMURA: *Tetsu-to-Hagané*, 1964, **55**, 347–54 (translation BISIT 8002, July 1970)
4 Y. K. CHUANG AND J. SZEKELY: *Int. J. Heat Mass Transfer*, 1971, **14**, 1 285–94

chapter 4: teeming and solidification

Heat losses from liquid steel in the ladle and in the tundish of a continuous-casting installation

R. Alberny and A. Leclercq

Depending on the installations and the methods of operation the temperature history of liquid steel in continuous casting can follow many different paths. It depends particularly, on the shape and thermal characteristics of the vessels (i.e. dimensions, materials) and on the operational practices used (i.e. cycle of the ladle and the tundish). The model presented here uses an iterative procedure to determine the temperature variations at the exit of the different vessels. The heat losses through the refractory, the slag or the topping powders, have been derived from the temperature history of these materials and calculated using a finite difference method. To these losses have been added the radiation losses of the exposed surfaces. A thermal balance allows the calculation at any time of the average temperature of the liquid steel in the ladle and the tundish. In the ladle the steel cooled at the walls moves by natural convection to the bottom. So a thermal layer formation is set up and the steel leaving the ladle has a lower than average temperature. The model takes this effect into account by introducing an empirically determined difference between the exit temperature and the mean ladle temperature. Treatment of existing installations shows that this model is in good agreement with plant data. Considering the different items of heat lost, the model stresses the influence of various factors, e.g. preheating of the ladle and tundish, type of refractory, tapping time, insulation of the surface of the steel in the ladle, the tundish, and argon stirring in the ladle. It helps in obtaining a greater constancy of the temperature in the tundish.

SYMBOLS

c	heat capacity (J/kgK)
h	heat exchange coefficient between liquid steel and solid steel at the solidification front (W/m^2K)
k	thermal conductivity (W/mK)
L	heat of solidification (J/kg)
m	mass of liquid steel kept in the considered vessel (kg) or (t)
ϕ	heat lost by the metal (W)
q	heat gain of the metal from the exterior (W)
$\mathring{m}$	quantity of steel entering or leaving the vessel (kg/s) or (t/h)
t	time (s) or (min)
T	temperature (K)
ΔT	temperature difference between the liquid steel and its solidification point (K)
ΔT_s	difference between the average ladle temperature and the ladle-exit temperature (K)
x	distance (m)
α	emissivity of liquid steel
ξ	position of the solidification front (m)
ρ	density (kg/m^3)
σ	Stefan Boltzman constant $(W/(m^2K^4))$
ϕ	heat flux density (W/m^2)
∇^2	Laplace operator
index 1	represents the upper surface of the vessel
index 2	represents the lateral surface of the vessel
$\bar{x}$	means the average of x
index a	refers to steel
index i	refers to refractory of the vessel
index r	refers to tundish
index e	refers to steel entering the vessel
index s	refers to steel leaving the vessel

In order to obtain good metallurgical results with a continuous-casting machine, the steelmaker has to

The authors are with Institut de Recherches de la Sidérurgie Française

control carefully the heat losses of the liquid steel going through the ladle and the tundish. Usually there is no heating system provided, so that correction during casting of the temperature deviations of the metal in the tundish is not possible. The effect of these losses and their control is relatively well known for ingot teeming. Hlinka[1] and Szekely[2] have treated the application to the case of continuous casting. These authors have shown that stratification in the ladle is an important factor and they have presented some means to control the effects. Sometimes stratification is not of much importance. The cycle of the equipment, the choice of the refractories or their preheat can strongly influence the behaviour of the observed variations. The model now presented has as its object to take into account all parameters relevant in the operation of the continuous-casting machine. It allows the calculation of the heat losses and the temperature of the liquid steel in the tundish as a function of time for any continuous-casting machine. In the first part of the paper a discussion on the role of the steel temperature in the tundish will be presented. In a second part the main hypotheses and the calculation method adopted will be explained. In the third part some applications of the model will be presented.

IMPORTANCE OF THE TEMPERATURE CONTROL IN THE TUNDISH OF A CONTINUOUS-CASTING MACHINE

In Fig. 1 we have recorded the temperature variations observed in the tundish of a conticaster for billets fed from an 18 ton ladle. This represents a specific example of an experimental curve. The temperature, which is rather low initially, rises during the first ten minutes and then falls again. The temperature varies over a region of 40°C during a cast. Adding the variations between casts, deviations over a range of 60°C can arise if no precautions are taken. The difference between the temperature of the liquid metal and the temperature of the start of solidification (depending on the composition of steel) is called superheat. The variations of this parameter in the tundish of a conticaster are very important (the superheat varies between 20° and 60°C in our case) and we shall see what the consequences are. The solidification speed of the skin formed in the mould depends on the superheat of the steel.

Supposing that the steel has a superheat of ΔT, that the heat transfer coefficient between liquid and solid steel is h, that the solidification is plane and one-dimensional, it is possible to calculate theoretically the displacement velocity of the solidification front $d\xi/dt$. As shown in Appendix 1, using the notation of Fig. 2, the solidification speed can be given by the following relation:

$$\rho_a L \frac{d\xi}{dT} = K_a \left(\frac{\partial T}{\partial x} \right)_{x=\xi} - h\,\Delta T . \qquad \qquad (1)$$

The solidification of the outer skin, therefore, is retarded by the existence of superheat. Taking into account the order of magnitude of the parameters, this phenomenon can be very important, especially when at certain points along the mould the jet touches the wall, e.g. an eccentric jet. Experimentally it has been shown by Muttitt[3] that a relation exists between the degree of superheat and the number of break-outs underneath the mould. The superheat should, therefore, be kept at a low level.

If the superheat is too low, often blocking of the teeming nozzles may occur. In a very complete study Duderstadt[4] has shown the influence of many operating parameters on blocking and the role of the teeming temperature seems to control quantitatively its occurrence. Other incidents to be avoided are the formation of a crust on the upper surface in the mould at places where the convective currents do not sufficiently stir the metal. The product quality is also affected by the superheat. When it has been too low, the shape of the teeming jet is uncertain, which results in increased oxidation from the atmosphere. The behaviour of the physical properties of steel in the neighbourhood of its fusion points

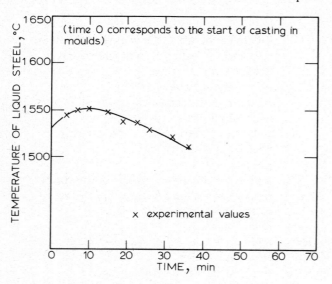

Experimental curve for the particular case of an 18 t ladle

1   Variation of the temperature of liquid steel in the tundish of a continuous-casting machine

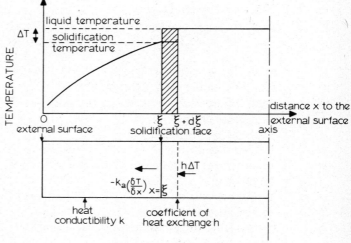

2   Propagation of the solidification front in a slice of a billet and profile of the corresponding temperature

limits the escape of inclusions. When the superheat is too high the solidification is columnar over a great part of the product, which increases the formation of internal cracks and the axial porosity.[5] These respective effects of superheat on the operation of continuous casting and its product quality makes limitation of the range of teeming temperatures desirable. Therefore, it is necessary to know how to influence these variations.

CALCULATION OF THE TEMPERATURE VARIATIONS OF LIQUID METAL IN THE TUNDISH

For the two vessels that play a part in the problem, the ladle and the tundish, the heat losses are of two types. These are losses by conduction in the refractories and losses by conduction and radiation at the upper surface, eventually protected by a slag, an insulating powder, or a lid (*see* Fig. 3). The heat losses by conduction to the refractories have been calculated analytically for a simple case.[6] The solution shows a decrease of the heat flux inversely proportional to the square root of time. The heat lost by the metal for this simple case of a semi-infinite, un-preheated, refractory wall is given in Fig. 4. This curve represents the results for refractory sand. For other refractories the results will have to be multiplied by the factor $(\sqrt{k_i \rho_i c_i})$. The approximate multiplication coefficients for some materials are given in Table 1.

TABLE 1 Physical coefficients for several refractory materials used for ladles

Material	Refractory sand	Fireclay	Mullite brick
Thermal conductivity, k_i W/(mK)	0·328	0·675	1·54
Density, ρ_i kg/m³	$1·5 . 10^3$	$2 . 10^3$	$2·3 . 10^3$
Specific heat, c_i J/(kgK)	$0·836 . 10^3$	$1·34 . 10^3$	$0·96 . 10^3$
$k_i \rho_i c_i$	$0·41 . 10^6$	$1·81 . 10^6$	$3·4 . 10^6$
$\sqrt{k_i \rho_i c_i}$ W s$^{\frac{1}{2}}$/(m²K)	$0·64 . 10^3$	$1·35 . 10^3$	$1·85 . 10^3$

We notice in Table 1 that the heat losses by conduction in mullite bricks are three times as much as those in sand. The effect of preheat in the ladle and the presence of an insulating layer behind the worklayer can be obtained by using a numerical method. The temperature distribution in the refractory can be determined for any time by integrating the general equation:

$$\frac{k_i}{\rho_i c_i} \nabla^2 T = \frac{\partial T}{\partial t} \quad . \quad . \quad . \quad . \quad . \quad (2)$$

The finite difference method permits an integration of this equation and so we can determine the amount of heat that enters the refractory as a function of time. We shall assume, for simplicity, that the same time origin can be taken for the calculation of the heat flux for the whole of the refractory of a vessel. Owing to lack of data to the contrary, we shall assume the physical properties of the materials do not vary with temperature. The heat losses from the upper surface and by the teeming jets are of a different nature for the respective periods of

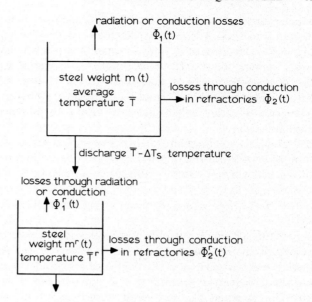

3 *Schematic representation of the losses of the system ladle–tundish*

time or for the different installations. For the teeming jets or for a free surface of steel there is a direct radiation to the surroundings that are always at ambient temperature. For a steel temperature of 1 600°C and for an emissivity of liquid steel of 0·4 the heat losses per unit surface are

$$\phi_1(t) = \alpha\sigma[T_a^4 - T_0^4]$$

where

T_a is the steel surface temperature
T_0 is the ambient temperature
$\phi_1(t) \simeq \alpha\sigma T_a^4 = 284 \text{ kW/m}^2$.

The metal tapped in the ladle can be covered by a slag tapped from the furnace.[7] The liquid slag solidifies downwards from the upper surface, which loses heat by convection and radiation.[8] The heat losses of the steel in contact with the slag are thus governed by the conduction in the liquid steel, the solidification of the slag and the conduction within the cooling slag. The complete

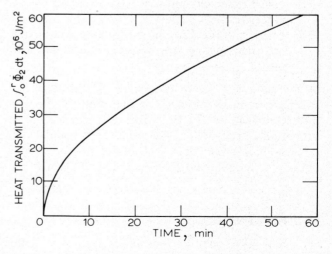

4 *Heat transferred by conduction to a refractory sand not preheated*

calculation of these losses can be made using a finite difference method. We assume that the emissivity of the slag is 0·8. An insulating slag is sometimes put on the upper surface. This suffers a thermal shock similar to that of the refractories. A lid placed on the tundish or the ladle also limits the heat losses.[9] The heat exchange takes place by radiation between two surfaces of different temperatures.

To calculate the temperature history of the liquid metal, we must now write the thermal balance of the different vessels. The general equation of such a balance is:

$$c_a \frac{d}{dt}(m\overline{T}) = \dot{m}_e c_a T_e - \dot{m}_s c_a T_s + q(t) - \phi_1(t) - \phi_2(t) \quad (3)$$

Depending on which vessel is considered and at which moment of the cycle $\dot{m}_e$ or $\dot{m}_s$ can be equal to zero. In the tundish it is assumed that the degree of stirring is such that the temperature is uniform. The exit-steel temperature will be equal to the average temperature in the tundish, ($T_s^r = \overline{T}^r$).

Ladle experiments by Irsid[10] have shown that a heterogeneity exists in the temperatures. The steel cools along the walls and runs to the bottom, and hot steel moves to the top under the slag layer. Dumont-Fillon[10] and Genkin[11] have found differences from 40° to 100°C. Depending on teeming practice the first steel teemed can have a temperature very different from the average. To include this phenomenon mathematically, a complex study of the natural convection and orifice withdrawal currents in the ladle is necessary. Szekely and Chen[2] have presented the foundations for such a study. Our model is based on experimental data and introduces a difference ΔT_s between the exit-steel temperature and the average temperature in the ladle at the moment considered. We let this difference decrease linearly from its initial value ΔT_{so} to 0°C at the end of the cast. In summarizing this, we have established a calculation method for determining the temperature variations in the tundish of a continuous-casting installation. The necessary data for running the model are:

(i) the geometrical characteristics of the different vessels and the physical characteristics of the materials used

(ii) the cycle of the different pieces of apparatus (preheat time, casting time, waiting time in the ladle), etc.

Of the data less easily obtainable, is the degree of stratification in the ladle; consideration of the convection currents in the ladle and tests can lead to an estimation of this factor. The other experimental data are the values of the emissivities of the radiating bodies and of the thermal conductivities of the refractories.

MODEL APPLIED

For using this model for continuous casting we define first the cycle of the different vessels, i.e. ladle and tundish. This cycle is given in Fig. 5. Here we see the schedule

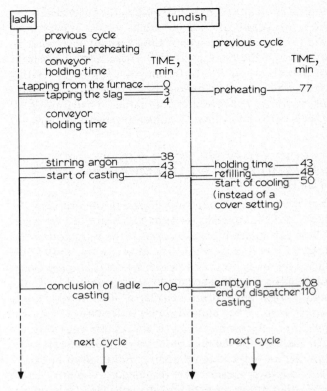

5   *Schedule of the ladle and tundish in continuous casting*

of the main operations and the instants when they affect the heat losses and the temperature evolution in the tundish. In this way, the model can be applied in several particular cases. We present two examples.

First example

We have recorded in Fig. 6 and Fig. 7 the case of a ladle of 18 t capacity, which is preheated for 1 h to a surface temperature of 1 000°C, and filled in 3 min. This ladle is transferred in 15 min to the conticaster and placed over

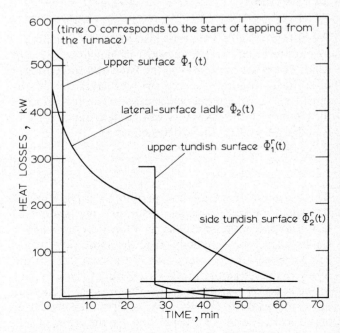

6   *Heat losses calculated for the system ladle–tundish*

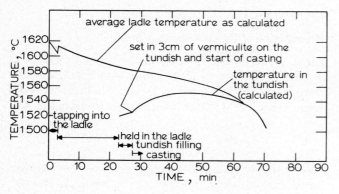

18 t ladle preheated for 1 h to 1 000°C

7 *Calculation of the temperature evolution in the tundish of a continuous-casting machine*

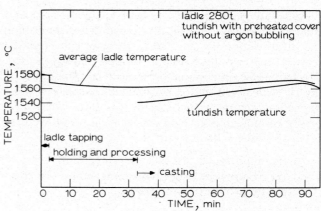

280 t ladle, not stirred

9 *Calculation of the temperature evolution in the tundish of a continuous-casting machine*

a similarly preheated tundish. Figure 6 represents the heat losses $\phi_1(t)$ by the upper surface of the ladle and $\phi_2(t)$ through the refractory, as well as the heat losses $\phi_1^r(t)$ and $\phi_2^r(t)$ of the tundish. The most important contributions are generally the radiation losses of the free surfaces. They decrease immediately when they are covered with an insulating slag. It appears important to put on this protection as soon as possible.

In Fig. 7 we have given the calculation results of the temperature in the ladle and the tundish as a function of time. It proves that our model confirms the initial rise of temperature at teeming followed by a decrease to the end. To avoid important temperature differences during the cast it is necessary to preheat the ladle carefully and to put a protective layer on the tundish as soon as possible. The model shows in Fig. 8 the case of a preheat for 2 h to a surface temperature of 1 200°C and installing the protective layer 2 min after starting to fill the tundish. The heat starts at a much higher temperature and the fall to the end does not show up until the ladle is empty. In this way, we observe a gain in temperature of 15°C after 10 min casting, and a gain of 20°C 10 min before the end for the case of a well preheated ladle with rapid protection of the steel surface in the tundish.

Second example

Figure 9 shows the evolution of the temperatures in a 280 t ladle with a non-preheated sand refractory, feeding a tundish of 12 t made in fireclay preheated for 2 h to 1200°C and covered with a lid. The cast is made on two slab lines in 1 h. A cast made without stirring results in a continuously rising temperature from start to finish. This can mean too low an initial temperature and too high a temperature near the end. Nemoto[12] mentions this case for a 90 t ladle resolving it by argon stirring before teeming. If we assume that it is also the function of argon stirring to suppress the stratification in the ladle, the model gives us (Fig. 10) a much more constant temperature in the tundish and a hotter start, that justifies the use of argon if only for this reason.

CONCLUSION

The temperature variations in the tundish of a continuous-casting machine have an effect on operation and product quality. To maintain the temperature as constant as possible, as little control is possible during casting, all must be done *a priori* to limit the reasons for variations. A mathematical model makes it possible

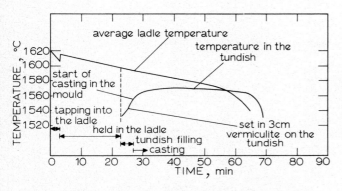

18 t ladle preheated for 2 h to 1 200°C. Protection of the surface in the tundish during filling.

8 *Calculation of the temperature evolution in the tundish of a continuous-casting machine*

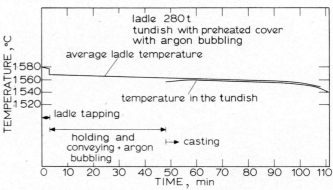

280 t ladle, argon stirred

10 *Calculation of the temperature evolution in the tundish of a continuous-casting machine*

to calculate the evolution of heat losses in ladle and tundish. Adapting empirically a parameter describing the stratification in the ladle, we can calculate the temperature evolution in the tundish during casting. The hypotheses introduced prove justified when comparing the calculated and experimental results. The most important factors and reasons for variations can theoretically be indicated for every specific case. For the case of an 18 t ladle is demonstrated:

(i) the importance of a well preheated ladle
(ii) the importance of applying an insulating layer on the tundish as soon as possible.

In the case of a large ladle the thermal losses are not sufficient to compensate for the effects of stratification. Argon stirring makes it possible to obtain a constant tundish temperature throughout the cast.

REFERENCES

1 J. W. HLINKA AND T. W. MILLER: *Iron Steel Eng.*, Aug., 1970, 123–33
2 J. SZEKELY AND J. H. CHEN: *Met. Trans.*, 1971, **2**, 1 189–92
3 F. C. MUTTITT: *Blast Furn. Steel Plant*, Mar., 1969, 215–24
4 G. C. DUDERSTADT *et al.*: *J. Met.*, April, 1968, 89–94 and *Translation CIT du CDS*, 1968, **9**, 1 905–18
5 R. CHOUVEL AND J. SELORON: La Documentation Métallurgique, 1956, **9**, 282–96
6 H. S. CARSLAW AND J. C. JAEGER: 'Conduction of heat in solids', 1959, Oxford University Press
7 J. SZEKELY AND R. G. LEE: *Trans. AIME*, 1968, **242**, 961–5
8 J. H. LUDLEY AND J. SZEKELY: *JISI*, 1966, **204**, 12–15
9 J. SZEKELY AND W. EVANS: *Trans. AIME*, 1969, **245**, 1 149–58
10 J. DUMONT-FILLON AND M. VIOLA: *Translation CIT du CDS*, 1968, **6**, 553–68
11 V. GENKIN AND O. A. SHANTAGIN: *Metallurg.*, 1959, **11**, 17
12 N. HIDETARO AND K. TAKAHO: *J. Met.*, Aug., 1969, 62–7

APPENDIX 1

Propagation of the solidification front

Let us make during the time dt the thermal balance of a volume element of unit section and a length of $d\xi$ along the x direction (*see* Fig. 2). The solidification of this volume element $d\xi$ leads to a change in enthalpy ΔH:

$$\Delta H = -\rho_a L \, d\xi$$

During the same time a certain amount of heat has been transferred to this volume element by the liquid through the surface indicated by its abscissa $\xi + d\xi$: assuming that a heat transfer coefficient h exists at this interface, this amount of heat is:

$$q_e = h \, \Delta T \, dt$$

A certain quantity of heat q_s has been taken from the volume element in the solid through the surface indicated by its abscissa ξ

$$q_s = K_a \left(\frac{\partial T}{\partial x} \right)_{x=\xi} dt$$

The thermal balance of the element runs:

$$\Delta H = q_e - q_s$$

or

$$\rho_a L \frac{d\xi}{dt} = K_a \left(\frac{dT}{\partial x} \right)_{x=\xi} - h \, \Delta T$$

Water model for the quantitative simulation of the heat and fluid flow in liquid-steel refractory systems

J. W. Hlinka

Mathematical proof supported by in-plant tests is given. This verifies that because of the unique relationship between their physical properties, hot water contained in acrylic plastic can be used to model liquid steel contained in refractory. To scale the heat flow, a mathematical description of a simplified system is written and this shows that only one dimensionless parameter needs to be satisfied. The parameter, termed a property ratio, is defined as the ratio of the volumetric specific heats of the liquid steel to solid refractory. The property ratio, which hot water and acrylic satisfy, together with the scaling of time (the Fourier number), temperature, and geometry define the simplified thermal model. A surprising outcome of this study, as is detailed in the paper, is that if the model is made to about one-third scale, then the model also satisfies the Froude, Grashof–Prandtl, Biot, Nusselt, Euler, and Peclet numbers. The Reynolds and Weber numbers require a 0·6 scale which is not far removed from one-third scale. Thus, the paper presents a unique model with which both the heat and fluid flow can be simultaneously simulated and quantitatively related to a steel system. Although the model was developed with a ladle-tundish-mould system in mind, as used in strand casting, it should be applicable to a variety of systems such as vacuum degassers, transfer ladles, sand moulds, runners, and the like.

SYMBOLS

A	area	m^2
γ	volume-expansion coefficient	1/deg K
c	specific heat	J/K kg
D	nozzle diameter	m
Fr	Froude number	—
Gr	Grashof number	—
g	gravitational constant	m/s^2
H	head of metal in the ladle or tundish	m
h	heat transfer coefficient	W/m^2K
k	thermal conductivity	W/m K
L	characteristic dimension	m
Nu	Nusselt number	—
Pe	Peclet number	—
Pr	Prandtl number	—
Q	volume flow rate	m^3/s
q	heat flow	J/s
q_F	heat flow scale factor	—
S_F	geometric scale factor	—
T	temperature	deg K
t	time	s
t_F	time scale factor	—
V	velocity	m/s
v	volume	m^3
x	space coordinate	m
α	thermal diffusivity	m^2/s
Δ	difference notation	—
θ	dimensionless temperature	—
θ_F	temperature scale factor	—
η	absolute viscosity	$N\,s/m^2$
ν	kinematic viscosity	m^2/s
ξ	dimensionless space	—
ρ	density	kg/m^3
τ	dimensionless time	—

The author is with Homer Research Laboratories, Bethlehem Steel Corporation, USA

Subscripts

a   ambient
i   initial temperature
m   in the model system
p   plexiglas, or in the plexiglas–water system
r   refractory, or in the refractory–steel system
s   steel, or in the steel–refractory system
w   water, or in the water–plexiglas system

In a joint research effort initiated by Bethlehem Steel in 1965, Inland, Republic, and Youngstown Steel Companies joined together with Bethlehem to operate a production-size pilot plant for the development of strand-casting technology. The objective of the five-year programme was primarily to produce high-quality aluminum-killed sheet-grade steels. In evaluating the many factors that were apparently contributing to the success of the programme, we observed that the temperature of the liquid steel in the tundish was essentially constant throughout most of a cast. This security of tundish temperature control enabled our people to operate at lower furnace-tap and tundish temperatures, a condition that means not only smooth operation but also uniformity of product quality. In contrast to our experience, other casters at that time were reporting that during a cast the tundish temperature would peak and that this peak was followed by a decay which followed the decay of the ladle temperature.

As a matter of fact, a mathematical analysis of the heat conduction within the ladle–tundish did predict that a peak and decay in the tundish temperature should be expected. The question asked was 'what conditions in our operating practice were conducive to our maintaining an essentially constant tundish temperature?' On reviewing the basic heat conduction equations (*see* Appendix), we noted that for the ladle–tundish system a single dimensionless ratio controlled the time–temperature–space relationship, i.e. the ratio of the volumetric specific heat of steel to that of refractory. The thought occurred to us that if two materials could be found that had the same ratio of volumetric specific heats as that of steel to refractory, a model could be developed to study the thermal response of the system and, if possible, observe conditions that might account for the discrepancy between theory and practice. Water, having the same kinematic viscosity as steel and easily handled, was an obvious choice to simulate liquid steel and a brief search led to another familiar and desirable material, plexiglas, to represent the refractory. The ratio of volumetric specific heats of water and plexiglas did in fact satisfy the thermal modelling criteria dictated by the mathematical description of the heat conduction within the system.

APPLICATION OF THE MODEL TO THE LADLE–TUNDISH SYSTEM

Our strand-casting pilot plant equipment was of 91 tonne heat scale producing 0.203×0.940 m single-strand slabs at rates in excess of 145 tonnes per hour. A model

1   Plexiglas–water model of the steel ladle–tundish system

(*see* Fig. 1) of the ladle and tundish was made from plexiglas, with boiling water simulating the steel. From heat transfer considerations, the boundary conditions at the surface of the steel had to be satisfied within the system. Since slag is an effective insulator, we assumed the adiabatic condition of no heat loss and simulated this condition by using a layer of mineral oil on the hot water to suppress the evaporative heat losses from the near-boiling water in the ladle and tundish. Indeed, in the first test with this oil-layer condition, the temperature of the water in the tundish, in contradiction to the mathematical analysis, remained essentially constant—in fact, increased during the latter part of the simulated 'heat'. In other tests that did not have an oil layer serving as the 'slag' cover, the tundish temperature peaked and decayed as predicted by the mathematics. In the mathematical formulation of the problem it was assumed that the steel in the ladle was stirred sufficiently (by natural convection), so that the mass of steel could be considered as being homogeneous in temperature. Therefore, we suspected that stirring in the ladle during teeming caused the peak and decay in the tundish temperature. Tests on

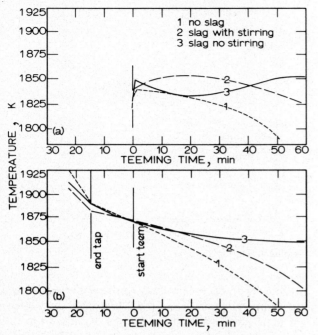

2 *Comparison of temperature response during teeming*

3 *Convection currents during teeming*

the water model proved this to be the case. Three tests were made:

(i) a ladle with no 'slag' cover, i.e. no mineral oil
(ii) a ladle with a 'slag' cover, and gentle stirring with a propeller during teeming
(iii) a ladle with a 'slag' cover, but no stirring.

Figure 2a shows three tundish temperature curves as measured during teeming in three 1/12 scale water-model tests. Temperature and time are scaled to a 91 tonne heat. Curves representing tests (i) and (ii) show a similar temperature pattern of a peak followed by a decay. Curve 3 with a 'slag' layer and not disturbed is distinctly different from the other two curves where convection was mechanically induced or occurred naturally in the absence of a 'slag' cover. Figure 2b gives the corresponding ladle temperature taken below the surface of the water.

Our interpretation of the contrasting patterns is that Szekely's mathematical model showed that a normal amount of slag, i.e. about 0·076 m, would be sufficient to hold temperature in a ladle.[1] Going to a thicker slag cover would make little difference in the bulk heat loss from the steel. For example, as between a 0·076 m and 0·254 m slag, the difference in temperature of the steel near the end of the teem was calculated by him to be only about 5·5 K. But, this is a bulk loss. Actually, at the slag–metal interface the local temperature loss with a 0·076 m slag cover can be far greater than 5·5 K. Owing to this larger localized temperature drop, the surface of the steel increases in density and descends, creating a mixing action in the central region of the ladle that tends to homogenize the ladle temperature. The tundish temperature pattern produced by this kind of mixing was like the pattern that had been reported by industry, i.e. the tundish temperature is initially low, then peaks, and

finally decays following the decay of the ladle temperature. In the water model we used dyes as tracers, which enabled us to observe the convection currents in the ladle during teeming. Figure 3 shows schematically the convection developed with and without an oil layer. The oil, by suppressing convection induced by the heat losses from the oil–water interface, established a bulk of stagnant water in the central region of the ladle. We observed that this bulk of stagnant water is the last to be discharged and that it remains relatively hot because it does not contact the colder sidewalls. Thus, near the end of teeming, when one is concerned about temperature, the hotter water becomes available. Only with an oil layer could we achieve this result. The oil cannot, however, affect the downward convection along the ladle walls. These cooler streams descend, flow to and along the bottom of the ladle, and, depending on the teeming rate, discharge directly through the nozzle or collect in a layerlike fashion in the lower central region of the ladle.

The principle that emerges from these tests and considerations is that if the oil layer, being an excellent preventive of evaporative heat losses in the model, was able to effectively suppress convection, then the same result could be obtained in actual practice by having a slag layer of sufficient thickness. This assumption was confirmed by the results of tests we conducted with 6·8 t electric-arc furnace heats. In these 6·8 t tests, made at Bethlehem Steel's Homer Research Laboratories, we found that when the slag thickness was only 0·051 m for a 12 min teeming time, the tundish temperature showed a peak followed by a decay (Fig. 4), whereas for the same teeming time but with a slag layer 0·153 m thick the tundish temperature remained essentially constant. Although in these tests 0·153 m cover was sufficient to produce a constant tundish temperature for a 12 min teeming time, the question was: what slag thicknesses are needed in production heats? Further tests on 6·8, 91, and 182 t heats showed that the slag layer thickness is a function of teeming time. A plot combining data from these tests is shown in Fig. 5, which gives the minimum slag thickness required to maintain an essentially constant tundish temperature during a cast. Results from water model tests showed that heats could be teemed for prolonged periods with a constant tundish

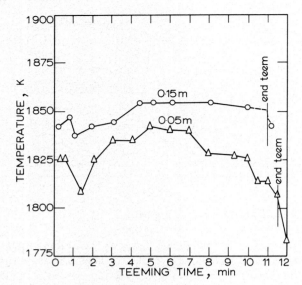

4   Tundish temperature in 6·8 t melt-shop heats

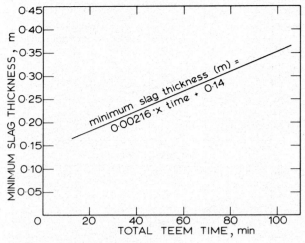

5   Minimum slag thickness, m

temperature, provided that the ladle had a thick slag layer and a sufficient tap temperature. To verify these findings, a 6·8 t heat (*see* Fig. 6 for composition) was made and teemed at a rate of 10·5 t/h through a tundish having a 0·0127 m metering nozzle. The results with a head of steel in the tundish of about 0·406 m, were a teeming time of 39 min and a total time, including tap and transfer, of about 45 min. A 0·254 m slag cover and a furnace tap temperature of 1 950 K were provided. The ladle and tundish temperatures were obtained with immersion thermocouples. The heat was teemed clean, i.e. without skull. Results of these tests are shown by the solid lines in Fig. 6. Note the different tundish-temperature patterns in Fig. 4, representing a 'fast cast', and Fig. 6, a 'slow cast', both cases having the condition of a heavy slag layer. In the case of the fast cast the tundish temperature is initially lower and then levels off at a somewhat higher temperature, whereas for the slow cast the tundish temperature is initially higher than the level-off temperature.

At very low casting rates and the necessarily high tapping temperatures, a low tundish preheat may be used to reduce the initial peak. This peak comes about because of the high rate of heat input into the tundish during the initial rapid filling as contrasted with the slow filling during the cast. At high casting rates, the tundish temperature was low initially because of the heat required to heat up the tundish. This initial 'heatup' occurs at low casting rates also. However, because the rate of metal input to the tundish drops sharply once the tundish is full, the tundish temperature continues to drop until its level-off point. The relationship between tundish temperature response and casting rate was presented in detail in our previous study.[2]*

An indication of the accuracy of the water model was made using the data from the 'slow cast' 6·8 t heat. A 1/6 scale plexiglas model was used. Results from the model are shown in Fig. 6 by the broken lines. Comparing the measure and model data, we see that in this test the model gave results which were accurate to within 11 K. The model was also used to predict the temperature response and values at which the tundish temperatures would level off in our 91 t pilot-plant unit. In our experience the agreement between the predicted and the measured temperatures did not deviate by more than 11 K. This consistent agreement over a broad range of heat sizes established the validity of the plexiglas–water model as a quantitative tool for the simulation of the heat flow in liquid steel–refractory systems.

MODELLING OF THE FLUID FLOW

The thermal model had no geometric scaling restrictions, i.e. any scale factor could be used. As a matter of fact, the water model tests were made in the same plexiglas ladle shown in Fig. 1, which represented a 1/6 scale when applied to the 6·8 t heats and a 1/2 scale when applied to the 91 ton heats. This freedom from geometric

---

* Other findings that were reported in a previous paper concern ladle temperature stratification, the relationship between casting rate and tundish levelling-off temperature, and the effect of ladle preheat on tap temperature

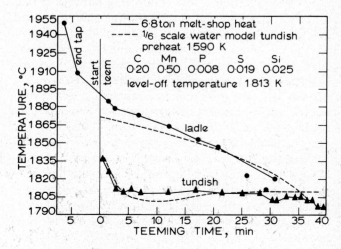

6   Comparison of the temperature response in the water model with a 6·8 t melt-shop heat during a slow cast

scaling restrictions permitted us to consider the scaling of the fluid flow in the system. Because natural convection controlled the fluid flow in the ladle, it would be the dimensionless Grashof–Prandtl number that should be satisfied. This number demanded a scale factor of about 1/3 for the model, i.e. to simulate the natural convection currents in the ladle the water model should have a 1/3 scale to the system being modelled. Mathematical analysis revealed that with a 1/3 scale factor the model satisfied the following dimensionless ratios:

  (i) the Grashof–Prandtl number for the simulation of the natural convection currents within the ladle

  (ii) the Biot number needed to simulate the heat transfer from the outer walls of the ladle and tundish to the surroundings

  (iii) the Nusselt number to simulate the heat transfer and fluid flow between the bulk fluid and ladle walls

  (iv) the Froude number which simulates the dynamic forces of the ladle stream as it is opposed by the body forces of the steel in the tundish and the subsequent currents developed

  (v) the Euler number which satisfies the relationship between the static pressure forces and the inertial forces

  (vi) the Peclet number which relates heat transfer by convection to that by conduction

  (vii) the Stanton number, since it is a ratio of the Nusselt and Peclet number.

Other critical numbers investigated were the Reynolds number (the ratio of inertial to viscous forces) and the Weber number (the ratio of inertial to surface tension forces). Under the constraints of the above-mentioned dimensionless ratios, these two numbers required a scale factor of about 0·6, which is not far removed from a 1/3 scale. It is unusual for any model to be able to simultaneously satisfy this many characteristic requirements for the modelling of both the heat and fluid flow. Yet not only does the 1/3 scale water–plexiglas system meet this test but it also permits the scaling of time (the Fourier number) and temperature, and, most important, the scaling of the volumetric specific heats. Thus, what evolved is a unique physical model that provides a tool with which one can quantitatively extract data about the heat and fluid flow in a complex refractory-contained liquid steel system such as the ladle–tundish used in strand casting.

REFERENCES

1 J. SZEKELY AND R. G. LEE: *AIME*, 1968, **242**, 961–5
2 J. W. HLINKA AND T. W. MILLER: *AISE*, 1970, **47**, 123–33
3 M. FISHENDEN AND O. A. SAUNDERS: 'An introduction to heat transfer', (1st Ed), 93, 1961, Oxford, Clarendon Press

APPENDIX 1
MATHEMATICAL BASIS OF THE WATER MODEL
Modelling the heat flow

Our first approach to the study of the ladle–tundish system was based on a mathematical description of the temperature loss in a well-stirred fluid in contact with a wall. These heat conduction equations were extended, using finite difference methods, to include the changing ratio of mass of steel to contact area in the ladle as the ladle is being teemed. Also, the non-linear heat transfer coefficients on the inside and outside of the ladle and tundish walls were included as boundary conditions. The system, as defined by these equations and boundary conditions, is shown in Fig. 7. For simplicity of expression, the equations are written in one-dimensional Cartesian coordinates with constant coefficients and for the ladle wall only. The solution of the equations led to a tundish temperature–time function characterized by a low tundish temperature initially (owing to conductive losses to the cold tundish walls), a peak as the tundish refractories warmed, and a decay as the ladle temperature decayed. Although these results seemed logical and were to be expected, they were in direct contradiction to the nearly constant tundish temperature which was measured daily on our pilot-plant strand-casting machine.

In an attempt to arrive at an explanation for this contradiction, we examined the system equations in their dimensionless form. Written functionally, the system may be expressed as:

$$\theta(\xi, \tau) = f_1\left[\left(\frac{\rho_s C_s}{\rho_r C_r}\right), \left(\frac{v}{v_r}\right), \left(\frac{h_s L_r}{k_r}\right), \left(\frac{h_a L_r}{k_r}\right), \theta_{ri}(\xi)\right] . \quad (1)$$

where

$$\tau = \frac{\alpha_r t}{L_r^2} \qquad \text{is dimensionless time}$$

$$\xi = \frac{x}{L_r} \qquad \text{is dimensionless space}$$

$$\theta = \frac{T - T_a}{T_{si} - T_a} \qquad \text{is dimensionless temperature.}$$

Equation (1) expresses the five dimensionless ratios that would be required for an ideal thermal model of the system. Examining the ratios, we found that:

  (i) the first term requires that the ratio of volumetric specific heats in the model system be the same as that of liquid steel to refractory

  (ii) the second term expresses a volume ratio, i.e. the model should be geometrically scaled

  (iii) the third and fourth terms, the Biot numbers, are not particularly significant in a ladle–tundish application because we may expect a heat transfer coefficient between the liquid steel and refractory, under the conditions of natural convection, to be in the order of 570–5 700 W/m² K. This is equivalent to a negligible thermal resistance of

$$\frac{\partial^2 T}{\partial x^2} = \frac{1}{\alpha_r} \frac{\partial T}{\partial t}$$

at x=0 and t>0

$$\frac{\rho_s c_s V_s}{A_r} \frac{\partial T_s}{\partial t} = h_s(T_s - T) = k_r \frac{\partial T}{\partial x}$$

at x=L and t>0

$$k_r \frac{\partial T}{\partial x} = -h_a(T - T_a)$$

at t=0 and 0<x<L

$$T_{ri} = f(x)$$

at t=0 and x=0

$$T_i = f(0)$$

7   *Schematic and mathematical description of refractory wall–steel system*

about 0·0025–0·00025 m of refractory. Thus the term $(h_s L_r/k_r)$ may be ignored. The external Biot number $(h_a L_r/k_r)$, between ladle and surroundings, is also a weak number, because during a casting period of about one hour the amount of heat transferred to the outer surface of the thick insulating refractory walls is small. Therefore, this ratio also may be ignored

(iv) the last term in Eq. (1) requires that the dimensionless initial temperature distribution be the same in the model as in the steel–refractory system.

This examination led to an interesting reduction in the requirements for simulating the heat conduction in the system. That is, the remaining requirements for a practical simulation of a liquid-steel refractory system are simply that, if the geometry and the initial temperature distribution are scaled in proportion to the steel system, then Eq. (1) may be written as:

$$\theta(\xi, \tau) = f_2\left(\frac{\rho_s C_s}{\rho_r C_r}\right) \qquad \qquad (2)$$

Equation (2) clearly shows that a thermal model of the ladle–tundish system can be developed if two materials can be found that have the same ratio of volumetric specific heats as steel to refractory. As was noted earlier in this paper, our search for the appropriate materials led to the finding that water and plexiglas satisfy this requirement (Table 1). Next, how to model a liquid steel–refractory system by equating each ratio in the water–plexiglas system to the steel–refractory system will be discussed.

SCALING OF SPACE

All dimensions in the water model are geometrically

TABLE 1 Physical Properties*

Symbol	Units	Iron	Refractory	Water	Plexiglas†
k	W/Km	41·0	1·39	0·68	0·19
ρ	kg/m³ × 10⁻³	7·5	2·09	0·965	1·19
c	J/K kg × 10⁻³	0·755	1·21	4·19	1·52
α	m²/s × 10⁵	0·717	0·055	0·0168	0·0105
v	m²/s × 10⁵	0·0666	—	0·0294	—
γ	1/K × 10³	0·0139	—	0·725	—
η	Ns/m² × 10⁴	48·0	—	2·81	—
Pr	—	0·089	—	1·67	—
Ratio $\rho c/\rho c$ liquid/solid		2·24		2·23	

* On the basis of our experience as well as the literature, the values given in this table represent the best numbers to use. They are not constant but vary with temperature

† Plexiglas is used in this paper as an abbreviation for polymethyl methacrylate

proportioned to the steel system. We may define a scale S_F as the ratio of characteristic dimensions of the model to those of the actual system. As an equation:

$$S_F = \frac{L_p}{L_r} \qquad \qquad (3)$$

SCALING OF TIME

Equating the Fourier numbers we have

$$\frac{\alpha_p t_m}{L_p^2} = \frac{\alpha_r t_s}{L_r^2} \qquad \qquad (4)$$

Time in the model is then related to the actual steel system by a time scale factor t_F, which, by rearrangement of Eq. (4), is

$$t_F = \frac{t_m}{t_s} = \left(\frac{L_p}{L_r}\right)^2 \left(\frac{\alpha_r}{\alpha_p}\right) = S_F^2 \frac{\alpha_r}{\alpha_p} \qquad (5)$$

SCALING OF TEMPERATURE

Much as in the case of space, temperature is scaled directly. Select the initial temperature and the ambient temperature as the characteristic temperatures, and define

$$\theta_F = \frac{T_{mi} - T_{am}}{T_{si} - T_{as}} \qquad \qquad (6)$$

As an example, in the steel system, T_a may be about 311 K and T_i about 1 890 K. In a laboratory, T_a would be 294 K, and a convenient value for T_i is 373 K. These values lead to a temperature scale factor of

$$\theta_F = \frac{373 - 294}{1\,890 - 311} = \frac{1}{20} \qquad \qquad (7)$$

This scale factor means that a 1 degree drop in water temperature in the model corresponds to a 20 degree drop in the steel temperature.

PHYSICAL PROPERTY RATIO

The ratio of the volumetric specific heats of steel to

refractory is made the same by selection of the model materials, i.e.

$$\frac{\rho_s C_s}{\rho_r C_r} = \frac{\rho_w C_w}{\rho_p C_p} \qquad \cdots \qquad (8)$$

Hot water and plexiglas satisfy this requirement for modelling steel and refractory.

Boundary conditions

The Biot number between the liquid steel and refractory is not important. However, for general application, if it is necessary to satisfy the Biot number between the refractory container and its surrounding, one needs to equate

$$\frac{h_{am} L_p}{k_p} = \frac{h_{as} L_r}{k_r} \qquad \cdots \qquad (9)$$

and determine the proper scale factor, namely

$$\frac{L_p}{L_r} = S_F = \left(\frac{h_{as}}{h_{am}}\right)\left(\frac{k_p}{k_r}\right)^* \qquad \cdots \qquad (10)$$

Thus, a thermal model was established based on the simplified one-dimensional system shown in Fig. 7. This model applies to a three-dimensional system as well. As for the heat losses in the ladle and in the tundish through the slag layer, we assumed the adiabatic condition of 'no heat loss' at the slag–metal interface. This condition was satisfied by providing a layer of mineral oil (heated with the water) to suppress the evaporative heat losses from the near-boiling water.

MODELLING THE FLUID FLOW

If, as in the case of a ladle and tundish, the Biot numbers are not significant, then according to Eq. (1) any geometric scale factor can be used to thermally simulate the system. We decided to use this freedom in modelling the fluid flow within the ladle. Natural convection along the vertical ladle wall prevails, and under these conditions the fluid flow is controlled by the product of the Grashof and Prandtl numbers. Equating this product for the liquid steel and water systems, we found that a 1/3 scale model would satisfy this requirement.[2] However, we found that 1/6 and 1/12 scale models gave good results, indicating that the Gr–Pr number was not a stringent requirement in modelling the heat flow. To study the fluid flow in the tundish, one would need to simulate the interaction of the inertial forces of the ladle stream with the body forces of metal in the tundish. In other words, the model should satisfy the Froude number. The Froude number is the ratio of the inertial forces of the ladle stream to the opposing body forces of the metal in the tundish. This number should be written as

$$Fr = \frac{\rho Q V}{g \rho L^3} \qquad \cdots \qquad (11)$$

---

* For the ladle–tundish system we found that a one-third scale model would satisfy the Biot number

Introducing the diameter of the ladle nozzle D, the driving force or head in the ladle H, and noting that the density of the stream and metal in the tundish are the same, we may write

$$Fr = \frac{D^2 V^2}{L^3} \cong \frac{D^2 H}{L^3} \qquad \cdots \qquad (12)$$

Here we have assumed that V is proportional to the square root of H. Since the head in the ladle at any time during teeming should be geometrically scaled, the Froude number becomes

$$Fr = \left(\frac{D}{L}\right)^2 \qquad \cdots \qquad (13)$$

Equating this ratio in the steel and water systems, we arrive at the simple conclusion that the ladle nozzle diameter, to satisfy the Froude number, should have the same scale factor as all other parts of the system. However, to satisfy the time scaling requirements dictated by the Fourier number, the rate of flow from the ladle must also be scaled. The volume of steel which has left the ladle at any time t is Qt or VAt. Again, assuming V is proportional to $\sqrt{H}$ and A to D^2, we may write

$$Qt = \pi \sqrt{H} D^2 t = v \qquad \cdots \qquad (14)$$

Equating the volume flow in the model and steel system, we have

$$\frac{(\sqrt{H} D^2 t)_m}{(\sqrt{H} D^2 t)_s} = \frac{v_m}{v_s} = S_F^3 \qquad \cdots \qquad (15)$$

and

$$\frac{t_m}{t_s} = \sqrt{S_F} = t_F \qquad \cdots \qquad (16)$$

But according to Eq. (5)

$$t_F = S_F^2 \left(\frac{\alpha_r}{\alpha_p}\right) \qquad \cdots \qquad (17)$$

To satisfy both the Fourier number and the flow requirements that satisfy the Froude number

$$t_F = \sqrt{S_F} = S_F^2 \left(\frac{\alpha_r}{\alpha_p}\right) \qquad \cdots \qquad (18)$$

or

$$S_F \equiv \left(\frac{\alpha_p}{\alpha_r}\right)^{\frac{2}{3}} \qquad \cdots \qquad (19)$$

Substitution from Table 1 for the thermal diffusivities of plexiglas and refractory leads to a scale factor of

$$S_F = \left(\frac{\alpha_p}{\alpha_r}\right)^{\frac{2}{3}} = \left(\frac{0 \cdot 00405}{0 \cdot 0213}\right)^{\frac{2}{3}} = 0 \cdot 332 \qquad \cdots \qquad (20)$$

or a 1/3 scale. Thus, with a 1/3 scale model we can describe:

   (i) natural convection currents in the ladle
   (ii) the dynamic forces between the ladle pouring stream and tundish

(iii) the temperature distribution in the steel and refractory
(iv) the heat transfer in both the ladle and tundish.

Further investigation led to additional fluid flow factors which a 1/3 scale model would satisfy. By satisfying the Grashof–Prandtl number the Nusselt number is satisfied, because under the conditions of natural convection these numbers are uniquely related.[3] We can also demonstrate that the Nusselt number, being a ratio of the heat flow by convection to that by conduction, is satisfied by a 1/3 scale model as follows. The Nusselt number Nu may be expressed as

$$\mathrm{Nu} = \left(\frac{q}{\Delta T}\frac{L}{k}\right) \qquad . \qquad . \qquad . \qquad . \qquad (21)$$

Equating this number to water and steel, we have

$$\left(\frac{qL}{\Delta Tk}\right)_\mathrm{w} = \left(\frac{qL}{\Delta Tk}\right)_\mathrm{s} \qquad . \qquad . \qquad . \qquad (22)$$

or by rearrangement

$$\frac{L_\mathrm{m}}{L_\mathrm{s}} = \frac{q_\mathrm{s}}{q_\mathrm{w}}\frac{k_\mathrm{w}}{k_\mathrm{s}}\frac{\Delta T_\mathrm{w}}{\Delta T_\mathrm{s}} = S_\mathrm{F} \qquad . \qquad . \qquad . \qquad (23)$$

The heat flow ratio, i.e. the scaled flow of heat in the model to that in the steel system, has been derived[2] and is related as

$$\frac{q_\mathrm{s}}{q_\mathrm{w}} = \frac{(kA\,\Delta T/\Delta X)_\mathrm{r}}{(kA\,\Delta T/\Delta X)_\mathrm{p}} = \frac{k_\mathrm{r}}{k_\mathrm{p}}\frac{1}{S_\mathrm{F}\theta_\mathrm{F}} \qquad . \qquad . \qquad (24)$$

Substitution of Eq. (24) into (23), rearranging, and using property values from Table 1 yields a scale factor to satisfy the Nusselt number of

$$S_\mathrm{F} = \left(\frac{k_\mathrm{r}k_\mathrm{w}}{k_\mathrm{p}k_\mathrm{s}}\right)^{\frac{1}{2}} = \left[\frac{(1\cdot39)(0\cdot68)}{(0\cdot19)(41\cdot0)}\right]^{\frac{1}{2}} = 0\cdot349$$

or, again about 1/3 scale. It can be rationalized that the Peclet number is satisfied by the model because the Peclet number is the ratio of the heat transferred by convection to that transferred by conduction. Since the model does in fact scale the heat flow, the Peclet number is satisfied. This conclusion can be arrived at as follows:

$$\mathrm{Pe} = \frac{(\rho cVA\,\Delta T)_\mathrm{s}}{(kA\,\Delta T/\Delta X)_\mathrm{r}} = \frac{(\rho cVA\,\Delta T)_\mathrm{w}}{(kA\,\Delta T/\Delta X)_\mathrm{p}} \qquad . \qquad . \qquad (25)$$

Note in Eq. (25) that the areas and temperature ratios cancel. Also, by equating the Froude numbers we get a velocity scale factor

$$\frac{V_\mathrm{w}}{V_\mathrm{s}} = \left(\frac{L_\mathrm{w}}{L_\mathrm{s}}\right)^{\frac{1}{2}} = S_\mathrm{F}^{\frac{1}{2}} \qquad . \qquad . \qquad . \qquad (26)$$

Substituting Eq. (26) into (25) and rearranging, we get

$$S_\mathrm{F}^{1\cdot5} = \frac{(\rho c)_\mathrm{s}}{(\rho c)_\mathrm{w}}\frac{k_\mathrm{p}}{k_\mathrm{r}} \qquad . \qquad . \qquad . \qquad (27)$$

and from Table 1 we see that the Peclet number requires a scale factor of,

$$S_\mathrm{F} = \left[\frac{(755 \times 10^3)(0\cdot755 \times 10^3)(0\cdot19)}{(0\cdot965 \times 10^3)(4\cdot19 \times 10^3)(1\cdot39)}\right]$$

$$= 0\cdot336 . \qquad . \qquad . \qquad . \qquad . \qquad (28)$$

The Euler number is the ratio of the static pressure force to the inertial force. Equating this number in the model to the actual steel system yields the scale factor relating the static pressures in the two systems. The Stanton number is satisfied by the model because this number is a ratio of the Nusselt and Peclet numbers, both of which have been satisfied. Two other numbers, namely the Reynolds and Weber numbers, were examined, and it was found that under the constraints of the other dimensionless ratios they required a scale factor of about 0·6.

Modelling of the flow field in the mould region of continuous-casting systems

J. Szekely and R. T. Yadoya

A mathematical representation is developed for the turbulent flow field, temperature field, and tracer distribution in the upper region of the liquid pool in continuous casting. The problem is formulated through the statement of the two-dimensional turbulent flow equations, which were then solved numerically, using the adaptation of a technique described by Spalding and co-workers. The computed results for the velocity fields were found to be in good qualitative agreement with the results of water model studies for both straight and radial flow nozzles. Further, the predictions based on the model for the temperature and tracer profiles within the pool seem to be consistent with expectations.

SYMBOLS

A_D, A_μ	turbulence parameters (*see* Table 2)
C	tracer concentration
C_D, C_μ	turbulence parameters (*see* Table 1)
C_p	specific heat
d	distance from the wall
$\mathbf{g}$	acceleration, owing to gravity
G_d	molecular diffusivity
k_c	thermal conductivity
N	dissipation term
P	pressure
$\mathbf{q}$	heat-flux vector
r	radial coordinate
t	time
T	temperature
$x_1, x_2,$	coordinates
$\mathbf{v}$	velocity vector
$v_1, v_2,$	components of the velocity vector
α	scaling factor (*see* Eq. (6))
ϵ	turbulent energy
Φ	dissipation term
λ_μ	length scale for turbulent viscosity (*see* Eq. (9))
ψ	stream function (*see* Eq. (6))
ξ	vorticity

μ	viscosity
μ_t	turbulent viscosity
ρ	density
τ	stress tensor
Ω	generation term

$$\frac{D}{Dt}\left(\ \right) = \frac{\partial}{\partial t}\left(\ \right) + v_x\frac{\partial}{\partial x}\left(\ \right) + v_y\frac{\partial}{\partial y}\left(\ \right) + v_z\frac{\partial}{\partial z}\left(\ \right)$$

Pr_ϵ	see Table 1
Pr_t	see Table 1
Sc_t	see Table 1

The widespread application of the continuous-casting technique and the growing demand for improved surface quality have stimulated extensive research into the behaviour of the liquid pool in the upper mould region. This work may be classified into three groups:

(i) mathematical modelling[1-2]
(ii) radioactive tracer studies on 'real systems'[3-5]
(iii) studies involving the use of water models.[6-10]

While the information provided by these investigations is helpful for the visualization of the general nature of the flow field within the mould region, it is essentially qualitative and no quantitative data are available on the numerical values of the fluid velocities.

The work to be described in this paper was undertaken with a view to obtaining a quantitative, or at least semi-

The authors are with Dept. of Chemical Engineering, State University of New York, Buffalo

quantitative description of the actual flow field within the upper mould region. The principal motivation for this work is provided by the fact that a proper quantitative description of the fluid flow field is a necessary pre-requisite of any future studies aimed at the better understanding of the criteria for the flotation of inclusions. In tackling this problem a dual approach is taken in that the mathematical representation of the system, through the solution of the turbulent flow equations, is accom-panied by water model studies devoted to actual velocity measurements. A reasonable agreement between measurements and predictions would then enable one to extrapolate the model to a .wider range of conditions. The theoretical description of the velocity (and tempera-ture) fields in the mould region, to be given in the subse-quent sections of the paper, is rigorous in a sense that it is based on the solution turbulent equation of motion. However, in viewing this matter more realistically, this representation should also be regarded as a model because of the simplifying assumptions introduced in the statement concerning the boundary conditions and in the representation of the Reynolds stresses.

It is noted that until quite recently the solution of multidimensional turbulent flow problems would have represented a formidable, if not impossible undertaking. However, recently Spalding and co-workers developed a method for the numerical solution of two-dimensional turbulent flow problems.[12] The technique to be used in the present paper is a modification of Spalding's approach. Since there exist a number of turbulent flow problems in metals processing operations, the analysis of which has yet to be attempted, it is hoped that this work may provide a stimulus for research in this area.

MATHEMATICAL REPRESENTATION

Let us consider a rectangular or a cylindrical mould into which molten steel is being poured from a nozzle and assume that in the upper mould region the thickness of the solidified layer is small enough so that any distortion in the geometry of the liquid pool may be neglected. The problem is then to calculate velocity distribution and the temperature field within the pool for a given mould and nozzle geometry, casting rate, inlet tempera-ture of the metal, and a specified heat flux at the walls.

General equations

For turbulent flow of an incompressible fluid the general form of the conservation equations is given as:

$$\nabla . \mathbf{v} = 0 \qquad . \qquad . \qquad . \qquad . \qquad . \qquad (1)$$

(equation of continuity)

$$\rho \frac{D\mathbf{v}}{Dt} = -\nabla P - \nabla . \tau + \rho \mathbf{g} \qquad . \qquad . \qquad (2)$$

(equation of motion)

where τ is the stress tensor which for an incompressible Newtonian fluid is related to the local velocity gradient. Since these relationships are readily available in texts

of fluid mechanics[12,13] they will not be reproduced here. We note that these expressions involve μ_e, the effective viscosity which is the sum of the molecular and the turbulent contributions, i.e.

$$\mu_e = \mu + \mu_t \qquad . \qquad . \qquad . \qquad . \qquad . \qquad (3)$$

The thermal energy balance equation may be written as:

$$\rho C_p \frac{DT}{Dt} = -(\nabla . q^e) + \Phi \qquad . \qquad . \qquad . \qquad (4)$$

(molecular   (viscous dissipation)
and
turbulent
conduction)

The dispersion of a tracer in the system may be repre-sented by an expression analogous to Eq. (4), by replacing the viscous dissipation term with a source (or sink) term for the tracer. Equations (1)–(4) are quite general and may be usefully simplified for the representation of specific systems.

Simplified form of the governing equations

Let us consider a two-dimensional system at steady state and define our coordinate system, such that x_1 is parallel to the mould walls (i.e. it is in the direction of the casting velocity) and x_2 is perpendicular to the mould walls.

EQUATION OF MOTION

Within the framework of these assumptions the equation of motion may be written in terms of the velocity components, v_1 and v_2. It may be shown[13,14] that the two components of the momentum balance equation may be consolidated into a single expression known as the vorticity transport equation:

$$\frac{\partial}{\partial x_1}\left[\frac{\xi}{\alpha}\frac{\partial \psi}{\partial x_2}\right] - \frac{\partial}{\partial x_2}\left[\frac{\xi}{\alpha}\frac{\partial \psi}{\partial x_1}\right] - \frac{\partial}{\partial x_1}\left[\frac{1}{\alpha}\frac{\partial}{\partial x_1}(\alpha\mu_e\xi)\right]$$
$$- \frac{\partial}{\partial x_2}\left[\frac{1}{\alpha}\frac{\partial}{\partial x_2}(\alpha\mu_e\xi)\right] = 0 \qquad . \qquad . \qquad (5)$$

where ψ is the stream function, defined as:

$$v_1 = \frac{1}{\alpha}\frac{\partial \psi}{\partial x_2}; \qquad v_2 = -\frac{1}{\alpha}\frac{\partial \psi}{\partial x_1} \qquad . \qquad . \qquad (6)$$

ξ is the vorticity and α is a scaling factor which is unity for the Cartesian coordinate system and $\alpha = r = x_2$ for cylindrical coordinates. Furthermore, ξ and ψ are related by the following expression:

$$\frac{\partial}{\partial x_1}\left(\frac{1}{\alpha}\frac{\partial \psi}{\partial x_1}\right) + \frac{\partial}{\partial x_2}\left(\frac{1}{\alpha}\frac{\partial \psi}{\partial x_2}\right) + \xi = 0 \qquad . \qquad . \qquad (7)$$

It is noted that by using the stream function the equation of continuity is automatically satisfied so that Eq. (1) need not be invoked in the subsequent manipulation of the governing equations. The quantity μ_e incorporating the turbulent viscosity appearing in Eq. (5) is strongly position dependent and is a function of the local velocity gradients. Numerous empirical relationships have been proposed for describing μ_e and here we shall use the Kolmogorov–Prandtl model:[15,16]

$$\mu_t = C_\mu \rho \epsilon^{\frac{1}{2}} \lambda_\mu \qquad . \qquad . \qquad . \qquad . \qquad (8)$$

where

ϵ is the turbulent energy

λ_μ is the length scale of the viscosity.

Following Wolfshtein,[17] we shall use van Driest's proposal for computing λ_μ in the following form

$$\lambda_\mu = d[1 - \exp(-A_\mu Re_t)] \qquad . \qquad . \qquad . \qquad (9)$$

where d is the (shortest) distance to the solid boundaries, and Re_t the turbulent Reynolds number is defined as:

$$Re_t = \frac{d\rho \epsilon^{\frac{1}{2}}}{\mu} \qquad . \qquad . \qquad . \qquad . \qquad (10)$$

the quantity A_μ will be taken as an empirical constant. ϵ is defined as the kinetic energy of the fluctuating motion. It may be shown that the spatial distribution of ϵ may be obtained from the following balance equation[11,17]

$$\frac{\partial}{\partial x_1}\left(\epsilon \frac{\partial \psi}{\partial x_1}\right) - \frac{\partial}{\partial x_2}\left(\epsilon \frac{\partial \psi}{\partial x_2}\right) - \frac{\partial}{\partial x_1}\left[\alpha\left(\mu + \frac{\mu_t}{Pr_\epsilon}\right) - \frac{\partial \epsilon}{\partial x_2}\right]$$

(convection)   (diffusion)

$$- \frac{\partial}{\partial x_2}\alpha\left(\mu + \frac{\mu_t}{Pr_\epsilon}\right)$$

$$= \alpha(\Omega - N) \qquad . \qquad . \qquad . \qquad . \qquad (11)$$

(generation)(dissipation)

Here

$$Pr_\epsilon = \left(\frac{\mu + C_p}{k_c}\right)$$

is a turbulent Prandtl number and expressions are available for relating Ω and N to the velocity components and their derivatives.

THERMAL ENERGY BALANCE EQUATION

The thermal energy balance equation may be written as

$$\frac{\partial}{\partial x_1}\left(T \frac{\partial \psi}{\partial x_2}\right) - \frac{\partial}{\partial x_2}\left(T \frac{\partial \psi}{\partial x_1}\right) - \frac{\partial}{\partial x_1}\left[\alpha\left(k_c + \frac{\mu_t}{Pr_t}\right)\frac{\partial T}{\partial x_1}\right]$$

$$- \frac{\partial}{\partial x_2}\left[\alpha\left(\frac{k_c}{C_p} + \frac{\mu_t}{Pr_t}\right)\frac{\partial T}{\partial x_2}\right] = \frac{\alpha \Phi}{C_p} \qquad . \qquad . \qquad (12)$$

where Φ is the viscous dissipation.

DISPERSION OF TRACERS OR INCLUSION PARTICLES

Finally, the dispersion of tracers, or inclusion particles may be expressed as:

$$\frac{\partial}{\partial x_1}\left(C \frac{\partial \psi}{\partial x_2}\right) - \frac{\partial}{\partial x_2}\left(C \frac{\partial \psi}{\partial x_1}\right) - \frac{\partial}{\partial x_1}\left[\alpha\left(G_d + \frac{\mu_t}{\rho Sc_t}\right)\frac{\partial C}{\partial x_1}\right]$$

$$- \frac{\partial}{\partial x_2}\left[\alpha\left(G_d + \frac{\mu_t}{\rho Sc_t}\right)\frac{\partial C}{\partial x_2}\right] = 0 \qquad . \qquad . \qquad (13)$$

where G_d is the molecular diffusivity for a dissolved tracer and for solid particles, such as inclusions; G_d may be estimated with the aid of the Stokes–Einstein relationship:

$$G_d = \frac{\tilde{k}T}{6\pi R_0} \qquad . \qquad . \qquad . \qquad . \qquad (14)$$

where

$\tilde{k}$ is the Boltzmann's constant

R_0 is the radius of the solid particle

Sc_t is the turbulent Schmidt number.

Equations (5), (6), (7), (11), (12), and (13) together with the boundary conditions and the subsidiary relationships ((8), (9), (10) (definition of Ω and N) represent a complete statement of the problem.

Boundary conditions

In a physical sense the boundary conditions have to express the following constraints:

   (i) zero turbulent energy on all solid surfaces (and also on the meniscus)

   (ii) prescribed temperature and heat flux at the mould wall

   (iii) prescribed entrance conditions

   (iv) the stream function is zero at the axis of symmetry

   (v) the gradient of the tracer concentration must be zero at the solid walls and at the axis of symmetry. (This condition could be relaxed to allow for the partial entrapment of the solid inclusion particles.)

These constraints are readily expressed and are available elsewhere.[14] The statement of the boundary conditions in terms of the vorticity is less obvious. In the finite difference formulation used, this boundary condition took the form of a relationship between the vorticity and the stream function, the details of which are available in the thesis upon which this paper is based.[14]

Method of solution

The governing equations, i.e. the vorticity transport equation, the thermal energy balance equation, and the turbulent energy balance equations are all elliptical differential equations. The numerical techniques available for tackling elliptic differential equations include the use of variational methods, a Taylor series expansion, and integral methods. In the present work we shall adopt the procedure described by Gosman *et al.*,[12] which in principle consists of the successive integration of the governing equations over a finite difference grid, which in turn yields a set of algebraic relationships for the dependent variables at the various spatial locations within the system. These simultaneous algebraic equations are then solved by using iterative procedures. The technique actually chosen was the Gauss–Seidel successive displacement procedure, which is known to give relatively rapid convergence.

    The actual finite difference representation involved the use of a 16 × 15 grid, which was almost certainly too coarse for some of the applications, but the use of a finer grid would have made the computational costs prohibitively high. The actual computation was done on the CDC 6400 digital computer of the State University of New York at Buffalo. In order to indicate the computer time requirements, one iteration cycle for the five differential equations, i.e. vorticity, stream function, tracer, temperature, and turbulent energy required about 4 s. The compilation of the program written in FORTRAN IV required 30 s, and a typical run consumed about 6–10 min of computer time. Computational details, including a complete listing of the program are available in the thesis on which this work is based. A selection of the computed results will be given later.

EXPERIMENTAL WORK[19]

The objective of the experimental part of the program was to obtain quantitative information on the velocity field within the simulated mould region so that these measurements could be compared with the predictions of the model described in the preceding section. In modelling the flow system, ideally one would have to meet the criteria for both geometric and dynamic similarity. Geometric similarity was attained by setting the physical dimensions of the model to be within the range of units used in practice. Dynamic similarity would be achieved if both the Reynold and the Froude numbers were the same in the model and in the prototype. The criteria for velocity were satisfied and the kinematic viscosity of water, used as the working fluid, is thought to be sufficiently close to that of steel.

Apparatus

The line diagram of the apparatus is shown in Fig. 1 and the principal components of the system are discussed below. The apparatus consisted of a plexiglass column, 73in long and $7\frac{1}{2}$in diameter, through which water was pumped, at rates corresponding to casting speeds of 30–50in/min. The column was encased in a square plexiglass prism, which was also filled with water so that parallaxis effects were eliminated. Along the column 20 tapholes were drilled, in pairs at corresponding levels, to allow both static pressure measurements and the insertion of probes, for the determination of the total impact pressure, needed in connexion with the velocity measurements. Water was introduced into the system through the inlet nozzles, which consisted of plexiglass tubes, 1in i.d. and 2 ft long. Several types of inlet nozzles were studied, including straight nozzles and radial flow nozzles. The details of these will be discussed later.

The static and dynamic pressures were determined by the use of a micromanometer, shown in Fig. 2, which is a direct reading device having the increased sensitivity brought about by the inclination of the manometer tube and the use of an optical device for the measuring of displacement. This sensitive pressure measurement device was necessary because of the relatively low values of the linear velocities encountered in the system. The total pressure reading was taken with the aid of an impact tube, which was constructed from a 19 gauge hypodermic needle, welded to a stainless steel tube and mounted on a United Sensor traverse unit. The static pressure was measured by taps in the wall, constructed so as to obey the recommended geometric configurations, thus minimizing the errors in static pressure measurements. These taps were $\frac{3}{64}$in in diameter, $\frac{1}{4}$in long, and were connected to acetate tubing, $\frac{3}{16}$in diameter. The other items in the circuit included rotameters for flow measurement, two circulating pumps, a surge tank, and arrangements for the injection of dye into the incoming stream for the flow visualization tests.

Experimental procedure

The experimental work done included flow visualization studies through the use of tracers and actual velocity measurements. In the velocity (i.e. total pressure) measurements the appropriate inlet nozzle was inserted and fluid was circulated through the system at predetermined rates as indicated on the rotameters. After a period of time, usually 30 min, when steady state had been reached, a traverse was made by the total impact

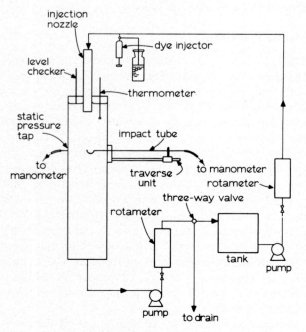

1   Schematic line diagram of the apparatus

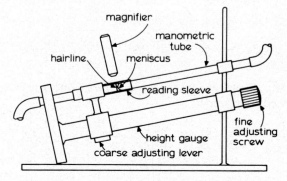

2   The micromanometer used for the pressure readings

probe, at various vertical levels. At each horizontal point total pressure readings were taken at about $\frac{1}{2}$ min intervals, until two consecutive readings agreed to within 0·002in water as indicated on the inclined manometer. In order to measure the flow in the reversal (backflow) region the impact tube was rotated about its axis by 180°. The mapping of a complete velocity field required about ten days' work.

In the determination of the static pressures a series of four to seven runs were done and the results were averaged. It was recognized that the measurement of the static pressure employed in this study could be subject to error, although Barchillon[18] has reported quite good agreement between static pressure measurements made with the use of wall probes and movable probes, within the interior of the fluid. Since erroneous measurements are most likely to occur when there is a velocity component normal to the wall, the method adopted for the radial flow nozzles was one where the total pressure profile was measured at a given vertical position, and then the probe was rotated to determine the total pressure profile for reverse flow. If these two curves did intersect, then the positive pressure reading corresponding to the intersection was taken as the static pressure. If the curves did not intersect, the static pressure was taken as the value corresponding to zero recirculation. A more detailed discussion of the experimental technique and of the possible error involved in the measurements is available elsewhere.[14,19] Some typical experimental results showing the velocity fields within the system will be described subsequently.

RESULTS

Experimental measurements

Measurements were made with both straight nozzles and with radial flow nozzles. In the case of straight nozzles the fluid stream was introduced into the system through a vertical tube, 1in i.d. or $\frac{3}{4}$in i.d. the outlet of which was submerged 2in below the liquid surface. The flow rates used corresponded to simulated casting rates of 33in/min and 45·5in/min. The radial flow nozzle used consisted of a 1in tube, which had a closed end but had six circular

holes some 1in above the closed end. The size of the holes was so selected that the total area available for flow was the same as the cross-sectional area of the pipe. Since the flow is not axisymmetrical in this case, in these measurements the probe was positioned parallel to the axis of two diametrically opposing slots. The flow rate in this run corresponded to a casting speed of 32in/min. The general nature of the velocity fields, corresponding to these two inlet nozzle configurations, is sketched in Fig. 3 which was deduced from tracer tests.

Actual velocity measurements are shown in Figs. 4–6. Figures 4 and 5 show the map of the axial velocity component and the corresponding streamline pattern for straight nozzles, whereas the axial velocity field for a radial flow nozzle is given in Fig. 6. Inspection of these plots indicates that for straight nozzles there exists a potential core, together with a region of strong recirculation near the walls. It is also seen that for the particular conditions considered it took some 3–5 mould diameters to establish a relatively flat velocity profile. The behaviour of the system is different for radial flow nozzles and as seen in Fig. 6, flat velocity profile in this case is reached within a very short distance, say $\frac{1}{2}$–1 mould diameters from the inlet. In some respects the fluid exiting from the radial flow nozzle behaves like a wall jet. It could be inferred from Fig. 6, and was found in the flow visualization tests, that two sets of recirculating eddies are formed. The upper rotates in a clockwise direction, whereas the lower eddy rotates in the opposite direction. A schematic sketch of these eddies has been given in Fig. 3a.

The experimental data described in this section seem to be consistent with the findings of other investigators. However, the principal reason for making these measurements was to produce a set of quantitative data with which the computed results may be compared.

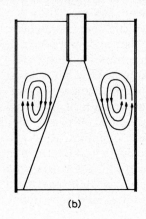

(a)   (b)

a Radial flow nozzle; *b* Straight nozzle

3   Schematic representation of the flow field

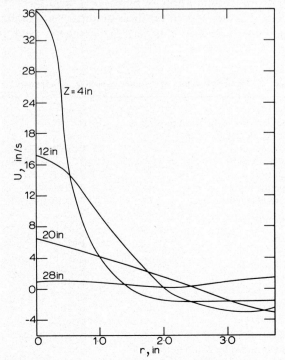

4   Velocity profiles for various axial positions for a straight nozzle, simulated casting rate 33in/min

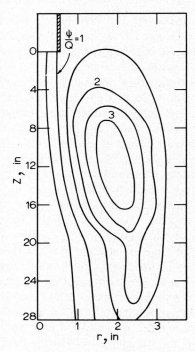

5 Typical recirculation pattern in the vicinity of the inlet, for a straight nozzle, shown on a streamline plot, simulated casting rate 33in/min

Computed results

The numerical values for the parameters used in the computation were so selected as to allow a direct comparison with the water model tests and at the same time to be representative of continuous-casting practice. In view of the very large number of parameters involved in the characterization of continuous-casting systems, the actual selection of the numerical values for the purpose of computation is necessarily arbitrary. The numerical values chosen for these quantities are thought to be representative. Further, the geometry and the

TABLE 1 Numerical values of parameters used in the computation

Casting speed	0·5in/s
Mould diameter (cylindrical mould)	8in
Mould width (square mould)	8in
ρ (liquid density)	0·283 lb/in³
μ (liquid viscosity)	$3·72 \times 10^{-4}$ lb/in s
T (inlet temp.)	3 280°R
C_p (specific heat)	0·12 Btu/lb°R
k_c (thermal conductivity)	0·0029 Btu/in s°R
Turbulence parameters	
$A\mu$	0·016*
A_D	0·263*
C_μ	0·220*
C_D	0·416*
Pr_ϵ	1·53*
Pr_t	0·71†
Sc_t	0·86‡

* Recommended by Wolfstein[17]
† Suggested by Gosman[11]
‡ Suggested by Okita[11]

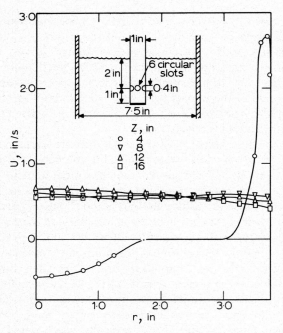

6 Velocity profiles at various axial positions for the radial flow nozzle, simulated casting rate 33in/min

casting rates were so selected as to allow a direct comparison with the previously reported water model experiments. The principal fixed parameters used in the computation are listed in Table 1 and the main variables are:

(i) nozzle type: axial or straight nozzle and radial flow or bifurcated nozzle
(ii) nozzle position: inclined nozzle,* off-centre nozzle, and double nozzle*
(iii) mould geometry: cylindrical mould, square mould
(iv) cooling conditions.

A typical set of the computed results is presented in Figs. 7–12. Figures 7 and 8 show the streamline pattern and the axial velocity profiles at various axial positions for a straight nozzle, (without swirl) discharging into a cylindrical mould. It is of interest to compare these computed results with experimental measurements described previously, and shown in Figs. 4 and 5. The reasonably good qualitative agreement between measurements and prediction is readily apparent, which should provide some confidence in the computed results even in the areas where such direct comparison is not possible. In comparing Figs. 8 and 5 it is interesting to note that in both cases a flat velocity profile is being approached upon reaching a distance of about 3–5 mould diameters downstream of the nozzle position. In this regard the agreement between prediction and measurements is quite quantitative.

Figure 9 shows the computed profiles of the turbulent energy for the same system. The behaviour shown by this graph is quite consistent with the computed velocity profiles and the streamline patterns given in the preceding

* Computed results are not reported here but are available in the thesis on which this paper is based[14]

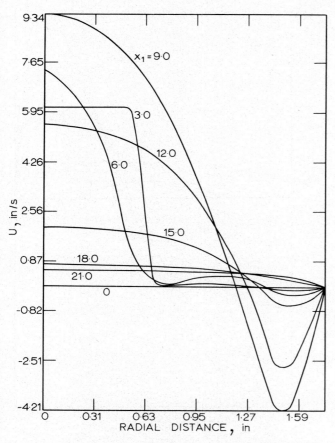

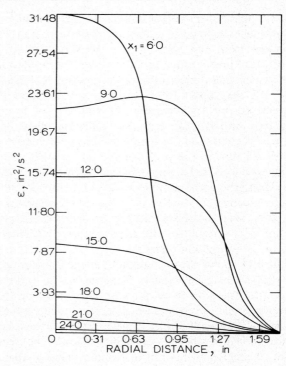

9   Computed values of the turbulent energy at various axial positions, for cylindrical mould, straight nozzle and a casting speed of 30in/min

7   Computed axial velocity profiles at various axial positions for a cylindrical mould, a straight nozzle and a casting speed of 30in/min

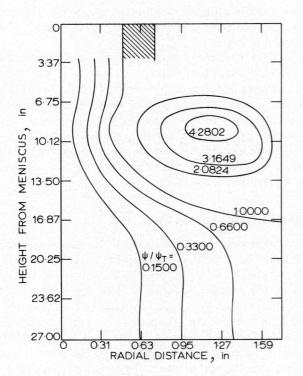

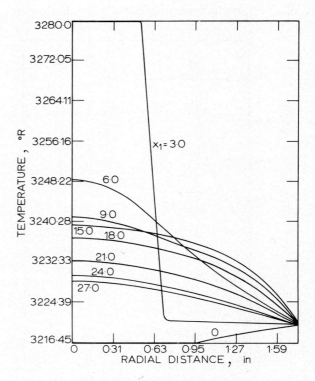

8   Computed streamline pattern for a cylindrical mould, a straight nozzle and a casting rate of 30in/min

10   Computed temperature distribution for a cylindrical mould, straight nozzle and a casting speed of 30in/min, prescribed wall temperature

Figs. 7–8, in that for straight nozzles the region of intense turbulence is confined to a distance of about 3–5 mould diameters from the inlet. Figure 10 shows a set of temperature profiles for the same system, computed for a prescribed wall temperature corresponding to 3 220°F. It is seen that apart from the uppermost region the temperature profiles are quite flat, which is, of course, consistent with the fact that the highly turbulent flow field would correspond to a high 'effective conductivity'. It is noted that in the previous thermal models of the liquid pool this behaviour was represented by either considering the pool 'completely mixed' or by assigning a high 'effective conductivity' to the liquid region. The approach taken in the present work is clearly more basic and could be combined with more realistic representations of the solidifying surface.

Figure 11 shows the dispersion of a tracer introduced into the system continuously from the inside walls of the nozzle. An alternative interpretation may be that the tracer particles represent inclusions eroded from the nozzle walls. Inspection of Fig. 11 shows flat tracer profiles, indicating the very rapid dispersion of the tracer within the region of intense turbulence. This predicted behaviour is in good agreement with the experimental findings of Weinberg and Brimacombe,[20] whose results could be interpreted on the assumption of 'perfect mixing' or a condition which is approached by the computed results shown here.

Figure 12 shows the map of the axial velocity component for the radial flow nozzle. It is seen that, as expected, there exists a region for reverse flow in the centre of the mould within the vicinity of the discharge level of the nozzle. Moreover, a relatively flat velocity profile is established within about $\frac{1}{2}$–1 mould diameters

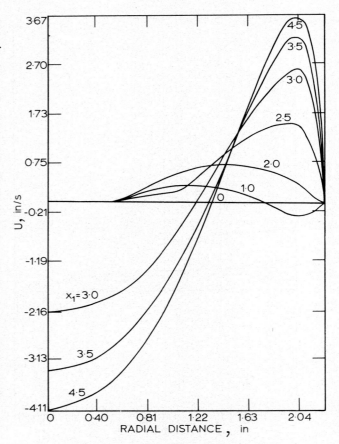

Numbers on the curves denote vertical distances in inches from the top of the nozzle

12   Axial velocity profiles for the radial flow nozzle

downstream of the nozzle. The velocity field seen in Fig. 12 is in reasonable qualitative agreement with the experimental results obtained in water model studies and as shown in Fig. 6.

Finally, Fig. 13 shows the distribution of the turbulent energy for a radial flow nozzle, which again is consistent with previous findings, both experimental and analytical, that the region of intense turbulence is confined to within about $\frac{1}{2}$–1 mould diameters. The model described here could be used for computing the velocity, temperature, and tracer fields for a variety of operating conditions. A selection of these results is available in the thesis on which this work is based.

CONCLUDING REMARKS

A mathematical representation is developed for the turbulent flow field, temperature field and tracer distribution in the liquid pool of a continuous-casting system. The problem is formulated by the statement of the turbulent fluid flow equations and the Kolmogorov–Prandtl model is used for the presentation of the turbulent viscosity. Thus, the solution of the fluid flow problem required the simultaneous solution of the equation of motion and the turbulent energy balance equation. In addition to the statement of the fluid flow equations the description of the problem required a statement of the

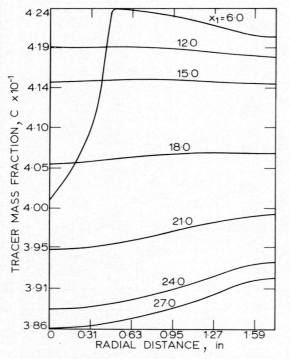

11   Computed tracer profiles in the liquid region, for a cylindrical mould, straight nozzle and a casting speed of 30in/min

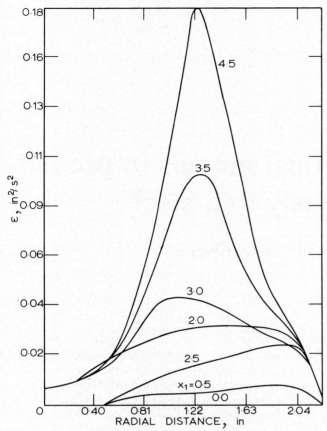

13 Distribution of the turbulent energy at various axial positions for a radial flow nozzle, cylindrical mould and casting rate of 30in/min

(turbulent) thermal energy balance equation and an equation expressing the conservation of a tracer material. The system of five simultaneous elliptical differential equations was put in a finite difference form, through an integral formulation, and the resultant non-linear algebraic equations were solved using the Gauss–Seidel technique.

The computed results for the velocity fields were found to be in reasonably good qualitative agreement with the results of water model studies for both the straight and the radial flow nozzles. Further, the predictions made by the model for the temperature and the tracer profiles within the molten pool appear to be consistent with expectations, at least in a qualitative manner. In a sense this work was a pioneering undertaking because in all likelihood it is the first attempt at the application of turbulent flow theory to metallurgical systems in general and continuous casting in particular. This approach shows considerable promise, especially as further refinements are made. In conclusion, it may be worthwhile to comment briefly on the areas where further work would be required:

(i) accuracy of the model. The considerable computational expense necessitated the use of a rather coarse grid and the use of finer grids with faster machines should provide a more accurate detailed description of the fluid flow field

(ii) boundary conditions for heat transfer and for the dispersion of inclusions particles were rather oversimplified. Future development in these areas could include the incorporation of solidification models into the overall heat transfer scheme, together with suitable source and sink terms for the inclusion particles. Neither of these refinements is likely to cause appreciable computational difficulties compared to the major task involved in the solution of the turbulent flow equations

(iii) it would be desirable to construct a realistic representation for the solid-melt interface in continuous casting in which full account is taken of the behaviour of the two-phase (mushy) region. The integration of such representation with the turbulent fluid flow equations given in this paper could provide a major forward step in our understanding of some of the factors that govern surface quality

(iv) it must be stressed that the formulation given here will apply only to the upper portion of the liquid pool where forced convection effects predominate. In the lower portion of the pool where the two-phase region occupies a substantial part of the system, natural convection should predominate, the description of which will require a drastically different approach. Nonetheless, the 'initial conditions' for this latter region are set by the turbulent flow regime the description of which was attempted here.

ACKNOWLEDGMENT

The authors wish to thank the American Iron and Steel Institute for partial support of the investigation under Grant No. 39–197.

REFERENCES

1 E. A. MIZIKAR: *Trans. Met. Soc. AIME*, 1967, **239**, 1 747
2 J. SZEKELY AND V. STANEK: *Met. Trans.*, 1970, **1**, 119
3 H. KRAINER AND B. TARMANN: 'Extrait de la Revue Universelle des Mines', 1958, Liege
4 J. ARNOULT *et al.*: *Rev. Mét.*, 1969, 585
5 K. I. AFANASEVA AND T. P. IVENTSOV: *Stal*, 1958, **18** (7), 599
6 A. A. SKVORTOV AND A. D. AKIMENKO: *Izvest. VUZ Chern. Met.*, 1958, **3**, 21
7 A. D. AKIMENKO: *Izvest. VUZ Chern. Met.*, 1963, **6**, 179
8 R. EASTON AND S. W. MEYER: *Iron and Steel Eng.*, 1965, 139
9 E. I. ASTROV *et al.*: *Stal in English*, 1966, **10**, 796
10 F. WILLIAMS AND F. NEUMANN, *Concast News*, 1968, **7** (2), 5–6
11 A. D. GOSMAN *et al.*: 'Heat and Mass Transfer in Recirculating Flows', 1969, Academic Press, London
12 R. B. BIRD *et al.*: 'Transport Phenomena', 1960, John Wiley, New York
13 H. SCHLICHTING: 'Boundary Layer Theory', 1968, McGraw-Hill, New York
14 R. T. YADOYA: PhD thesis, State University of New York at Buffalo, 1972
15 A. N. KOLMOGOROV: *Izvest. AN SSSR*, 1952, 56
16 L. PRANDTL: *Nach. Akad. Wiss.*, 1945, 6, Gottingen
17 M. WOLFSHTEIN: *Int. J. Heat Mass Transfer*, 1969, **12**, 301
18 M. S. BARCHILON: *Publ. Sci. et Techn. Minist. Air*, 1969, No. 442
19 J. SZEKELY AND R. T. YADOYA: *Met. Trans. ASM-AIME*, 1972, **3**, 2 673
20 F. WEINBERG AND K. BRIMACOMBE: *Ironmaking Steelmaking*, 1974, **1**, 35, 90

Application of mathematical models to predict pool profiles in continuously cast steel

J. K. Brimacombe, J. E. Lait, and F. Weinberg

The liquid pool profiles of continuously cast steel are calculated with mathematical models and compared to profiles measured using radioactive tracers. The agreement between model predictions and experiment is good over the upper half of the mould. In the lower half of the mould and upper spray regions the measured shell thickness is greater than calculated. The factors which may contribute to this discrepancy are analysed using heat flow data from several hundred casts. The validity of various surface boundary conditions for the mould, including the measured heat flux relation of Savage and Pritchard, is considered. Heat transfer coefficients for different types of moulds in different casting machines are compared as a function of casting rate. A general plot of shell thickness and surface temperature against time in the mould is given which is applicable to all the cases considered.

SYMBOLS

b	constant in general heat flux equation, $\mathrm{kcal\,m^{-2}\,s^{-\frac{3}{2}}}$
C	specific heat, $\mathrm{kcal\,kg^{-1}\,{}^\circ C^{-1}}$
h_M	heat transfer coefficient between the shell surface and mould water, $\mathrm{kcal\,m^{-2}\,{}^\circ C^{-1}\,s^{-1}}$
$\bar{h}_M, \bar{h}_s$	average heat transfer coefficient for the mould and sprays respectively
h_0	heat transfer coefficient at the meniscus
k	thermal conductivity, $\mathrm{kcal\,m^{-1}\,{}^\circ C^{-1}\,s^{-1}}$
k_{eff}	effective thermal conductivity
l	width of billet, m
L	latent heat, $\mathrm{kcal\,kg^{-1}}$
q_0	heat flux from the shell surface, $\mathrm{kcal\,m^{-2}\,s^{-1}}$
$\bar{q}_0$	average heat flux from the shell surface
$q_{0,0}$	surface heat flux at the meniscus
t	time, s
t_M	dwell time, s
T	temperature, °C
T_0, T_W	temperatures of casting surface and cooling water, respectively
T_s	solidus temperature
ΔT_{sh}	superheat of liquid steel
u	casting speed, $\mathrm{m\,s^{-1}}$
x	distance below meniscus, m
X	effective mould length, m
y	distance from shell surface, m
y'	distance from shell surface over which new temperature profile is established after abrupt cooling change, m
y_t	thickness of steel shell, m
$[y_t]_{\max}$	maximum possible shell thickness (defined by Eq. (22)), m
Y^*	maximum shell thickness at the bottom of the mould (defined by Eq. (21)), m
Y_M	shell thickness at the bottom of the mould, m
η	constant determining rate of decrease of h_M with $x(\mathrm{m^{-1}})$
ρ	density, $\mathrm{kg\,m^{-3}}$

Dimensionless groups

h^*	ratio of heat transfer coefficients between mould and sprays defined by Eq. (19)
h_{M1}^*, h_{12}^*	ratio of heat transfer coefficients between mould and zone 1 sprays, and between zone 1 and zone 2 sprays respectively.
Q	dimensionless heat flux from the surface, $= q_0/q_{0,0}$

The authors are with Dept. of Metallurgy, University of British Columbia, Vancouver

174

Q' described by Hills and Moore[14] as the imaginary surface heat flux during the transition period

Q^* heat extracted by the mould per unit length of mould perimeter, $= -q_0\sqrt{X}/\sqrt{u\rho ckT_s}$

Y thickness of solid shell, $= -q_{0,0}y_t/T_sk$ for mould, $= \bar{h}_s y_s/k$ for sprays

y^* square of depth of penetration of new temperature profile after a sudden cooling change, $= y'q_{0,0}^2/T_sk$ for mould; $= y'\bar{h}_s/k$ for sprays

X^* effective length of mould, $= q_{0,0}^2 X/T_s^2 u\rho Ck$

β constant in dimensionless surface heat flux equation, $= bT_s\sqrt{\rho Ck}/q_{0,0}^2$

γ parameter determining rate of decrease of $h_M = \eta u\rho Ck/h_0^2$

θ surface temperature, T_0/T_s

λ effective latent heat of solidification, $= L + C\Delta T_{sh}/CT_s$

ξ distance below the meniscus, $= q_{0,0}^2 x/T_s^2 u\rho Ck$ for mould, $= \bar{h}_s^2 x/u\rho Ck$ for sprays

τ_{M1}^*, τ_{12}^* value of ξ at end of the transition period between the mould and zone 1 sprays, and between zone 1 and zone 2 sprays

Λ, Γ, Ω parameters in Eq. (8)

MATHEMATICAL MODELS

Several mathematical models[1-9] have been formulated to describe the heat transfer and solidification processes in the continuous casting of steel. The models are based on the unsteady state conduction of heat from the interior of the steel to the casting surface. Conduction in the withdrawal direction is assumed to be negligible. Mathematically, the heat conduction along a single axis is described by Eq. (1).

$$\rho C\frac{\partial T}{\partial t} = \frac{\partial}{\partial y}\left(k\frac{\partial T}{\partial y}\right) \quad . \qquad . \qquad . \qquad . \qquad (1)$$

The models differ from one another in their treatment of the heat transfer processes inside the liquid pool and at the outside surface of the steel shell. To describe the transfer of superheat from the liquid pool to the solidification front Donaldson and Hess[3] and Gautier et al.[7] have assumed the pool to be stagnant and used Eq. (1). Mizikar[4] and Kung and Pollock[9] took into account the convection that the input metal stream creates by replacing k in Eq. (1) with an effective thermal conductivity, k_{eff}, which is about seven times greater than the normal value at that temperature. Hills[2] neglected conduction in the liquid pool altogether assuming that it was completely mixed. Superheat was then assumed to be released at the same time as the latent heat. Although these assumptions differ markedly it is unlikely that they have a large effect on the calculated rate of solidification since the superheat is normally a small fraction of the latent heat.

Mathematical formulation of the heat flux from the casting surface, q_0, for use in the surface boundary condition (Eq. (2))

$$q_0 = -k\frac{\partial T}{\partial y}\bigg|_{surface} \qquad . \qquad . \qquad . \qquad . \qquad (2)$$

has posed a more difficult problem, particularly for the mould region, because q_0, which is a complex function, can significantly influence the rate of solidification. Various approaches have been taken for the mould. Donaldson and Hess[3] and Gautier et al.[7] have divided the mould into two zones, i.e. an upper zone where the shell surface and the mould wall are in good contact and a gap zone over which the surfaces are separated by an air gap. The initiation of the gap was calculated by Donaldson and Hess from the theoretical considerations of Savage[10] while Gautier et al.[7] obtained it from a heat balance on the mould. In the contact zone q_0 was characterized by an empirical heat transfer coefficient; in the gap zone it was calculated assuming that radiation and conduction across the gas in the gap were important. Mizikar[4] took a simpler approach and used a heat flux relation (Eq. (3))

$$-q_0 = 640 - 80\sqrt{t} \qquad . \qquad . \qquad . \qquad . \qquad (3)$$

that had been determined experimentally by Savage and Pritchard[11] earlier on static moulds. The average heat flux to the mould is then given by

$$-\bar{q}_0 = 640 - 53\sqrt{t_M} \qquad . \qquad . \qquad . \qquad . \qquad (4)$$

Both Hills[2,5] and Kung and Pollock[9] have described q_0 according to Eq. (5)

$$-q_0 = \bar{h}_M(T_0 - T_W)\dagger \qquad . \qquad . \qquad . \qquad (5)$$

where $\bar{h}_M$ is a constant overall heat transfer coefficient between the shell surface and the mould water. Hills[5] has also suggested that a coefficient which decreased linearly with distance below the meniscus (Eq. (6))

$$h_M = h_0(1 - \eta x) \qquad . \qquad . \qquad . \qquad . \qquad (6)$$

might be more realistic. h_0 is the value of h_M at the meniscus and η is a constant. The question of which boundary condition to use for the calculation of pool and surface temperature profiles has been difficult to resolve because of the lack of reliable data from continuous-casting operations. Certainly the approaches taken by Hills, Kung and Pollock, and Mizikar are appealing due to their simplicity. Moreover Brimacombe and Weinberg[12] have now shown experimentally that if one chooses Eq. (5) or (6), where h_M or $\bar{h}_M$ are calculated from an integral heat balance over the mould, pool profiles can be predicted which agree closely with measured profiles. However, for this model to achieve widespread use, reliable values of $\bar{h}_M$ need to be ascertained under a variety of casting conditions.

In this work the choice of Eq. (3) and (5) as suitable boundary conditions is analysed in detail. The equations are used in the calculation of pool profiles which are then compared to profiles measured in tests conducted at

---

† T_0 may be expressed relative to a water temperature of zero. Then Eq. (5) is $-q_0 = \bar{h}_M T_0$

Manitoba Rolling Mills, Selkirk, Canada where radioactive tracers were added to the mould to delineate the solid shell. Casting data have also been gathered from several hundred casts which make it possible to consider the effect of withdrawal rate on heat flux to the mould.

METHOD OF CALCULATION

The integral profile solution of Eq. (1), presented by Hills,[5] has been used predominantly in the theoretical calculations. Although the formulation assumes constant thermophysical properties, a negligible freezing range and unidirectional conduction, it has been found by Brimacombe and Weinberg[12] to predict realistic pool profiles for billets in the mould region. In the present work, also involving square billets, unidirectional conduction is assumed to apply only for the centre of the faces from which shell thickness measurements were taken. The calculations are restricted to the mould and upper spray zones where the steel shell is still thin relative to the half width of the billet. Using a quadratic equation to approximate the temperature profile in the solid shell, Hills[5] derived Eqs. (7) and (8) for the case of zero superheat

$$\frac{d\theta}{d\xi} = -\frac{\lambda(dY/d\xi)^2 + Y(\partial Q/\partial \xi)}{1 + Y(\partial Q/\partial \theta)} \quad . \quad . \quad . \quad (7)$$

$$\frac{dY}{d\xi} = \frac{2\Lambda}{\Gamma + \sqrt{\Gamma^2 + 4\Lambda\Omega}} \quad . \quad . \quad . \quad (8)$$

where

$$\Omega = \lambda Y[4 + Y(\partial Q/\partial \theta)] \quad . \quad . \quad . \quad (9)$$

$$\Gamma = [6\lambda + 4(1 - \theta) - 2YQ][1 + Y(\partial Q/\partial \theta)] \quad . \quad (10)$$

$$\Lambda = 6Q[1 + Y(\partial Q/\partial \theta)] - 3Y^2(\partial Q/\partial \xi) \quad . \quad (11)$$

Here Q is the dimensionless form of the surface heat flux, q_0, obtained for the three types of boundary conditions by recasting Eqs. (3), (5), and (6) in dimensionless terms:

assumed heat flux

$$Q = 1 - \beta\xi^{\frac{1}{2}} \quad . \quad . \quad . \quad . \quad . \quad (12)$$

constant heat transfer coefficient

$$Q = \theta \quad . \quad . \quad . \quad . \quad . \quad . \quad (13)$$

linearly increasing heat transfer coefficient

$$Q = (1 - \gamma\xi)\theta \quad . \quad . \quad . \quad . \quad (14)$$

Equations (7) and (8) with the appropriate Q must be solved simultaneously to obtain the dimensionless surface temperature, θ, and the dimensionless shell thickness, Y, of the billets as a function of dimensionless time (or dimensionless distance below the meniscus), ξ. The zero superheat approximation applies to continuous casting if the superheat is lumped in with the latent heat. For low carbon steel, λ normally has a value of 0·3. Hills[2] has presented plots of Y and θ v. ξ for the case of the constant heat transfer coefficient. Brimacombe and Weinberg[12] have provided similar graphs for the linearly decreasing heat transfer coefficient. Plots for the

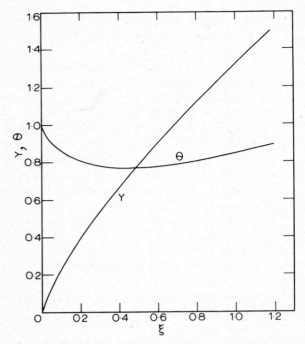

1 *Plot of dimensionless shell thickness, Y, and dimensionless surface temperature, θ against dimensionless time in the mould, ξ, with Eq. (3) as the surface boundary condition; β = 0·834*

assumed heat flux case are shown in Fig. 1 where $\beta = 0.834$.

To obtain real pool and surface temperature profiles from the dimensionless plots given by Hills and Brimacombe and Weinberg the value of the heat transfer coefficient must be known. For the spray region the heat transfer coefficients have been determined for each zone in which the physical characteristics of the sprays are known from the correlations of Mizikar.[13] For the mould region $\bar{h}_M$ or h_0 can be obtained from an integral heat balance over the mould as shown by Hills.[2] The integral heat balances for the two cases have been presented graphically as dimensionless heat extracted by the mould per unit length of mould perimeter, Q^* v. dimensionless mould length, X^*, by Hills[2] and Brimacombe and Weinberg[12] respectively.

The abrupt change in cooling at the surface of the billet as it passes from the mould through successive spray zones has been treated using a method recently formulated by Hills and Moore.[14] A transition time, defined as the time taken for the new temperature profile in the solid shell to be established after a sudden cooling change is calculated, employing Eq. (15) which is solved simultaneously with Eqs. (7) and (8)

$$\frac{dy^*}{d\xi} = \frac{6Q' - y^*(\partial Q'/\partial \xi) - y^*(\partial Q'/\partial \theta)(d\theta/d\xi)}{y^*(\partial Q'/\partial \xi) + Q'} \quad . \quad (15)$$

The expression for Q' depends on the relationship used to describe the surface heat flux before and after the change. Three examples are given below for a mould to sprays transition

$\bar{h}_M T_0$ changing to $\bar{h}_s T_0$

$$Q' = \frac{(h^* - 1)\theta}{1 + 0.5h^*\sqrt{y^*}} \quad . \quad . \quad . \quad (16)$$

$h_0(1 - \eta x)T_0$ changing to $\bar{h}_s T_0$

$$Q' = \frac{(h^* - (1 - \gamma\xi)\theta}{1 + 0.5h^*\sqrt{y^*}} \qquad \qquad (17)$$

$q_{0,0} - b\sqrt{t}$ changing to $\bar{h}_s T_0$

$$Q' = \frac{h^*\theta - (1 - \beta\sqrt{\xi})}{1 + 0.5h^*\sqrt{y^*}} \qquad \qquad (18)$$

where

$$h^* = \frac{\bar{h}_s T_s}{q_{0,0}} \qquad \qquad (19)$$

The use of Eq. (15) is illustrated in Fig. 2 which shows the transition zone between the end of the mould and the zone 1 sprays for test 3 (to be described later). $\sqrt{y^*_{M1}}$ is the dimensionless depth in the solid shell to which the newly established temperature profile has penetrated after the cooling change. When $\sqrt{y^*_{M1}}$ is equal to Y, the dimensionless shell thickness, the transition period is ended. The value of ξ at this point is designated τ^*_{M1}. Over the transition period the rate of solidification proceeds as if the billet were still in the mould. After the transition period is ended, the surface temperature is recalculated and the calculation of Y and θ as a function of ξ is continued with the new surface boundary condition for the sprays. The same procedure is followed as the billet passes from the zone 1 to zone 2 sprays. h^*_{12} is then the ratio of heat transfer coefficients of zone 2 to zone 1. Finally, the theoretical shell thickness has also been calculated for the mould region with an expression given by Mizikar[4]

$$y_t = 2.82(10^{-3})\sqrt{t} - 7.6(10^{-4}) \qquad \qquad (20)$$

from his finite difference solution of Eq. (1).

EXPERIMENTAL

Continuous-casting machines

Manitoba Rolling Mills has two twin strand continuous-casting machines designed to produce several sizes of billets including the 10·1 and 13·3 cm square billets used in the tests. A schematic drawing of one of the strands is given in Fig. 3. The strands each have a low head, curved mould which is lubricated with rapeseed oil at a rate of about 110 cm³ per 1 000 kg of billets. The moulds are 0·814 m long, have a radius of curvature of 6·7 m and are oscillated with a stroke length of 3·8 cm. During normal operations steel is poured continuously from a single tundish into the two moulds of a machine. The billets emerging from the moulds, usually at a casting rate of 3·6 to 6·4 cm s^{-1} (for 10·1 cm and 13·3 cm sizes), enter a spray region which consists of three zones. Details of the spray zones are listed in Table 1. Below the sprays the billets enter a radiation cooling zone, then pass through straightener rolls, and finally are cut into lengths by diagonal downcut shears. Further details on the continuous-casting machines and the facilities at Manitoba Rolling Mills in general are given by Hester et al.[15]

Procedure

ADDITION OF RADIOACTIVE MATERIAL

Four tests were performed in which a small piece of radioactive gold, Au^{198}, with an activity of 75 millicuries was added to the liquid in the mould. The gold in the form of a cylinder, 0·3 cm diameter by 0·64 cm, was held in the end of a 0·64 cm diameter steel rod which was inserted into the liquid steel about 15 cm beneath the surface directly below the input steam. The gold then melted within 5 s and mixed into the liquid pool. Simultaneously with the gold addition in tests 2 to 4, a small pellet of tungsten, 1·25 cm diameter by 1·25 cm, with 2 millicuries of Co^{60} sealed inside was added to the liquid pool to mark the bottom. This method has

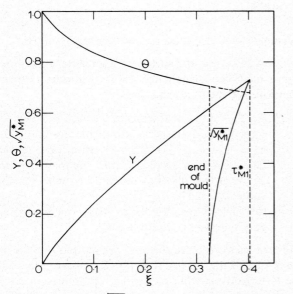

2 Plot of Y, θ and $\sqrt{y^*_{M1}}$ v. ξ showing the transition period between the mould and the zone 1 sprays for test 3

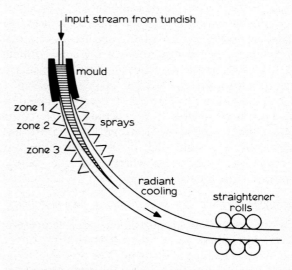

3 Schematic drawing of a continuous-casting machine at Manitoba Rolling Mills

TABLE 1   Characteristics of spray regions

Zone	Zone length, m	Spray configuration, per face	Distance between nozzle and billet face, m × 10²		Spray pressure,† N m⁻² × 10⁻⁵	Average water flux,‡ m³m⁻² s⁻¹ × 10²		Heat transfer coefficient, kcal m⁻² s⁻¹ °C	
			10 cm	13·3 cm		10 cm	13·3 cm	10 cm	13·3 cm
1	0·3	1 pair of nozzles* every 7·6 cm. Nozzles in pair 5–7 cm apart	12·7	14·6	2·07	2·24	2·04	0·45	0·41
2	1·52	Single nozzle every 10·2 cm	12·7	14·6	2·07	0·95	0·78	0·22	0·21
3	3·66	Single nozzle every 30·5 cm	12·7	14·6	1·04	0·20	0·20	0·1	0·1

* Nozzles are Spraying Systems Type $\frac{1}{4}$ HH 10 SQ
† Estimated for the spray header from pressure gauges located upstream from the sprays
‡ Estimated from graphs presented by Mizikar[13] for $\frac{1}{4}$ GG 10 nozzles

been used previously by Varga and Fodor,[16] Gomer and Andrews,[17] and Weinberg and Morton.[18] The tests were conducted during normal casting operations in the plant. The radioactive additions were made about half an hour after casting had begun to ensure that casting conditions were relatively stable and at steady state. Tests 1 and 2 were conducted sequentially during the casting of a single heat.

MEASUREMENT OF POOL DEPTH AND SHELL THICKNESS

Once the steel had cooled the position of the tungsten pellet was located (to within 2·5 cm) with a geiger counter. The pool depth was taken as the distance between the pellet and the meniscus which was subsequently found from autoradiographs. The position of the pellet relative to the centreline of the billet was ascertained by flame cutting the billet transversely next to the pellet. The pellet was then visible on the newly exposed surface. The billets were torch cut into 18 cm lengths, then, with a band saw, each section was cut in half along its longitudinal axis. In the case of test 4 the high manganese content of the steel severely reduced the rate of the saw cutting with the result that fewer sections were cut. The cut surfaces were faced on a lathe, then exposed to X-ray film for autoradiography. Also some faces were surface ground and exposed to contrast-process ortho film to obtain better resolution of the solid structure. Solid shell thicknesses were measured to ±0·05 cm from the autoradiographs at intervals of 1·27 cm (except for test 4) allowing for a 1·27 cm gap between sections where steel had been melted away during flame cutting. Measurements were taken from both sides of the autoradiographs. The solid shell in these autoradiographs corresponded to the sides which faced the centre of curvature of the billets.

MEASUREMENT OF CASTING PARAMETERS

With the exception of the liquid pool temperature, casting parameters were measured with instruments permanently installed in the plant. The flow rate of water through the mould was continuously monitored by a magnetic flow meter while the temperature rise of the

water was measured with thermocouples located in the inlet and outlet mould manifolds. Mould-water† flow rate and temperature rise as well as the withdrawal rate were read from a strip recorder. The instruments had been calibrated before the tests. The water pressure for each zone of the sprays was read on pressure gauges some distance upstream from the spray manifold. The temperature of the molten steel in the mould in tests 1 and 2 was measured with a Pt–Pt 13%Rh thermocouple sheathed in quartz. The liquid pool temperature measurement was made immediately before the radioactive materials were added. The effective mould length was estimated to be 0·685 m since the meniscus was about 0·13 m below the top of the mould during the tests.

RESULTS

Heat flow measurements

The flow rate and temperature rise of cooling water in the mould, casting speed and other parameters are given in Table 2. Heat transfer coefficients estimated from Mizikar's data[13] for the three spray zones are presented in Table 1.

Calculated shell thickness and surface temperatures

The shell thickness and surface temperature in the mould region have been calculated using the integral profile equations for the following cases:

(i) $\bar{h}_M$, the mould heat transfer coefficient, has a constant value over the length of the mould

(ii) $h_M = h_0(1 - 0.73x)$, the heat transfer coefficient decreases with distance below the meniscus until at the mould bottom its value is half the initial value, h_0

(iii) the surface heat flux is given by the Savage and Pritchard relationship, Eq. (3).

The profiles for each of the tests are plotted in Figs. 4–7. Cases (i) and (ii) are given as dot-dash lines, marked A and B respectively while case (iii) is represented by a solid

---

† Mould-water temperature was taken on average to be 10°C

TABLE 2 Casting conditions and heat flow data for the mould

							Mould water			
Test	Billet size, m × 10²	%C	Mould length, m	Casting speed, m s⁻¹ × 10²	Pool temp., °C	Surface temp. straightener, °C	Pool depth,† m	Flow rate, m³ s⁻¹ × 10²	Temp. rise, °C	Heat flux, kcal m⁻² s⁻¹
1	13·3 × 13·3	0·11–0·16	0·685	3·50	1 501	1 055	—	2·78	4·7	358
2	13·3 × 13·3	0·11–0·16	0·685	4·40	1 501	1 055	6·1	2·78	5·0	380
3	10·1 × 10·1	0·13–0·18	0·685	4·65	—	1 010 ± 11	3·36	2·54	5·6	510
4	10·1 × 10·1	0·33–0·37*	0·685	5·50	—	—	3·66	2·61	6·1	572

* Mn: 0·9–1·05%
† As determined from position of tungsten pellet

TABLE 3 Thermophysical properties of the steel

Property	Value
Thermal conductivity, k	7·02 (10⁻³) kcal m⁻¹ s⁻¹ °C⁻¹
Specific heat, C	0·16 kcal kg⁻¹ °C⁻¹
Latent heat of solidification, L	65 kcal kg⁻¹
Density, ρ	7 400 kg m⁻³
Solidus temperature, 0·1 to 0·2%C	1 495°C
Solidus temperature, 0·35%C	1 465°C

line. The physical properties of the steel employed in the calculations are listed in Table 3. The values of dimensionless heat flow, Q^*, dimensionless mould length, X^*, and heat transfer coefficients for the tests are presented in Table 4. In addition the shell thickness calculated from Mizikar's Eq. (20) are included as dashed lines in Figs. 4–7. The pool and surface temperature profiles have also been calculated for the zone 1 and part of the zone 2 sprays using the integral profile Eqs. (7), (8), and (15), and the spray heat transfer coefficients given in Table 1. For tests 1 and 2 the case (ii) profiles only have been extended into the sprays while for tests 3 and 4 only the case (i) profiles have been calculated beyond the mould bottom (Figs. 4–7). The dimensionless time, τ^*, and the ratio of heat transfer coefficients used in the calculations, h^*, are presented in Table 4.

Autoradiographs

A composite of the autoradiographs obtained in tests 1 and 2 is shown in Fig. 8. The billet sections have been outlined in black by exposing the X-ray film to light. The bottom of the mould is shown at sections 1-D and 2-D by horizontal line segments. The dark area within the billets indicates the presence of radioactive gold while the white strip running down either side is the solid shell where the gold had not penetrated.

It is important to note that from the meniscus down to section 1-E for test 1 and 2-F for test 2, the boundary between the dark and light areas is sharp. Below these sections, however, the boundary becomes indistinct with the solid shell appearing to thicken rapidly. In test 3 the boundary was sharply defined further, down to section J, on which it too became blurred. The sharp boundary is thought to result from good mixing of the gold in the liquid pool and should, therefore, coincide closely with the solid/liquid interface. The poorly defined boundary

is then believed to be caused by poor mixing in the liquid. As a result, measurements of shell thickness for comparison with model predictions have been taken only from the upper sections where the pool profile was clearly defined. It is also evident that the shell thickness fluctuates within the mould. In sections 1-A and 2-A a thin segment of shell was observed well above the continuous shell. This would indicate that the shell had torn, probably on the upstroke of the mould.

From the autoradiograph of the cross-section obtained between sections 2-C and 2-D one sees that the solid shell is not uniform for all faces. For example, the upper and lower shell are slightly thicker than the left-hand shell. The shell for the right face does not seem to be sharply

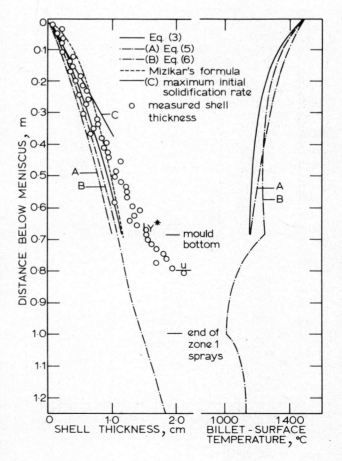

4 *Liquid pool profiles and surface temperature profiles for test 1*

TABLE 4   Parameters used in the integral profile calculations

Test	Q*	X*	Constant, $\bar{h}_M$ $\bar{h}_M$ (kcal m⁻² s⁻¹ °C⁻¹)	τ^*_{M1}	h^*_{M1}	τ^*_{12}	h^*_{12}	$h_M = h_0(1 - 0.73x)$ X*	h_0 (kcal m⁻² s⁻¹ °C⁻¹)	τ^*_{M1}	h^*_{M1}	τ^*_{12}	h^*_{12}
1	0·372	0·189	0·283	—	—	—	—	0·330	0·373	0·405	1·10	0·753	0·512
2	0·351	0·164	0·295	—	—	—	—	0·286	0·390	0·344	1·05	0·582	0·512
3	0·459	0·325	0·427	0·403	1·05	0·695	0·49	0·558	0·560	—	—	—	—
4	0·484	0·375	0·499	0·475	0·903	0·597	0·49	0·651	0·658	—	—	—	—

defined. For the 10·1 cm billets the shell thickness also varied significantly from the centre of the faces to the corners as seen in Fig. 9.

Measured shell thickness

Thicknesses of the solid shell for the two sides facing the centre of curvature for test 3 are given in Fig. 10. The top and bottom faces refer to the faces closest to and furthest from the centre of curvature respectively. It is seen that a reasonable average curve can be drawn through the points. The average shell thicknesses for the four tests, shown by open circles, are presented in Figs. 4–7. The depth at which the shell boundary became unclear is indicated by the letter U.

Pool depths

The depths of the liquid pools, as determined from the position of the tungsten pellets,† are given in Table 2. The tungsten pellets were found to lie well below the bottom of the dark cone delineated by the radioactive gold, the difference being about 1·2 m in tests 3 and 4 and 3·05 m in test 2. Thus, it is clear that the gold was poorly mixed in the lower regions of the pool.

---

† Falling rate of the pellet was calculated to be about 1 m s⁻¹

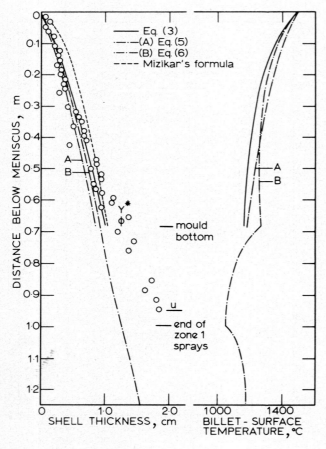

○ measured shell thickness

5   Liquid pool profiles and surface-temperature profiles for test 2

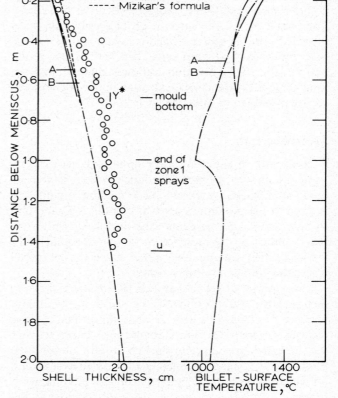

○ measured shell thickness

6   Liquid pool profiles and surface-temperature profiles for test 3

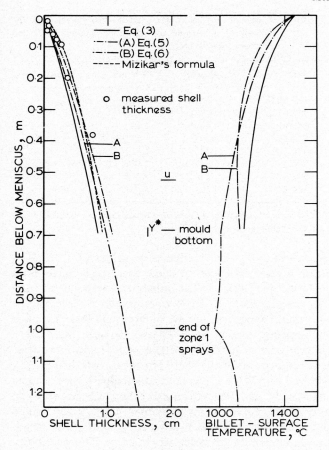

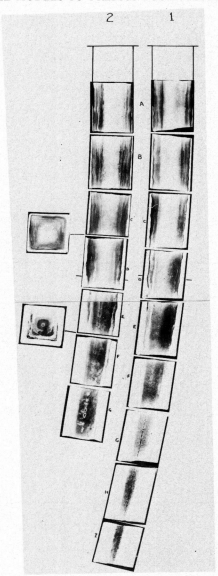

7 Liquid pool profiles and surface-temperature profiles for test 4

DISCUSSION

Comparison between calculated and measured pool profiles

MOULD

Considering first the pool profiles calculated from the measured heat flow data-curves *A* and *B* in Figs. 4–7 it is apparent that close agreement with the measured profiles is obtained only over the upper half of the mould in tests 2–4. Curve *B*, calculated for the case of a mould heat transfer coefficient which decreased with distance below the meniscus to half its initial value, seems to give a better fit than *A* for which a constant heat transfer coefficient was assumed. In the lower half of the mould the measured shells are significantly thicker than the calculated values, culminating in a difference of about 0·5 cm at the bottom of the mould. In test 1 the measured shell appears to be thicker than calculated over most of the mould. This lack of agreement is puzzling when compared to results obtained previously in tests on a triple billet Weybridge mould at the Western Canada Steel Company.[12] There, for most tests a good fit was obtained between measured billet shell thicknesses and calculations based on the same model. The pool profile from one of the tests, the centre billet (14 cm × 14 cm) cast at a rate of 0·0221 m s^{-1}, is given in Fig. 11.

The reason for the misfit in the Manitoba Rolling Mill tests appears to be related to uncertainties in either the measured shell thickness or measurement of the mould

8 Composite of autoradiographs from tests 1 and 2

9 Autoradiograph of cross-section from test 4 taken from 0·6 m below meniscus

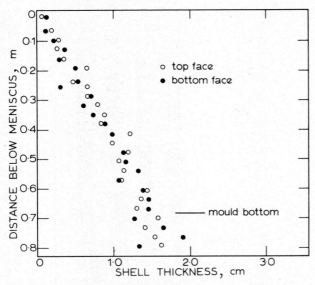

10   *Shell thickness of top and bottom faces from test 3*

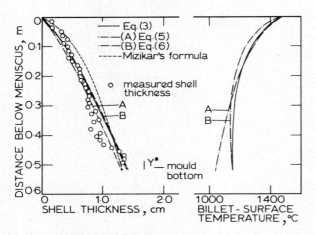

11   *Liquid pool profiles and surface temperature profiles for test 3
—Western Canada Steel*

heat flow data. This is based on a comparison of the measured shell thickness at the bottom of the mould, Y_M, with the maximum possible shell thickness there, Y^*. The hypothetical Y^* is defined as the shell thickness which would be obtained at the bottom of the mould if the entire shell was at the solidus temperature. It is calculated from Eq. (21) which is based on an overall heat balance on the mould.

$$Y^* = \frac{1}{2}\left[l - \sqrt{l^2 - \frac{(\bar{q}_0 - u\rho C\,\Delta T_{sh}l^2)}{u\rho L}} \right] \quad . \qquad (21)$$

Since the actual shell results from the withdrawal of both latent heat and heat to bring the shell temperature well below the solidus temperature (*see* the surface temperature profiles in Figs. 4–7), it is clear that $Y^* > Y_M$ for each test. The Y^* have been calculated for the tests, assuming that five degrees of superheat, ΔT_{sh}, were also removed from the liquid metal in the mould. They are compared to the Y_M in Table 5 and Figs. 4–7. It is seen that for tests 1 and 2, Y_M and Y^* are virtually the same, an improbable situation, whereas for test 3 Y^* is 21%

TABLE 5   Measured and maximum possible shell thickness at the bottom of the mould for Manitoba Rolling Mills and Western Canada Steel

Test	Y_M, cm	$Y,*\ddagger$ cm	Difference, %
MRM 1	1·5	1·51	1
MRM 2	1·2	1·25	4
MRM 3	1·46	1·76	21
MRM 4	—	1·63	—
WCS 3	1·37	2·13	56
WCS 12	1·27	2·36	86
WCS 13	1·27	1·69	33
WCS 14	1·12	2·13	91

‡ Y^* calculated assuming 5°C superheat removed by the mould and no heat removed from billet shell

greater than Y_M. For comparison, values of Y^* and Y_M from several Western Canada Steel tests have been included in Table 5. The difference between Y^* and Y_M, ranging from 33 to 91%, is greater for these tests. One might expect the greater difference in this case since the casting speeds at Western Canada Steel were generally lower (0·0212 to 0·0339 m s^{-1}) and more heat was removed from the shell. However, two of the tests, MRM 1 and WCS 13, were conducted with similar casting speeds, and the percentage differences between Y_M and Y^* are still markedly dissimilar. The low percentage difference for both tests 1 and 2 suggests that one of the measurements in the tests was in error. The possibility that errors had been encountered in the measurement of the heat flow data has to be considered seriously. The measurement of the temperature rise of the mould water is probably the most suspect since the temperature differences were relatively small, 5–6°C (Table 2).

To investigate the heat flow question further casting data were gathered from 500 casts at the Manitoba Rolling Mills and the average mould heat fluxes were calculated. They are presented as a function of withdrawal rate in Figs. 12 and 13 for the 13·3 cm × 13·3 cm and 10·1 cm × 10·1 cm billets respectively. The heat fluxes measured in the tests are identified by a closed

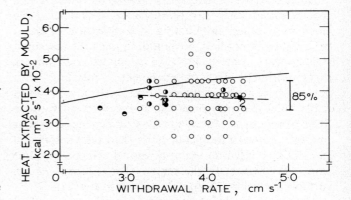

12   *Relation between average heat flux to the mould and the withdrawal rate, 13·3 cm billets*

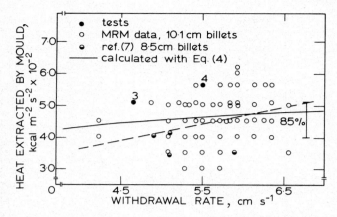

13 Relation between average heat flux to the mould and the withdrawal rate, 10·1 cm billets

circle and the appropriate number. Least square plots, denoted by dashed lines, have been superimposed on the graphs. The scatter of the data is deceiving since 85% of the heat fluxes for the 13·3 cm billets lay between 340 and 435 kcal m^{-2} s. For the 10·1 cm billets the same percentage of heat fluxes were found between 400 and 510 kcal m^{-2} s^{-1}. These ranges are denoted by a vertical bar in Figs. 12 and 13. Clearly the heat fluxes measured for tests 1 and 2 lie very close to the average. This coincidence reduces the possibility that the instruments had been misread during tests 1 and 2. It is still quite possible, however, that the instruments were reading incorrectly at the time of the tests and had done so over a period of months, despite having been calibrated. The heat fluxes for tests 3 and 4 are considerably higher than average although still within the range of the other data. The reason for the high fluxes is uncertain, although, as discussed previously, there is no reason to suspect their accuracy.

It is interesting to compare the measured heat fluxes with the flux calculated from the relationship, Eq. (4), experimentally determined by Savage and Pritchard.[11] In previous work[12] at the Western Canada Steel Company it had been found that Eq. (4) gave a reasonable estimate of actual heat fluxes. A plot of average heat flux *v*. withdrawal rate, calculated from Eq. (4), is drawn as a solid line in Figs. 12 and 13. The agreement between it and the data for the 10·1 cm billets is remarkably good. However, for the 13·3 cm billets the line lies roughly 10% above the average of the measured heat fluxes and 13% above the fluxes for tests 1 and 2. This comparison lends further weight to the argument that the heat flux measurements for tests 1 and 2 may be somewhat low.

Since the measured heat flux appears to be acceptable for the 10·1 cm billets another reason must be sought to explain the misfit between calculated and measured pool profiles in test 3. One of the assumptions that has been made in the calculations is that the shell thickness is the same at any point on the perimeter of the billet at a given distance below the meniscus. This seems to be true for the 13·3 cm billets as shown by the cross-section in Fig. 8. However, upon examination of the autoradiograph of a

cross-section from test 4 (Fig. 9) it can be seen that the centres of the faces of the 10·1 cm billet have considerably thicker shells than the corners. Although autoradiographs were not taken of cross-sections in test 3 it is likely that the same behaviour would have been observed. Under these circumstances the measured shell thickness taken from the centre of the faces would be greater than the calculated value. Further measurements are required to determine whether the non-uniformity in shell thickness could cause the observed discrepancy. There remains the possibility that the gold had not mixed well enough throughout the liquid pool to reach the solid/liquid boundary. If this were the case the apparent solid shell delineated by the gold-rich region would be thicker than the actual shell. This is thought to be unlikely, however, in view of the sharp boundary which was observed to separate the gold-rich and gold-free areas.

The pool profiles calculated with the integral profile equations and the assumed heat flux (solid lines in Figs. 4 to 7) provide a better fit to the measured profiles than curves *A* or *B* for tests 1 and 2. This is an expected result since the average rate of heat extracted by the mould according to Eq. (4) is greater than the measured rate for both tests. The fit for tests 3 and 4 is poorer than *A* or *B* for the opposite reason, i.e. the calculated rate is less than the measured rate. The pool profiles predicted from Mizikar's model[4] are noticeably thicker than any of the integral profile curves in the upper half of the mould. Since Mizikar appears to have used a larger latent heat in his calculations one would have expected his profiles to be thinner. Hills[5] has shown, however, that the shell thickness predicted by Mizikar is greater in the upper regions of the mould than the theoretical maximum, $[y_t]_{max}$ which, like Y^*, can be calculated assuming no cooling of the solid shell occurs (Eq. (22)).

$$[y_t]_{max} = \frac{640x}{u\rho L} \qquad . \qquad . \qquad . \qquad . \qquad (22)$$

$[y_t]_{max}$ has been calculated with the thermophysical properties used by Mizikar for test 1, and is shown as line *C* in Fig. 4. It can be seen that the shell thickness predicted by Mizikar remains above the line for the first 36% of the mould. Identical results were obtained for the other tests. At the bottom of the mould, however, the Mizikar line agrees quite well with the integral profile solutions.

SPRAYS

The agreement between the measured and calculated pool profiles is best for test 3 (Fig. 6) in which the solid shell was sharply outlined to the furthest depth. The profiles are almost parallel from the mould bottom, eventually meeting at 1·4 m below the meniscus. From this, the calculated rate of solidification in the sprays appears to be reasonable, indicating further that the values of the zone 1 and 2 spray heat transfer coefficients (Table 1) used in the surface boundary condition were correct. Contrary to the above results the measured shells from tests 1 and 2 (Figs. 4 and 5) thicken more rapidly in the zone 1 spray region than the predicted shells. The results for test 1 may not be meaningful, however, since in the short space between the bottom of the mould and the beginning of the diffuse shell outline the gold may not have been mixed sufficiently well in the liquid pool to reach the shell wall. In test 2 a higher zone 1 spray heat transfer coefficient would seem to be required to boost the measured rate. The conflicting results from tests 2 and 3 leave the question of the applicability of Mizikar's heat transfer coefficient data unresolved at this time.

Calculated surface temperatures

The most important feature of these calculations is that the surface temperature of the billets in the spray region remains well above 870°C, the austenite to ferrite phase transformation. This is desirable, as Mizikar[4] has pointed out, since this transformation is accompanied by a large volume change which could lead to cracking of the shell. Within the mould the three calculated temperature profiles are quite similar. Only for the case of the decreasing mould heat transfer coefficient (curve B) is any reheating of the surface of the billet predicted.

Surface boundary condition in the mould

The processes of heat transfer in the mould are very complex as illustrated by the observations of tearing of the shell in the mould (Fig. 8) and the non-uniform shell thickness between the centre of the face and the corners (Fig. 9). From these observations it is apparent that the heat flux from the surface of the billets must be an extremely complicated function of position relative both to the meniscus and the centre of the faces. It is therefore unlikely that attempts to simulate these processes with a simple two-zone model, as formulated previously, will be successful. Rather it is suggested that the surface boundary condition in the mould can be better and more simply characterized either by a constant overall heat transfer coefficient as first proposed by Hills[2] and later confirmed by Brimacombe and Weinberg,[12] or the assumed heat flux, Eq. (3), initially adopted by Mizikar.[4] The problem with the first suggestion in the past has been the lack of reliable heat transfer coefficients reported in the literature. Similarly with the assumed heat flux, there appears to have been little effort, beyond that originally made by Savage and Pritchard[11] and Krainer and Tarmann,[19] to confirm that Eq. (4) related to the heat fluxes measured in the mould of a commercial continuous-casting machine. The data presented in Figs. 12 and 13 now make it clear that Eq. (4) does give a good approximation of the average heat flux in the mould. The data have also been used to calculate average overall heat transfer coefficients with the equation

$$\bar{h}_M = 1.551 \left[\frac{X}{upCk} \right]^{0.141} \cdot \left[\frac{\bar{q}_0}{T_s} \right]^{1.282} \qquad . \qquad . \qquad (23)$$

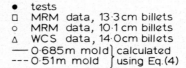

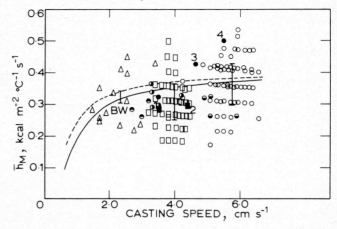

14   Effect of casting speed on the average mould heat transfer coefficient

Equation (23) has been obtained from the relationship between dimensionless rate of heat extracted by the mould and the dimensionless effective mould length. These coefficients and others reported previously[12] from the Western Canada Steel Company are plotted as a function of casting speed in Fig. 14. Again the closed symbols with the appropriate numbers indicate the test heat transfer coefficients. The vertical bar marked BW shows the range of heat transfer coefficients which were suggested by Brimacombe and Weinberg[12] to be most typical for a casting speed of 2.35 cm s^{-1} at Western Canada Steel. The vertical bars situated in the midst of the open squares and circles signify the ranges over which 85% of the heat transfer coefficients were found for the 13.3 and 10.1 cm billets respectively. Heat transfer coefficients also have been calculated for different casting speeds with average heat fluxes given by Eq. (4). These are superimposed on Fig. 14 as a dashed line for the 0.51 m mould from Western Canada Steel and a solid line for the 0.685 m mould at Manitoba Rolling Mills. With the exception of the 13.3 cm billets the agreement between these curves and the data is good. This is not a surprising result in view of the coincidence between calculated and measured heat fluxes in Figs. 12 and 13.

An important conclusion which may tentatively be drawn from Fig. 14 is that the mould heat transfer coefficient may be more predictable than originally supposed. With relatively little data at his disposal Hills[2] had suggested that the heat transfer coefficient would vary widely between different moulds. Here it is seen that the coefficients for a triple billet Weybridge mould correlate well with coefficients from a curved single billet mould. This correlation is being investigated further with data from slab, bloom, and beam blank moulds. The development of this correlation does not mean that the heat transfer processes in the mould are characterized for every cast, however. From Fig. 14 it is obvious that the heat transfer coefficient can be well above or below the expected value. Thus other factors may play an important role in determining the rate of heat extraction by the mould. These may include the quantity and type of mould lubricant, the mould taper, condition of the mould surfaces, radius of curvature at the mould corners, and alignment of the mould with the withdrawal rolls.

RECOMMENDED LIQUID POOL AND SURFACE TEMPERATURE PROFILES IN THE MOULD

Since the Savage and Pritchard heat flux relationship holds well over a range of casting speeds it has been used with Eqs. (7) and (8) to calculate the shell thickness and surface temperature as a function of time in the mould (*see* Fig. 15). Figure 15 can be employed to determine the pool and surface temperature profiles under real process conditions although its use should be restricted to $<0.35\%$ carbon steels since the physical properties of low carbon steel were employed in the calculations. Also for billets the plots apply only to the centre region of the faces. Gautier *et al.*[7] have made measurements of the surface temperatures of 8·5, 10·5, and 12·0 cm square billets which allow an independent check on the validity of the surface temperature profile in Fig. 15. These workers used light pipes to channel light, from the billets emerging from the mould, to a two-colour pyrometer. The measured temperatures and mould heat flow data are presented in Table 6. The mould heat fluxes are plotted as a function of casting speed in Figs. 12 and 13, and the $\bar{h}_{\mathrm{M}}$ derived from the casting

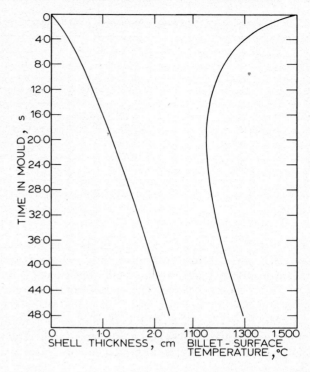

15   *Shell thickness and surface temperature as a function of time in the mould*

data are given in Fig. 14. The data can be seen to fit into the same range of values that were obtained from Manitoba Rolling Mills. The dwell times, X/u, have been calculated ($X = 0.65$ m) and the predicted surface temperatures obtained using Fig. 15. From Table 6, the predicted temperature is seen to be 2 to 4% less than the measured value for the 8·5 cm billets and, with one exception, 7 to 8% greater than measured for the 10·5

TABLE 6   Calculated and measured surface temperatures at the bottom of the mould

Cast no.	$\bar{q}_0$, kcal m^{-2} s^{-1}	u, m s^{-1}, $\times 10^2$	$\dfrac{X}{u}$, s	T_0, °C Measured‡	From Fig. 15	Calculated with $\bar{h}_{\mathrm{M}}$
8·5 × 8·5 cm						
42 771	406	4·9	13·3	1 237	1 188	1 142
13 440	411	5·1	12·8	1 234	1 190	1 142
13 401	350	5·9	11·0	1 228	1 200	1 242
13 407	345	5·1	12·8	1 210	1 190	1 220
10·5 × 10·5 cm						
13 755	362	3·3	19·7	1 084	1 175	1 100
13 756	401	4·2	15·5	1 099	1 180	1 108
13 757	396	3·5	18·6	1 091	1 176	1 070
13 761	369	3·5	18·6	1 093	1 176	1 107
13 767	404	3·3	19·7	1 089	1 176	1 038
13 763	430	3·3	19·7	1 089	1 176	1 007
12·0 × 12·0 cm						
42 803	330	3·0	21·7	1 100	1 178	1 123
13 427	346	2·7	24·1	1 106	1 184	1 075
13 428	378	3·7	20·7	1 054	1 177	1 070

‡ Average of the four faces of the billet measured by Gautier *et al.*[7]

TABLE 7   Calculated and measured thicknesses at the bottom of the mould

Test	$\bar{q}_0$, kcal m^{-2} s^{-1}	u, m s^{-1} $\times 10^2$	$\dfrac{X}{u}$, s	Y_M, cm Measured‡	From Fig. 15	Calculated with $\bar{h}_M$
3	392	2·12	24·0	1·37	1·36	1·27
9	286	2·75	18·5	0·79	1·13	0·80
12	469	2·34	21·8	1·27	1·28	1·37
13	515	3·39	15·0	1·27	0·96	1·02
14	465	2·54	20·0	1·12	1·20	1·20

‡ Average of two sides of the billet, reported by Brimacombe and Weinberg[12]

and 12·0 cm billets. This agreement is considerably better than was obtained by Gautier *et al.*, whose model predicted surface temperatures were consistently 7 to 18 % greater than measured. The surface temperature at the mould bottom has also been calculated using the $\bar{h}_M$, displayed in Figs. 12 and 13, in the surface boundary condition. This gives values that are ± 1 to 3 % differerent from the measured values, although in four cases the difference was 8 %.

Measured shell thicknesses reported by Brimacombe and Weinberg[12] can be utilized to check the reliability of the shell thickness plot in Fig. 15. The shell thicknesses measured at the bottom of the mould for five tests are given in Table 7. The calculated values from Fig. 15 agree very well with these for three of the tests. For the other two tests it should be noted that the measured heat fluxes were far from the average value. Good agreement between measured and calculated values is obtained for four tests if $\bar{h}_M$ is used. From these comparisons it may be concluded that Fig. 15 can be used with confidence in predicting liquid pool and surface temperature profiles for the mould region of a commercial continuous-casting machine.

CONCLUSION

Model predicted pool profiles of continuously cast billets for the mould and upper spray region have been compared to measured profiles. The predicted shells, calculated using a mould heat transfer coefficient or an assumed surface heat flux relationship coincided reasonably well with the measured shell in the upper half of the mould for three of four tests. However, in the lower half of the mould and in the spray zone the predicted shell was thinner than the measured shell. In two of the tests involving 13·3 $\times$ 13·3 cm billets the discrepancy was traced to apparent errors in the measurement of the rate of heat extraction by the mould. For 10·1 $\times$ 10·1 cm billets non-uniformity in the shell thickness between the centre of the faces and the corners may have caused the measured shell to be too thick. Additional heat-flux data for the mould has established the reliability of the

Savage and Pritchard heat flux relationship for use as a surface boundary condition in the mould. Overall heat transfer coefficients for the mould, calculated from this data for a curved mould, have been successfully correlated to coefficients previously obtained for a Weybridge mould.

ACKNOWLEDGMENTS

The authors are deeply grateful to the management and production staff of Manitoba Rolling Mills, in particular Messrs. A. R. Caton, melting superintendent, and H. Shimizu, divisional metallurgist, for their full cooperation during the tests. The facilities provided by the AECL, Pinawa, Manitoba for the machining and autoradiography of the billets were greatly appreciated since they helped to make the tests possible.

REFERENCES

1 R. D. PEHLKE: *ASM Met. Eng. Q.*, 1964, **4**, 42–7
2 A. W. D. HILLS: *JISI*, 1965, **203**, 18–26
3 J. W. DONALDSON AND M. HESS: Met. Soc. AIME Conf., 1966, **49**, 299–319
4 E. A. MIZIKAR: *Trans. Met. Soc. AIME*, 1967, **239**, 1 747–53
5 A. W. D. HILLS: *Trans. Met. Soc. AIME*, 1969, **245**, 1 471–9
6 T. Z. FAHIDY: *JISI*, 1969, **207**, 1 373–6
7 J. J. GAUTIER *et al.*: *JISI*, 1970, **208**, 1 053–9
8 J. SZEKELY AND V. STANEK: *Met. Trans.*, 1970, **1**, 119–26
9 E. Y. KUNG AND J. C. POLLOCK: ISA Proceedings, 1967, **17**, 8–1, 8–2
10 J. SAVAGE: *JISI*, 1962, **200**, 41–7
11 J. SAVAGE AND W. H. PRITCHARD: *JISI*, 1954, **178**, 267–77
12 J. K. BRIMACOMBE AND F. WEINBERG: *JISI*, 1973, **211**, 24–33
13 E. A. MIZIKAR: *Iron Steel Eng.*, 1970, **47** (6), 53–60
14 A. W. D. HILLS: 'Continuous casting of ferrous and nonferrous metals', 1966, A1–A9, Heywood-Temple, London (also A. W. D. Hills and M. R. Moore, paper presented at Sheffield conference, 1971)
15 K. D. HESTER *et al.*: *Can. Met. Q.*, 1968, **7** (2), 97–107
16 C. VARGA AND J. FODOR: Proceedings of the second international conference on the peaceful uses of atomic energy, UN, 1959, 235–236
17 C. R. GOMER AND K. W. ANDREWS: *JISI*, 1969, **207**, 26–35
18 S. K. MORTON AND F. WEINBERG: *JISI*, 1973, **211**, 13–23
19 H. KRAINER AND B. TARMANN, *Stahl Eisen*, 1949, **69**, 813–9

Two-dimensional heat transfer model for continuous casting of steel

A. Perkins and W. R. Irving

A two-dimensional heat transfer model of the continuous-casting process is described. This model is sufficiently flexible to apply to both bloom and slab sections and allows variable surface heat transfer data to be used both around the perimeter of the section and down the length of the strand. Several numerical techniques are investigated for the solution of the heat diffusion equation and the merits of each method are discussed. The model can be used to predict the spray cooling water distribution necessary to maintain any specified surface temperature distribution. The model has been validated by obtaining both solidified shell thicknesses and surface-temperature measurements on plant and comparing these with predicted values. The application of the model for work on optimizing operating conditions and the design of control systems is also briefly discussed.

SYMBOLS

λ thermal conductivity
c specific heat
L latent heat
h heat-transfer coefficient
τ solidification time
u casting speed, maximum
v casting speed
E Young's modulus
v Poisson's ratio
d_m ex-mould shell thickness
α aspect ratio
T throughput
ω width of bloom/slab
t thickness of bloom/slab
d depth below meniscus

Worldwide, increasingly more steel billets, blooms, and slabs are being produced by the continuous-casting process. Within the General Steels Division of the BSC three new large tonnage continuous-casting machines will be operational before the end of 1973. These consist of an eight strand bloom machine with strand sections ranging from 254 × 254 mm to 483 × 305 mm and two wide slab machines which range in size from 1 000 × 152 mm to 1 830 × 305 mm. The bloom machine was commissioned in July 1972 while the first of the slab machines is at present being commissioned. The second slab machine will be commissioned later in the year.* Late in 1971 it was recognized that a flexible two-dimensional simulation model describing the complex heat transfer phenomena in these machines would be a valuable asset in examining the effects of various operating parameters both before and after these plants became operational. Before any of the plants were installed, it was necessary to investigate the effects of the extent of the secondary cooling zone, particularly on the throughput. After commissioning, such a model would facilitate the establishment of satisfactory operating practices for each strand size and steel quality.

Several workers have in the past developed mathematical models of the heat extraction process in continuous-casting machines but these have mainly been confined to one-dimensional solutions. Analytical solutions[1,2] of the heat transfer equations involved limit the degree of flexibility of the surface-boundary conditions while a one-dimensional approach using numerical techniques,[3,4,5] or a two-dimensional approach with axial symmetry,[6,7] only allow the surface-boundary conditions to be varied down the length of the strand. The

---

The authors are with BSC, General Steels Division, Teesside

* Since the date of the Conference all these machines have been fully commissioned.

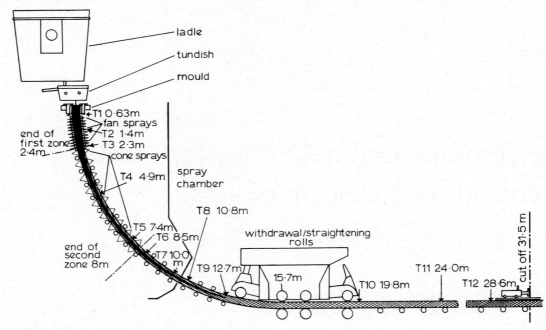

1   Section through bloom caster

distribution of cooling conditions around the strand is often important and for some sections a one-dimensional calculation can lead to predicted throughputs which are underestimates. It was therefore considered that a two-dimensional model which handled thermal diffusion in the plane normal to the strand axis was necessary. Further, such a model should be capable of dealing with boundary conditions which vary round the perimeter of the section as well as down the length of the strand. In cases where surface-temperature control is envisaged the model is also required to predict the cooling water which would allow such conditions to be achieved. Controlled cooling[8,9] is thought to be essential to prevent overcooling of the surface. Experience has shown that overcooling[3] can produce casting defects in the bloom/slab and can also lead to difficulties in straightening at the tangent point. After investigating both implicit and explicit methods of numerically solving the basic Fourier heat transfer equation the usual explicit finite difference method was selected.

The validity of the model has been examined by comparing calculated results with data obtained on the bloom machine and by a comparison with other models. Measured plant data consisted of solidified shell thicknesses and surface temperatures down the strand. The model has been used to investigate the effect of various operating parameters on the temperature distribution of the bloom/slab at any position down the strand. These investigations have been used to determine the maximum casting speeds (and thus throughputs) for various section sizes and for complete solidification at specific points down the strand. It is envisaged that the model will be used extensively for optimizing process conditions to achieve sound operating practice on the machines described and to determine parameters for the auto-

matic control of secondary cooling. To date, work has been concentrated on the bloom machine.

A typical section through a strand on the bloom machine is shown in Fig. 1. This shows the various cooling zones, namely the mould, secondary sprays, and radiation zones respectively. The thin shell in the top section of the secondary spray zone requires closely spaced support rolls, and fan sprays have to be used between the rolls. At lower levels where less support is required, particularly for smaller sections, full cone sprays are generally used. Laboratory work has been carried out to obtain heat transfer coefficients for both fan and cone sprays on steel surfaces at the surface temperatures likely to be encountered in the secondary cooling zone.

MODEL

General considerations

The model considers a rectangular section normal to the axis of the strand and solves numerically the heat diffusion equation subject to the time-dependent boundary conditions encountered by the section as it passes down the strand. It has been shown[1] that the high lateral heat fluxes produced by mould or spray cooling allow a two-dimensional treatment since conduction along the strand is negligible. Mixing in the liquid core does occur and is three-dimensional. Along the strand this has been ignored but an estimate of the effect of mixing across the section has been made by increasing the effective thermal conductivity as described by Mizikar.[3] Heat fluxes varying around the perimeter of the section can be treated but normally mirror symmetry can be assumed about both *x*- and *y*-axes (defined parallel to the section sides) so that only one quarter of the total section need be covered by the finite difference mesh. The model can be used conversely to calculate the spray-cooling distribution necessary to produce a required surface-temperature distribution. Thermal conductivity (λ) and specific heat (c) can be taken to be temperature-dependent in which case they are evaluated at any temperature by an interpolation procedure. Latent heat (L) is incorporated into the model by firstly calculating temperatures ignoring latent heat and then correcting for its evolution by essentially multiplying temperature drops by the ratio $c/(c + L)$ in the solidus–liquidus region.

An estimate has been made of the effect of using constant values of λ and c, taken to be typical values[3,10] over the range 870–1 550°C, as opposed to temperature-dependent values, for the case where surface temperatures are maintained above that at which the phase change commences (870°C). The effect on shell thickness and on mid-broad face temperatures is shown in Figs. 2 and 3. The small differences involved can be tolerated in discussing the effects of various operating parameters leading to a substantial saving in computer time. In cases where temperatures are likely to fall below the phase-change value, variable properties are used since large variations can occur during the change of phase.

Finite difference scheme

Three methods of solving numerically the heat diffusion equation have been examined:

(i) normal explicit method (EX)
(ii) explicit method of Dufort–Frenkel (DFF)
(iii) implicit method of Peaceman–Rachford (PR).

DFF was investigated because of the potential time-saving in computation associated with the three-level nature of the method which necessitates computation only at alternate mesh points at each time level. DFF is roughly twice as fast as EX and PR. However, it was found that sufficiently rapid convergence could not be achieved and the method was rejected. This problem, confirmed independently[11] is believed to be associated only with computations involving latent heat.

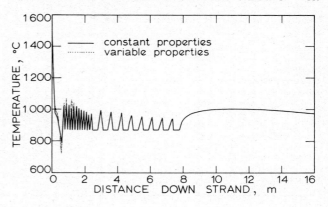

3 *Effect of variable properties, temperature*

The choice between EX and ER is complicated by the boundary conditions. Controlled cooling necessitates explicit evaluation of the boundary conditions and so rules out PR. However, the possibility exists of taking advantage of the unconditional stability of PR by using that method for interior points only together with explicit evaluation on the surface. Thus, both methods have been tested for convergence and accuracy and for the case where $L = 0$, the solutions have been compared with the analytical solution. Table 1 shows that the results are satisfactory even for the coarse mesh. It is obvious that the advantage of the almost unrestricted time step of PR opens up the possibility of large-scale time savings. However, two problems remain before this can be implemented. First, the basic speed of PR has been impaired by the use of temperature-dependent thermal properties which have introduced non-linearity. This makes the straightforward application of standard algorithms for the solution of tridiagonal systems a slow procedure. Second, a satisfactory link between the PR solution on the interior points and the explicit evaluation of the boundary conditions is still needed. In view of these complications, it was felt to be expedient to proceed with EX but at the same time to keep open and develop an improved model based on PR.

Boundary conditions

MOULD

Table 1 shows that the accuracy of the numerical solution is somewhat mesh-dependent at early times of the order of a minute. This causes difficulties in the mould region where the problem is compounded by the existence of large temperature gradients and by the lack of reliable data on the distribution of heat transfer coefficients. To improve the latter situation, a 483 × 305 mm mould has been instrumented with 108 thermocouples, inserted in the mould plates, to experimentally determine, on plant, the heat flux distributions in the mould and how these depend on casting speed and mould lubricants. At the same time, the use of a hyperfine mesh for the mould region is proposed for the model. To date,

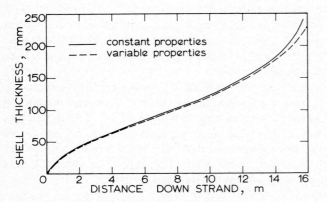

2 *Effect of variable properties, shell thickness*

TABLE 1   Comparison of finite difference schemes

Mesh Timestep, s	Explicit 54 pt 10	 5	 2	 187 pt 10	 5	 2	Peaceman–Rachford 54 pt 20	 10	 5	 2	 1	 187 pt 10	 5	 2	Analytic
Temp. @ 120 s $L = 0$	787	794	797		788	791	—	789	795	798	—	785	789	791	792
$L \neq 0$	880	890	896	UNSTABLE	905	910	863	883	892	897	898	904	908	911	—
Temp. @ 240 s $L = 0$	638	641	642	UNSTABLE	643	645	—	638	640	642	—	641	643	645	646
$L \neq 0$	761	762	763	UNSTABLE	749	750	756	759	761	763	763	747	749	751	—
Temp. @ 360 s $L = 0$	557	559	560	UNSTABLE	562	563	—	557	559	560	—	560	562	563	564
$L \neq 0$	646	648	649	UNSTABLE	658	659	642	646	648	649	650	657	658	659	—
Temp. @ 480 s $L = 0$	503	504	504	UNSTABLE	507	507	—	502	503	504	—	505	506	507	508
$L \neq 0$	594	595	596	UNSTABLE	596	597	589	593	595	596	596	594	596	597	—

however, two simple approaches have been tried. Normally, the mould heat transfer coefficient (h) is taken to be a constant based on published measured overall values, obtained from mould-heat balances. To investigate possible effects of the mould, however, on surface temperatures further down the strand, a simple model of the heat transfer in the mould has been tried. The mould is considered to be divided into three zones. In the top zone, contact between strand and mould is assumed and a high constant heat transfer coefficient is estimated. In the bottom zone, heat transfer from strand to mould is by radiation only. The central zone uses a linearly decreasing heat transfer coefficient which matches at the boundaries with the top and bottom zones. So far the length of each zone is only guessed but as data is collected from our plant work more meaningful figures will be used. The values used in the present investigation are:

(i) constant heat transfer in mould: $h = 1\ 257\ \mathrm{W/m^2 K}$
(ii) three-zone model: top zone (200 mm), $h = 1\ 257$ $\mathrm{W/m^2 K}$, central zone (200–300 mm), bottom zone (300–600 mm).

A comparison between (i) and (ii) in terms of their effect on surface temperatures and shell thicknesses below the mould has been made. The mid-broad face temperature is shown in Fig. 4 for each case. Predicted temperatures for case (i) (solid line) are much lower than for case (ii) (dotted line) in zone 1 of the secondary cooling region. However, the effect quickly damps out and at the end of zone 1 only a 2% differential is detected. The resulting effect on solidification time, τ is that predicted values for

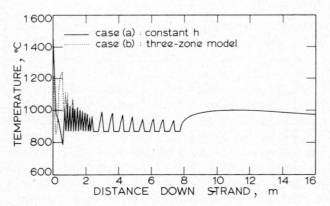

4   Effect of mould parameters on temperature

case (i) are about 1·5% lower than for case (ii). Ex-mould shell thicknesses are about 2 mm greater for case (i). All results given in this paper are based on case (i). Figure 4 shows that valid comparisons can be made between measured and calculated surface temperatures beyond the end of zone 1 of secondary cooling (2·4 m down the strand).

SECONDARY COOLING ZONES

Heat is lost from the strand surface by transfer to the water in the sprays and by radiation to the surroundings. All quoted values and references to heat transfer coefficients concern only the linear heat transfer to the water. That owing to radiation is treated separately and is always taken into account. The value of h at each surface mesh point is evaluated at each time step in a separate procedure which describes the periodicity of the sprays throughout the secondary cooling zone. The surface temperature is then calculated and if the point lies within a spray, the h-value at that point is output. If the point lies in the gap between sprays, a nominal value of zero for h is output and cooling is by radiation alone.

When controlled cooling is employed, the surface temperature is calculated in the usual way until it falls below the control (minimum) value. At this point, it is set equal to the control value and the corresponding h-value required to maintain that temperature is computed and output, provided the mesh point is within a spray. If it is between sprays the original calculated temperature stands and h is set to zero. It soon becomes necessary to reduce h to zero at the corner since it will readily cool to the control value by radiation alone. Gradually, this effect spreads across the face and surface temperatures cannot be maintained at the control level. By reducing the cooling earlier from the maximum possible with a given set of sprays, this effect can be delayed but in so doing, τ will be increased and maximum casting speed, u, will be decreased.

Heat transfer coefficients have been measured in the laboratory for several sprays and their dependence on water flow rates has been determined. Thermocouples were embedded at intervals along the axis of a cylindrical specimen, insulated over its curved surface to give approximately axial heat flow only. The specimen was heated up and its initial temperature distribution noted. One flat surface was then exposed to spray cooling and the temperature distribution recorded as it cooled. A one-dimensional model was used to match the observed heat flow with a series of calculated profiles parameterized by *h*-values. The specimen size was sufficiently small to allow sampling to be done in different parts of the spray. The results described later are based on the following idealized spray system which is similar to that on the bloom machine:

(i) fan sprays: width = 50 mm, gap = 100 mm, h = 1 676 W/m²K
(ii) cone sprays: width = 380 mm, gap = 240 mm, h = 838 W/m²K.

The end of each spray zone is indicated in Fig. 1. During the design stage of the bloom machine consideration was given to the inclusion of a third zone of spray cooling. The effect on maximum casting speeds of extending the spray cooling to as far as 13·5 m down the strand was examined. Given that surface-temperature control would be required, the critical factor which determines the advantage to be gained by having this extended cooling is the point at which solidification is required. For solidification at the tangent point no significant increase in casting speed can be achieved but for solidification at cut-off, the resulting increase would be about 7%.

RADIATION ZONE

Radiation according to Stefan's Law is the dominant cooling mechanism in this zone although some account is taken of the spray water which runs down the strand from the secondary cooling zone above. All surface points are assumed to radiate to a nominal ambient temperature, usually taken to be 20°C. Emissivity is taken to be 0·8. It is in this region that mirror symmetry is least accurate but errors from this source cannot be significant.

EVALUATION OF THE MODEL

In evaluating the model three comparisons were made. These were:

(i) comparison of the predicted temperature distributions with those predicted by other models using the same data
(ii) comparison of predicted shell thicknesses with those obtained on plant
(iii) comparison of predicted surface temperatures with those measured on plant.

Comparison with other models

The temperature profile at the centre of, and normal to, the broad face of a bloom (508 × 254 mm) was found to agree exactly with that predicted by a one-dimensional model previously developed. The two-dimensional effect, due to lateral heat flow, was found to be negligible at this aspect ratio. The one-dimensional model had been previously checked with a similar model developed by Mizikar[3] and a comparison of the calculated temperature distributions gave very good agreement.

330 mm × 254 mm SECTION   DISTANCE DOWN STRAND

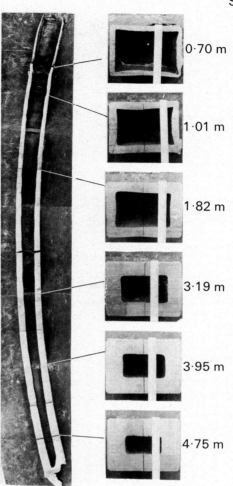

0·70 m

1·01 m

1·82 m

3·19 m

3·95 m

4·75 m

5   *Solidified shell after breakout*

Predicted and measured skin thicknesses

Shortly after commissioning, the bloom machine described above suffered a break out at the dummy-bar head. This left a hollow shell over five metres long which was retrieved and sectioned for shell thickness measurements. Figure 5 shows a photograph of the hollow bloom and the shell thicknesses at various distances down the strand. The thickness of the shell was measured along certain vertical sections and the results for a broad face are shown in Fig. 6. The section size was 330 × 254 mm. The predicted shell thicknesses for the average casting speed used (0·5 m/min) are also shown. As can be seen the agreement is satisfactory. Figure 7 shows the predicted isotherms at 3·95 m down the strand which are almost identical to the actual shell at that depth. (*See* Fig. 5.)

Predicted and measured surface temperatures

Seven locations for the installation of optical pyrometers were chosen in the spray chamber and these are indicated in Fig. 1 as the points T1–T7. These pyrometers were fitted with sight tubes and purged with air at a flow

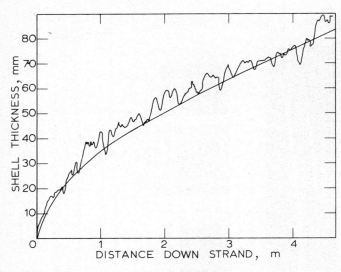

6   *Calculated and measured shell thickness*

8   *Pyrometer installation*

TABLE 2   Measured surface temperatures for cast 0116

| Time from start of cast, min | Casting speed, m/min | Measured surface temp., °C | | | | | | | | |
		T4	T5	T6	T7	T8	T9	T10	T11	T12
27	0·44	729	806	870	872	—	—	—	—	—
28	0·48	712	800	870	868	—	—	—	—	—
29	0·52	815	814	868	858	940	980	—	—	—
30	0·52	760	790	855	862	—	—	—	—	—
31	0·52	766	794	844	868	—	982	—	—	—
32	0·52	750	802	848	864	935	980	—	—	—
33	0·52	760	800	849	858	—	—	—	—	—
34	0·52	747	791	850	854	—	—	912	—	—
35	0·55	700	780	850	852	—	—	—	825	800
36	0·53	700	783	845	849	—	—	920	—	—
37	0·50	700	810	840	853	—	—	—	—	—
38	0·53	700	802	850	850	—	—	—	—	—

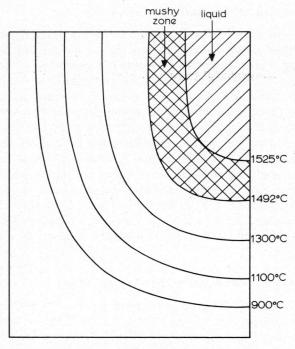

7   *Isotherms at 3·95 m for 330 × 254 mm strand*

rate sufficient to maintain the target area free of water and steam. A photograph of the installation of some of these pyrometers is shown in Fig. 8. The temperature recorded by the pyrometers T4–T7 along with additional measurements at points indicated by T8–T12 in Fig. 1 made by using a gold-cup surface pyrometer are shown in Tables 2, 3, and 4 for three casts on a 483 × 305 mm bloom with about the same cooling water conditions, but casting speeds (v) of 0·52, 0·63, and 0·75 m/min. No results have yet been obtained from positions T1, T2, and T3. The model was used to predict the surface temperatures along the centre of the top broad face for these conditions and these results are compared with the measured values in Figs. 9, 10, and 11. The input data for these runs were calculated from the water flows recorded during the cast to each of the spray zones and from the number and types of spray nozzles used. (Table 5). The input data were as follows:

Mould $h = 1\,257\,\mathrm{W/m^2K}$

Zone 1 (top) Impact area of fan
    sprays $h = 2\,280\,\mathrm{W/m^2K}$

TABLE 3   Measured surface temperatures for cast 0120

Time from start of cast, min	Casting speed, m/min	Measured surface temp., °C								
		T4	T5	T6	T7	T8	T9	T10	T11	T12
40	0·63	814	820	882	884	—	—	—	—	—
41	0·60	820	812	882	890	—	—	—	—	—
42	0·63	845	839	882	882	—	—	—	—	—
43	0·64	814	830	882	882	—	—	—	—	—
44	0·64	820	842	877	894	970	—	—	—	—
45	0·63	830	828	891	896	—	1 000	—	—	—
46	0·63	852	810	873	870	—	—	—	—	—
47	0·63	850	820	877	877	—	—	—	—	—
48	0·61	864	832	879	873	—	—	960	—	—
49	0·60	860	836	874	874	—	—	—	930	—
50	0·61	840	844	874	886	—	—	—	—	870
51	0·64	856	839	873	884	—	—	—	—	—
52	0·65	823	853	880	888	—	—	—	—	—
53	0·65	818	851	882	882	—	—	—	—	—
54	0·64	836	848	882	890	—	—	—	—	—
55	0·57	868	838	893	881	970	—	—	—	—
56	0·52	864	839	891	880	—	—	—	—	—
57	0·54	862	830	890	888	—	995	—	—	—
58	0·63	874	839	896	889	—	—	940	—	—
59	0·54	849	848	888	888	—	—	—	920	—
60	0·54	856	860	878	880	—	—	—	—	865

TABLE 4   Measured surface temperatures for cast 0122

Time from start of cast, min	Casting speed, m/min	Measured surface temp., °C								
		T4	T5	T6	T7	T8	T9	T10	T11	T12
30	0·75	919	903	952	934	—	—	—	—	—
31	0·75	900	900	950	932	—	—	—	—	—
32	0·75	924	900	948	934	970	—	—	—	—
33	0·75	927	905	946	933	—	1 010	—	—	—
34	0·75	928	900	942	930	—	—	—	—	—
35	0·75	924	900	949	933	—	—	1 000	—	—
36	0·69	925	908	948	929	—	—	—	—	985
37	0·75	919	916	951	928	970	—	—	—	—
38	0·80	928	913	955	—	—	1 015	995	—	—
39	0·79	934	913	951	930	—	—	—	970	920
40	0·78	919	905	951	933	—	—	—	—	—
41	0·74	924	906	950	934	—	—	—	—	—

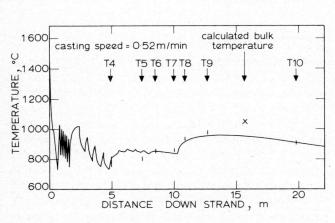

9   Temperatures for cast 0116

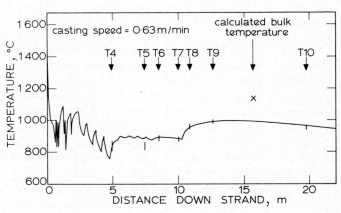

10   Temperatures for cast 0120

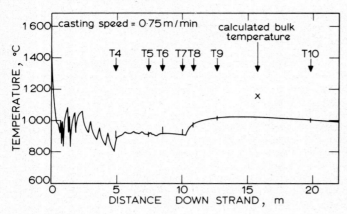

11   Temperatures for cast 0122

TABLE 5   Secondary water distributions

Metered sections	Cast 0116 m³/h	Cast 0120 m³/h	Cast 0122 m³/h
Ring	4·83	4·44	5·00
Zone 1 (top)	15·36	15·20	15·20
Zone 1 (bottom)	9·80	9·70	9·65
Zone 2 (front face)	4·15	4·04	3·94
Zone 2 (both side faces)	4·86	4·91	4·86
Zone 2 (back face)	4·26	4·31	4·24

Zone 1 (bottom) Impact area of fan sprays	$h = 1\,420\ \text{W/m}^2\text{K}$
Zone 2 (top) Impact area of fan sprays	$h = 500\ \text{W/m}^2\text{K}$
Zone 2 (bottom) Impact area of fan sprays	$h = 220\ \text{W/m}^2\text{K}$
Gaps between sprays	$h = 150\ \text{W/m}^2\text{K}$
End of sprays to the exit from the spray chamber	$h = 150\ \text{W/m}^2\text{K}$

As can be seen from these comparisons quite good agreement between measured and predicted surface temperatures has been obtained.

RESULTS UNDER STANDARDIZED CONDITIONS

The basic output of the model is the temperature distribution throughout the strand. From this, two further quantities can be deduced, i.e. shell thickness and solidification time. These three quantities have been determined for each section size under standardized conditions. Eight sections have been considered although only five of these are expected to be cast in practice. The other three have been included to obtain a more complete picture. Controlled cooling to 870°C is applied using the spray configuration described earlier. Constant thermal properties and constant heat transfer coefficient in the mould are also used. Casting temperature is 1 550°C.

TABLE 6   Casting speed under standardized conditions

Section, mm	Casting speed u, m/min			
	Solid at tangent point	Solid at cut-off	Manufacturers recommended	Throughput, t/h
483 × 305	0·49	0·90	0·55	32·4
406 × 279	0·60	1·10	0·65	30·6
508 × 254	0·65	1·18	—	37·8
406 × 254	0·68	1·26	—	31·5
330 × 254	0·76	1·40	0·85	28·8
254 × 254	0·95	1·72	0·85	27·5
406 × 203	0·96	1·73	1·10	35·6
203 × 203	1·37	2·50	—	25·2

Casting speed

By assuming complete solidification at the tangent and at the cut-off points respectively, values of u have been calculated. Table 6 shows these results together with corresponding throughputs and where appropriate, the manufacturer's recommended casting speeds. By extending the point of solidification from tangent point to cut-off, an increase in u of about 80% can be achieved for all sections. If controlled cooling were not applied and temperatures were allowed to fall below 870°C, the gains in u would be 12% and 4% respectively for tangent point and cut-off solidification.

Shell thickness

In Table 7, estimated values of mid-face shell thickness are given at different points along the strand. For solidification at the tangent point no significant difference can be detected between broad and narrow face shell thickness until the end of the secondary cooling zone. A difference is not apparent until the tangent point in the case of solidification at cut-off. In Table 7, where two values per strand position are given, the larger value refers to the narrow face. The smaller sections, being cast at higher speeds, have thinner shells at any given point along the strand. This may lead to some limitation on u which will adversely affect throughput rates on smaller sections since thinner shells increase the probability of breakouts.

Temperature

Surface temperature is much more sensitive to fluctuation in h than either casting speed or shell thickness. In practice, the step-function variation used in the model will be smoothed out by the spray water present between sprays. Thus, the variations shown in Fig. 4, in which the mid-broad face temperature on the 483 × 305 section has been plotted, will not be encountered to the same extent on plant. It is estimated that the fluctuation will fall from a maximum of 100 K at the start of zone 2 to 20 K at the end of secondary cooling. In general, the surface temperature reaches the control temperature in less than one minute after leaving the mould and

TABLE 7 **Shell thickness (mm) under standardized conditions**

Section, mm	Solid at tangent point				Solid at cut-off			
	ex-mould	ex-fans	ex-cones		ex-mould	ex-cones	ex-pinch rolls	
483 × 305	20	50	102	95	11	68	104	95
406 × 279	18	44	92	87	10	61	91	86
508 × 254	18	43	89	82	11	57	90	80
406 × 254	18	44	92	86	11	55	87	77
330 × 254	17	41	83	78	9	52	80	73
254 × 254	13	36	71	71	9	44	66	66
406 × 203	13	31	69	64	9	44	71	63
203 × 203	10	25	53	53	6	34	52	51

Casting speed u, m/min

subsequent temperature control confines temperature differences between bloom sections to a narrow range. For example, for solidification at the tangent point, the mid-narrow face temperature for each section at the tangent point lies approximately within the range 890–1 010°C, while the bulk temperatures are within the range 1 080–1 110°C. Similar ranges apply at cut-off for solidification at that point although they are slightly higher because of the proportionately shorter time spent in the spray zone. The temperature distribution across the section at the tangent point is important in that it is some measure of the force required to straighten the bloom/slab. Table 8 shows estimated temperatures at the tangent point for solidification at each of the two points considered.

EFFECT OF VARIATION IN OPERATING PARAMETERS

The effects of variations in four operating parameters have been examined for the 483 × 305 mm section. Mixing in the liquid core has also been considered. Percentage variations quoted refer to deviations from the results found for the standardized conditions described in the previous section with solidification at the tangent point.

Effect of casting temperature

As the casting temperature increases from 1 550°C to 1 575°C and then to 1 600°C, τ increases from 1 915 s to 1 970 s and then to 2 025 s. Thus, each 10 K of superheat adds 20 s to τ leading to a corresponding decrease in u of 1 %. Over the same range, no discernible change in shell thickness can be detected until exit from the fan sprays. If v is held constant, the narrow side thickness at exit from the cone sprays has decreased from 103 mm to 97 mm. For each degree of superheat above 1 550°C, ex-mould mid-broad face temperature increases by 0.5 K and in-spray/out-spray fluctuations increase from an average of 135–150 K in the fan sprays and from 95–110 K in the cone sprays. Bulk temperature at the tangent point increases by 0.3 K for each degree of superheat.

Effect of surface temperature

If the control temperature is 800°C instead of 870°C, τ drops from 1 915 s to 1 850 s, representing an increase in u of 4.7 %. Controlling to 950°C increases τ to 2 050 s, reducing u by 7 %. Mid-narrow side shell thickness decreases as the control temperature increases if v is held constant. At the end of the fan sprays, shell thickness varies by 1 mm (2 %) per 40 K of control-temperature variation. The corresponding rate at the end of the

TABLE 8 **Temperature under standardized conditions**

Section, mm	Solid at tangent point, Temps. at tangent point, °C				Solid at cut-off, Temps. at tangent point, °C			
	Mid-narrow face	Mid-broad face	Corner	Bulk	Mid-narrow face	Mid-broad face	Corner	Bulk
483 × 305	894	979	769	1 082	1 012	1 057	839	1 236
406 × 279	915	988	790	1 086	1 035	1 074	862	1 241
508 × 254	906	1 020	795	1 115	1 031	1 087	870	1 263
406 × 254	918	1 007	802	1 096	1 039	1 087	875	1 248
330 × 254	939	994	815	1 088	1 059	1 089	888	1 244
254 × 254	981	981	838	1 095	1 098	1 098	914	1 254
406 × 203	937	1 058	838	1 131	1 066	1 124	916	1 280
203 × 203	1 014	1 014	882	1 112	1 132	1 132	960	1 266

Casting speed u, m/min, as in Table 6

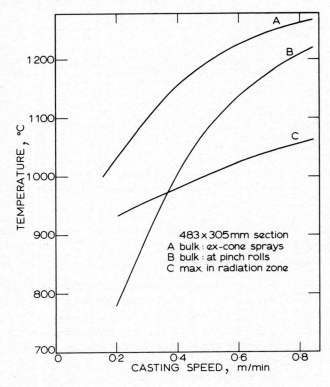

12   *Strand temperature*

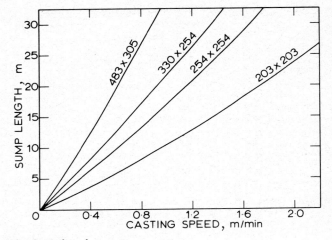

13   *Sump length*

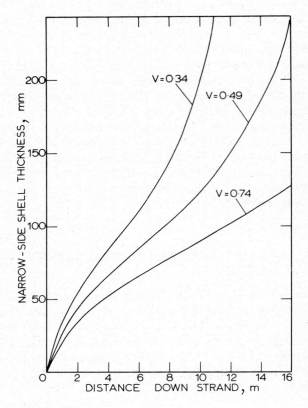

14   *Shell thickness*

cone spray region is 2·7 mm (2·7%) per 40 K. Bulk temperature shows an approximately constant increase of 0·4 K per degree down the strand.

Effect of spray heat transfer coefficient

The standardized distribution of heat transfer coefficient was modified by diverting one-third of the spray value into the gaps. This resulted in an increase in u of 4%. Initially, little change occurs in shell thickness but by the end of the cone spray zone, mid-narrow side thickness has increased by 6 mm (6%). Bulk temperature at the end of the spray zone drops by 50 K (5%) and at the tangent point the drop is 30 K (3%).

Effect of casting speed

The variation of bulk temperature ex-cone sprays and at the tangent point as casting speed is varied over a wide range is shown in Fig. 12. The maximum temperature reached in the radiation zone is also shown. Fluctuations in both spray zones increase slightly with increasing casting speed. The increase in ex-mould temperature is more marked. Over a range of v from 0·34–0·74 m/min, τ was found to vary by only 135 s (6%) and thus, sump length is essentially proportional to casting speed. These results are summarized in Fig. 13 together with the results for other sections. Shell thicknesses down the strand are given in Fig. 14 for three values of v. The graphs have the familiar parabolic shape until the two-dimensional effect becomes significant, at which time accelerated solidification occurs. Ex-mould mid-face shell thickness (d_m), which is about the same for all sections for the same v, is plotted against v in Fig. 15. As expected, the calculated values, taken from all sections, lie approximately on the line vd_m^2 = constant, in accordance with the relationship given above.

Effect of mixing in the liquid core

The method of artificially increasing the thermal conductivity of the liquid core has been used to try to take some account of the improved heat transfer brought about by mass transfer. λ was increased by a factor of 8 for the liquid region. As a result, τ dropped from 1 915 s to 1 865 s representing an increase in u of 2·6%. No increase in shell thickness was apparent till the end of the

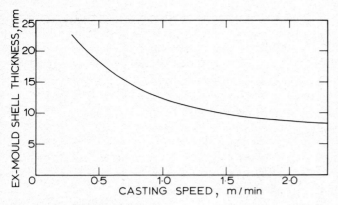

15   Ex-mould shell thickness

fan sprays where the shell was 3 mm thicker, becoming 4 mm thicker by the end of the cone sprays. The ex-mould mid-broad face temperature increased by 15 K and fluctuations in the sprays fell by about 10 K.

APPLICATION OF THE MODEL

To date, our attention has been directed towards the bloom caster but the model will be applied to both slab machines at some stage in the future. General applicability to the design of continuous-casting machines is also considered in this section.

Prediction of throughputs

Table 6 gives the calculated throughput for each section, based on the calculated casting speeds for solidification at the tangent point. The results have been plotted in Fig. 16 which shows that throughput (T) of a single strand increases with aspect ratio (α), defined as the ratio of width (w) to thickness (t). As α increases, maximum casting speed (u) tends to a constant value and, therefore, T becomes proportional to α. Further, for solidification at a fixed point along the strand, in this case at the tangent point, our results show that, for all sections, ut^2 is approximately constant. Since

$$T \sim uwt = \alpha ut^2$$

it therefore follows that the relationship between T and

α, shown in Fig. 16 is unique and independent of thickness. Thus, from heat transfer considerations, the throughput of a single strand is linearly proportional to aspect ratio when this is greater than about 2. This conclusion has also been reached by other workers.[12]

Bulging and roller spacing

The estimates of shell thickness have been applied to a brief study of bulging. The solidified shell along the broad face of a rectangular section can be considered as a series of rectangular plates constrained at the edges by the adjacent faces and by two adjacent support rolls. Suppose the dimensions of such a plate are a (= section width) and b (= roller separation). Applying the standard theory for the deflection of such a plate (with a thickness equal to the shell thickness) the deflection at the centre (δ) under the uniform loading caused by the ferrostatic pressure is

$$\delta = AF(a, b)(1 - v^2)d/Et^3$$

where A is a constant, $F(a, b)$ is a known function, d is the depth below the meniscus and t is the shell thickness. Thus, making the assumption that all sections are roughly at similar temperatures at corresponding positions in the strand, and that therefore they have similar values of E and v, it follows that

$$\delta = A^1 F(a, b)/t^3$$

for each section at the same value of d. Thus, by assuming a given roller spacing for the 254×254 mm section, the roller spacings which produce an equal bulging for each of the other sections can be calculated. The results are shown in Fig. 17 for spacings on the 254×254 mm

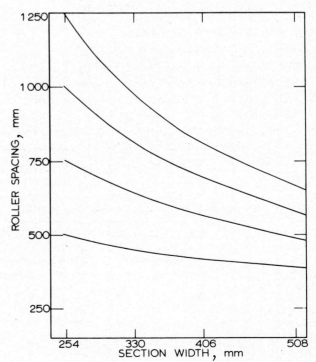

17   Roller spacing

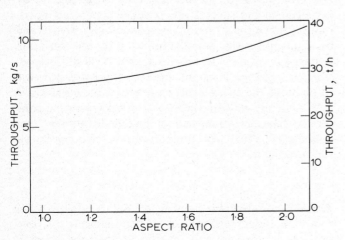

16   Throughput

of 500, 750, 1 000, and 1 250 mm. These results are applicable at $d = 2$ m but further calculation has shown that they apply at all values of d. However the assumptions made in obtaining the expression for the deflection become untenable at large values of d when t becomes comparable to a or b.

Figure 17 shows for example, that a spacing of 750 mm on a 254 mm square section needs to be reduced to one of 500 mm on the 508×254 mm section for the same bulging, i.e. 50% more support rolls are needed. This problem becomes significant when slab casting is considered. Some of the advantage gained in throughput is offset by the need for heavier plant. The graphs of Fig. 17 can be extrapolated to make rough estimates for slabs. Thus, a $1\,524 \times 254$ mm slab requires a spacing of slightly less than half the spacing for the 254 mm square section, to give the same bulging. For wide slabs the inter-roll spacing below the mould must be quite small to contain the thin shell, particularly at higher casting speeds. This has led to the development of cooling plates or cooling grids for constraining the solidifying shell just beneath the mould.

Design of spray cooling configuration

To keep surface temperature constant, the heat transfer at any given point on the strand must be increased as casting speed increases. Thus, higher values of h are needed when casting smaller sections at their maximum rate than for the larger sections. This is demonstrated by the results shown in Table 9 which gives the required value of heat transfer coefficient at the mid-face points at the end of the spray zone. The difference between narrow and broad side values increases with aspect ratio as expected before reaching a limiting value when the solidification is essentially one-dimensional.

VARIATION DOWN STRAND

Once the surface temperature has been driven down to the desired value, it is maintained at that value by reducing h. Considering only the mid-point of the broad side, the required value of h, as a function of distance down the strand, is shown in Fig. 19 for the 483×305 mm section. Thus, knowing the dependence of h on water flux, the surface temperature can be controlled by controlling water fluxes via pressure control and spray nozzle design.

TABLE 9   Heat transfer coefficient at end of spray zone, W/m²K

Section	Solid at tangent point	
	Mid-narrow face	Mid-broad face
483×305	145	183
406×279	168	204
508×254	169	224
406×254	178	227
330×254	216	250
254×254	271	271
406×203	279	336
203×203	355	355

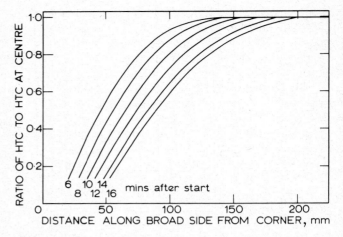

18   *HTC distribution across strand*

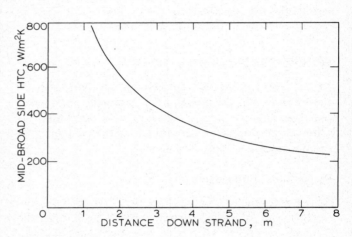

19   *HTC distribution down strand*

VARIATION ACROSS STRAND

The possibility exists of designing spray nozzles and combinations of them which will produce the necessary distribution of heat transfer to give uniform surface temperature over the strand surface. This distribution is shown in Fig. 18 for various times after teeming for the broad side of the 483×305 mm section. Alternatively, for any given v, the distributions are applicable to fixed positions down the strand. Thus, by designing nozzle arrangements to successively produce the correct distributions down the strand in accordance with Fig. 19 and by controlling the water flux to give the variation required by Fig. 18 across the strand, it should be possible to produce constant strand surface temperature throughout the spray zone. In practice, the situation is more difficult because the sprays, particularly the cone sprays, have two-dimensional flux distributions. Not only does the flux vary across the strand face, but it also varies along it.

Control

As has been shown the required secondary cooling water to obtain a predetermined surface-temperature distribution is a complex function of section size, casting speed, and position down the strand. It is proposed to use this model together with comprehensive plant measurements to determine parameters which will enable a control system to be designed and commissioned which will automatically adjust the water supply to the various banks of spray nozzles when the casting speed changes to achieve required surface temperatures. This control is particularly required for the bloom machine. Some of the reasons why casting speed variation occurs are as follows:

(i) metering nozzles are in use on the tundish and the casting speed is automatically controlled (from mould level detection) by adjusting the speed of the withdrawal rolls. If the nozzles wear due to erosion the casting speed must be increased, or, if partial blockage occurs the speed must be decreased

(ii) during the changing of ladles during sequential casting the level in the tundish decreases and the flowrate through the nozzles decreases

(iii) 'finish casting' procedures require that the strand be virtually stopped until solidification of the top surface has occurred. If intense spray water is maintained in the secondary cooling zone the bloom is difficult to straighten and curved blooms often result.

If these variations occur it is necessary to adjust the water to maintain the surface temperature within specific limits thus improving the probability of good quality blooms and ensuring that no problems occur in straightening. Curved blooms can lead to difficulty in the reheating furnaces. Before the parameters for such a control system can be determined, comprehensive plant data are necessary and these are at present being acquired. Further, the data will be correlated with quality and yield to assess the value of such a control system.

ACKNOWLEDGMENTS

The authors wish to thank Mr J. Mackenzie, Head of Research, General Steels Division, BSC for permission to publish this paper and their many colleagues, both on the works and at the Teesside Research Centre for their assistance.

REFERENCES

1 A. W. D. HILLS: Inst. Chem. Engs. Symposium on Chemical Engineering in Metallurgical Industries, 1963, 128–40
2 W. R. IRVING: *JISI*, 1967, **205**, 271–7
3 E. A. MIZIKAR: *Trans. Met. Soc. AIME* 1967, **239**, 1 747–53
4 K. FEKETE: Concast Metalurgical Seminar on Slab Casting, March 1971, Zurich
5 J. J. GAUTIER et al.: 'Mathematical models in metallurgical process development', 1970, London, The Iron and Steel Institute
6 H. G. BAUMANN: BISI Trans. no. 8 392
7 D. A. PEEL AND A. E. PENGELLY: 'Mathematical models in metallurgical process development', 1970, London, The Iron and Steel Institute
8 A. V. WIEBEL: *Blast Furnace Steel Plant*, 1969, Sept., 741–5
9 D. R. THORNTON: *Steel Times*, 1972, Jan., 99–105
10 BISRA: 'Physical constants of some commercial steels at elevated temperatures', 1953, Butterworths
11 D. ELLISTON: Private Communication
12 L. S. RUDOI: *Metallurg i Gornorudn Prom.*, **12** (4), 1971, HB Translation no. 8 744

Models for macrosegregation in rimmed and semikilled steel ingots

H. W. den Hartog, J. M. Rabenberg, and R. Pesch

The subject of this paper is the quantitative treatment of the concentration distribution in rimmed and semikilled steel ingots. Two new models are developed. The first one describes the mass transfer and the resulting segregation during rimming action. A relationship between the effective distribution coefficient and the velocity of the solidification front is predicted and confirmed by experiments. The second model describes the segregation in the ingot core and is based on the fact that crystals, growing in the melt, are a major source of macrosegregation in steel ingots. The core segregation model contains a single independent variable which incorporates both the ingot geometry and the process variables affecting the solidification rate. This variable can be evaluated with a mathematical model of the ingot solidification process. Moreover, the core segregation model shows the exponential character of the concentration distribution in the ingot core, a fact which has not been recognized so clearly till now. Finally, the models are used in a quantitative discussion of the influence of ingot dimensions and process variables on the segregation pattern.

SYMBOLS

A	surface area of solidification front, cm^2
c	concentration, wt-%
c_0	concentration at the start of segregation process in the ingot core, wt-%
c_{ladle}	concentration in the ladle, wt-%
c_{max}	maximum concentration in the ingot, wt-%
c_p	specific heat, J/°C
d	thickness of solidified shell, cm
D	diffusion coefficient, cm^2/s
k_0	equilibrium partition coefficient for binary alloy
k_e	effective partition coefficient for binary alloy
p	empirical parameter in core segregation model, cm/s
q	specific volumetric growth rate crystals in the melt, cm^3/cm^2 s
s	surface renewal rate, s^{-1}
t	time, s
v	linear velocity of solidification front, cm/s
V	volume of the liquid core in the ingot, cm^3
x	cartesian coordinate, cm
y	cartesian coordinate, cm
$\alpha_{1,2,3,4}$	heat-transfer coefficient, W/cm^2 °C
ϵ	gas-bubble release parameter, cm^{-1}
δ	diffusion layer thickness, cm
λ	heat conduction coefficient, W/cm^2 °C
ρ	specific weight, g/cm^3
ψ	lifetime distribution function

Segregation of foreign elements in solidifying steel is a phenomenon of great importance in steelmaking. The inhomogeneous concentration distribution in the steel ingot results in an inhomogeneity of the mechanical properties of the final products. Under certain circumstances the segregation of harmful elements such as sulphur and phosphorus leads to severe defects within the ingots which appear already in the semiproducts from those ingots. Since segregation is an essential part of the solidification mechanism of steel ingots and thus cannot be prevented it requires close attention to keep its effects within acceptable limits. Practical measures to this end are:

(i) minimizing the concentration of the harmful elements during steelmaking

The authors are with Hoogovens, IJmuiden BV

(ii) discrimination of slabs produced from top and bottom parts of the ingots.

Inspection of the literature shows an extended discussion of the problem. A first comprehensive survey has been given in the reports of the Heterogeneity of Steel Ingots Committee of the ISI,[1] followed by an abundance of other literature in later years. Especially the influence of the ingot dimensions, the length of track time and the initial concentration of the alloying elements have been studied. In spite of all the efforts, no working theory which provides a quantitative description of the segregation in large ingots exists. It is the purpose of this paper to provide simple models which are based on the physics of the segregation process. This is in contrast to earlier attempts to relate the segregation pattern to the process variables by the use of statistical methods.[2] The general pattern of the concentration distribution in a rimmed steel ingot is shown in Fig. 1. The ingot is surrounded by the rimlayer, which is solidified during the period of rimming action. In the core of the ingot the concentration rises from the bottom to the top and from the outside to the centre of the ingot.

A region with a high concentration is located in the top half of the ingot. Aspects of this concentration distribution that are of great practical interest and consequently have received a lot of attention in the literature, are the concentration in the rim layer, the value of maximum concentration in the ingot and the concentration distribution in the strip rolled from the ingot. As shown by Mayo *et al.*[3] for example, apart from the rimlayer and the consequently higher starting concentration, the segregation pattern in the core of a rimmed ingot is similar to that in a semikilled steel ingot. The segregation in killed steel ingots takes place basically according to the same mechanism as in the core of rimmed or semikilled steel ingots. However, the subject is of much greater importance for the latter ingot types since a disadvantage of these ingot types is the existence of a segregation peak well within the ingot. Moreover, the greater part of the world steel production is made in the form of rimmed or semikilled steel ingots. The segregation as a result of rimming action in rimmed-steel ingots will be dealt with first. Next, the mechanism of macrosegregation in the ingot core is discussed and formulated in a quantitative model, which is combined with a mathematical model of ingot solidification. The experimental verification of the quantitative model is also given in this section. With a combination of these models several important aspects of the concentration distribution can be predicted as a function of the process variables. Finally, several applications of these models will be illustrated.

MACROSEGREGATION DURING RIMMING ACTION

Mass transfer resulting from rimming action

The special feature of the mechanism by which segregation takes place during rimming action is the development of carbon monoxide at the solidification front. As a result of this a circulating flow in the liquid core of the ingot exists, which enhances the mass transfer between the solidification front and the liquid steel. A part of the excess of the alloying elements at the solidification front, resulting from the lower solubility in solid steel, is transported to the bulk liquid, thus producing a solute concentration in the rimlayer which is considerably lower than the concentration in the liquid steel. In recent years several papers describing a quantitative study of the segregation during rimming action have been published.[4,5,6,7] Following Nilles,[4] who was the first one to apply simple mass transfer theory to the case of rimmed-steel ingots, in all these papers use has been made of the film theory of mass transfer to interpret the experimental results. In this theory it is assumed that the mass transfer takes place by diffusion through an imaginary stagnant liquid layer, with thickness δ, next to the solid–liquid interface, while outside this layer the liquid is completely mixed. The general idea of the film theory is that the parameter δ is completely determined by the liquid flow field and thus has the same value for the different diffusing species. Evaluation of experimental data on rimmed-steel ingots with this mass transfer model shows that δ is a function of the velocity, v, of the solidification front indicating that the liquid flow field is also dependent on the movement of the solidification front. A satisfactory quantitative description of this phenomenon cannot be given by the film theory.

To this end a more elaborate mass transfer model, closer to the physical reality, must be used. Particularly suited for the case of rimming steel is the surface renewal model.[8] In this model it is assumed that the mass transfer takes place by the transport of small elements of liquid from the bulk liquid to the interface and back. During their stay at the interface a non-steady diffusion takes place in these liquid elements. From a solution of the non-steady diffusion equation and by specifying the lifetime distribution of the liquid elements at the interface the net mass transfer rate from the solidification front to the liquid and the effective distribution coefficient can be calculated. The non-steady diffusion field in the liquid elements is obtained by integration of the partial

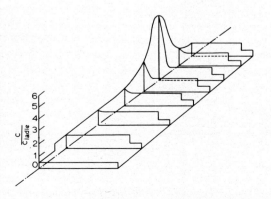

1   Concentration distribution in a vertical cross section through a rimmed-steel ingot

differential Eq. (1) together with the boundary conditions.[2]

$$\frac{\delta c}{\delta t} + v\frac{\delta c}{\delta x} = D\frac{\delta^2 c}{\delta x^2} \qquad (1)$$

$$t = 0 \qquad x > 0 \qquad c = c_0 \qquad (2a)$$

$$t > 0 \qquad x = 0 \qquad (1 - k_0)vc = -D\frac{\delta c}{\delta x} \qquad (2b)$$

$$x = \infty \qquad c = c_0 \qquad (2c)$$

A solution to this problem has already been given by Smith et al.,[9] from which the following expression for the time dependent effective distribution coefficient can be deduced:

$$k_e(t) = \frac{1}{2}\left[1 + \mathrm{erf}\left(\frac{v^2 t}{2D}\right)^{\frac{1}{2}} + (2k_0 - 1)\right.$$

$$\times \exp\left(-k_0(1 - k_0)\frac{v^2 t}{D}\right)$$

$$\left. \times \mathrm{erfc}\frac{(2k_0 - 1)(v^2 t/D)^{\frac{1}{2}}}{2}\right] \qquad (3)$$

If $\psi(t)\,dt$ stands for the fraction of the surface with a lifetime between t and $t + dt$ the average value of the effective distribution coefficient is given by:

$$k_e = \int_0^\infty k_e(t)\psi(t)\,dt \qquad (4)$$

In this case use is made of a random surface renewal model defined by Eq. (5):[8]

$$\psi(t) = s\,e^{-st} \qquad (5)$$

It can easily be seen that the lifetime distribution defined by Eq. (5) satisfies the condition:

$$\int_0^\infty \psi(t)\,dt = 1 \qquad (6)$$

In Eq. (5) s has the physical meaning of a surface renewal rate and $1/s$ can be regarded as the average lifetime of the fluid elements at the interface. Introducing (3) and (5) into (4) and performing the integration leads to:

$$k_e = \frac{1}{2}\left[1 + \left(\frac{1}{2Ds/v^2 + 1}\right)^{\frac{1}{2}} + (2k_0 - 1)\right.$$

$$\times \frac{Ds/v^2}{Ds/v^2 + k_0(1 - k_0)}$$

$$\left. \times \left\{1 - \left(\frac{(2k_0 - 1)^2}{4Ds/v^2 + 1}\right)^{\frac{1}{2}}\right\}\right] \qquad (7)$$

It now remains to relate the surface renewal rate, s, to the fluid flow conditions and the solidification rate. During rimming action a large number of carbon monoxide bubbles are generated at the solid-liquid interface. It is plausible to assume that the local mixing in the liquid caused by the formation and the release of the gas bubbles will play a major role in the transport

of fluid elements to and from the solid-liquid interface. In view of this the surface renewal rate, s, can as a first approximation be considered as proportional to the frequency with which bubbles are released at their growth sites on the solid-liquid interface. The gas volume and the number of gas bubbles released at the solid-liquid interface are proportional to the amount of carbon and oxygen rejected during solidification, and thus as a first approximation proportional to the solidification rate. Consequently the following simple expression can be written down for the surface renewal rate:

$$s = \epsilon . v \qquad (8)$$

The reciprocal value of the factor ϵ can be considered as a measure for the average distance traversed by the solidification front between the release of two gas bubbles from the same growth site. Introduction of (8) into (7) leads to:

$$k_e = \frac{1}{2}\left[1 + \left(\frac{1}{2\epsilon D/v + 1}\right)^{\frac{1}{2}} + 2(k_0 - 1)\right.$$

$$\times \frac{\epsilon D/v}{\epsilon D/v + k_0(1 - k_0)}$$

$$\left. \times \left\{1 - \left(\frac{(2k_0 - 1)^2}{4(\epsilon D/v) + 1}\right)^{\frac{1}{2}}\right\}\right] \qquad (9)$$

Inspection of Eq. (9) shows that if $\epsilon D/v$ has a very large value $k_e = k_0$ and if $\epsilon D/v$ has a very small value $k_e = 1$.

Figure 2 shows k_e for sulphur as a function of the solidification rate, v, as calculated from (9) for several values of the parameter ϵ. Also shown are experimentally determined values of k_e in ingots ranging from 0.5 ton to 13 ton. The data of the 0.5 ton and 5.5 ton ingots are taken from the ingots investigated and described by Nilles.[4,5] The 13 ton ingot was recently investigated at the CRM. The agreement between the experimental results and the calculated relationship between the effective distribution coefficient and the solidification rate for a value of 300 cm^{-1} for ϵ is very good. For this value of ϵ the average lifetime of the fluid elements at the interface

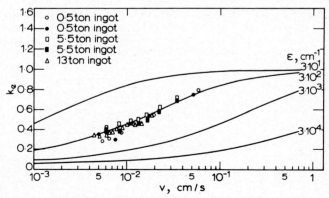

$D = 5 \cdot 10^{-5}\ (\mathrm{cm}^2/\mathrm{s}); k_0 = 0.05$

2   *Relationship between the effective distribution coefficient of sulphur during rimming action and the velocity of the solidification front*

ranges from 0·07 s to 0·7 s during the rimming period. Since ϵ is dependent upon the carbon monoxide development at the interface its value will undoubtedly be a function of the steel composition. The present value pertains to the composition normally encountered in rimming steel, i.e. $\pm 0\cdot 1\%$ C and $\pm 0\cdot 4\%$ Mn.

Concentration in rimlayer and liquid core

The concentration distribution of the non-reacting alloying elements can be calculated by combining expression (9) with a mass balance over the liquid core of the ingot. In this early part of the solidification the thickness of the solidified shell can be calculated very well with a semi-empirical relationship of the type:

$$d = 2\cdot 8\sqrt{t} - 2\cdot 5 \qquad . \qquad . \qquad . \qquad . \qquad (10)$$

Results of these calculations for a 13 ton ingot are given in Figs. 3a and b and compared with experimental results. Figure 3a shows the sulphur concentration of the liquid core as a function of the thickness of the solidified shell, and Fig. 3b the sulphur concentration distribution in the rimlayer. In the first instance a small systematic difference of about 10% exists between the experimental results and the calculations. This can be explained by the fact that during the rimming period also, a certain quantity of steel solidifies in the form of free crystals floating in the melt. Assuming that the amount of free crystals is determined by the radiative heat loss from the free surface of the liquid in the ingot and assuming that the effective distribution coefficient of the free crystals has the same value as that of the rimlayer, the calculated curves in Figs. 3a and b are corrected for the segregation caused by these crystals. The corrected curves are in excellent agreement with the experimental results. For

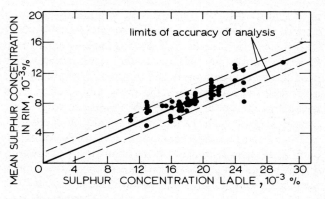

Ingot weight from 12–30 tons

4   *Mean sulphur concentration in the rim as a function of the concentration in the ladle*

ingots larger than about 12 tons, the decrease of k_e of sulphur with time (Fig. 2) and the increase of the sulphur concentration in the liquid core (Fig. 3a) combine in such a way that the sulphur concentration remains approximately constant over the whole rimlayer at a level of about 50% of the ladle concentration. This is also illustrated in Fig. 4 where the average sulphur concentration of the rimlayer as determined in a large number of slabs rolled from rimmed-steel ingots, is given as a function of the sulphur concentration in the ladle. This circumstance makes the calculation of the macrosegregation during rimming action in large ingots particularly simple.

MACROSEGREGATION IN INGOT CORE

Mechanism of solidification and macrosegregation in ingot core

The mechanism by which macrosegregation develops in the ingot core after capping of the ingot is completely different from the segregation mechanism during rimming action. The currently accepted theory regarding this mechanism has its origin in the growth of relatively pure crystals in the melt, which settle toward the bottom of the ingot. This theory has a long history and is already expounded in the reports of the Heterogeneity of Steel Ingots Committee.[1] The main arguments that support it are the general pattern of the concentration distribution as outlined in Fig. 1 and the crystal structure of the solid ingot core. Metallographic investigation of the ingot shows the existence in the bottom part of the ingot of a cone of so-called globulitic crystals, which are distinctly different from crystals in other parts of the ingot in magnitude, shape and concentration of alloying elements.[10] Early work of BISRA[11] and of West[12] has proved clearly that these crystals are deposited on the bottom of the melt under the influence of gravity forces. Recently Kohn[13] and Andrews and Gomer[14] have been able to make the contour of the mass of settled crystals in the bottom of the ingot visible through the addition of a radioactive tracer to the solidifying ingot. This contour appears to be funnel-shaped. From this it is concluded that the crystals are deposited preferentially

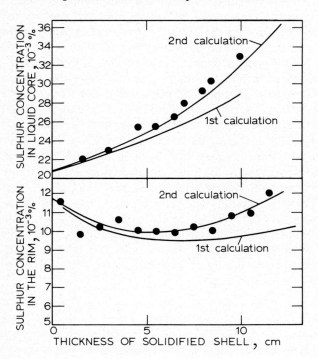

Ingot dimensions 680 × 1 350 × 2 100 mm

3   *Segregation during rimming*

at a short distance before the solidification front. Experiments with radioactive tracers[13-19] have further shown the existence of a persistent natural convection flow along the side walls of the liquid core, which produces in comparison to the solidification rate a rapid mixing of the liquid. Also, the presence of a clear and well defined boundary between the liquid and solid along the vertical side walls of the liquid core is observed.

These experimental observations lead to the following picture of the solidification mechanism. A necessary condition for the growth of crystals in the liquid core of the ingot is that at least a part of the liquid is supercooled. Moreover, in order to allow the removal from the melt of the latent heat of solidification generated by the growing crystals, a temperature gradient towards the macroscopic solidification front must exist. This temperature gradient is also responsible for the natural convection flow in the liquid metal. A pseudo steady state will develop in which the heat transport from the liquid to the solidification front will be balanced by the latent heat of solidification of the crystals growing in the liquid.

The origin of the supercooling and the temperature gradient in the liquid is not yet completely clear, but must be found in the mechanism of the dendritic solidification in the two-phase zone behind the macroscopic solidification front. A qualitative explanation can be given with the help of the model of the dendritic growth in the two-phase zone introduced by Fleming *et al.*[20,21] Figure 5a shows a schematic picture of the growing

dendrites. Figure 5b gives the concentration distribution in the liquid and the dendrites in a direction perpencircular to the macroscopic growth direction. Figures 5c and 5d give respectively the concentration and temperature distribution in the liquid of the two-phase zone in the macroscopic growth direction. Recent research into the mechanism of solute redistribution during dendritic solidification[20-23] has shown that in any cross section through the interdendritic channels the solute concentration in the liquid can be considered as uniform (Fig. 5b).

The solute redistribution resulting from this mode of solidification gives rise to a fraction of solid material with increasing concentration in the liquid part of the two-phase zone. The concentration and temperature distributions are mutually connected through the existence of local equilibrium (Figs. 5c and 5d). The characteristic distance for a diffusion process in the macroscopic growth direction is given by D/v. Typical values of D and v in the case of ingot solidification are 5×10^{-5} cm^2/s and 2×10^{-3} cm/s respectively. This leads to a value of the characteristic diffusion distance of 2.5×10^{-2} cm. Comparison of this value with the estimated thickness of the two-phase zone, which is, except during the first 30 min of the solidification, at least 3–5 cm in the case of low carbon steel, shows that the concentration gradient in the liquid part of the two-phase zone will not have any appreciable influence on the concentration field ahead of the macroscopic solidification front. However, the situation is radically different when the heat-flow field is considered. Since the thermal diffusivity of liquid steel is about 7×10^{-2} cm^2/s, which leads to a characteristic distance of about 40 cm, the temperature gradient in the liquid of the two-phase zone will extend itself into the liquid ahead of the macroscopic solidification front (*see* dotted line in Fig. 5c) and provide the driving force for the natural convection and the growth of crystals in the liquid core of the ingot.

The argument concerning the diffusion in the macroscopic growth direction given above shows also that no net mass transfer between the solidification front and the bulk liquid is to be expected. Although an extensive local solute redistribution takes place, the overall effect is that the solid steel growing in the two-phase zone behind the macroscopic solidification front has the same average concentration as the bulk liquid and does not contribute to the development of macrosegregation. On the other hand, the crystals that grow in the natural-convection boundary layer do so, by the nature of the mechanism responsible for their growth, at small supercooling. This means that they must grow virtually in equilibrium with the surrounding liquid and thus are an effective source of macrosegregation.

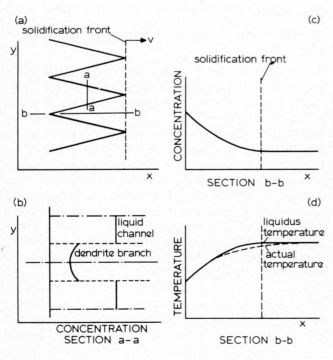

a Schematic representation of dendrites; *b* concentration distribution in liquid channel and dendrite perpendicular to macroscopic-growth direction; *c* concentration distribution in liquid channel in macroscopic-growth direction; *d* temperature distribution without and with convection in macroscopic growth direction

5   *Dendrite solidification in two-phase zone*

Mathematical model of macrosegregation in ingot core

The formulation of a quantitative model for the macrosegregation in the ingot core according to the mechanism described in the preceding section can be divided into two separate problems:

(i) the description of the development of the liquid concentration during solidification
(ii) the relationship between the liquid concentration and the concentration of the solid material that grows from the liquid.

These two problems will be treated here in this order.

As was explained earlier, the increase of the liquid concentration is predominantly due to the formation of relatively pure free crystals in the supercooled region in front of the macroscopic solidification interface. The key problem in the development of a mathematical model of macrosegregation lies in the determination of the fraction of the solid material that is solidifying in the form of crystals floating in the melt. Since the growth of these crystals is determined by the heat transport from the liquid to the solidification front by the natural convection flow, the total growth rate of the crystals in the melt is proportional to the surface area of the solidification front. Under these conditions the mass balance for an alloying element in the melt is given by:

$$V\frac{dc}{dt} = (1 - k_e)cqA \qquad . \qquad . \qquad . \qquad . \qquad . \qquad (11)$$

Integration of this equation leads to:

$$\frac{c(t)}{c_0} = \exp\left[\int_0^t (1 - k_e)q\frac{A}{V}\,dt\right] \qquad . \qquad . \qquad (12)$$

The heat transfer rate between the liquid core and the macroscopic solidification front, and thus the value of q, cannot be calculated *a priori* since the boundary condition of the natural convection flow along the two-phase zone is not very well defined. As is discussed in the preceding section the heat transfer and the convection flow in the liquid core are generated by the temperature gradient in the two-phase zone. In view of this it can be expected that a flux boundary condition, proportional

to the temperature gradient in the two-phase zone, exists for the natural convection flow. Since the temperature gradient in the two-phase zone is in first approximation proportional to the velocity of the macroscopic solidification front, the flux boundary condition and thus the value of q can also be considered as being proportional to this velocity. A typical example of the behaviour of the solidification rate, v, as a function of time, is given in Fig. 6. After an initial transient the solidification rate reaches a nearly constant value during the last part of the solidification. Consequently it can be expected that q is also approximately constant during this part of the ingot solidification. Figure 6 gives also the ratio A/V as a function of time. From this it can be concluded that the integral in Eq. (12) grows rapidly near the end of solidification and is determined to a large extent by the behaviour of the ratio A/V, which places a heavy emphasis on the last part of the solidification. This being so Eq. (12) is approximated by

$$\frac{c(t)}{c_0} = \exp\left[p\int_0^t \frac{A}{V}\,dt\right] \qquad . \qquad . \qquad . \qquad . \qquad (13)$$

in which p contains the average volumetric growth rate of the crystals and the average effective distribution coefficient of the alloying element under consideration. The parameter p in equation (13) must be determined experimentally. The interesting point of this equation is that it relates the development of the solute concentration in the liquid core of the ingot through the integral $\int_0^t (A/V)\,dt$ directly to the primary variables of the ingot solidification process like ingot dimensions and cooling conditions. It is to be noted that, due to the singularity of the ratio A/V at the axis of the ingot, Eq. (13) predicts an extremely rapid rise of the liquid concentration near the end of solidification. The value of the integral can be calculated in different ways, i.e. by the use of a semi-empirical rule like Eq. (10), by direct experimental observation or by the use of a mathematical model of the ingot solidification process.

In this case the latter method has been used among others, as it offers a greater flexibility with respect to the ingot dimensions and ingot-cooling conditions that can be treated. Appendix 1 gives a short summary of the mathematical model. A more detailed description is given in another paper by H. W. den Hartog et al.[24] It suffices here to say that in the mathematical model used the macroscopic solidification front is treated as a discrete front where a fraction of the latent heat of solidification, depending upon the concentrations of the alloying element in the steel, is set free. The model is two-dimensional and the calculations of $\int_0^t (A/V)\,dt$ are performed in a horizontal cross section through the ingot. Thus the liquid core of the ingot is considered as an infinitely long cylinder, with no influence of the top and bottom surfaces of the liquid core on the macrosegregation. This seems to be permitted since the bottom surface is anyway covered with a blanket of settling crystals through which the natural convection flow cannot penetrate, while the area of the top surface is usually

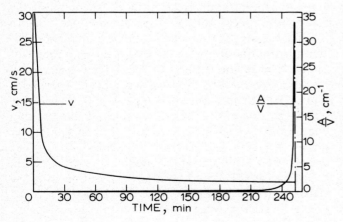

Ingot dimensions 852 × 1 560 × 2 200 mm; cooling time in mould, 110 mins; cooling time in air, ∞

6   *Velocity of solidification front and the ratio A/V as a function of time*

small compared with the surface area of the sidewalls (less than 10 %) and becomes progressively less important near the end of solidification.

A consequence of the two modes of solidification taking place in the ingot core is that the relationship between the final concentration distribution in the solid ingot and the development of the liquid concentration is rather complicated. As is explained in the preceding section it is plausible that the solid steel growing at the macroscopic solidification front has an average concentration equal to the concentration of the liquid from which it originates. The concentration distribution in a cross section through the solid ingot thus reflects directly the development of the liquid concentration, provided that no settled crystals are incorporated in the solid. This is the case at the level where the last liquid solidifies and as a consequence the segregation peak is positioned. At lower levels the inner part of the cross section is occupied by the settled crystals. To calculate the complete concentration distribution in the solid ingot it is not only necessary to have knowledge of the development of the liquid concentration as a function of time, but also of the amount of crystals that are formed, the solute concentration in these crystals and their settling behaviour. Since the value of the concentration in the segregation peak and its relation to the process variables is the most important piece of information in the study of macrosegregation and since this value can be calculated directly from Eq. (13), the present study will be restricted to the validity of this equation.

Experimental verification of mathematical model

In order to verify Eq. (13) the concentration distribution in a number of ingots and slabs has been determined very carefully. The dimensions of the ingots, together with the cooling times used are given in Table 1. It can be seen from this table that three different ingot types, solidified under rather different cooling conditions, are investigated. The ingots are sectioned vertically along a plane of symmetry parallel to the narrow sides of the ingot. The general concentration distributions of sulphur, carbon, phosphorus, and manganese in the ingots are determined by drilling samples with a diameter of 10 or 15 mm. An example of a concentration distribution of sulphur determined in this way is shown in Fig. 7.

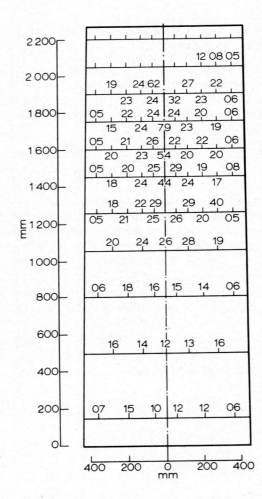

Ingot dimensions 852 × 1 560 × 2 200 mm; cooling time in mould, 110 mins; cooling time in air, ∞

7   *Sulphur concentrations (10^{-3} %) in a vertical cross section*

In view of the sharp increase of the concentration in the neighbourhood of the segregation peak predicted by Eq. (13), the concentration distribution in this region must be determined with a much higher resolution.

To this end samples are taken at distances of 10 mm with a drill of 5 mm diameter. In these samples only the sulphur concentration is determined. To diminish the influence of local concentration fluctuations, due to internal fissuring during solidification etc., the concentration distribution in the cross section through the ingot at the level of the segregation peak is determined by averaging the concentration over a height of 7·5 cm above and below the concentration maximum and by averaging about the axis of the ingot. Examples of the resulting concentration distributions in the thickness direction are given in Fig. 8. This figure illustrates already very well the steep concentration gradients near the centre of the ingots. The concentration distribution in a few slabs (*see* Table 1) has also been determined. The slabs are cut in sections with a size of 5 % of the total length of the slab. Samples are taken from the centre of these sections to determine the longitudinal concentration distribution. Once the position of the concentration maximum is determined, at this location a piece is cut from the slab with a cross section of 40 mm × 40 mm and

TABLE 1   Ingots used in the experimental verification of core segregation model

No.	Dimensions, mm	Cooling times min in mould	in air	Analysed in ingot	slab
1	852 × 1 560 × 2 200	110	—	x	—
2	852 × 1 560 × 2 200	108	5	x	—
3	852 × 1 560 × 2 200	72	159	—	x
4	852 × 1 560 × 2 200	50	180	—	x
5	792 × 1 185 × 2 100	112	—	x	—
6	792 × 1 185 × 2 100	114	5	x	—
7	680 × 1 350 × 2 080	—	—	x	—

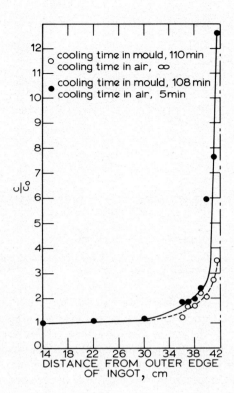

Ingot dimensions 852 × 1 560 × 2 200 mm

8 Dimensionless sulphur distribution in horizontal cross sections through ingots

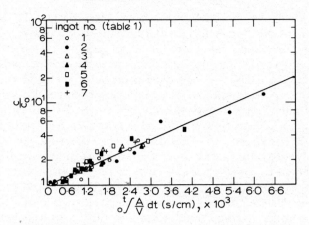

10 Dimensionless sulphur concentrations in the liquid core as a function of $\int_0^t (A/V)\,dt$

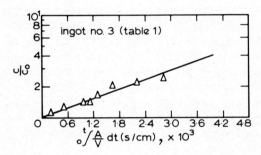

11 Dimensionless phosphorus concentration in liquid core as a function of $\int_0^t (A/V)\,dt$

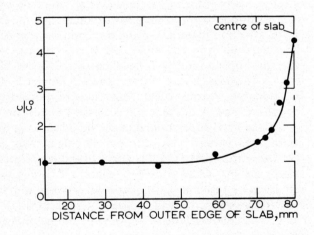

Ingot dimensions 852 × 1 569 × 2 200 mm; slab thickness 160 mm; cooling time in mould, 72 mins; cooling time in air, 159 mins

9 Dimensionless sulphur distribution in a cross section through a slab

which contains the complete thickness of the slab. The concentration distribution of sulphur in the direction of the thickness of the slab is then determined by cutting with a small milling cutter layers with a thickness of 0·2 mm at distances of 2 mm from the cross section of the sample and analysing these. An example of a concentration distribution determined in this way across a slab is given in Fig. 9.

Using the assumption that the concentration in the solid steel growing at the solidification front is equal to the concentration in the liquid and by calculating the position of the solidification front as a function of time with the mathematical model of ingot solidification the development of the liquid concentration as a function of time is determined from the concentration distributions given in Figs. 8 and 9. In using the data of the slabs the concentration distribution in the original ingot is recalculated by assuming that during rolling the deformation has been uniform over the cross section of the ingot. The integral $\int_0^t (A/V)\,dt$ is also calculated as a function of time with the mathematical model. Figure 10 gives a half-logarithmic plot of the sulphur concentrations in the investigated ingots and slabs against the integral $\int_0^t (A/V)\,dt$. This figure shows that all concentration distributions can be represented with a single straight line, thus confirming,

(i) the exponential nature of the development of the concentration predicted by Eq. (13)

(ii) the fact that the integral $\int_0^t (A/V)\,dt$ can be considered as the fundamental independent variable in the segregation process, which takes into account both the influence of ingot dimensions and of the cooling conditions.

In one case the phosphorus concentration has also been determined with a fine resolution. The results are given in Fig. 11, and show that in this case also the concentration distribution can be described very well with Eq. (13). The values of the parameter p for sulphur and phosphorus which can be determined from Figs. 10 and 11 are 4.2×10^{-4} cm/s and 3.4×10^{-4} cm/s respectively.

An additional piece of experimental evidence is available for one of the assumptions in the present model, i.e. the equality of the concentration in the solid shell and in the liquid. In a large number of slabs rolled from rimmed steel ingots the sulphur concentration in the outer core (region of constant concentration adjacent to the rimlayer) has been determined. According to the assumption quoted above this concentration should be equal to the sulphur concentration in the liquid core at the moment of capping of the ingot. This liquid concentration can be obtained by a simple mass balance calculation from the average concentration in the rimlayer and the thickness of the rimlayer, which is also measured. The two concentrations are compared with each other in Fig. 12. There is a slight tendency of the actual concentration in the outer core to be somewhat higher than the concentrations calculated from the mass balance. This can be explained very well by the fact that in these calculations the effect of the formation of free crystals in the melt during the rimming period is not taken into account. It appears that both concentrations agree rather well with each other, particularly when the accuracy of the mass balance calculations, which is estimated to be $\pm 15\%$, is taken into account.

Discussion of the core segregation model

In the first place a remark will be made here on the general shape of the concentration distribution in the ingot. Inspection of Eq. (13) shows that for a given value of the parameter p, the concentration only starts to rise perceptibly above its original value when the integral $\int_0^t (A/V)\,\mathrm{d}t$ has reached a certain value. The value of the integral $\int_0^t (A/V)\,\mathrm{d}t$ is dominated to a large extent by the development of the dimensions of the liquid core. As a result the thickness of the heavily segregated region in the ingot is almost independent of the ingot dimensions and the cooling conditions. On the other hand the maximum concentration in the segregated region is dependent upon the value of the integral in the centre of the ingot. Since this value grows with the ingot

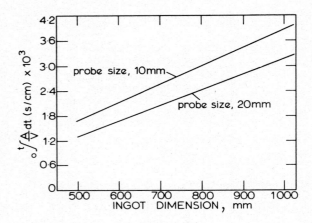

The ingots are solidified in the mould

13 *Value of the integral $\int_0^t (A/V)\,\mathrm{d}t$ for square ingots as a function of ingot dimension*

dimensions as illustrated in Fig. 13, the maximum concentration in the ingot grows also with ingot size.

Thus far the model has only been verified for sulphur and in a single instance for phosphorus. However, ample evidence can be found in the literature on macrosegregation that, apart from the magnitude of the concentration differences the general shape of the concentration distributions for different elements is the same.[1,26] Thus, it can safely be concluded that the present model applies also for other alloying elements in steel, when appropriate values of the parameter p are introduced. A first estimate of the value of p for other elements can be made by a further consideration of the growth kinetics of the free crystals. From the nature of the mechanism generating the supercooling in the liquid core it is to be expected that this supercooling will only be of the order of a few °C. The growth rate of the crystals is limited by the fact that the freezing point depression resulting from the solute build up at the interface of the crystals cannot exceed the local supercooling in the liquid. Taking into account that carbon is the principal alloying element and that the slope of the liquidus curve of the iron–carbon system is about 90°C/% it is clear that the crystal growth rate must be such that at the most an increase of a few hundredth of a percent in the carbon concentration at the crystal interface exists. In view of the equilibrium distribution coefficient of carbon ($k_0 \approx 0.12$) in steel with an average concentration of 0.1% carbon this would amount to an effective distribution coefficient only slightly higher than the equilibrium distribution coefficient. Since the solute build up around the crystals is governed primarily by the growth rate the same conclusion applies to the other alloying elements. This means that for a first approximation of the parameter p the effective distribution coefficient can be set equal to the equilibrium distribution coefficient.

The above reasoning is supported by the experimental results of Figs. 10 and 11. The ratio of the values of p for sulphur and phosphorus determined from these figures is 1.25. From different literature sources values of the equilibrium distribution coefficient for sulphur between 0.03 and 0.06 and for phosphorus between 0.13

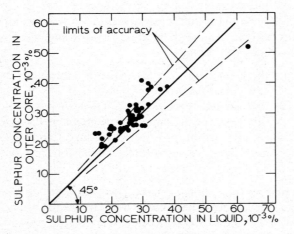

12 *Sulphur concentration in the outer-core region compared with the concentration of the liquid at the moment of capping*

and 0·18 can be found. The ratio between the p values calculated on the basis of these data varies between 1·1 and 1·2. This compares very favourably with the experimentally determined ratio. With the assumption of a negligible solute build up around the crystals it is also possible to calculate the order of magnitude of the crystal growth rate in the melt. From the value of $4·2 \times 10^{-4}$ cm/s for p and with a value for k_0 for sulphur of 0·05, the average crystal growth rate is calculated to be $4·4 \times 10^{-4}$ cm^3/cm^2 s. This value must be compared with the growth rate at the macroscopic solidification front in the ingot. A typical value for the solidification velocity in big ingots during a large part of the solidification is 2×10^{-3} cm/s. This means that near the end of solidification about 20 % of the solid material is growing in the ingot in the form of crystals floating in the melt.

APPLICATIONS OF THE SEGREGATION MODELS

Scatter in experimental data on macrosegregation

The most striking fact appearing in a survey of the literature on macrosegregation is the large scatter in the experimental data.[2,25-29] In fact, this scatter is often so large that it overshadows any possible effect of the process variables to be studied. The present study provides the possibility to explain the origin of the scatter. One of the most important sources is the sampling technique by which the segregation pattern is determined. Very often this is done by taking samples along the axis of slabs or blooms with sizes reported to range from 10 mm to 25 mm. Considering the exponential behaviour of the liquid concentration predicted by the core segregation model and inspecting the resulting concentration distributions in slabs or blooms illustrated in Fig. 9, it is clear that the above mentioned sample sizes are much too large in view of the concentration gradients in the centre of the slabs. Particularly when it is taken into account that as a result of asymmetric cooling or rolling of the ingot, the concentration maximum is not necessarily located at the centre of the slab. Figure 8 shows that even in ingots sectioned along the axis the concentration distribution must be determined very carefully and with a proper resolution in the sampling pattern near the concentration maximum.

A second source of error lies in the variability of the volume fraction of the ingot occupied by the rimlayer. The liquid concentration at the end of the rimming period is the starting concentration for the segregation process in the ingot core. The large ratio between the maximum and the starting concentration in the ingot core, about 4 to 5 for normally solidified ingots, results in a relatively large influence of variation in the volume fraction occupied by the rimlayer on the concentration in the segregation peak. The results of investigations where these two factors are not properly taken into account, which is the case for the great majority of the data reported in the literature, cannot be used for a quantitative discussion of macrosegregation.

Ingot dimensions

The present models provide the possibility to calculate the relationship between the segregation pattern and the ingot dimensions. To illustrate this calculations are made for two series of ingots with thicknesses ranging from 500 mm to 1 000 mm. The first series has a square cross section and the second series a rectangular cross section with a constant width to thickness ratio of 3. Moreover, the cooling times of the ingots are chosen in such a way that they are solidified completely in the mould. To judge the influence of the segregation during rimming action on the overall results, the calculations are performed both for semikilled steel ingots and for rimmed-steel ingots. For the rimmed steel-ingots a rimlayer with a thickness of 10 cm has been assumed. The results are presented in Figs. 14 and 15 for semikilled and rimmed-steel ingots respectively. The maximum concentration predicted in sample sizes of 10 mm and 20 mm is given. The influence of the sample size on the observed maximum concentration is very clearly illustrated. Comparison of Figs. 14 and 15 shows the relatively large increase of the maximum concentration in the smaller ingots as a consequence of the larger volume fraction of the ingot occupied by the rim. This explains the relative insensitivity of the maximum concentration

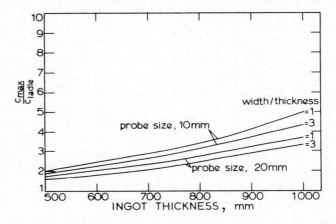

14   Maximum concentration in semikilled steel ingots as a function of ingot thickness

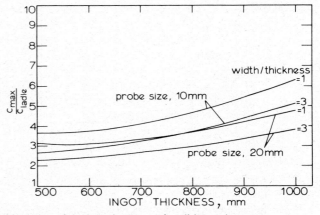

Dimension of the layer is 100 mm for all ingot sizes

15   Maximum concentration in rimmed-steel ingots as a function of ingot thickness

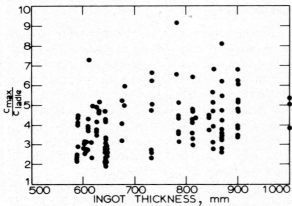

16 *Experimental data on maximum concentration of ingot thickness*

in rimmed-steel ingots to the ingot size as shown in Fig. 15.

A typical set of experimental data on the relationship between the maximum concentration and the ingot thickness is given in Fig. 16. The data in this figure are taken from a survey conducted by the CRM among its members.[30] The relationship between the maximum concentration and the ingot thickness as established in Fig. 15 is almost completely obscured by the scatter in the experimental data in Fig. 16. Comparison of Figs. 15 and 16 shows that a large part of the scatter in Fig. 16 can be explained by factors such as the differences in ingot geometry and sample sizes. It can be concluded that with the present models a much better insight into the relationship between the segregation pattern and the

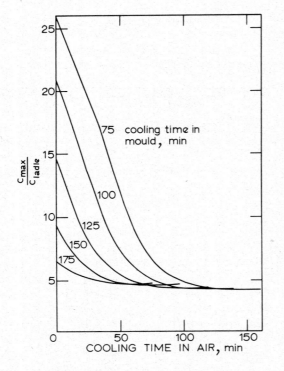

Ingot dimensions 852 × 1 560 × 2 200 mm; thickness of rim 100 mm

17 *Relationship between maximum concentration and cooling times in rimmed-steel ingots*

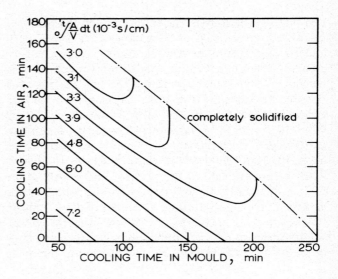

Ingot dimensions 852 × 1 560 × 2 200 mm

18 *Value of the integral $\int_0^t (A/V)\,dt$ as a function of the cooling times in the mould and in the air*

process variables can be obtained than from the existing experimental data.

Track times

The influence of the cooling times in the mould and in air after stripping of the ingot is calculated for rimmed-steel ingots of dimensions 852 mm × 1 560 mm × 2 200 mm. In the calculations it is again assumed that the rimlayer has a thickness of 10 cm. Moreover, it is assumed that at the end of the cooling time in air the ingot is charged into the soaking pit where reheating of the ingot takes place.

Figure 17 shows the results of the calculation. The maximum concentration in the ingot (sample size 10 mm) is given as a function of the cooling time in air for different values of the cooling time in the mould. Very interesting is the horizontal part of the curves. Apparently above a certain value a change in the cooling time in air does not have any influence on the maximum concentration. The physical explanation for this phenomenon is that for a certain combination of cooling time in the mould and cooling time in air the thickness of the solidified shell reaches such a value that the heat wave introduced in the ingot after charging in the pit furnace cannot influence the solidification before its completion.[24] When on the other hand the cooling time in air is reduced below the critical value the solidification is retarded, resulting in an increase of the maximum concentration. The extremely rapid rise of the maximum concentration can be explained by the fact that the retardation takes effect during the last part of the solidification, where the dimensions of the liquid core give rise to a high value of the ratio A/V. The influence on the value of $\int_0^t (A/V)\,dt$ is thus relatively large.

The results of the calculations can also be represented in the diagram of Fig. 18. The cooling time in the mould and in air are plotted on the horizontal and vertical axis respectively. In the diagram curves of constant value of the integral $\int_0^t (A/V)\,dt$ are drawn. For a given length of the rimming period the maximum concentration in the ingot is also constant along these curves. In the region above the dotted line the ingot is completely solidified before charging in the soaking pit. The vertical branches of the lines of constant value of $\int_0^t (A/V)\,dt$ show again that for certain combinations of the cooling times the solidification velocity is insensitive towards the length of the cooling time in air. The diagram of Fig. 18 can serve as a useful reference for the determination of the cooling times necessary to meet certain segregation requirements, such as the absence of internal defects in slabs.[24]

CONCLUSIONS

The mass transfer during rimming action is governed by the local mixing resulting from the formation and the release of carbon monoxide bubbles at the solidification front. The model describing this process leads to a relationship between the effective distribution coefficient, k_e, and the solidification velocity, v, independent of the ingot size. For large ingots (> 12 tons) the simultaneous decrease of k_e and the increase of the concentration in the liquid core with time lead to an approximately constant value of the sulphur concentration in the rimlayer, which is 0·5 times the ladle sulphur concentration. The core segregation model shows that the concentration distribution in the horizontal cross section through the ingot at the height of the segregation peak is governed by the integral $\int_0^t (A/V)\,dt$. This integral is an independent variable for the segregation process which includes both the influence of the ingot geometry and of the process variables governing the solidification process.

The ingot core can be divided into an outer core region with an almost uniform concentration and an inner core region with a sharply increasing concentration. This is a result of the exponential nature of the concentration distribution together with the singularity of $\int_0^t (A/V)\,dt$ on the axis of the ingot. The size of the inner core region is almost independent of the ingot dimensions, while the maximum concentration in the inner core grows with increasing ingot dimensions. Consideration of the growth mechanism of the free crystals and of the experimental evidence shows that it is plausible to assume that the concentration in the free crystals is in equilibrium with the bulk liquid concentration. Under these conditions the average crystal growth rate is calculated as $4\cdot4 \times 10^{-4}$ cm^3/cm^2 s. The value of the parameter p in the core segregation model (*see* Eq. (13)) for other alloying elements can be estimated by multiplying this value with the factor $(1 - k_0)$.

The scatter usually encountered in the experimental data on macrosegregation from the literature is a result of variations in factors such as the sample sizes, length of rimming period, length of track time, and ingot geometry. Application of the models presented here allows the quantitative estimation of the influence of ingot dimensions and cooling times on the segregation pattern.

REFERENCES

1 1st–9th Reports on steel ingots, 1926–1939, London, The Iron and Steel Institute
2 K. ASANO AND T. OHASHI: *Tetsu-to-Hagané*, 1966, **52**, 1 517
3 W. H. MAYO *et al.*: Proceedings of the Open Hearth Conference, 1956, **39**, 146
4 P. NILLES: *JISI*, 1964, **202**, 602
5 P. NILLES *et al.*: *Stahl Eisen*, 1965, **85**, 1 025
6 A. MASUI *et al.*: *Trans. ISI Japan*, 1968, **8**, 195
7 K. NARITA: *Tetsu-to-Hagané*, 1968, **54**, 876
8 P. V. DANCKWERTS: *Trans. Faraday Soc.*, 1950, **46**, 300
9 V. G. SMITH *et al.*: *Can. J. Phys.*, 1955, **33**, 722
10 A. KOHN: *Rev. Mét.*, 1963, **60**, 711
11 BISRA: *JISI*, 1949, **162**, 437
12 D. R. F. WEST: *JISI*, 1950, **164**, 182
13 A. KOHN: 'The solidification of metals', 1968, London, The Iron and Steel Institute
14 K. W. ANDREWS AND C. R. GOMER: *ibid*
15 A. KOHN AND J. ARNOULT: *Rev. Mét.*, 1965, **62**, 311
16 A. A. ZBORORSKI *et al.*: *Steel*, 1957, **17**, 24
17 H. MORI *et al.*: *Tetsu-to-Hagané*, 1966, **52**, 419
18 H. KOSMIDER: *Stahl Eisen*, 1957, **77**, 133
19 K. O. JONSSON: *Jernkont. Ann.*, 1969, **153**, 193
20 H. D. BRODY: *Trans. Met. Soc. AIME*, 1966, **236**, 615
21 T: E. BOWER: *Trans. Met. Soc. AIME*, 1966, **236**, 624
22 S. V. SUBRAMANIAN *et al.*: *JISI*, 1968, **206**, 1 027
23 S. V. SUBRAMANIAN *et al.*: *JISI*, 1968, **206**, 1 124
24 H. W. DEN HARTOG *et al.*: to be published
25 J. F. ELLIOTT *et al.*: Proceedings of the Open Hearth Conference, 1955, **38**, 142
26 K. K. ASCHENDORFF *et al.*: *Stahl Eisen*, 1962, **82**, 1 356
27 K. MORINAGA *et al.*: *Tetsu-to-Hagané*, 1964, **4**, 288
28 H. RELLERMEYER AND R. HAMMER: *Stahl Eisen*, 1958, **78**, 1 505
29 K. KUPZOG *et al.*: *Stahl Eisen*, 1962, **82**, 393
30 R. PESCH: CRM Internal Report
31 L. FOX: 'Numerical solution of ordinary and partial differential equations, 1962, Oxford
32 R. SÉVRIN: 'Mathematical models in metallurgical process development, 1970, London, The Iron and Steel Institute

APPENDIX 1

Solidification model

The solidification model consists of a numerical solution of the two-dimensional heat conduction Eq. (A1) in horizontal cross section through the ingot.

$$\rho c_p \frac{\delta T}{\delta t} = \frac{\delta}{\delta x}\left(\lambda \frac{\delta T}{\delta x}\right) + \frac{\delta}{\delta y}\left(\lambda \frac{\delta T}{\delta y}\right) \qquad . \qquad . \qquad . \quad \text{(A1)}$$

The boundary conditions are given by the relations which govern the heat transfer between ingot mould and surroundings. The heat flux from the mould to the ambient air is described by a heat transfer coefficient α_1, which takes into account the heat transport by radiation as well as by free convection. The heat flux between ingot and mould is described by a heat transfer coefficient α_2, which varies with the formation of the air gap between ingot and mould. To take this phenomenon into account α_2 is regarded as a function of position on the ingot perimeter and of time. In the limit, after complete separation between ingot and mould has been achieved, the dominant mode of heat transport is radiation. After stripping during cooling in free air and during reheating of the ingot in the pit furnace, the heat transfer between ingot and surroundings is described by a heat transfer coefficient α_3. As in this case radiation is the primary mode of heat transport, α_3 is strongly dependent on the temperature of both ingot surface and the surroundings. Considerable attention has been given to the treatment of the solidification front, which constitutes a moving boundary to the heat conduction problem of Eq. (A1).

In an alloy the solidification takes place over a temperature traject between the liquidus temperature at the composition of the liquid and the eutectic temperature of the alloy. However, calculations based upon a dendritic growth model[20,21] show that the liberation of the latent heat of solidification is very unevenly distributed over this temperature range. From the model calculations it can be concluded that steel with a low carbon content can be treated to a good approximation as a pure metal, i.e. the latent heat of solidification is completely set free at the liquidus temperature of the alloy. For steel with a higher carbon content only part of the latent heat can be considered as set free at the liquidus temperature. The remaining part has to be taken account of in the specific heat of the steel in the solidification range. The displacement of the solidification front is given by the relation:

$$L_c \frac{dn}{dt} = \lambda \frac{\delta T}{\delta n} + \alpha_4 (T_m - T_s) \qquad . \qquad . \qquad . \qquad (A2)$$

In this relation L_c is the corrected heat of solidification. The last term on the right-hand side of (A2) represents the convective heat transfer from the liquid metal to the solidification front. In general this term is not very important in ingot solidification. For the calculation of the thermal field in the mould and in the solidified part of the ingot Eq. (A1) together with the boundary conditions is transformed with the aid of an implicit finite difference method into a set of simultaneous linear algebraic equations, which can be solved by standard techniques of numerical analysis.[31] A serious problem is constituted by the presence of a moving boundary whose movement is dependent again on the thermal field.

This problem is solved by a prediction-correction type of method. An outline of this procedure is given in Fig. 19. At the start of a time step the new position of the solidification front is calculated, using the thermal field resulting from the former time step. With the new position of the solidification front new values of the thermal field are calculated. Subsequently this procedure is repeated, using the updated values of the thermal field and the position of the solidification front. In this way the temperature dependence of the specific heat and the thermal conductivity can also be taken into account in a

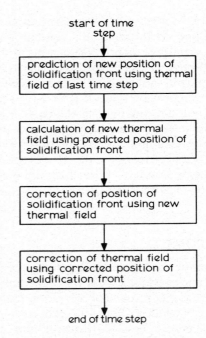

start of time
step

prediction of new position of solidification front using thermal field of last time step

calculation of new thermal field using predicted position of solidification front

correction of position of solidification front using new thermal field

correction of thermal field using corrected position of solidification front

end of time step

19   *Diagram of the prediction-correction method used in the numerical calculations*

proper way. The implicit nature of the calculation procedure ensures stability. This means that the maximum allowable time step is only determined by the desired accuracy.

Both the mesh width of the grid and the time steps used are selected so as to have no influence on the results of the calculations. Another source of error is found in the physical properties of steel and mould material used in the calculations. Particularly at higher temperatures these values are not very accurately known. A series of calculations made to check the influence of this inaccuracy on the results of the model showed an insignificant sensitivity to the values of the properties of the mould material used. A change of as large as 25 % in the thermal conductivity of steel resulted in only a 10 % change in the value of the thickness of the solidified shell. These results are in agreement with those of Sévrin.[32] The calculations of $\int_0^t (A/V) \, dt$ are performed in a horizontal cross section through the ingot. The liquid core in the ingot is considered as an infinitely long cylinder. From the position of the solidification front the surface area and the length of the circumference of the horizontal cross section through the liquid core are calculated. In this way the ratio A/V is determined as a function of time and subsequently integrated by standard methods of numerical analysis.[31]

Discussion on chapter four: Teeming and solidification

CHAIRMAN: PROF. F. OETERS (TECHNICAL UNIVERSITY OF BERLIN)

The following papers were discussed: *Models for macrosegregation in rimmed and semikilled steel ingots* by H. W. den Hartog, J. M. Rabenberg, and R. Pesch; *Heat losses from liquid steel in the ladle and tundish in a continuous-casting installation* by R. Alberny and S. Leclercq; *Water model for the quantitative simulation of the heat and fluid flow in liquid-steel refractory systems* by J. W. Hlinka; *Two-dimensional heat-transfer model for continuous casting of steel* by A. Perkins and W. R. Irving; *Application of mathematical models to predict pool profiles in continuously cast steel* by J. K. Brimacombe, J. E. Lait, and F. Weinberg.

Considering first the paper by den Hartog *et al.*, **Mr R. Alberny** (IRSID, France) was concerned to know how the authors dealt with reactions among carbon, oxygen, and manganese. He wondered whether consideration had been given in some implicit way.

Mr den Hartog reiterated that his model of the rimmed part of the ingot takes into account only diffusion mechanisms from the solidification front. Similar mechanisms apply in the cases of carbon, manganese, and oxygen, but, although there must clearly be interactions between these elements, it would be too complicated to try to account for them.

The Chairman, commenting on Eqs. (11) and (13) (forms of Scheldt's equation) pointed out that these took no account of solid diffusion and he wondered whether this would be important in the case of very hot soaked ingots. **Mr den Hartog** felt that since the characteristic distances for macrosegregation are between 5 and 10 cm, solid diffusion processes would not interfere. He also emphasized his view that solid crystals in an otherwise liquid phase should be regarded as being in an independent world with its own scale of velocity.

Opening the discussion on Mr Alberny's paper, **Mr Hlinka** said that although the use of lids and covers on tundishes was one way of controlling tundish temperature, another approach which he had described consisted simply of using enough slag on the ladle. **Mr Alberny** agreed that this was indeed another approach, but pointed out that in practice, both heat parameters (insulation and diffusion) and fluid parameters (convection) play a part in setting up stratification of temperature within the ladle.

Mr Verhoog then presented the following contribution:

HEAT BALANCE AND TEMPERATURE STRATIFICATION IN LIQUID STEEL IN LADLES

H. W. den Hartog, S. Rosier, A. B. Snoeijer, and H. M. Verhoog

The control of the temperature of liquid steel in ladles and tundishes is of great importance for steelmaking practice. Since there are only limited possibilities to adjust the liquid-steel temperature in the ladle the control of the teem stream or tundish temperature has to take place principally in the converter. This makes it necessary to describe quantitatively the heat losses in ladle and tundish. In this respect the papers of Alberny and Leclercq[1] and of Hlinka[2] are to be welcomed as important contributions to this subject. Comparable work has been done at Hoogovens, i.e. the development of numerical models for the calculation of the heat balance of steel in the ladle and for the estimation in the ladle under the influence of gravity forces. In order to supply the correct values of the parameters in the process models and to verify the calculations a large amount of experimental work has been carried out in the BOF shop no. 2 of Hoogovens. It is of interest to compare the methods used and the results obtained with the work presented here today.

HEAT BALANCE OF THE STEEL IN THE LADLE

A numerical model has been developed to calculate the heat balance of the liquid steel in the ladle. The calculation covers the period between the last temperature measurement in the converter and the end of teeming. It takes into account:

(i) the heat losses of the steel by radiation during its residence in the converter from the tapping stream and the free surface of the steel in the ladle

(ii) the heat effects of the additions to the steel in the ladle during tapping

(iii) the heat fluxes into the refractory lining of the ladle

(iv) the heat losses through the slag layer on the steel in the ladle.

It is a special feature of the present model that measurements of temperature profiles in the refractory lining have been used to derive values of the thermal conductivity as a function of the temperature. These measurements indicate that there is no shift in material properties during the ladle campaign and consequently no influence of the number of heats already made in the ladle. The numerical calculation of the temperature field in the refractory lining makes it also possible to take the influence of any temperature distribution in the lining at the start of tapping into account. In this way allowance is made for the influence of the cycle time of the ladle and wear of the lining on the heat balance. Figure 1 gives

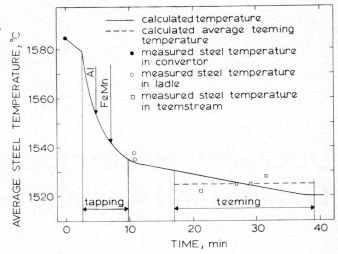

2 Evolution of steel temperature, calculated and measured in heat M 8795

for two heats the temperature profiles in the refractory lining at the beginning of tapping and after 30 min. During tapping and during teeming the variation of the height of the steel is taken into consideration. Shadow factors are introduced to calculate the exchange of radiation between the surface of the steel bath, respectively the slag cover, the ladle walls and the surroundings. Table 1 and Fig. 2 give an example of the results of a heat balance calculation for a 280 ton ladle of BOF shop no. 2 at Hoogovens, in terms of the average

TABLE 1   Calculated temperatures of heat M 8795 BOF shop No. 2, assuming uniform steel temperature

Steel weight 309 ton	Quality: semikilled medium carbon steel	
18 ingots of 17 ton		
nozzle diameter 90 mm	Ladle: wall, sand lining bottom, fire	
slag weight 4·6 ton	clay bricks	

	Temp., °C	Time, min
Last measurement in converter	1 585	0
Time between measurement and start of tapping	−3·8	2·5
Beginning of tapping	1 581·2	2·5
Ferromanganese 3 400 kg	−21·5	
Aluminium 37 kg	+3·5	
Temperature loss of steel in converter	−11·0	
Radiation during tapping loss from tapjet	−2·8	
Heat loss to ladle wall	−4·0	
Heat loss to ladle bottom	−2·3	
Heat loss to stopper rod	−2·0	
Radiation loss from steel surface in the ladle	−6·4	
End of tapping	1 534·7	9·7
Calculated steel temperature at moment of measurement in ladle	1 534·0*	10·7
Heat loss during transport and teeming		
to ladle wall	−7·0	
to ladle bottom	−2·9	
to slag layer	−0·03	
Calculated teem stream temperature	1 524·8†	
End of teeming		40·1

* Measured temperatures in ladle one minute after the end of tapping, 1 538 and 1 535°C

† Measured temperatures in the teem stream, 1 522, 1 525, 1 524, and 1 528°C

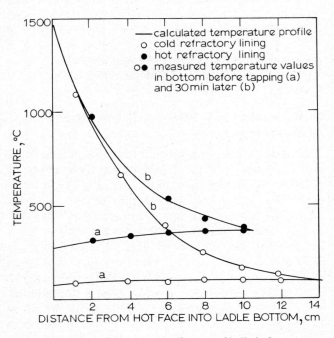

1 Temperature profiles in fireclay bottom of ladle before tapping and 30 min later

temperature of the steel in the ladle. The teem stream temperature given in Table 1 and Fig. 2 is calculated with the assumption that this temperature remains essentially constant over the complete teeming period. The teem stream temperature is calculated from the heat balance over the complete teeming period. The assumption of a constant teem stream temperature is based on measurements in the BOF shop and is in agreement with the analysis of the stratification phenomenon in the ladle given by Hlinka.[3] This method of calculating the teeming jet temperature from the steel enthalpy differs from that proposed by Alberny and Leclercq. These authors calculate the temperature of the steel leaving the ladle by a correction on the calculated average temperature of the steel in the ladle. The correction decreases linearly from an initial value to zero at the end of teeming. In doing so it appears that heat is allowed to disappear unaccountedly from the heat balance of the ladle–liquid steel system.

A number of measurements of the temperature of the liquid steel at different moments in the process cycle have been carried out in order to check the results of the heat balance calculations. All the experiments are done with 280 ton ladles of BOF shop no. 2 of Hoogovens. The first instance where a meaningful measurement of the temperature of the steel in the ladle can be made is shortly after tapping of the steel from the converter. At that moment the liquid steel can be considered as reasonably well mixed and uniform in temperature. The steel temperatures are measured with disposable thermocouples at an immersion depth of about 0·5 m below the slag cover. Figure 3 gives a comparison of the measured and calculated average steel temperature in the ladle. The 2σ values indicated in this figure are determined from a series of readings of two thermocouples which are simultaneously immersed in steel in the converter or ladle. The results in Fig. 3 show a good agreement between the calculated and the real temperature of the

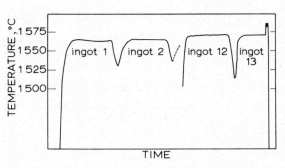

4 *Responses of the thermocouple mounted in the stopper rod head*

steel in the ladle. The second place where a meaningful temperature measurement can be carried out is in the teem stream. Several methods have been tested. In the first instance measurements are made with a thermocouple protected with a cermet sheath which penetrates axially through the head of the stopper rod. Figure 4 shows a typical response of the thermocouple on the lifting of the stopper rod. Figure 5 shows the teem stream temperature measured in this way as a function of ingot number. Also shown are the results of measurements made with disposable thermocouples inserted with a lance into the teeming jet. It is shown by laboratory experiments that the difference in the temperature between the two methods is not real but is caused by the different thermocouple wires applied in the temperature probes. It follows that the temperature is essentially constant over the period the measurements are made. Equipping stopper rod heads with temperature probes is rather complicated and interferes with the routine handling in the shop when preparing the ladles for the next charge. Therefore, most of the teeming jet temperature measurements are carried out by means of disposable probes. Figure 6 gives the teeming jet temperature for ladles with slag layers of different thickness. For a very thin slag layer (M8793, 5 cm) the teem stream temperature shows a tendency to decrease during teeming. In the other cases the temperature remains virtually constant. Figure 7 gives a comparison of the calculated and the measured teem stream temperatures. The 2σ values indicated are again calculated from reproducibility measurements in converter and teem stream. The value of 9°C is somewhat greater than the value of 7·6°C in Fig. 3. This is due to the larger scatter

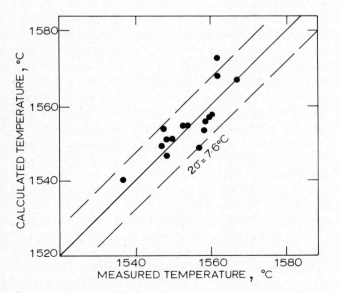

Each point is the average of two subsequent measurements in the same ladle

3 *Calculated v. measured temperature in the ladle after tapping*

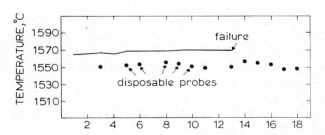

5 *Teem stream temperature measured with a thermocouple mounted in the stopper rod head with disposable thermocouples inserted in the teem stream*

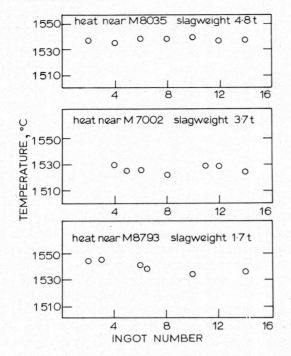

6   Temperature measurements in the teem stream with thermo-couples inserted into the jet

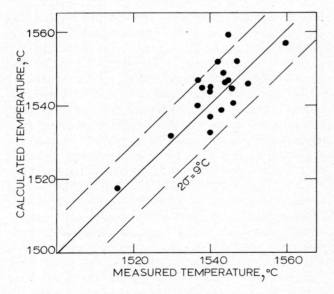

The measured value is the average of at least six measurements during teeming

7   Calculated v. measured temperature in the teem stream

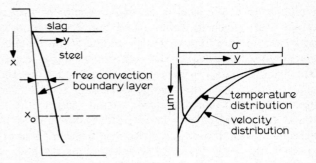

8   Temperature and velocity distribution in the free convection boundary layer in the ladle

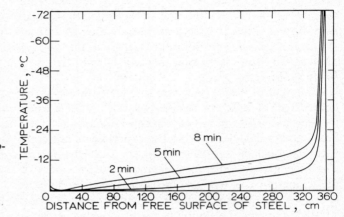

9   Temperature stratification in ladle at different times after tapping of the steel

in the temperature measurements in the teem stream. Again the agreement between the temperature calculated with the heat balance model and the measured values is very satisfactory.

TEMPERATURE STRATIFICATION IN THE LADLE

A numerical model has been developed for the natural convection flow in the ladle in order to estimate the influence of process variables such as argon stirring and

casting speed on the teem stream temperature evolution. The natural convection boundary layer flow along the sidewalls of the ladle (Fig. 8) is calculated in an approximate manner with the momentum and heat balance integral method, described in detail by Eckert.[4] The method is modified to take into account the effect of the longitudinal temperature gradient in the bulk liquid. The heat fluxes into the refractory lining calculated with the heat balance model serve as boundary conditions for the calculation of the flow field. The velocity of the bulk liquid is calculated from the continuity equation assuming that apart from the boundary layer the flow velocity is uniform over the complete cross section. It is assumed that during teeming the steel is discharged layer-like from the ladle. Furthermore, it is assumed that the slag cover on the steel is thick enough to limit the mixing effect from the adverse temperature gradient near the free surface of the steel to a relatively small part of the ladle.

The calculations show the determining influence of the vertical temperature gradient in the ladle on the boundary layer flow. Figure 9 shows the bulk liquid temperature distribution at different times after the end of tapping. The sharp decrease of the temperature near the bottom is a result of the almost stagnant layer at this place. Figures 10 and 11 show respectively the thickness of the boundary layer and the volumetric flow rate as a function of distance to the free surface of the liquid steel. The influence of the temperature gradient in the bulk

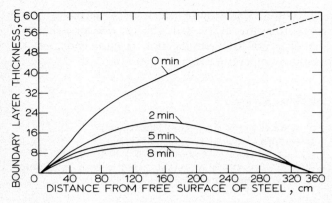

10 *Thickness of free convection boundary layer at different times after tapping of the steel*

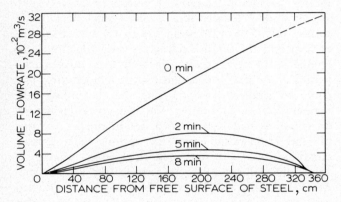

11 *Volume flowrate in free convection boundary layer at different times after tapping of the steel*

liquid is clearly illustrated in these figures. An important conclusion is that, notwithstanding the large decrease under the influence of the temperature stratification, the volumetric flow rate remains of the same order of magnitude as the flow rate in most casting operations.

A number of measurements of the temperature stratification are carried out in a 280 ton ladle. In these experiments three thermocouples protected by cermet sheaths are mounted in the wall of the ladle at 75 cm, 200 cm, and 270 cm from the bottom. The length of the thermocouples penetrating through the refractory lining into the ladle (± 15 cm) is long enough to reach after a reasonably short time through the boundary layer and to measure the bulk liquid temperature. Together with the temperature measurements inside the ladle the temperature of the teem stream is measured with disposable thermocouples. A typical example of a result of these measurements is shown in Fig. 12. Also shown are the calculated bulk liquid temperatures at the levels of the thermocouples and the calculated value of the teem stream temperature. The agreement between the calculations and the results of the measurements is rather good.

EXAMPLES

To illustrate the possibilities and the flexibility of the models two examples are shown in Figs. 13 and 14. The examples can be compared with the calculations for a combination of a 280 ton ladle and a 12 ton tundish with or without argon stirring in the ladle given in the paper of Alberny and Leclercq. Starting from a converter temperature of 1 600°C the temperature distribution in the ladle, the teem stream temperature and the tundish temperature are calculated. In the calculation of the tundish temperature this vessel is considered to be perfectly mixed, while the heat losses to the refractories

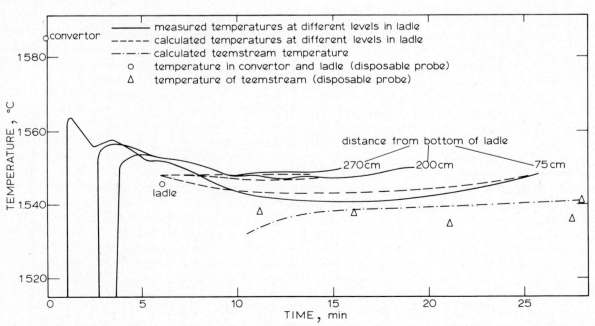

12 *Comparison of measured and calculated values of the temperature at different levels in the ladle and of measured and calculated values of the teem stream temperature*

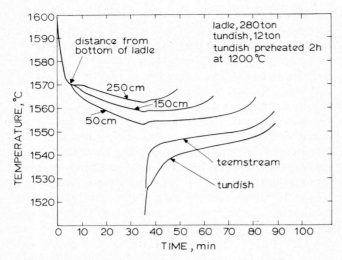

13   *Stratification in ladle and teem stream and tundish temperature calculated with heat balance and stratification models*

and the surroundings are calculated in the same manner as is done for the ladle. The influence of argon stirring on the temperature stratification in the ladle and on the initial temperature evolution in the tundish is clearly illustrated.

CONCLUSIONS

The results of the calculations and experimental determinations of the temperature of the liquid steel in the ladle presented in this discussion agree within the limits set by the accuracy of the measuring methods. This supports the conclusion put forward in the paper of Alberny and Leclercq that heat balance calculations can serve as a useful tool to control teeming temperature.

It is shown that a mathememematical model of the natural convection flow in the ladle can provide an estimate of the effect of the stratification phenomenon on the teeming temperature.

REFERENCES

1 R. ALBERNY AND A. LECLERCQ: This volume
2 J. W. HLINKA: *ibid*
3 J. W. HLINKA AND T. W. MILLER: *AISE*, 1970, **47**, 123
4 R. G. ECKERT AND R. M. DRAKE: 'Heat and Mass Transfer', 1959, New York, McGraw-Hill

Mr W. R. Irving starting a discussion on the contribution presented described similar work on temperature losses from ladles and large multiple strand continuous-casting tundishes. Excellent agreement had been obtained between calculated heat losses from the steel to the refractory bricks and those determined by measuring thermal profiles in the refractory bricks. Figures 15 and 16 show the temperature profiles and heat fluxes respectively. The implication was that a decreasing loss of heat into the tundish refractory with time might be compensated by a decrease in ladle teem stream temperature to obtain a constant casting temperature. This could be achieved by optimizing and controlling ladle temperature by preheating and slag-cover insulation. Calculations had been carried out to predict the rate of steel temperature drop for various ladle preheat conditions and different slag thicknesses. Figure 17 shows the difference in steel temperature for two preheat conditions and two slag thicknesses. Gas stirring certainly tends to generate homogeneity but **Mr Irving**

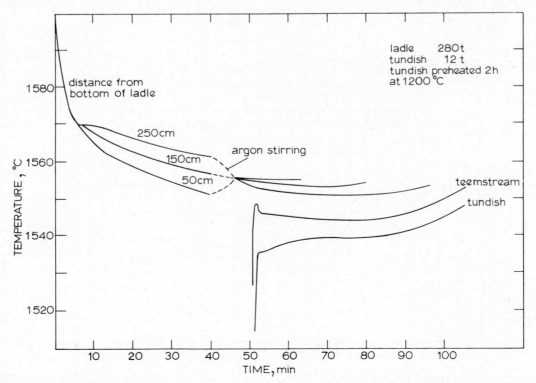

14   *Stratification in ladle and teem stream and tundish temperatures calculated with heat balance and stratification models*

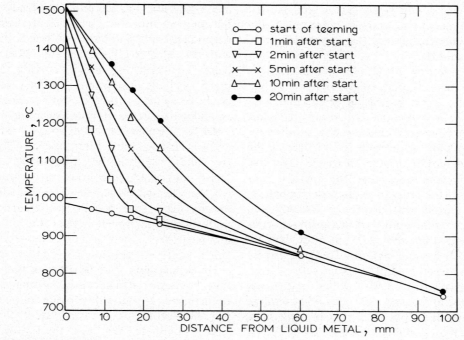

15 *Temperature distribution in brick*

asked whether the authors could comment on the relative effectiveness of bottom stirring through diffusers and stirring through lances. He was also concerned to hear views on the effectiveness and relative values of ladle cooling by the addition of scrap or the suspension of a slab in the ladle.

Mr Alberny, also replying to Mr Verhoog, said that in his model the heat balance for the tundish and ladle systems was indeed conserved. It was in fact this heat balance conservation which led to adequate explanation of the different performances of large and small ladles. Concerning argon stirring, it was most important to choose the right time. Gas stirring should be carried out when heat losses through the wall and upper surface are low so that there will be no reappearance of stratification. The longer that stirring is continued the better will

be the results. It is equally important not to use too much gas for if the surface cover is broken heat losses and stratification can reappear.

Mr Alberny asked Mr Hlinka whether he was satisfied with the similarity of his physical models and asked about changes of scale and geometry. Mr Hlinka was quite adamant that changes of scale were thoroughly well treated in the combined thermal/fluid model and

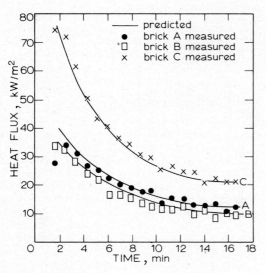

16 *Heat flux through wall bricks*

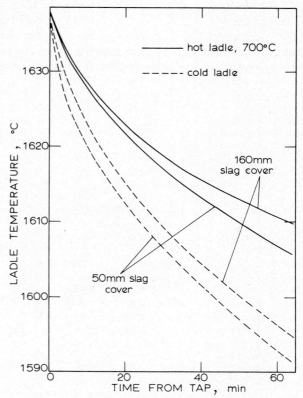

17 *Temperature losses from 250 ton ladle*

referred to the previous papers on the subject. He felt that the combined model was so much more practically useful than mathematical models that it should supercede them in the context.

Prof. Szekely, referring to Hlinka and Verhoog's work pointed out that although simple boundary-layer concepts provided a good indication of thermal fluid flux behaviour, it was dangerous to presume too far. He was specifically concerned that the flow model proposed by Verhoog took no account of vortices at the nozzle which he felt would certainly upset the 'layer like process', although conceding that the method was perfectly satisfactory for order of magnitude prediction. **Mr den Hartog** agreed with Professor Szekely and quoted evidence of the invalidity of the layer sequence model but affirmed that the main purpose was to establish a general behaviour pattern. This had proved to be quite satisfactory in guiding works practice.

Prof. Collin, commenting on Mr Hlinka's paper and views was concerned at the cost and inflexibility of large physical models, pointing out that only organizations with large resources and specific problems could follow the line taken by Mr Hlinka. Nevertheless, it was felt that a systematic study in physical models of some of the more complex features of (for e.g.) convection flow would be very valuable and might perhaps result in empirical techniques which could be used in subsequent mathematical models.

Mr Hlinka, replying, said that it certainly was not his intention to deny the validity of mathematical models. Nevertheless, in complicated circumstances such as those under discussion the physical model provided a very flexible tool in which regions of particular interest could readily be singled out and appropriately detailed measurements made. This was the point to which Prof. Collin was speaking. Concerning stratification, **Mr Hlinka** felt that it was naïve to presume that this started from the bottom of the ladle. In fact, it could occur in

any plane and was certainly affected by vortices. He felt that stratification was not as important as had been made out. In this context he was unimpressed also with the value of gas stirring and, incidentally, vacuum degassing which also induces stirring. By proper treatment of ladle insulation, perfectly adequate results could be achieved. As for cooling the ladle, the melter should get the temperature right in the first place.

Dr N. A. Robins then put two questions to Dr Perkins and Dr Brimacombe. First, he asked for a view about the validity of using break-out shells as a measure of liquid cool profile in continuous casting. He wondered whether the flush of metal leaving after a break-out would modify the profile. Second, he wondered whether the authors could comment on the value of mould lubricants and particularly their effect on heat-transfer coefficients either in the mould or the secondary cooling section.

Dr Brimacombe and **Dr Perkins** both took the view that break-out shells, while fortunately being a rare occurrence, do indeed provide a good measure of solidified profile. The superheat in continuously cast steel is eliminated very near the top of the mould and the large difference between subsequently available sensible heat and the latent heat of solidification is such that it is difficult to envisage any modification of the profile during runout. Dr Brimacombe said that his method of using radioactive pellets was quite effective but tended not to give good profiles at the bottom of the liquid sump because pellets stick in the partially solidified mush at about half the calculated pool depth. Practical measurements on the plant clearly indicated that the calculated depth was more or less right.

Commenting on mould lubricants, **Dr Brimacombe** referred to Fig. 18 in which dwell time in the mould of a large range of commercial continuous-casting plants was plotted against a mean heat flux. The reference line on this graph is the Savage and Pritchard model and it can be seen that all the practical measurements are

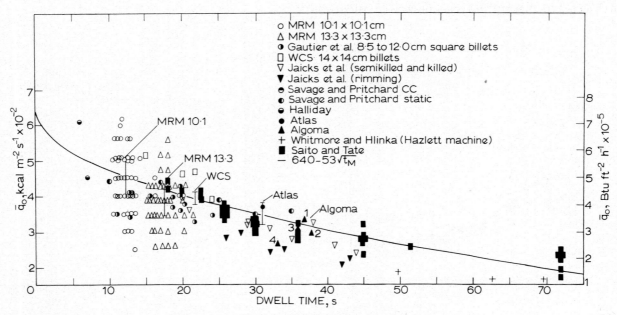

18 Dependence of average heat flux extracted by the mould on dwell time for continuously cast steel

spread about this line fairly uniformly. Of the plants for which results were quoted, **Dr Brimacombe** knew of a number of cases (marked on Fig 18) where a variety of practices with and without mould lubricant or rapeseed oil were common. In broad terms, however, all these results straddled the theoretical line as did some confidential figures which he had from a Japanese plant. It thus seemed that mould lubricants had only a modest effect on heat transfer. 10% had been suggested as a measure of the effect.

Mr Torp had been interested by Perkins and Irving's paper and particularly their discussion on boundary conditions. He suggested that the so-called 'box' integration in space together with an exponential alternating splitting method in time integration could be used radically to reduce computing time. Basically, the latter presumes that temperature behaves exponentially with time, i.e.:

$$O(t) = e^{wt} \cdot (t)$$

This is substituted into the heat conduction equation:

$$D \text{———} = AO + S$$

where the matrices D, A, and S contain the heat capacity, heat conduction, and heat source coefficients, respectively. Splitting the resulting Ae^{wt} matrix into triangular matrices and solving the time step in two half-steps, gives an extraordinarily fast solution algorithm. **Mr Torp** gave two examples of problems in which the method has been helpful. The first concerned mould casting of steel ingots in which the ingot and mould were divided into 122 mesh points with radiation and convection at the mould and an air gap formed at the ingot surface after 150 s. 1 000 s real time from teeming to stripping was simulated in 4·5 s. The second example concerned semicontinuous casting of aluminium. Vertical central cross-sections were divided into 600 mesh points and different assumptions about lubrication mechanisms at the mould were assessed. A 1 000 s real time was simulated in 100 s. The computer used in both cases was a Control Data 'CYBER 74'.

chapter 5: heating furnaces

Mathematical modelling of furnaces and primary rolling

F. Fitzgerald

There is a considerable volume of published work concerning the modelling of furnace systems. Accordingly, this review has been restricted to recently published work, except where reference has been made to classic papers, or those where some aspect of the treatments presented is considered sufficiently novel or different from those generally used to warrant their inclusion.

MELTING FURNACES

Open-hearth furnace

The earliest models of the open-hearth furnace were presented by Thring and co-workers.[1,2,3] The original model assumed a thin triangular flame starting from a point source and 'fanning out' to cover the whole of the bath at the exit. Air at constant temperature ran side by side with the flame and was gradually used up in the combustion process. Recirculation and convective effects were ignored, as also was longitudinal radiation. To simplify the calculation, radiant heat transfer was assumed to vary linearly with temperature in the range 1 300°–1 900°C and the heat capacities of the materials in the process were assumed constant at their mean values between 0° and 1 500°C. The effect of slag resistance was allowed for quite simply. Obviously these assumptions introduced errors but they did not greatly affect the comparative results which were sought. The model was used to investigate the effects of different flames on heat transfer in the open-hearth furnace and the effect of preheating and excess air were investigated. It was shown that the slag properties are overriding in controlling the heat transfer to the bath. Perhaps the most recent model of this type, of a reverberatory copper

The author is with BSC, Corporate Advanced Process Laboratory, Teesside

smelter, has been described by Harris.[4] The aims of the model were stated to be:

(i) provision of a means of detailed analysis of temperature profile and heat transfer under existing operating conditions
(ii) estimation of the response of the furnace to possible changes in operation and design
(iii) examination of alternatives proposed as ways of increasing efficiency, throughput, or bulk temperature
(iv) estimation of the ultimate capacity of the furnace under the most favourable conditions.

The furnace was 33 m long, by 10 m wide, by about 3·5 m high and was fired by four pulverized coal burners. Calculation was carried out in exactly the same way as by Thring[1,2,3] and the assumptions made were similar in many respects.

LD furnace

Modelling of the LD furnace has been treated by Oeters[5] and in other papers presented in this volume.[6,7]

Electric-arc furnace

No completely descriptive model of the electric-arc furnace has been found, presumably owing to the lack of knowledge concerning the mechanisms of energy transfer from AC arcs in furnace conditions. A number of descriptive models of parts of the electric-arc process have, however, been presented. Bowman[8] has considered the mechanism of electrode wear. He concluded that evaporation of the electrode tip due to arcing is made up of two components, i.e. evaporation at the mobile roots of the arc, the anode, and cathode spots and simultaneous evaporation from the whole end face of the tip due to the heating effect of the arc. The arc root loss is linearly proportional to arc current, whereas the evaporation from the whole tip face is a function of arc power and tip diameter. Good qualitative and quantitative agreement between predictions from a model based on these facts, and laboratory measurements made on electrodes of tip diameter 75, 100, and 150 mm at currents up to 10 kA, tended to confirm the validity of the model. However, measurements made on a large arc furnace at a constant current of 54 kA showed no simple dependence on electrode-tip diameter but a dependence on the angle of the tip face to the horizontal. It was therefore proposed that the lack of dependence of tip loss on tip diameter in a large arc furnace is due to the conflicting mechanisms of evaporation from the end face of the electrode, which decreases with increasing electrode diameter and slag attack which increases with diameter. The author noted large cast-to-cast variations in tip loss rates which were not explained.

Schwabe[9] has considered the hot-spot phenomenon in arc furnaces and deduced a refractory-wear index incorporating arc length, arc power and electrode-pitch circle, and furnace shell diameter. Arc length and power can be expressed as functions of the circuit characteristics and operating parameters, and the inverse square law of radiation incorporates the geometry of the system. Schwabe presents graphs allowing estimation of the index as a function of power factor and circuit reactance.

Bowman and Fitzgerald[10] in experiments have demonstrated the importance of the transmissivity of the furnace atmosphere and the overriding effect of arc flames which are projected to the furnace walls by the magnetic forces of interaction between the arcs. It is thus concluded that the models proposed by Schwabe are incomplete. A dynamic model for electric melting of continuously charged pre-reduced iron has been reported by Woodside.[11] The model predicts bath temperature in steelmaking with SLRN pellets and is used as the basis of a control system which allows the bath temperature to increase gradually, so that the desired tapping temperature is reached at the same time that the continuous feeding of the pellets is completed. Mass and energy balances were used to draw up the basis of the model, which was then expressed in the form of a difference equation with intervals corresponding to the irregular intervals between bath temperature measurements. Experimental data were analysed by the statistical techniques of regression analysis and quasi-linearization, to find the coefficients needed in the model. A scheme of 'optimal' control of the bath temperature using Kalman filtering is described and the dependence of the control accuracy on the number and accuracy of the measurements is demonstrated.

Woodside et al.[12] have also attempted to produce a model to optimize electric steelmaking. Using carbon, mass, and energy balances, a second order non-linear model was drawn up and solved using the method of steepest descent to reach the optimum. The authors concluded that with an adequate process model of the furnace as a pre-requisite, it would be possible to refine steel to specification and then to tap immediately, because there would be no need to hold to achieve temperature or carbon analysis checks. A dynamic

power input control system of an electric-arc furnace during the refining period, based on a simple arc energy model has been presented by Wheeler.[13] Nicholson and Roebuck[14] have examined electrode position controllers and these will be discussed in this volume.[15]

REHEATING AND TREATMENT FURNACES

Batch furnaces

In a previous conference[16] the use of a simple method for calculating heat transfer in furnaces with substantially uniform stock surface and enclosure temperatures was outlined. The boundary condition at the upper surface of a heated steel plate was assumed to be

$$F\sigma(T_f^4 - T_n^4) + h(\theta_f - \theta_n) = -K\frac{\partial \theta}{\partial x}\bigg|_n \quad . \quad . \quad (1)$$

T and θ are absolute and normal temperatures respectively. f and n define the furnace and the steel surface temperatures, σ is the Stefan Boltzmann constant, K the thermal conductivity of the steel, and x the distance from the surface. Measurements of the variation with time of the furnace temperatures (T_f, θ_f) and the steel temperatures (T_n, θ_n) obtained in an experiment were used in a 'calibration' calculation to deduce values of F and h for use in subsequent calculations. F and h have no true physical significance although the form of the terms on the left hand side of the equation corresponds to the laws of radiation and convection. In the 'calibration', the values of F and h were arrived at merely by 'weighting' the fourth power and linear terms so as to reproduce in the calculation the measured steel surface temperatures. The 'furnace' temperature was an effective enclosure temperature measured, for example, by a thermocouple inserted in the furnace roof. After the calibration the F and h values and Eq. (1) were used in the example quoted in Ref. 16 to deduce optimum conditions for normalizing plates of varying thickness, by means of a statistical correlation of the results of a large series of calculations. There appear to have been no recent papers which improve on this technique.

Continuous furnaces

Also, in a previous conference,[16] the use of the boundary condition Eq. (1) to describe the heat transfer to a slab passing through a pusher reheating furnace was described. In this case the furnace temperature (T_f, θ_f) varied in different parts of the furnace and the terms F and h determined by calculation based on experimental data as before, contained allowance for the effects of radiant interaction between the different parts. The value of this method of calculation in modifying existing designs of furnace was clearly demonstrated. Reinitzhuber[17] and co-workers have published the basis of a similar calculation for a continuous normalizing furnace with a roller hearth, in which plates were heated. The boundary equation in this case had only a linear term on the left hand side

$$f(\theta_f - \theta_n) = -K\frac{\partial \theta}{\partial x}\bigg|_n \quad . \quad . \quad . \quad . \quad (1a)$$

This simplification was justified, in that the difference between θ_f and θ_n in each of the different parts of the furnace was comparatively small. The results of calculations were analysed and a general furnace model deduced from which the heating times of plates could be calculated as a function of steel composition, thickness, and furnace temperature distribution. Optimum rates of passage of plates through the furnace could also be deduced and it was suggested that in a simpler form the model could be used as the basis of an on-line computer control model for the furnace. While these methods are suitable for optimization and examination of relatively minor changes in existing plant, there are considerable uncertainties in their application to radically different designs of furnace.

In Ref. 16 the efforts being made to apply the Hottel and Cohen[18] type of calculation to prediction of heat transfer in pusher reheating furnaces were reviewed. The zonal predictive techniques based on Ref. 18 have considerable scope for examining new and radical furnace designs, and since the last conference appreciable advances have been made in their application. Fitzgerald and Sheridan[19] have reported the prediction of temperature and heat transfer using the Hottel–Cohen technique in two small pusher reheating furnaces, both 3·6 m long by 1·07 m wide but with different roof lines. One furnace was rectangular with a chamber height of 0·457 m, and the other had a sloping roof and a maximum chamber height of 1·07 m. Both furnaces were used for reheating steel billets of dimensions 1 m by 60·8 mm and 63·5 mm^2, and were fired with town gas through burners located in the discharge end walls. The throughput of the furnaces was in the range 30–60 billets per hour. The furnaces were 'zoned', being considered to be split into a series of cubical gas zones and square surface zones. A zone dimension of 0·53 m was used.

After zoning and determination of the radiant interchange configuration factors from data in Ref. 18, the flow and mixing patterns of the flame and furnace gases were specified. In the cases reported, values were estimated from published data on aerodynamics of jets for the rectangular furnace and deduced from cold model experiments for the sloping roof furnace. From a knowledge of the fuel, air, and stock input rates, the furnace geometry and the gas flow and mixing patterns, it was possible to predict the temperature distributions and heat transfer in the different parts of the two furnaces. Comparison of predicted and measured temperatures showed that the method is satisfactory for predicting the variation of stock temperature through the furnaces despite the crude zoning used and the assumption made in the paper that the gas was effectively a grey emitter and absorber. Predicted gas and refractory temperatures were appreciably in error in those parts of the furnace where active combustion was taking place, but the authors concluded that finer zoning and a better description of

the flame gases in these regions would reduce the discrepancies quite considerably.

While it is thus apparent that the Hottel and Cohen zoning technique of prediction is at least proving useful in the case of non-luminous flame fired furnaces, the situation has not improved significantly in so far as luminous flames are concerned. Despite considerable effort by a number of workers, including the International Flame Research Foundation, it has not yet proved feasible to predict the generation of luminosity in a flame. This has prompted some workers to propose that heat-transfer prediction should be attempted by substituting into the furnace models details of experimentally determined flame parameters, e.g. data from the International Flame Research Foundation. Salter and Costick[20,21] have applied this suggestion in the construction of a novel mathematical model of a pusher reheating furnace. In the model the effects of burner design and the rates of flow of fuel and oxidant on the patterns of combustion and radiation were replaced by assumed distributions of gas temperature and gas emission characteristics which resembled those obtained in experiments. The distributions were represented as surfaces defined by a family of similar elliptical contours, parameters describing which were used to represent flame properties. Having thus defined the flame properties, the steel and refractory temperatures were calculated for a given furnace geometry and steel throughput. Alternatively, to achieve a desired steel temperature the flame shape and properties could be adjusted. The basis of the calculation was again a zonal one. A square grid was used and as the calculations were two-dimensional (there were assumed to be no variations across the furnace width) the furnace was divided into a series of square gas zones and linear surface zones. It was further assumed that

(i) all heat transfer within the furnace chamber was by radiation
(ii) all surfaces were black
(iii) all radiation was emitted diffusely
(iv) the roof and wall surfaces were non-conducting
(v) the gas was grey (but with a varying extinction coefficient)
(vi) allowance was made for variable thermal properties with temperature of the stock which was assumed to be of uniform thickness and to move through the furnace at a constant rate.

Some of these assumptions apply only to the type of reheating furnace considered and are made so as to reduce the computational time. The model is thus specific rather than generally applicable. Assumed luminous flame characteristics could however be fed into the Hottel and Cohen model and generality maintained, though uncertainties would also be introduced as the flame's properties are a function of its environment and in the proposed method the coupling between the flame and the environment is ignored.

The model was 'checked' against published data from KHNS[22] and BSC Llanwern furnaces and although comparisons of predicted and practical values were not good, the model was later used to assess the principles of design of the OZRF furnace which has been installed at BSC's Lackenby Works. Salter and Costick assumed the steel surface to be black and Fitzgerald and Sheridan assumed it to have an absorptivity of 1, but an emissivity which was a function of its temperature. Neither paper dealt with either the heat generated in the formation of scale or the thermal properties of a scale layer and the scale/metal interface. There does not seem to be any reliable data on the thermal properties of scale layers.

Macedo[23] used the model as presented by Costick[21] to examine the problem of control of the OZRF furnace. Costick had shown that the furnace shape is of secondary importance in heat transfer to the stock and that flame position, shape and fuel input are overriding. Accordingly, variable flame burners were introduced to facilitate control under transient mill demands. The descriptive model[21] is a steady-state one and therefore not suitable for control purposes, but its limitations were overcome by Macedo who used an empirical model, fitted in the steady state to Costick's results. The OZRF furnace has central offtakes for the waste gases, so interaction between the different furnace zones is virtually non-existent. It therefore presents a different control problem from those for conventional furnaces. The latter however have been the subject of much attention in the last two years and a number of studies have been reported.[24,25] Much time is required in deducing manually the interchange factors needed for drawing up the matrix in the Hottel and Cohen solution though a computer routine would reduce it, and in Ref. 20, the simpler two-dimensional radiation factors are determined as part of the furnace-simulation program. The effort might be reduced by the use of the Monte Carlo technique which is the subject of an important paper by Steward and Cannon.[26] In this paper results from the Monte Carlo method are compared with those from the zonal technique obtained by Hottel and Sarofim[27] for a cylindrical furnace.

For the same conditions, the Monte Carlo method and the Hottel–Cohen solution gave results generally differing by no more than 5%. Moreover, the computation time for the Monte Carlo method was of the same order as that of the Hottel–Cohen and there was no need to make a preliminary calculation of the interchange factors. Additional modifications were introduced into the calculations so that the concentration of radiating and absorbing gases within the system could be taken into account and thus measured properties in the case of luminous flames are easily introduced. Also, conical volume elements were used to give a better representation of the jet flow pattern, so that more accurate temperature and heat flow distributions could be obtained, and directionally dependent radiative properties of surfaces might be considered. These refinements are easily introduced into the Monte Carlo simulation, while they would require extensive labour before each single example could be studied using the Hottel and Cohen technique.

It is concluded that the Monte Carlo method compares favourably with that of Hottel and Cohen regarding accuracy and computation time. The Monte Carlo method is also considerably more flexible in dealing with rapidly varying temperatures and concentration profiles since the volume geometry can be changed with little change in procedure. Thus as the problem becomes more sophisticated it appears that the Monte Carlo method becomes more advantageous. The application of the Monte Carlo method to heat transfer problems generally has been considered by Howell.[28]

Rapid heating or convective furnaces

A paper from the Gas Council describing a model of a single-cell convection furnace was presented at the last conference.[29] This model has now been extended to consider transient temperature changes in the refractory structure and thus the transient thermal response of the furnace.[30] The convective heat transfer coefficients were obtained, as before, by mass transfer measurements (naphthalene sublimation) in cold models. More recently, McBride[31] has combined both cold and hot model determinations of heat transfer coefficients from impinging flame jets with the calculations of Spalding and co-workers[32,33] in an attempt to procure data for use in the design of rapid heating furnaces. A Spalding finite difference solution of the general two-dimensional equations of vorticity, stream function, and enthalpy under steady, turbulent conditions and in the absence of chemical reaction was made the basis of a mathematical model of an impinging gas jet. While the solution was not totally successful the predicted heat fluxes were of the right order and the radial distribution of flux was sensible.

Carburizing/decarburizing

In a previous conference[16] Birks and Nicholson[34] presented a treatment of decarburization based on the calculation of the carbon concentration as a function of time and position by means of a solution of the diffusion equation. The carbon content at the limit of decarburization was defined from the results of a metallographer's assessment of decarburization depth in a heated sample, which was then subjected to 'quantovac' analyses after successive surface grinding treatments. This carbon content was found to be 92.5% of the initial value in the steel. Values of the diffusion coefficient of carbon were also estimated by examination of published practical data, and the corrosion constant of steel was obtained by measurement on samples of steel in the relevant atmosphere. This latter figure was needed to define the extent of scaling. With the model the effect of variables such as temperature distribution and throughput rate in reheating on the degree of decarburization of steel could be quickly and cheaply assessed without the expense and inconvenience of works trials.

Collin and co-workers[35] have presented a similarly based mathematical model for predicting the carbon concentration in steel as a function of distance from the surface and the carburizing time. Required reaction rate constants, activities, and diffusion coefficients were deduced from the author's own experimental work and published data. The predictions from the model have been verified using experimental results from continuous and pit furnaces.

SOAKING PITS AND PRIMARY ROLLING

At a previous conference[16] Sévrin[36] presented a method of calculating the cooling of an ingot and its subsequent reheating. This was based on the well-known model due to Sarjant and Slack[37] which is rooted in the classic paper of Ayres et al.[38] Since the conference,[16] a number of papers have dealt with the problem.[39,40,41,42] Most have made the assumption that a two-dimensional calculation at the mid-height of the ingot was satisfactory for the calculation of solidification and subsequent soaking requirements and that:

(i) the steel was poured instantaneously
(ii) flow patterns in the ingot, both residual and convective had negligible effect
(iii) a surface skin was formed immediately and it shrank from the mould leaving a gap after two minutes
(iv) heat transfer across the gap after the skin had formed was by radiation
(v) heat losses through the mould surfaces were uniform
(vi) after stripping, the ingot lost heat by radiation and convection, the effect of the proximity of other ingots, e.g. on the same bogie, being allowed for.

Sévrin showed that superheat of the steel on pouring did not markedly affect the rate of solidification and that the degree of superheat was rapidly dissipated in the presence of convection currents. Reference 40 confirms the conclusions reached by Sévrin and examines the effects of mould thickness and temperature. For the case considered (115 cwt square ingot), doubling the mould thickness reduced the solidification time by 7% and raising the mould temperature from 20° to 100°C resulted in a 2% increase in solidification time. The authors in Ref. 42 similarly concluded that mould thickness had little effect on solidification time and claimed that as a result of their work a saving of 2 000 Kg of iron per ingot mould (10 t ingot) had been achieved. In Ref. 40, data are presented allowing the solidification time of rectangular ingots to be calculated directly from the data for the solidification of square ingots. This shows that a rectangular ingot of the same cross-sectional area as a square one solidifies faster, but the effect is not appreciable until the ratio of the sides of the rectangular ingot is greater than about 1·5 to 1. Finally, also in Ref. 40, the application of the solidification calculation to the estimation of the time required in the soaking pit by the ingot before its rolling is outlined. This involves the development of an acceptable model of the soaking pit and the assumption of a 'ready for rolling' criterion based on the temperature distribution in the ingot after soaking. The soaking pit model developed in Ref. 40 uses the simple heat transfer equation

$$q = \sigma \epsilon A F(T_p^4 - T_i^4) \qquad . \qquad . \qquad . \qquad . \qquad (2)$$

q is the heat transfer to the ingot per unit time, σ is the Stefan Boltzmann constant, A the surface area of the ingot, T_p the pit temperature indicated by the control thermocouple, and T_i the ingot surface temperature. (ϵF) is a factor for which values are chosen for each face of the ingot so that calculated temperature distributions agree with those measured in trials of the heating of cold-charged ingots in a soaking pit. The procedure and some of the results were discussed at the last conference.[44] All the calculations made by Massey and Sheridan[40] have used the values of (ϵF) determined in the way described from experiments on a particular pit with one ingot size. They would obviously be incorrect in systems which are radically different geometrically from the original experiment.

Kung et al.[43] describe a more detailed soaking pit model in which flue and wall losses were considered. It was then possible to draw up a heat balance on the pit for which it was necessary to define the flue gas temperature. This was done by use of an empirically determined constant. With this model could be calculated the required fuel flow, pit wall temperatures, and ingot temperatures during soaking. Comparison of calculated and measured fuel flows and temperatures indicated that the model was satisfactory for estimating ingot heating in pits. There has been wide variation between the criteria for rolling used by different workers. Pengelly[45] used an ingot bulk temperature of 1 300°C for 75 cwt ingots, Bijl and Hollander,[46] for slab ingots suggested as the best criterion a temperature of 1 325°C at the surface, rising to 1 450°C at the centre, and in Ref. 40 the criterion was that the temperature in any section must be below the solidus temperature of the steel and not less than 30°C below the pit setting temperature. A true criterion of readiness for rolling is however dependent on the ingot size and quality and the mill characteristics. In Ref. 41, the rolling load of an ingot as a function of

(i) the reduction of thickness
(ii) the temperature distribution in the ingot
(iii) its dimensions
(iv) the steel quality
(v) the radius and speed of rotation of the rolls

was calculated using the data by Cook and McCrum.[47] Despite a number of assumptions, comparison of calculated and measured roll loads was good. The calculation proceeded using first the ingot solidification model considering the ingot in the mould, then stripped and finally, soaking in the pit. Temperature losses from drawing to entering the first pass were computed and the temperature distribution at this stage was the initial condition of the rolling calculation. The calculation considered cooling in the roll pass by radiation, convection and conduction, and between passes by the same mechanisms but with conduction losses limited to the bottom face in contact with the roller table. Heat generation due to the work of plastic deformation was considered and rotation of the ingot between passes was allowed for. The effects of scale and water sprays on temperature losses were not considered. Obviously, this model allows the estimation of a criterion for rolling for individual cases under consideration, which takes account of the load and torque capacity of the mill, the pass sequence and other ingot and mill variables.

Whatever criterion of readiness for rolling is used, there is a certain track time which gives for any ingot a minimum soaking time. This is clearly shown in Ref. 40 where the authors plot the time the ingot was in the mould v, the time the ingot was standing in air before being charged to the pit, with necessary times in the pit as parameters on the resulting curves. All the authors claim significant reductions in soaking times of ingots and increased throughput of the pits as a consequence of application of the results of the model work. A number of models of the soaking-pit–rolling-mill complex have been used to study the optimum number of pits and operating strategies. One of the more recent is that presented by Ashour and Bindingnavle.[48] A discrete-event-simulation model has been used to predict the improvement in capacity of the complex as a result of adding more pits and to predict the effect of breakdowns and maintenance or the shutdown of a pit. Data for the simulation were taken from operating and economic data for a steel mill in Kansas City, Missouri, USA. The model results showed that the charging strategy of the ingots (first come, first charged or last come, first charged) is only important when there are fewer than the optimum number of pits and that the penalty for having a number of pits smaller than the optimum is far greater than having the same number in excess. Other authors have applied to the problem critical path analysis techniques,[49] queuing theory,[50] and a probabilistic approach based on Monte Carlo techniques.[51] It should be noted that the reviewer has been unable to obtain copies of Refs. 50 and 51. Welburn and Nicholson[52] have outlined the basis of a diffusion model to be used in a study of soaking pit practices aimed at homogenization of 1% C–Cr steel ingots.

REFERENCES

1 M. W. THRING: *JISI*, 1952, **171**, 381–92
2 M. W. THRING AND D. SMITH: *JISI*, 1955, **179**, 227
3 J. H. CHESTERS et al.: 'Combustion and heat transfer in an open-hearth furnace', 65, 1956, London, The Iron and Steel Institute
4 I. J. HARRIS: 'Development of a mathematical model for reverberatory furnace heat transfer', *Trans. AIMME*, June, 1972
5 F. OETERS: This volume
6 R. WEEKS: *ibid*
7 J. R. MIDDLETON AND R. ROLLS: *ibid*
8 B. BOWMAN: 'Measurement and theory of electrode tip wear', UIE Conference, Warsaw, 1972
9 W. E. SCHWABE AND C. G. ROBINSON: New developments in UHP: Theory and practice. Congres International sur le four electrique arc en acierie, France, June, 1971
10 B. BOWMAN AND F. FITZGERALD: *JISI*, 1973, **211**, 178
11 C. M. WOODSIDE: *TMS. AIME*, 1970, **28**, 191–7
12 C. M. WOODSIDE et al.: IEEE Transactions on Automatic Control, October, 1970, 549–56

13 F. M. WHEELER et al.: 'Dynamic power control during the refining period on electric arc furnaces', AIME Electric Furnace Proceedings, December, 1972, Chicago
14 H. NICHOLSON AND R. ROEBUCK: *Automatika*, 1972, **8**, 683–93
15 R. ROEBUCK: This volume
16 F. FITZGERALD AND A. T. SHERIDAN: 'Mathematical models in metallurgical process development', 18, 1970, London, The Iron and Steel Institute
17 F. REINITZHUBER et al.: *Stahl Eisen*, 1969, **89**, 578–99
18 H. C. HOTTEL AND E. C. COHEN: *J. American Inst. Chem. Eng.*, 1957, **4**, 3
19 F. FITZGERALD AND A. T. SHERIDAN: *J. Inst. Fuel*, 1974, **47**, 21–7
20 F. M. SALTER AND J. A. COSTICK: *ibid.*, 3–19
21 J. A. COSTICK: 'Slab reheating', 101, 1973, London, The Iron and Steel Institute
22 F. HOLLANDER: *ibid.*
23 F. X. MACEDO: *ibid.*
24 F. HOLLANDER AND R. L. HUISMAN: 'On-line computer control for five-zone reheating furnaces in a modern strip mill', *Internationale Eisenhüttentagung*, 1970
25 H. E. PIKE AND S. J. CITRON, *Automatika*, 1970, **6**, 41–50
26 F. R. STEWARD AND P. CANNON: *Int. J. Heat and Mass Transfer*, 1971, **14**, 245–62
27 H. C. HOTTEL AND A. F. SAROFIM: *Int. J. Heat and Mass Transfer*, 1965, **8**, 1,153
28 J. R. HOWELL: 'Advances in heat transfer', vol 5, 1968, New York, Academic Press
29 R. M. DAVIES et al.: 'Mathematical models in metallurgical process development', 29, 1970, London, The Iron and Steel Institute
30 D. M. LUCAS AND A. J. BARBER: *JISI*, 1970, **209** (10), 790–6
31 R. N. MCBRIDE: *J. Inst. Fuel*, 1974, 47, 29–37
32 S. V. PATANKAR AND D. B. SPALDING: 'Heat and mass transfer in boundary layers', International Textbook Co. Ltd., 1970, London
33 A. D. GOSMAN et al.: 'Heat and mass transfer in recirculating flows', 1969, Academic Press, London
34 N. BIRKS AND A. NICHOLSON: 'Mathematical models in metallurgical process development', 219, 1970, London, The Iron and Steel Institute
35 R. COLLIN et al.: *JISI*, 1972, **210**, 785–9
36 R. SÉVRIN: 'Mathematical models in metallurgical process development', 147, 1970, London, The Iron and Steel Institute
37 R. J. SARJANT AND M. R. SLACK: *JISI*, 1954, **177**, 428
38 N. E. AYRES et al.: *Proc. Roy. Soc.*, 1946, **240**, 1–57
39 M. TAKASUKE AND M. KÜCHI: *Trans. ISI Japan*, 1972, **12**, 83–91
40 I. D. MASSEY AND A. T. SHERIDAN: *JISI*, 1971, **209** (5), 391–5
41 I. D. MASSEY et al.: *J. Inst. Fuel*, 1974, 47, 373–82
42 K. A. CHEREPANOV AND V. K. KALASHNIKOVA: *Steel in the USSR.*, 1971, **1** (6), 442–3
43 E. Y. KUNG et al.: *ISA Transactions*, 1967, **6**, 162–8
44 F. FITZGERALD: 'Mathematical models in metallurgical process development', 158, 1970, London, The Iron and Steel Institute
45 A. E. S. PENGELLY: Unpublished work
46 C. L. BIJL AND F. HOLLANDER: *De Ingenieur*, 1964, April, 65–73
47 P. M. COOK AND A. W. MCCRUM: 'The calculation of load and torque in hot flat rolling', BISRA, 1958, London
48 SAID ASHOUR AND S. G. BINDINGNAVLE: *Simulation*, 1972, Jun., 207
49 A. V. BRANCKNER et al.: *JISI*, 1950, **164**, 67–84
50 J. A. BUZACOTT AND J. R. CALAHAN: *Canadian Journal of Operational Research and Information Processing*, 1971, **9** (2), 87–95
51 E. Y. KUNG et al.: *Westinghouse Eng.*, 1965, **25**, 148–52
52 R. W. WELBURN AND A. NICHOLSON: 'Homogenisation of an alloy steel containing a liquated phase', International Symposium on Metallurgical Chemistry, University of Sheffield, 1971

A computer model describing the heating of material in industrial furnaces

F. K. Reinitzhuber

There are many uncertainties concerning the heat transfer in the chambers of industrial furnaces, owing to the large effort required for measurements or calculations. Therefore, the construction and operation of furnaces is generally governed by empiricism. However the demands for more science and higher quality products requires valid fundamentals on the design and control of furnaces. These can only be obtained with the aid of computers and in this paper some of the required hypotheses and relations are described, as well as the method of solution and certain applications. Fundamentally there are two ways to calculate heat transfer to the stock in a furnace; on the one hand, by the laws of radiation and convection in the furnace chamber, on the other by the laws governing conduction inside the charge. The mathematical combination of these relations gives the evolution of the heat supplied to the charge and the evolution of the temperatures within the charge. Of course the temperature, composition and velocity fields in the furnace chamber must be introduced into the equation system as boundary conditions. The computer program can be adapted to any heating problem in industrial furnaces and is generally valid. Therefore, it constitutes a valid tool not only for the optimal control of existing furnace installations, but also for the development of the best design and for the comparison of planned furnace installations. It is important to know which parameters influence the heat transfer and how. For radiation from the furnace walls, seven parameters play a part, for convection and for gas radiation five, and for conduction, three. The order of magnitude of these influences have been systematically calculated and ranked in order of importance.

SYMBOLS

a	cm/s	thermal diffusivity
C_s	$W/K^4\,m^2$	radiation of a black body
D	—	catch number for the temperature and surface dependent radiation number
$\dot{q}$	W/m^2	heat-flow density
S	m	(layer) thickness
t	s	time
T	K	absolute temperature
v	m/s	velocity
x	cm	path
z	%	composition
α	$W/K\,m^2$	heat-transfer coefficient
ϵ	—	radiation emission rate
θ	°C	temperature
ν	m^2/s	cinematic viscosity
λ	$W/K\,m$	thermal conductivity
ψ	—	ratio of heat receiving and heat emitting surface

B	convection
g	combustion gas
G	gas radiation
i	index of place ($i = 0, 1, 2, \ldots n$)
k	index of time ($k = 0, 1, 2 \ldots$)
L	heat conduction
O	slab surface
u	surroundings
w	furnace inside wall
wg	charge, stock
W	wall radiation

In principle it is known which laws govern the heat transmission inside industrial furnaces, what boundary conditions exist and how heat flows within the material

The author is with Thyssen Niederrhein AG, Oberhausen

to be heated. However, owing to the great effort needed to carry out measurements and calculations, only a limited number of cases have been thoroughly treated. Moreover, information is not available to the engineer for the optimal construction, development, and operation of the furnace. The complete analysis of the total heat transmission can, however, be carried out with computers, so that in this way the engineering design and operation of a furnace can be deduced. This paper describes the required hypotheses and relations as well as the solution method and general applications of this computer analysis.

HEAT TRANSMISSION

For describing the heat transmission between the material surface and its surroundings the following relation is used:

$$\dot{q} = \alpha(\theta_u - \theta_0) \qquad . \qquad . \qquad . \qquad . \qquad . \qquad . \qquad (1)$$

In this the heat flow per unit time through unit surface is equated to the temperature difference between the surroundings and the material $(\theta_u - \theta_0)$. The heat transfer coefficient α serves as proportionality factor. Equation (1) only represents a simple relation defining α, as it has been assumed that α is a constant and only dependent on the nature of the material to be heated and its surrounding medium. Owing to its simplicity, this heat-transfer coefficient α is often used although it is occasionally replaced by a more general dimensionless number. In fact, α must depend on the overall behaviour of the furnace and material. Therefore, the question is what mechanisms are relevant. Figure 1a shows the relations valid for heat transfer in industrial furnaces. Basically, in the furnace chamber, heat is transferred by radiation and convection to the surface of the material and from there conducted into the inside. According to

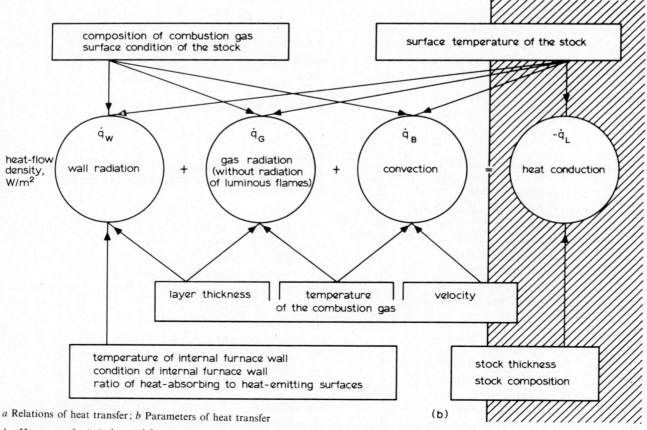

a Relations of heat transfer; *b* Parameters of heat transfer

1   Heat transfer in industrial furnaces

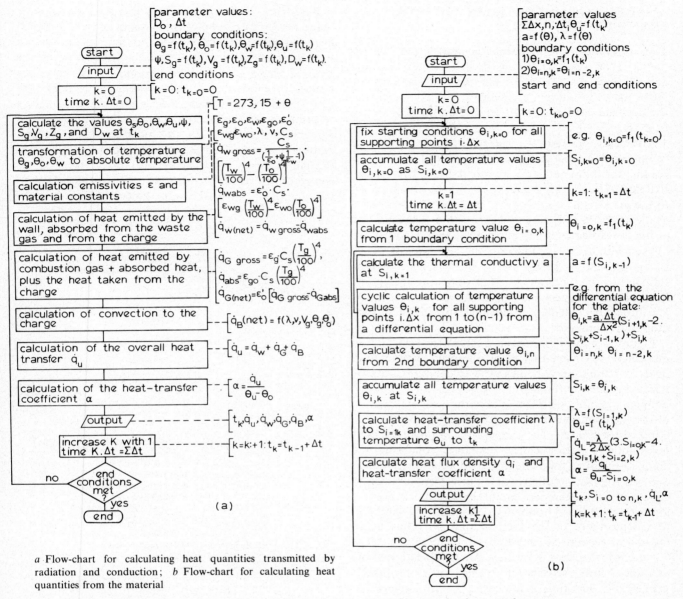

a Flow-chart for calculating heat quantities transmitted by radiation and conduction; b Flow-chart for calculating heat quantities from the material

2 Simplified flow-chart for the calculation of the contributing heat quantities, knowing the charge-surface temperature

the law of conservation of energy, the heat supplied to the surface $\dot{q}_u$ must be equal to the heat conducted away $\dot{q}_L$ on condition that no transformations or changes of state take place. So:

$$\dot{q}_u = -\dot{q}_L \quad . \quad . \quad . \quad . \quad . \quad . \quad (2)$$

There is thus the possibility of determining the amount of heat in question and also α in two different ways, i.e. on the one hand according to the laws of radiation and convection, on the other hand according to the laws of conduction. In this way all factors can be taken into account that directly influence the heat transfer between the furnace chamber and the material to be heated.[1] Figure 1b shows what quantities have to be considered and to what heat transfer mechanisms they are related. The wall radiation is influenced by seven parameters, the gas radiation and the convection by five, the conduction within the material by three. The following eleven

quantities must be considered for heat transfer calculations:

(i) the waste gas temperature θ_g
(ii) the surface temperature of material to be heated θ_0
(iii) the inside furnace wall temperature θ_w
(iv) the nature and shape of the furnace wall D_w
(v) the nature and shape of the material D_0
(vi) the ratio ψ between the heat-absorbing and heat-supplying surfaces (sink and source surfaces)
(vii) the layer thickness S_g of the combustion gases
(viii) the velocity V_g of the combustion gases
(ix) the composition Z_g of the combustion gases
(x) the composition Z_{wg} of the material to be heated.

From Z_{wg} the thermal diffusivity and heat conductivity of the material can be derived.[2]

MATHEMATICAL TREATMENT OF HEAT TRANSFER

The calculation for obtaining the transferred heat $\dot{q}_u$ by radiation and convection in the furnace chamber and the heat $\dot{q}_L$ conducted into the material must be undertaken by computer owing to the complexity of the problem. First the flowsheet of the calculation must be designed.

The heat supplied to the material from the outside can be determined according to the scheme of Fig. 2a. After reading the input data and the calculation of the respective emissivities and material constants the heat supplied to the material can be obtained by applying the laws of heat transfer by radiation and convection. The radiation of luminous flames is negligible when gaseous fuels are burned with excess combustion air. The addition of the heat contributions $\dot{q}_w$, $\dot{q}_G$, and $\dot{q}_B$ gives the net total heat supplied to the material $\dot{q}_u$. After obtaining the results for a given condition the time is increased by step Δt and the whole calculation repeated until the final conditions are achieved.

Figure 2b shows a flowsheet of a numerical calculation that can serve for one-dimensional transient temperature fields in plate-shaped bodies. The calculation starts by reading in the input data and by determining the initial boundary conditions. Then follows the cyclic calculation of the temperature values $\theta_{i,k}$ at all matrix points from 0 to n at the time Δt. The temperature at the first matrix point follows from the first boundary condition; the temperature of all following matrix points is determined consecutively as a solution of the Fourier heat-conduction equation and the temperature of the last matrix point is given by the second boundary condition. The temperature dependence of the thermal diffusivity has to be taken into account at each step. All temperature values $\theta_{i,k}$ are now stored as $S_{i,k}$ values. After calculation of the amount of heat absorbed up to this time all results are printed out. The time is increased by an increment Δt and all temperatures at the new time can be calculated in the same way from the stored values. A check loop ensures that the calculation stops when prescribed conditions are met. Further details will not be treated here. Such flow-sheets form the basis for the construction of computer programs. Next it must be checked whether at the material surface the mathematically calculated heat supply and heat absorption are equal. For this purpose the necessary boundary conditions prevailing in the heating process of thick plates in an industrial roller hearth annealing furnace were measured.[3] The results of such a test are shown in Fig. 3a. As a function of the throughput time could be represented: the strongly fluctuating combustion temperatures measured by suction pyrometers, the inner wall temperatures of the furnace measured by selective radiation pyrometers, and the surface temperatures of the 92 mm thick test plate measured by trailing thermocouples. Moreover, the O_2 and CO_2 content had been determined in the combustion gases using Orsat gas analysers. Also known were the layer thickness and velocity of the combustion gases as well as the radiative source to sink surface ratio.

Based on these measured values calculations were made per furnace zone of the amount of heat $\dot{q}_u$ transferred to the test plate by roof and flame radiation and by convection on the one hand, and on the other, the amount of heat $\dot{q}_L$ that has been conducted into the plate. Figure 3b shows the result of these calculations. On comparison of the corresponding curves for $\dot{q}_u$ and $\dot{q}_L$, respectively the thick and fine drawn lines, a reasonable agreement is shown. The unavoidable measuring and reading of errors of only a few degrees cause the jumps in the curve for $\dot{q}_L$. The figure also gives the separate contributions of convection, gas, and roof radiation to the quantity $\dot{q}_u$. Also shown is the overall heat-transfer

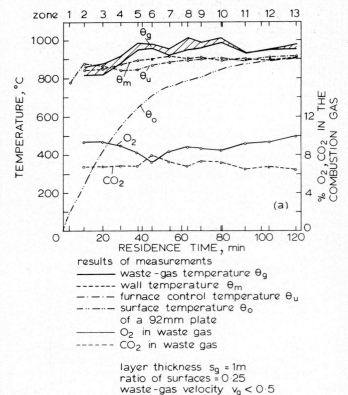

results of measurements

— waste-gas temperature θ_g
------- wall temperature θ_m
—·—·— furnace control temperature θ_u
—··—··— surface temperature θ_o
of a 92mm plate
— O_2 in waste gas
------- CO_2 in waste gas

layer thickness $s_g = 1m$
ratio of surfaces $= 0.25$
waste-gas velocity $v_g < 0.5$

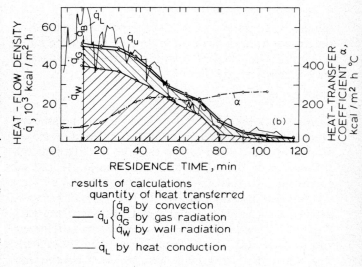

results of calculations
quantity of heat transferred
$\dot{q}_u$ { $\dot{q}_B$ by convection
$\dot{q}_G$ by gas radiation
$\dot{q}_W$ by wall radiation }
— $\dot{q}_L$ by heat conduction

a Measurements; *b* Calculated results

3   Measured and calculated results of a furnace test[3]

coefficient. The small dip in the middle zone of the furnace is caused by the change in material constants in the neighbourhood of the transition from ferritic to austenitic texture. In the same way more experiments have been run. The results have been represented in Fig. 4. Always good agreement has been found between the heat supplied and the heat absorbed. The agreement is also good if the thickness of the plate is changed, or if the plates are heated to different temperatures. This good agreement therefore confirms the validity of both the mathematical solutions for the heat transfer.

MATHEMATICAL FURNACE MODEL

Two possibilities exist for calculating the transferred heat, on the one hand with the laws of radiation and convection, on the other hand with the law of conduction. Both methods have their drawbacks. In the first case nine input data are required, but the calculation gives the transferred heat $\dot{q}_u$ and the heat transfer coefficients differentiated between the contributions from gas and roof radiation and convection. In the second case only three input data are required, but only the overall transferred heat $\dot{q}_L$ is obtained and the overall heat-transfer coefficients. For both calculations the material surface temperatures have to be known values, which is seldom the case for industrial heating furnaces. Moreover the result of this calculation, i.e. the evaluation of the heat transferred to the material, can only serve for the layout of the heat supply, for the drawing-up of heat balances or for certain comparisons of furnaces.

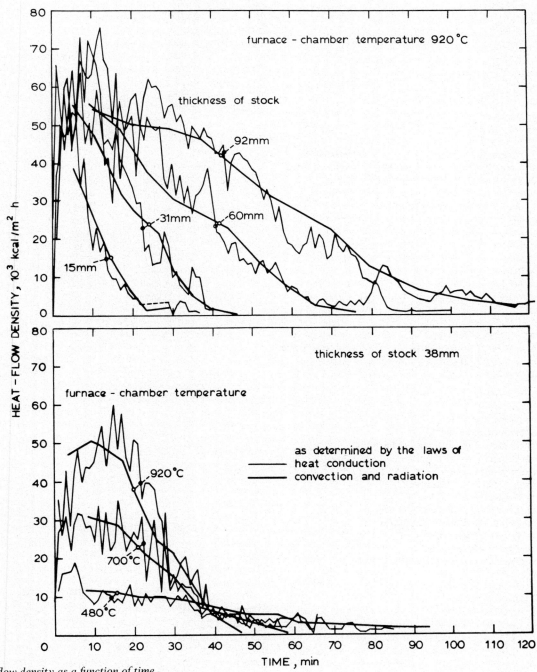

4 *Heat-flow density as a function of time*

TABLE 1 Output sheet of heat-transfer calculation

Test 15/8 (15 mm, 925°C, Steel 15)

Input

14 000	Charge temperature before heating, °C
5	Number of layers of the charge
0·839	Sum of all layer thicknesses, cm
0·100	Time step, s
0·000	Throughput velocity, m/mm
0·300	Average layer thickness of refractory, m
600	Catchword for print out
4	Catchword for steel surface
2	Catchword for refractory
1·871	Theoretical water-vapour content, Nm^3/m^3 or Nm^3/kg
8·212	Theoretical dry waste-gas volume, Nm^3/m^3 or Nm^3/kg

Temp., °C	Thermal diffusivity of steel, cm^2/s		Temp., °C	Thermal conductivity of steel, W/cm k
0	0·1200		0	0·4300
175	0.1040		100	0·4270
275	0·0980		250	0·4140
350	0·8800		400	0·3880
425	0·0820		650	0·3260
475	0·7300		700	0·3100
575	0·0610		815	0·2580
690	0·0510		900	0·2720
725	0·0240		1 100	0·2960
825	0·0600			
975	0·0610			

Time, min	Waste-gas temp., °C		Time, min	Waste-gas velocity, m/s		Time, min	CO_2%	O_2%	
0·0	850·0		0·0	0·600		0·0	6·200	10·800	0·000
5·5	869·0		5·5	0·596		5·5	6·200	10·800	0·000
11·3	862·5		11·3	0·547		11.3	6·200	10·800	0·000
14·8	887·5		14·8	0·527		14·8	6·700	9·900	0·000
19·3	880·0		19·3	0·483		19·3	6·300	10·600	0·000
23·3	893·0		23·3	0·215		23·3	5·400	12·300	0·000
29·0	905·0		29·0	0·296		29·0	5·800	11·500	0·000
33·3	915·0		33·3	0·228		33·3	5·900	11·300	0·000
37·8	918·5		37·8	0·296		37·8	5·800	11·600	0·000
43·3	925·0		43·3	0·160		43·3	5·800	11·500	0·000

Time, min	Charge surface, m^2/m	Wall surface, m^2/m	Gas layer thickness, m	Temp., °C	Heat conductivity of wall, W/cm k
0·0	2·130	6·452	1·802	0	0·0087
43·3	2·130	6·452	1·802	1 200	0·0142

Output

Z	= time, min
TR	= temperature waste gas, °C
TM	= temperature furnace inside, °C
TA	= temperature furnace outside (not insulated), °C
TO	= temperature surface charge, °C
TK	= temperature surface core, °C
TD	= maximum temperature difference, °C
Q	= heat flow density overall, $kcal/m^2h$
QW	= heat flow density wall radiation, $kcal/m^2h$
QG	= heat flow density gas radiation, $kcal/m^2h$
QK	= heat flow density convection, $kcal/m^2h$
QM	= heat flow density wall losses, $kcal/m^2$
A	= heat transfer coefficient, $kcal/m^2h\,k^2h$

Z	TR	TM	TA	TO	TK	TD	Q	QW	QG	QK	QM	A
0·000	850·0	773·0	235·5	14·0	14·0	0·0	37 790·9	22 113·6	14 302·4	1 375·0	1 696·6	47·4
1·000	853·5	774·9	235·9	102·0	97·6	4·4	38 524·6	22 744·1	14 487·5	1 293·1	1 702·2	54·1
2·000	856·9	776·9	236·4	183·6	179·1	4·5	38 870·3	23 164·6	14 500·1	1 205·6	1 707·9	61·4
3·000	860·4	778·9	236·8	262·2	257·6	4·6	38 724·3	23 315·9	14 297·5	1 110·9	1 713·7	69·5
4·000	863·8	781·0	237·3	336·9	332·3	4·6	37 948·0	23 110·0	13 826·5	1 011·5	1 719·7	78·2

TABLE 1 Output sheet of heat-transfer calculation—*continued*

Z	TR	TM	TA	TO	TK	TD	Q	QW	QG	QK	QM	A
5·000	867·3	783·1	237·8	405·1	400·5	4·6	36 521·3	22 452·7	13 158·2	910·4	1 725·8	86·9
6·000	868·4	783·8	237·9	467·2	462·8	4·5	34 251·7	21 139·7	12 305·6	806·4	1 727·9	95·4
7·000	867·3	783·1	237·8	520·3	516·0	4·3	31 573·9	19 521·7	11 345·1	707·0	1 725·9	103·5
8·000	866·2	782·5	237·6	566·5	562·4	4·0	28 819·5	17 805·5	10 396·9	617·1	1 723·9	111·8
9·000	865·1	781·8	237·5	606·2	602·5	3·7	25 789·6	15 825·0	9 427·5	537·1	1 721·9	118·7
10·000	864·0	781·1	237·3	640·4	637·0	3·4	22 638·2	13 658·7	8 513·1	466·4	1 720·0	124·3
11·000	862·8	780·4	237·2	669·3	666·3	3·0	19 523·2	11 473·2	7 645·1	405·0	1 718·0	128·2
12·000	867·5	783·3	237·8	693·9	691·2	2·7	17 267·4	9 740·1	7 163·6	363·7	1 726·2	131·4
13·000	874·6	787·8	238·8	712·4	709·9	2·5	15 889·0	8 573·6	6 975·6	339·8	1 739·3	133·7
14·000	881·8	792·5	239·9	725·0	722·6	2·4	15 190·5	7 899·4	6 963·9	327·2	1 753·0	135·5
15·000	887·2	796·2	240·7	735·6	733·2	2·4	14 486·5	7 269·7	6 902·0	314·9	1 763·8	136·6
16·000	885·5	795·0	240·4	746·7	744·5	2·1	12 628·4	5 921·8	6 419·7	286·9	1 760·4	134·9
17·000	883·8	793·9	240·2	757·6	755·8	1·8	10 656·0	4 547·4	5 849·4	259·3	1 757·1	131·2
18·000	882·2	792·7	239·9	768·0	766·4	1·5	8 711·5	3 180·2	5 298·1	233·2	1 753·8	125·4
19·000	880·5	791·6	239·7	777·2	776·0	1·2	6 886·0	1 888·9	4 787·6	209·5	1 750·5	117·0
20·000	882·3	792·8	240·0	785·3	784·2	1·0	5 653·6	1 013·6	4 453·4	186·6	1 754·0	108·1
21·000	885·5	795·0	240·5	792·5	791·7	0·9	4 717·9	345·4	4 207·9	164·6	1 760·5	98·8
22·000	888·8	797·3	241·0	798·9	798·2	0·7	3 909·9	−232·3	3 998·4	143·8	1 767·1	88·7
23·000	892·0	799·6	241·5	804·5	803·9	0·6	3 236·3	−722·4	3 835·2	123·5	1 773·8	78·4
24·000	894·5	801·4	241·9	809·4	808·9	0·5	2 682·1	−1 188·2	3 752·8	117·5	1 779·0	69·6
25·000	896·6	802·9	242·2	813·5	813·1	0·4	2 242·8	−1 591·4	3 715·8	118·3	1 783·6	62·0
26·000	898·7	804·5	242·6	817·2	816·8	0·4	1 907·4	−1 911·9	3 699·6	119·7	1 788·2	55·4
27·000	900·8	806·1	242·9	820·3	820·0	0·3	1 659·3	−2 163·1	3 700·9	121·4	1 792·8	50·1
28·000	902·9	807·7	243·3	823·1	822·9	0·3	1 478·5	−2 360·7	3 715·7	123·6	1 797·6	46·0
29·000	905·0	809·3	243·6	825·7	825·5	0·2	1 348·4	−2 518·0	3 740·5	125·9	1 802·4	42·9
30·000	907·3	811·2	244·0	828·1	827·9	0·2	1 266·7	−2 621·1	3 765·8	122·4	1 807·8	40·7
31·000	909·6	813·0	244·4	830·4	830·1	0·2	1 214·1	−2 700·8	3 795·8	119·0	1 813·2	39·2
32·000	912·0	814·9	244·8	832·5	832·3	0·2	1 181·7	−2 764·0	3 830·1	115·6	1 818·8	38·2
33·000	914·3	816·8	245·2	834·7	834·5	0·2	1 163·4	−2 815·5	3 866·7	112·1	1 824·5	37·7
34·000	915·5	817·9	245·5	836·6	836·4	0·2	973·6	−2 977·8	3 838·8	112·5	1 827·5	32·4
35·000	916·3	818·5	245·6	838·1	838·0	0·1	780·3	−3 132·5	3 798·4	114·9	1 829·5	26·7
36·000	917·1	819·2	245·8	839·4	839·3	0·1	650·3	−3 238·4	3 771·1	117·6	1 831·4	22·6
37·000	917·9	819·8	245·9	840·4	840·3	0·1	562·2	−3 310·9	3 752·6	120·5	1 833·3	19·8
38·000	918·7	820·5	246·1	841·3	841·2	0·1	519·3	−3 349·9	3 747·3	121·9	1 835·5	18·3
39·000	919·9	821·6	246·3	842·2	842·1	0·1	545·6	−3 343·2	3 771·8	117·0	1 838·5	19·1
40·000	921·1	822·6	246·5	843·2	843·1	0·1	564·3	−3 342·1	3 794·6	111·8	1 841·5	19·7
41·000	922·3	823·6	246·7	844·1	844·0	0·1	577·8	−3 344·6	3 816·2	106·2	1 844·6	20·1
42·000	923·5	824·6	246·9	845·1	845·0	0·1	587·8	−3 349·3	3 836·9	100·2	1 847·7	20·3
43·000	924·6	825·7	247·2	846·1	846·0	0·1	595·4	−3 355·3	3 857·0	93·7	1 850·8	20·5

Generally, it is of more interest to obtain the temperature development along the surface to be heated, without measuring it with trailing thermocouples or resorting to precarious guessing. This is possible if the relations for the radiation and convection are combined with those for conduction. The surface temperature can be calculated for each time step with the equation

$$\theta_{i=0} = 0·66 \cdot \frac{\Delta x}{\lambda_{wg}} \cdot \dot{q}_u + 1·33 \cdot \theta_{i=1} - 0·33 \cdot \theta_{i=2} \qquad (3)$$

(the development of this equation is given in the Appendix). In this equation all quantities are known (Δx, λ_{wg}) or can be calculated according to the laws of heat transfer by radiation, convection and conduction ($\theta_{i=1}$, $\theta_{i=2}$, $\dot{q}_u$). It is possible therefore to calculate step-wise from ten input data the eleventh, which is the changing surface temperature of the material to be heated. All temperatures in the material and the relevant heat quantities can be determined depending on time for all present and future furnaces. For the solution of

this set of equations certain boundary conditions must be given, especially the temperature, concentration, and velocity fields of the combustion gases.

The question remains of the accurate determination of the boundary conditions, only now they have been transferred from the material surface to the furnace chamber. These boundary conditions can be more easily measured without disturbing furnace operation. The set of equations for complete description of the heat transfer mechanisms in industrial furnaces is most complex, as it contains all relations regarding radiation, convection, and conduction. The calculation can only be performed on large computer systems. After reading in the input data the initial boundary conditions at zero time are determined. These describe the wall temperatures as well as the overall radiation from the walls and the combustion gas to the charge. A finite difference calculation with a time increment Δt is used for calculation of the charge temperatures in all matrix points $i \cdot \Delta x$ from 1 to n. Next the surface temperature at the first matrix point

$i \cdot \Delta x = 0$ is calculated with Eq. (3). A choice of the most important results is printed out. All heat quantities and temperatures will be calculated step-wise at time increments Δt, until all final boundary conditions are met. The results of a calculated example are given in Table 1 together with the corresponding input data. With the help of a computer all empirical data for any time can be taken into account such as the prevailing temperature inside or outside the furnace, the surface and the core of the charge, the maximum temperature difference within the charge, the separate heat quantities transmitted by wall or gas radiation and convection, the heat losses through the walls and the heat-transfer coefficient.

APPLICATIONS

Before organizing large-scale trials it is necessary to check with measurements the validity of the calculation results. In Figs. 3a and 3b good comparison has already been shown between the amount of heat supplied to the charge surface and the heat absorbed by the charge. Measured surface temperatures were the basis of this comparison. Now it has to be proved that by equating both amounts of heat, surface temperatures can be found that agree with measurements. Therefore, from the same test in the annealing furnace a comparison is derived in Fig. 5 between the measured and calculated surface temperature of the 92 mm thick plate. For reasons of clear presentation the measured curve is given as a full line, the calculated values being represented by a small number of points. Both curves differ little from each other. Greater deviations are to be expected for higher heating velocities (lower part of Fig. 5).

These results and those from comparable tests,[4] confirm that it is possible to describe the heat-transfer mechanism in an industrial furnace sufficiently accurately with a mathematical model. As the computer program with the boundary conditions can be adapted to the heating problem in any industrial furnace and therefore is generally valid, it is a valuable tool in many respects, first, for better control and optimal operation of existing furnace installations, second, for the development of the optimal layout and technical comparison of furnace installations to be constructed, and third, for fundamental trials. Several industrial applications are discussed in this volume. A more precise theoretical study about the importance of different influences on heat transfer will be presented now. When constructing and operating industrial furnaces, it is often important to know how the respective influences affect the overall heat transfer and the heating process itself. In systematic calculations numerous heating-up curves are studied, in each of which one of the ten parameters is varied within its usual limits under otherwise equal conditions. (These conditions are given in the lower part of Table 2.) It must be noted, that this assumption does not correspond with reality, as with the change of one quantity, e.g. the combustion gas temperature, a series of other quantities vary, in this case the gas composition and the gas velocity, and so the radiative power of the furnace walls. This study can only be a first stage for further comparable tests. Some of the results are shown in the following figures and tables.

Figure 6 shows the thermal changes of the heating-up of the charge to different high temperatures. The heating times grow shorter due to the greater radiation contribution with rising combustion gas temperatures. With this the temperature differences in the charge increase as well as the heat transfer to the charge. The influence of the

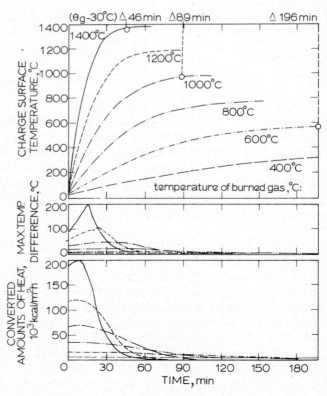

5   *Measured and calculated heat-up curves for 92 mm thick slab*

6   *Thermal events at heating up a 100 mm thick slab to various end temperatures*

TABLE 2 Thermal state in a 100 mm thick slab at the end of heating

Combustion gas temperature Time			$\theta_g = 1\,400°C$ $t = 46$ min			$\theta_g = 1\,000°C$ $t = 89$ min			$\theta_g = 600°C$ $t = 196$ min		
			θ_0	$\Delta\theta_0$	$\Delta\theta_{wg}$	θ_0	$\Delta\theta_0$	$\Delta\theta_{wg}$	θ_0	$\Delta\theta_0$	$\Delta\theta_{wg}$
	Considered quantity		°C	K		°C	K		°C	K	
θ_w	Furnace-wall temperature	$\theta_g - 20°C$	1 370·9		8·1	970·1		5·1	570·3		1·2
		$\theta_g - 100°C$	1 302·7	150·5	11·1	906·1	136·7	8·3	527·2	86·3	1·3
		$\theta_g - 200°C$	1 220·4		16·0	833·4		10·8	484·0		1·3
D_w	Refractory	Fire clay 50% SiO$_2$	1 377·4		4·4	977·0		3·1	572·8		1·1
		Alum. por. 16% Silica	1 375·3	7·4	5·8	974·5	6·9	3·9	571·7	2·5	1·2
		Fire clay 60% Al$_2$O$_3$	1 370·9		8·1	970·1		5·1	570·3		1·2
D_0	State of steel surface	Slagged	1 373·3		6·7	976·4		3·2	579·5		0·7
		Rusted	1 370·9	7·4	8·1	970·1	22·8	5·1	570·3	33·3	1·2
		Blasted	1 365·9		11·2	953·6		9·7	546·2		2·2
ψ	Surface ratio	0·3	1 370·9		8·1	970·1		5·1	570·3		1·2
		0·5	1 357·5	33·7	14·1	957·8	29·0	7·9	566·1	9·0	1·4
		0·7	1 337·2		21·2	941·1		11·1	561·3		1·6
S_g	Gas-layer thickness	4 m	1 372·6		8·1	972·3		5·0	572·7		1·2
		3 m	1 371·7		8·1	971·1		5·1	571·3		1·2
		2 m	1 371·1	3·1	8·2	970·3	4·8	5·1	570·3	5·0	1·2
		1 m	1 369·5		8·3	967·5		5·3	567·7		1·3
V_g	Gas velocity	20 m/s	1 372·6		7·4	977·5		3·3	586·4		0·4
		10 m/s	1 372·0	1·7	7·7	973·2	7·4	4·3	581·2	16·1	0·7
		1 m/s	1 370·9		8·1	970·1		5·1	570·3		1·2
Z_g	Fuel	Coke-oven gas	1 371·4		8·1	970·5		5·1	570·8		1·2
		Natural gas	1 370·9		8·1	970·1		5·1	570·3		1·2
		Light-oil gas	1 370·5	2·1	8·2	969·4	2·9	5·2	569·2	4·4	1·2
		Mixed gas	1 370·2		8·2	969·0		5·2	568·6		1·2
		Blast-furnace gas	1 369·3		8·3	967·6		5·3	566·4		1·2
	O$_2$ in combustion gas	0%	1 370·9		8·1	970·1		5·1	570·3		1·2
		5%	1 370·7	1·0	8·2	969·7	2·0	5·2	569·9	2·1	1·2
		10%	1 369·9		8·3	968·1		5·3	568·2		1·2
Z_w	Steel type	Carbon steel	1 370·9		8·1	970·1		5·1	570·3		1·2
		Low-alloy steel	1 375·7	4·8	5·2	975·9	9·5	3·5	569·6	4·4	1·5
		Alloy steel	1 375·3		5·5	979·6		2·2	574·0		1·7

At further constant parameters $\theta_w = \theta_g - 20°C$; $D_w =$ fire clay 60% Al$_2$O$_3$; $D_0 =$ rusted steel; $\psi = 0.3$; $S_g = 2.1$ m; $V_g = 1$ m/s; $Z_{wg} =$ carbon steel; $Z_g =$ natural gas burned stoichiometrically

thickness of the charge on its heating-up is represented in Fig. 7. Of course a greater thickness leads to a longer heating time, but also to greater temperature differences inside the charge. It is remarkable that the maximum net heat transfer shifts to longer heating times, but that its value stays unchanged. In normal furnace operation eight other parameters, apart from combustion gas temperature and plate thickness, influence heat transfer. Through changing each of these one at a time the calculated results have been obtained (*see* Table 2). The temperatures θ_0 at the charge surface and the greatest temperature differences $\Delta\theta_{wg}$ inside the charge at three combustion gas temperatures at fixed times at the end of heating are shown in Fig. 7.

An increase of the charge surface temperature together with a decrease in the temperature differences within the charge can be achieved by raising the furnace wall temperature θ_w, the wall emissivity D_w and that of the charge D_0, the gas-layer thickness S_g, the velocity V_g, and the water vapour content of the combustion gases as well as by a decrease of the surface ratio ψ and the oxygen content O$_2$ of the combustion gases. Various steel compositions Z_{wg} are the exception in that they

do not lead to unequivocal changes for the heat transfer and soaking times, owing to the spurious dependencies of the thermal diffusivity and conductivity, especially in ranges of the α–γ transition. On comparison of the values of θ_0 and $\Delta\theta_{wg}$ in Table 2 it can be found that they behave differently within the range considered. In order to obtain an idea of the order of magnitude of these changes, the temperature differences $\Delta\theta_0$ have been determined for each parameter. So it can be shown how important the influence is of e.g. the inner-wall temperature θ_w. Also, it is possible to rank the parameters in order of importance. Table 3 shows this ranking of the 10 parameters in the order of their contribution to the heat transfer to a 100 m thick slab for various combustion gas temperatures under known conditions. Together with the combustion gas temperature θ_g and the slab thickness S_{wg} the inner furnace wall temperature θ_w must be taken into account. In fuel heated furnaces, this wall temperature is not considered for operating control, owing to the long time lags caused by heat diffusion into the refractories of discontinuously operated furnaces. Therefore, the importance of this quantity has not been considered properly. In Oberhausen, we are

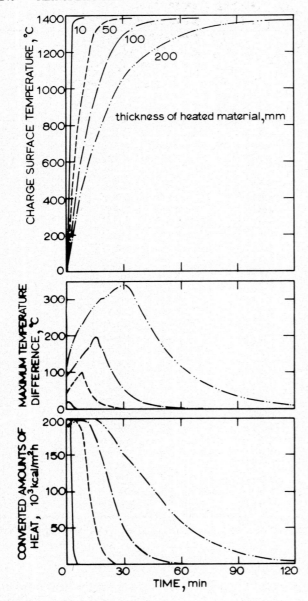

7 *Thermal events at heating slabs of various thicknesses at combustion temperatures of 1 400°C*

engaged in studying the heat transfer to the furnace inner wall.

In relation to the furnace inner wall, the influence of the surface ratio ψ of the heat absorbing and radiating surfaces and of the charge surface emissivity D_0 is small. The other parameters, with one exception play a relatively small part in the heat transfer, as by changing them within the usual spans a change in the surface temperature results of only up to 10 K. The only exception is the velocity V_g of the combustion gases which has a considerable influence on heat transfer in the lower temperature region. From these considerations follow important indications for the use of the furnace model. In general, most parameters can be taken as known quantities, as they are fixed by the dimensions and type of the furnace chamber and of the charge. The composition and velocity fields of the combustion gas only have to be roughly estimated, as they usually have little influence on the heat transfer.

However, the temperature fields in the furnace chamber must be known well in every case. The wall temperatures can be calculated for a steady case, or must be measured during unsteady operation. The temperatures of the combustion gases must be introduced from measurements. Calculations lead only to overall values in this case. This also leads to the limits of the furnace model. The actual events of the heat transmission in industrial furnaces can only be accurately simulated, if, next to the constructional details and general operational data, the evolution in time of the combustion gas temperatures is available. The further object of this study, therefore, has to be to include the combustion reactions in the mathematical furnace model. Then, from the input data on fuel and combustion air quantities and their mixing conditions can be calculated the temperature, composition, and velocity fields in the furnace chamber. But at the present state of research valid relations are not available for the description of the combustion phenomena, on the one hand because the events are only known accurately for simple cases, on the other hand because complete calculations lead to such complex equation systems, that even with large computers it is necessary to introduce simplifying assumptions. If generally valid and simple relations were available for the complete description of the combustion phenomena, then by introducing the treatment of the heat transfer by radiation, convection, and conduction, a furnace model, in every respect fundamental, would be available, that would allow the quantitative prediction of all·processes in the furnace chamber.

TABLE 3   Ranking of parameters; heat transfer to a 100 mm thick slab

Rank	Parameter*			Remark
1	$\theta_g = 1\,400°C$	$\theta_g = 1\,000°C$	$\theta_g = 600°C$	*See* Fig. 5
2	$S_{wg} = 100$ mm	$S_{wg} = 100$ mm	$S_{wg} = 100$ mm	*See* Fig. 6
3	θ_w	θ_w	θ_w	
4	ψ	ψ	D_0	$\Delta\theta_0 > 10°$
5	D_0	D_0	v_g	
6	D_w	Z_{wg}†	ψ	
7	Z_{wg}	v_g	S_g	
8	S_g	D_w	Z_{wg}	$\Delta\theta_0 < 10°$
9	Z_g	S_g	Z_g	
10	v_g	Z_g	D_w	

* Considered spans (*see* Table 2)
† Due to α–y recrystallization

REFERENCES

1 F. REINITZHUBER: *Arch. Eisenh.*, 1972, **43**, 413–21
2 F. REINITZHUBER: *Stahl Eisen*, 1971, **91**, 281–2
3 F. REINITZHUBER *et al.*: *Stahl Eisen*, 1969, **89**, 587–99
4 F. REINITZHUBER AND H. WEINECK: *Stahl Eisen*, 1973, **93**, 1106–14

APPENDIX

Deduction of Eq. (3)

The net heat $\dot{q}_u$ transferred to the charge from the furnace chamber by radiation and convection corresponds to the heat $\dot{q}_L$ conducted from the surface to the inside of the charge. So

$$(\dot{q}_u) = (\dot{q}_L) \qquad . \qquad . \qquad . \qquad . \qquad . \qquad (A1)$$

The heat quantity $\dot{q}_L$ can be expressed as:

$$\dot{q}_L = \lambda_{wg} \cdot \left(\frac{\partial \theta}{\partial x}\right)_0 \qquad . \qquad . \qquad . \qquad . \qquad (A2)$$

In this $(\partial \theta / \partial x)_0$ is the temperature gradient inside the charge at the surface and λ_{wg} the heat conductivity of the steel. This temperature gradient can be approximated by

$$\left(\frac{\partial \theta}{\partial x}\right)_0 \simeq \frac{3\theta_{i=0} - 4\theta_{i=1} + \theta_{i=2}}{2\Delta x} \qquad . \qquad . \qquad . \qquad (A3)$$

from the temperatures of three matrix points $\theta_{i=0}$, $\theta_{i=1}$, $\theta_{i=2}$, being a distance Δx removed from each other. From the equations (A1), (A2), and (A3) results after some transformations

$$\theta_{i=0} = 0.66 \frac{\Delta x}{\lambda_{wg}} \dot{q}_u + 1.33\theta_{i=0} - 0.33\theta_{i=2}$$

Discussion on chapter five: Heating furnaces

CHAIRMAN: A. E. PENGELLY (BSC, GENERAL STEELS DIVISION, TEESSIDE)

The following paper was discussed: *A computer model describing the heating of material in industrial furnaces* by F. K. Reinitzhuber.

The Chairman opening the discussion said that Dr Reinitzhuber had indicated that it was now necessary to develop a combustion model, but he had given examples of calculations on some very large furnaces and one in particular where he had examined the effects of variation in the roof height; Dr Reinitzhuber must have made some assumptions as to what the gas distribution was like in those furnaces. Mr Pengelly asked for details. Was the fuel gas or oil, and were the conclusions affected by the choice of fuel?

Dr Reinitzhuber in reply said the fuel was gas, and in one case the temperature of the waste gas was measured and in another case it was guessed, to find out whether the height was important for heat transfer or not.

Dr F. Fitzgerald (BSC, Corporate Advanced Process Laboratory, UK) said that he found the paper interesting, because it seemed at first that he agreed with it entirely, and then later that he disagreed with it entirely. He did not think that anybody could disagree with Dr Reinitzhuber technically. The equations of heat transfer were very well known, and as Dr Reinitzhuber quoted them they were quite correct. However, Dr Fitzgerald could not agree with Dr Reinitzhuber's interpretation of the present situation concerning furnace predictions. It seemed to Dr Fitzgerald that quite contrary to what was said during the presentation of the paper, there had been many experimental and mathematical studies of furnaces, and that the bibliography in the paper was severely limited. Dr Fitzgerald said that the results of many of the studies were already generally applied by furnace operators and by research workers. They already used models of the type described by Dr Reinitzhuber though it was true that all models do have uncertainties in the physical parameters which are needed in them. Dr Fitzgerald agreed that the emissivities of the surfaces, the effects of scale, and the question as to whether scale formation provides added heat transfer, were perhaps important topics. Their importance, however, depended on whether or not better predictions would result from knowing better values for these parameters.

Regarding the calculation of aerodynamics, mixing, and combustion in furnace models, Dr Fitzgerald recommended the work of Prof. Spalding and co-workers at Imperial College. He would, however, point out that the methods of calculation were not proved in many practical systems and he would advise Dr Reinitzhuber to examine afresh cold-modelling techniques, because he thought that Dr Reinitzhuber could get all the information on flow, mixing, and combustion that he needed without doing any calculations at all.

Finally, Dr Fitzgerald asked why Dr Reinitzhuber was calculating heat transfer to the insides of furnace walls, because it seemed that the mechanisms of heat transfer involved were exactly the same as the mechanisms of heat transfer to the stock in the furnace if one assumed that scale had no overall effect.

Dr Reinitzhuber in reply to the question said that the calculation of the heat transfer to the walls had not yet been made completely although the fundamental mechanisms were the same as for heat transfer to the stock. First, there were a number of layers in a furnace wall so that by knowing the temperature distribution through it one could hope to optimize its thickness. However, Dr Reinitzhuber agreed with the comment that it was not always necessary to know the wall temperatures exactly for furnace modelling purposes.

With regard to the calculation of combustion patterns. Dr Reinitzhuber knew that Prof. Spalding had done a lot of work and that calculations to evaluate the concentration, temperature, and velocity pattern in the furnace were very complicated. Further, the Spalding calculation must be combined with the Hottel and Cohen method in order to achieve furnace predictions and, therefore, Dr Reinitzhuber did not think that at this stage it was easy to build these rather complicated techniques into mathematical models which were already themselves quite extensive.

Written discussion contribution to the paper on *Mathematical modelling of furnaces and primary rolling* by F. Fitzgerald

Mr L. Fawcett (British Steel Corporation, Corporate Advanced Process Laboratory, Teesside) wrote that although induction furnaces and other alternatives are now being given serious consideration, the cupola remains the most widely used plant in foundries. Despite this, it had not been mentioned in the review of furnace models made by Dr Fitzgerald, perhaps because little work seems to have been done to produce a mathematical model of the process.

Breen[1] calculated metal, coke and gas temperature distributions for an experimental cupola using heat balances. Necessary to these calculations were data from a water-cooled copper probe inserted into the cupola bed. Although this type of work contributes to the understanding of the process physics and chemistry, it is of no direct value in improving the performance of a particular cupola or at predicting the design criteria or performance of others.

A different but equally restricted approach was taken by Surovskii et al.[2] who derived equations for charge and gas temperature distributions in the charge heating zone only. Nomograms were produced so that the temperatures could be calculated given a knowledge of the values of the following quantities: heat capacities and consumptions of charge materials and gas; linear speed of the charge materials; volumetric coefficient of heat transfer between the gas and charge materials; depth of charge heating zone and gas temperature at the bottom of that zone.

A more useful approach was taken by Briggs[3] who developed a model of the cupola using data from an experimental cupola at BCIRA and 18 industrial furnaces. The model consists of linear regression equations representing output quantities (melting rate, metal temperature and composition) in terms of operating conditions and design variables (coke charge, blast rate, etc.). It can be used either to predict how the furnace will perform for a given set of operating conditions or to predict the operating conditions necessary to provide a specified cupola output. This type of model has the most practical value and the version developed by Briggs shows fairly good agreement between observed and predicted results, almost all points on observed versus predicted value plots lying within 95% confidence limits. A 'net' diagram has been constructed using the model enabling the necessary coke charge and blast rate to be easily derived for a given melting rate and metal temperature.

Considering the surprisingly good correspondence between the linear regression model and observed results, it is doubtful whether a detailed physico-chemical model based on the reactions occurring in the process has much more to offer. Although such a model would be more flexible in use and more theoretically based, it also involves a great deal more effort to produce.

References

1 J. G. BREEN: *Proc. Australasian Inst. Min. Met.*, 1963, No. 208.
2 V. M. SUROVSKII et al.: *Steel in the USSR*, 1971, **1**(11), 852.
3 J. BRIGGS, *BCIRA J.*, 1973, 21 (May), 233.

chapter 6 : hot and cold rolling

Review of mathematical rolling models

M. Economopoulos

The mathematical model of a process is essentially an instrument of prediction. In fact, according to the definition of Peck et al.[1] 'the term mathematical model applies to any mathematical relationship that can be used to predict anything with regard to the output variables of the process as a function of the input variables'. The predictive capacity of mathematical rolling models is put to good use in three different types of problem:

(i) calculations for new rolling mills
(ii) determining the optimal control conditions in an existing mill by off-line studies on the model
(iii) determination and on-line application of the control parameters (set-up).

It will be appreciated that the demands made on the models will be different for every category of these problems. The accent will be placed on the predictive capacity of the model, on its accuracy or simplicity, and on the speed of calculation it permits, as the case may be. Thus the applicability of mathematical rolling models affords a possible means of classification. The type of rolling mill to which they are adapted forms another such means. For this reason we are not interested in mills for elongated products as the rolling theory for grooved rolls or universal stands is practically non-existent. Empirical formulae alone allow the approximate determination of the rolling forces and torques.[2,3,4,5,6,7] In what follows we are going to examine only the hot and cold rolling of 'flat' products, i.e. of products whose width to thickness ratio exceeds 20 or 30. It is well known that in this type of rolling the total widening of the product is practically nil, and the hypothesis of the state of plane strain is admissible for any point sufficiently remote from the edges. Consequently we will not discuss some attempts, notably by Russian authors, to tackle the rolling problem from the standpoint of triaxial strain.[8,9,10,11,12,13,14,19]

Even after having thus severely limited the subject, we are faced with an extremely abundant literature which it would be pointless to analyse here in detail. We shall,

therefore, be constrained to make a choice and more particularly to introduce a classification. To begin with we will examine the mathematical models of a rolling pass, to investigate later on the more practical case of rolling in several passes, either on a reversible stand or on several stands arranged in tandem.

MATHEMATICAL MODELS OF A ROLLING PASS

From the mechanical point of view hot and cold rolling are similar operations. They differ mainly in the properties of the rolled material and in the boundary conditions. Constructing the mathematical model of a rolling pass and its application to a specific case is a complex operation, which we can subdivide for clarity of exposition into successive stages or phases:

(i) formulating the rheological properties of the rolled material
(ii) setting up the differential equations describing the tensor field of stress and strain in the gap
(iii) determining tool strain (rolls, stand)
(iv) defining and formulating mathematically the boundary conditions
(v) determining the numerical values of the physical quantities involved in the model
(vi) solving the equations.

It will be understood that this division is of didactical importance only and the stages thus defined are not mutually independent. For instance, what plasticity equations are used will depend on the formulation of the properties of the material.

Rheological properties of the rolled material

One of the difficulties encountered in the study of plastic deformation of metals derives from the fact that it is not possible to define for them an equation of state in the same way as for perfect gases or liquids.[15] Indeed, the plastic state of the metal depends on all its preceding states. Owing to this none of the simple rheological

The author is with CRM, Belgium

bodies[16-18] gives a viable idealization for metals in the plastic state. Yet, in view of the mathematical difficulties entailed by adopting a complicated model of the rolled metal, most authors of rolling theories have accepted the simplest possible hypothesis. The rolled metal is assimilated to the 'rigid–perfectly plastic' body, well known to theoreticians of plasticity. Actually the real metal has a much more complicated behaviour. In addition to its antecedent thermo-mechanical history its resistance to plastic flow is affected by three variables (for a given composition and working method):

(i) the temperature
(ii) the strain
(iii) the strain rate.

These three factors vary considerably from point to point in the roll gap. So far as the temperature is concerned, it is assumed to be constant in all theories employed in practice. Now it is well known that the cooling at contact with the roll and the plastic deformation generate in the gap a thermal field that is far from uniform.

Johnson and Kudo,[20] inspired by the work of Tanner[21] and Bishop[22] on extrusion, have proposed a method of approximate calculation for the thermal field in the roll gap, but so far as we know this work has not been followed up. We will also refer in this connexion to the work of Finne et al.,[23] who take into account the thermal field in the roll gap in their mathematical model, as well as the observations by Tselikov[23] and the experiments made by Chelishev,[24] who has determined the effect on the strain of strongly inhomogeneous thermal fields. With regard to the influence of strain and strain rate upon the properties of plastic flow of metals, after numerous attempts, whose history need not be entered on here, the following philosophy, which has been clearly set forth by Rossard and Fazan,[25] has been derived. On the basis of the criteria of plasticity (generally after Tresca or von Mises)[26] are defined the generalized stress($\bar{\sigma}$) and the generalized strain and strain rate ($\bar{\epsilon}$ and $\dot{\bar{\epsilon}}$), which are respective functions of the six components of the stress, strain, and strain rate tensors at any point in the metal. The principle of equivalence is then introduced whereby:[25] 'if one considered any two strains imparted to the same metal and according to the same laws of strain–time $\bar{\epsilon} = f(t)$ and temperature–time $T = g(t)$, in both cases the metal will be at any moment in an equivalent condition from the point of view of mechanical behaviour and will assume at any moment the same value in both cases'. A simple laboratory test is then chosen during which the plastic deformation is carried out according to the laws

$$\bar{\epsilon} = f(t)$$

$$T = g(t)$$

and the characteristic stress G_0 of the test is measured. This is regarded as an intrinsic property of the metal and will be employed in the rolling theories through the principle of equivalence. The simulation tests most fre-

quently used are those of torsion[27-30] and compression.[31-35,40] Tests based on other principles, such as compression in the state of plane stress and compression on rectangular dies, have, however, been proposed.[36-39] These tests have been used to elicit the effect of the principal factors (temperature T, strain $\bar{\epsilon}$, strain rate $\dot{\epsilon}$) and to determine the characteristic function of a metal

$$G_0 = f(T, \bar{\epsilon}, \dot{\bar{\epsilon}})$$

This function is presented either in the form of a diagram[41] or in analytical form.[42] We would finally refer to the attempts at approximating the flow of a metal to that of a viscous fluid, which have given rise to hydrodynamic theories of rolling.[43-45]

Equations of rolling

Equations can be set up to describe the stress field in the roll gap in terms of the following hypotheses:

(i) the rolling is symmetrical
(ii) the temperature of the product in the roll gap is uniform
(iii) the inertial forces are negligible and the strain rate constant
(iv) von Mises's criterion of plasticity is valid, which presupposes that the metal behaves identically under tension and compression, and the generalized stress $\bar{\sigma}$ does not depend on the first invariant of the tensor of stresses
(vi) Levy von Mises's plasticity laws are applicable, which presupposes that the rolled metal is homogeneous and isotropic and may be regarded as a continuous medium and the rolled metal may be regarded as a perfectly plastic–rigid body
(vii) the equivalent stress is independent of the strain rate
(viii) we are dealing with a plane state of strain.

It can be shown that these equations are reducible to four equations with partial derivatives of hyperbolic type with four unknowns, i.e. two stress components and two speed components. Despite the considerable simplification arising from the adopted hypotheses, no general solution of these equations has been obtained yet. The precursors Siebel, von Karman, Tselikov, Nadai, Sachs, Klinger[46-51] etc. have by-passed the difficulty by making hypotheses that are still more restrictive and more remote from reality; the main one consisted in assuming that metal sections that were initially plane and perpendicular to the direction of rolling stayed plane in the roll gap (it can be easily shown that the hypothesis contradicts the fundamental equations of equilibrium). Despite these deficiencies, this conception of rolling has given birth to a school which has over several decades produced numerous works both theoretical and experimental (see Refs. 52–61).

An important advance has been achieved by Orowan's theory[62] which eliminates the hypothesis that plane sections remain plane in the roll gap. Orowan approximates the roll gap to a succession of planes tangential to the rolls and assumes that the product is compressed between successive corners. The distribution of stresses in the plate is found by extending the investigations by Prandtl and Nadai.[63,64] Orowan's theory is often held out to provide the exact solution of the rolling problem. It must, however, be observed that it takes no account of the elastic properties of the rolled material. Moreover, Nadai's solution applies only to the case where the material is depressed towards the apex of the angle subtended by two non-parallel planes. In rolling this situation arises on the exit side of the contact arc, but is reversed on the entry side. Orowan must assume that Nadai's equations apply with sufficient approximation to the entry side of the roll gap. Finally, there is a fundamental objection to be raised. On the basis of a theorem enunciated by Hencky in 1923 it has often been assumed, in the case of plastic plane strain problem, that the distribution of stresses can be determined without introducing the equations of displacement. Owing to the equations of equilibrium and to the criterion of plasticity, three equations, containing only σ_X, σ_Y, and τ_{XY} as unknowns, are combined, and the problem may be regarded as statically determined. This is done in Orowan's theory. As a result of more recent work on plastic deformation[65-68] it can be affirmed that this point of view is inexact and the equations of displacement must intervene, especially in the boundary conditions. In the plastic domain one distribution of stresses may be associated with an infinite number of solutions to the equations of displacement and thus with an infinite number of problems of plastic flow. As stated by Lee,[68] the solutions derived solely from the equations of stress may rather be regarded as probable, but may equally well come nowhere near the correct distribution of stresses. In spite of these fundamental objections, Orowan's theory is at present the most widely accepted in the sphere of hot rolling, notably thanks to the work done by Hockett[69] and especially to the simplifications introduced by Sims.[70]

More recently Ford, Alexander, Crane, Troost, and Potapkin have tried to eliminate the restrictive hypotheses of the previous theories and to solve the general rolling equations by having recourse to the slip line theory.[71-76] These attempts open up a new chapter in the theoretical investigation of rolling.

Boundary conditions

This is the most difficult problem in the theory of rolling for three reasons:

(i) there exists no means of directly investigating the conditions of contact between the roller and the product

(ii) the boundary to which the differential equations must be integrated is only partly defined, and in fact, the surfaces separating the rigid and plastic parts of the metal at the entry and exit sides of the contact arc are *a priori* unknown

(iii) the boundary conditions are of the mixed type, i.e. stress conditions are defined on some parts of the boundary and velocity conditions on others.

In view of these difficulties, which are at present insurmountable, more or less arbitrary hypotheses have been formulated.

(i) von Karman has proposed the hypotheses of dry friction according to which the tangential stress at any point of contact with the roller is proportional to the normal stress

(ii) Siebel assumes that the tangential stress is constant

(iii) Nadai assumes viscous friction

(iv) Orowan assumes dry friction over a portion of the contact arc and sticking over the rest and sets forth criteria for determining these two regions

(v) Sims assumes that sticking occurs over the whole of the contact arc.

Deformation of the rolls

Whereas the early researchers considered the rolls as rigid, it was soon proved that it is necessary to take into account the flattening of the rolls, especially in passes that generate a high specific pressure in the gap. Among the various simplified formulae that have been proposed[77-79] that of Hitchcock has been the most used and appears satisfactory, at any rate for most applications to hot rolling.[80,81] However, in the case of cold rolling thin plates the simplified formulae are inadequate. Recourse is then had to the point by point calculation of the deformation of the roll,[82,83] which yields results in excellent agreement with the experiments.[84,85]

Experimental results

A considerable volume of work has been dedicated to the experimental verification of the theories of rolling. (*See* Refs. 86–93.) The results of these investigations, which are sometimes contradictory, are difficult to summarize. It is found, however, that none of the present theories can provide *a priori* reliable numerical values of the rolling force and torque. We think that the chief advantage of these theories is to provide formal laws that qualitatively describe the effect of various parameters. The quantitative application of these laws to the processes has been made possible by the introduction of statistically determined coefficients and by the extensive use of methods of adaptative control. This aspect of the problem will be discussed in the following chapter.

MODELS OF ROLLING IN SEVERAL PASSES

While the problem of calculating a rolling pass is of particular interest to the rolling mill constructor, the utilizer has always to deal with rolling in several passes, continuous passes or on a reversible stand. The mathematical rolling models have found a vast field of application in the steel industry with the introduction of on-line computers for determining in advance the set-up values. In this case the mathematical models are indispensable owing to the fact that *a priori* control is essentially an operation of prediction. It is to be noted that the qualification 'mathematical' does not apply to every model used in practice, as some of them are simple empirical relations fed into the computer memory in the form of tables. In the case of rolling in several passes the difficulties mentioned earlier are greatly magnified by the fact that the model of rolling in the proper meaning of the term is insufficient. It is necessary to take into additional consideration the temperature of the product, the thermal state of the rolls, the mill stretch, etc. New solutions have become necessary in view of the complexity of the problem and the exigencies of on-line calculation:

(i) the models are simplified to the utmost and in some cases reduced to simple numerical tables

(ii) the whole production of the mill is divided into narrow classes according to the thickness, width, and composition of the rolled product, and the coefficients of the models are defined for every class

(iii) intensive use is made of the technique of adaptative control.

To sum up, the models employed for on-line control of rolling are simple, even simplistic, but specific to space and time. They correctly portray a particular machine for a particular subdivision of rolled products and at a given moment. In view of this specificity it would be devoid of interest to analyse here the various formulae that have been proposed. In Table 1 we give a list of publications relating to various models and processes.

REFERENCES

1 P. E. PECK *et al.*: *JISI*, 1967, **205** (4), 387
2 Z. ZAMYSLOVSKY AND V. CRHA: *Hutn. Listy*, 1966, **21**, 23
3 'Roll Pass Design', The United Steel Companies Ltd, 1960, Percy Lund Humphries and Co. Ltd, London

4 G. WALLQUIST: *Jernkon. Ann.*, 1960, 144, 192
5 A. HELMI AND J. M. ALEXANDER: *JISI*, 1968, **206** (2), 1 110
6 S. YANAGIMOTO AND I. AOKI: *Bull. JSME*, 1968, **11** (43), 165
7 E. BORGES AND S. ZAMPROGNO: *Metallurgia*, 1969, **25** (134), 32.
8 V. P. SEVERDENKO AND S. A. PASECNYJ, *Inzhen. Fiz. Zhur.*, 1960, **3** (5), 67
9 POLUKHIN AND VORONCOV: *Cernaja Metallurgija*, 1966, **9** (11), 57
10 POLUKHIN AND VORONCOV: *Cernaja Metallurgija*, 1966, **9** (5), 102
11 C. S. RUDISILL AND C. F. ZOROWSKI: International Conference Manufacturing Technology, ASME, 1967, 1 083
12 R. J. MURPHY: Thesis, Carnegie Institute of Technology
13 A. P. CEKMAREV *et al.*: *Trudy Dnepropetr. Chern. Met.*, 1969, 29, 44
14 A. P. CEKMAREV *et al.*: *Trudy Dnepropetr. Chern. Met.*, 1969, 29, 90
15 J. LEBOURS-PIGEONNIERE: *Métaux*, 1952, **27**, 119
16 F. R. EIRICH: 'Rheology', Theory and Applications, Academic Press, 1958, New York
17 W. PRAGER AND P. G. HODGE: 'Perfectly Plastic Solids', Dover Publication, 1968, New York
18 B. PERSOZ: 'Introduction à l'étude de la rhéologie', Duønod, 1960, Paris
19 Z. NIKEL: *Trans. Inst. Min. Met.*, Metallurgy series, 1969, **15** (3) 193
20 W. JOHNSON AND H. KUDO: *Internat. J. Meeh. Sci.*, 1960, **1**, 175
21 R. TANNER AND W. JOHNSON: *Internat. J. Mech. Sci.*, 1959, **1**, 28
22 J. W. F. BISHOP: *Quart. Appl. Math.*, 1956, **9**, 236
23 A. I. TSELIKOV: Theory of force calculations in rolling mills, Metallurgizdat, 1962
24 N. A. CHELYSHEV *et al.*: *Steel in the USSR*, 1971, **1** (2), 131
25 C. ROSSARD AND B. FAZAN: *Cessid*, 1968
26 R. HILL: 'Mathematical Theory of Plasticity', Clarendon Press, 1950, Oxford
27 P. PASTORET AND J. MATHONET: CRM Metallurgical Report, 1971, **29**, 57
28 C. ROSSARD AND P. BLAIN: *Rev. Mét.*, 1962, Mar, 223
29 D. S. FIELDS AND W. A. BACKOFFEN: *Proc. ASTM*, 1957, **37**, 1 259
30 H. J. WHITTAKER *et al.*: *Proc. ICSTIS*, Section 4, Suppl. *Trans. ISI Japan*, 1971, **11**, 662
31 A. HANNICK AND J. M. JACQUERIE: CRM Metallurgical Report, 1965, **3**, 49
32 B. LENGYEL AND M. MOHITPOUR: *J. Inst. Met.*, 1972, **100**, 1
33 N. H. POLAKOWSKI: *JISI*, 1949, **163** (3), 250
34 B. HUMBERT *et al.*: *Mét. Corr. Ind.*, 1969, **523**, 83

TABLE 1   List of publications relating to various models and processes

| Process | Models | | | | | |
	Description of the control assembly	Force and power models	Temperature models	Mill stretch models	Transverse profile of the strip	Results of application
Hot strip mill	95, 96, 98, 102, 103, 111, 114, 116, 131, 132, 133	94, 95, 96, 97, 98, 99, 104, 106, 131	95, 97, 98, 131	94, 97, 98	135	102, 105, 114
Plate mill	100, 108, 109, 115, 124, 128, 129, 134	97, 99, 100, 101, 104, 107, 108, 134	97, 100, 101, 134	97, 100, 115, 134		109, 128, 129, 134
Cold tandem mill	110, 113, 117, 120, 121, 122, 123, 127, 130	125, 126		112, 125	112, 119	117, 121, 122, 130
Skin-pass	118					

35 E. VOCE, *J. Inst. Met.*, 1948, 537
36 A. KÖLERUD: CIRP Conference, Ann Arbor, 1967, Sept.
37 R. B. SIMS: *JISI*, 1954, **178** (2), 393
38 A. B. WATTS AND H. FORD: *Proc. IME*, 1952, **10**, 448
39 A. S. WEINSTEIN AND A. MATSUFUII: *Iron Steel Eng.*, 1968, Sept., 121
40 G. R. DUNSTAN AND R. W. EVANS: *Metallurgia*, 1969, Mar., 96
41 P. M. COOK AND A. W. MCGRUM: 'The calculation of load and torque in hot flat rolling', BISRA, 1958
42 J. E. HOCKETT: Los Alamos Scientific Labs., LA2233, Jan., 1959
43 K. H. WEBER: *JISI*, 1965, **203** (1), 27
44 K. H. WEBER: *Arch. Eisenh.*, 1966, Oct., 783
45 K. H. WEBER: *Neue Hütte*, 1971, Feb., 81
46 E. SIEBEL: *Ver. Deutsch. Eisenh.*, 1924, **37**
47 E. SIEBEL: *Stahl Eisen*, 1930, **50**, 1 769
48 T. VON. KARMAN: *ZAMM*, 1925, **5**, 139
49 A. I. TSELIKOV: *Metallurg*, 1939, **6**, 61
50 A. NADAI: *J. Appl. Mech.*, 1939, **6**, A54
51 G. SACHS AND L. J. KLINGER: *J. Appl. Mech.*, 1947, **14**, 88
52 N. H. POLAKOWSKI: *Sheet Metal Ind.*, 1950, **27**, 389 and 667; *ibid.*, 1951, **28**, 885, 981, and 1 081; *ibid.*, 1952, **29**, 581
53 A. H. EL-WAZIRI: *Iron and Steel Eng.*, 1963, Oct., 73
54 E. OROWAN AND K. J. PASCOE: First report of the rolling-mill research sub-committee of the Iron and Steel Industrial Research Council, 124, 1946, London, The Iron and Steel Institute
55 S. GUPTA AND H. FORD: *JISI*, 1967, **205**, 186
56 A. P. CEKMAREV: *Bull. Sidérurgie*, 1967, Sept., 52
57 G. F. MICHELETI: *Int. J. Mech. Tool Des. Res.*, 1965, **4**, 157
58 A. GELEJI: *Acta Techn.*, 1964, **45**, 275
59 A. GELEJI: *Acta Techn.*, 1964, **46**, 171
60 A. GELEJI: *Arch. Eisenh.*, 1963, **34**, 565
61 A. I. TSELIKOV: *Steel*, 1958, **5**, 434
62 E. OROWAN: *Proc. IME*, 1943, 140
63 L. PRANDTL: *ZAMM*, 1923, **3**, 401
64 A. NADAI: 'The Plasticity', McGraw-Hill, 1931
65 R. HILL: *Quart. J. Mech. Appl. Math.*, 1949, **2**, 40
66 K. S. YAJNIK AND J. FRISH: *J. Eng. Ind.*, 1962, Feb., 81
67 R. HILL *et al.*: *J. Appl. Mech.*, 1951, 46
68 E. H. LEE: *J. Appl. Mech.*, 1952, **19**, 97
69 J. E. HOCKETT: *Trans. ASM*, 1960, **52**, 675
70 R. B. SIMS: *Proc. Inst. Mech. Eng.*, 1954, **168**, 191
71 H. FORD AND J. M. ALEXANDER: *J. Inst. Met.*, 1963, **92**, 397
72 J. M. ALEXANDER: *Proc. Inst. Mech. Eng.*, 1965, **169**, 1 021
73 F. A. A. CRANE AND J. M. ALEXANDER: *J. Inst. Met.*, 1968, **96**, 289
74 A. TROOST AND J. BETTEN: *Arch. Eisenh.*, 1969, **40**, 301
75 V. F. POTAPKIN: *Bull. de la Sidér*, 1971, **9**, 79
76 V. F. POTAPKIN: *Bull. de la Sidér*, 1971, **7**, 83
77 J. H. HITCHCOCK: 'Roll neck bearings', *ASME*, 1935
78 H. FORD: *Met. Review*, 1957, **5**, 1
79 W. L. ROBERTS: *Iron Steel Eng.*, 1965, Oct., 75
80 R. B. SIMS: *JISI*, 1954, **178**, 19
81 B. FAZAN: 'La théorie du laminage', CESSID, 1968
82 C. F. ZOROWSKI AND A. S. WEINSTEIN: *Iron Steel Eng.*, 1961, **38**, 99
83 D. JORTNER *et al.*: *Internat. J. Mech. Sci.*, 1960, 179
84 P. COSSE AND M. ECONOMOPOULOS: *CRM Met. Reports*, 1968, **17**, 15

85 O. PAWELSKI AND H. SCHROEDER: *Arch. Eisenh.*, 1969, (11), 867
86 G. WALLQUIST, *Jerkon. Ann.*, 1955, **129**, 923
87 G. WALLQUIST: *ibid.*, 1962, **146**, 873
88 G. WALLQUIST: *ibid.*, 1960, **144**, 194
89 G. WALLQUIST: *ibid.*, 1969, **153**, 5
90 R. STEWARTSON: *Proc. Inst. Mech. Eng.*, 1954, **168**, 201
91 Z. WUSATOWSKI AND W. KUSCHKA: *Arch. Hutn.*, 1963, **8**, 259
92 H. FORD: *Proc. Inst. Mech. Eng.*, 1948, **159**, 115
93 R. B. SIMS AND H. WRIGHT: *Iron Steel*, 1962, 627
94 I. IMAI AND T. KIMURI: British Patent Specification No. 1.089.847
95 O. G. MUZALEVSKII: *Stal in English*, 1970, 220
96 T. ISAHAYA *et al.*: *Int. Eisenh.*, 1970, Autom. in Hüttenwerken
97 K. GEDIN: *Jerkon. Ann.*, 1966, **150**, 537
98 U.S. Patent, no. 3 332 263, 1967
99 E. S. ROKOTYAN: *Stal'*, 1962, 797
100 R. G. SCHULZ AND A. W. SMITH: *Iron Steel Eng.*, 1965, May, 127
101 C. MCKENZIE: *Steel Intenational*, 1968, Jan., 8
102 D. J. RAY: Third BISRA Automation Conference, paper no.7
103 M. VAVRECKA AND R. SOBOTA: *Hutnik*, 1967, **17**, 276
104 S. A. F. BUXTON AND R. W. SUTTON: *J. Sci. Tech.*, 1969, **36**, 19
105 H. E. MILLER: *Iron Steel Eng.*, 1969, Sept., 67
106 V. P. POLUSHKIN: *Stal'*, 1968, Mar., 231
107 M. TAROKH AND F. SEREDYNSKI: *JISI*, 1970, **208** (2), 695
108 French Patent no. 1.581.023, 1969
109 D. R. JONES AND A. W. SMITH: *Iron Steel Eng.*, 1965, May, 134
110 W. E. MILLER: *Blast Furnace and Steel Plant*, 1964, 642
111 J. ULLMANN: *Blech*, 1964, **5**, 222
112 French Patent no. 1 500 452, 1967
113 H. SCHMIDT: *Stahl Eisen*, 1967, **87**, 1 565
114 R. J. DARNALL: *Iron Steel Eng.*, 1968, 128
115 A. W. SMITH AND L. P. GRIPP: *Iron Steel Eng.*, 1962, 77
116 E. FIEBIG: *Stahl Eisen*, 1969, **89**, 160
117 G. R. GRIFFITHS: Third BISRA Automation Conference
118 T. E. BRYAN AND J. E. HORN: *Iron Steel Eng.*, 1968, June, 121
119 Belgian Patent no. 708.052, 1967
120 M. M. BUTTERFIELD AND R. D. KILLICK: Automation Conference, Scarborough, 1963
121 M. H. BUTTERFIELD: *Trans. Soc. Inst. Tech.*, 1965, 76
122 G. F. BRYANT *et al.*: Int. Conf. on Iron and Steelmaking, Düsseldorf, 1965
123 H. D. MORGAN AND M. H. BUTTERFIELD: *Control*, 1962, 92
124 W. J. LINK: AISI, San Francisco Regional Technical Meeting, 1968
125 J. H. COURCOULAS AND J. M. HAM: *Trans. AIEE*, 1956, 363
126 G. LIANIS AND H. FORD: *Proc. IME*, 1957, 757
127 ANON.: *Fiji Steel Rev.*, 1969, (1), 7
128 K. E. MAYER *et al.*: *Stahl Eisen*, 1969, Feb., 178
129 M. OSHIMA *et al.*: Automatizierung in Hüttenwerken, Düsseldorf, 1970
130 Y. YOSHITANI *et al.*: *ibid.*
131 K. TODA *et al.*: *ibid.*
132 G. BADUSHE *et al.*: *Tech. Mih. Aeg-Telefunken*, 1969, 47
133 E. S. LODICS: *Control Eng.*, 1969, 89
134 J. BOUVARD *et al.*: *Rev. Mét.*, 1960, June, 433
135 S. WILMOTTE *et al.*: *CRM Metallurgical Report*, to be published

Criteria for hot rolling of plates with respect to the flatness and the crown of the plates

G. Fritsch, G. Haralamb, and J. C. Illaire

The deformation produced during rolling of a slab determines the flatness (form of the main surfaces) and the crown (difference between centre and edge) of the plate. Carrying out of the rolling operation requires that the development from pass to pass of the flatness and the crown of the slab should be known in advance, and for this purpose the use of analytical models of deformation phenomena is necessary. The models of flatness and crown defined by IRSID describe an interpretation of the deformation of the sheet. 'Primary' deformation is considered as that which reduces the thickness of the sheet and gives it the cross-section of the roll gap on leaving the rolls, and 'secondary' deformation as that which changes this cross-section or causes, if it is too great, the appearance of defects in flatness by warping of the plate. Secondary deformation results from the lack of affinity of the cross-sections of the roll gap on the exit side and of the plate on the entry side. The optimum rules for rolling practice with regard to the flatness and crown of plates, as defined by IRSID, make it possible to achieve much higher productivity levels than those obtained by the application of traditional rolling practice. The rules consist of carrying out primary deformation which causes secondary deformation to the warping limit.

SYMBOLS

σ	stress
ϵ	deformation
t	temperature
b	crown of the plate
h	thickness of the plate at the edge
H	thickness of the plate at the axis
$\bar{H}$	mean thickness along the cross-section of the plate
l	length of the plate
V	velocity of the plate
F	rolling force
F_0	rolling force, that compensates the crown of the rolls
A	bending modulus of all the rolls
C, μ	mechanical characteristics of the metal
i, j	characteristics of the warping of the plate
n	characteristics of the profile of the plate
w	width of the plate
—	state at the entry of the roll bite
'	state at the exit of the roll gap before secondary deformation
+	state at the exit of the roll gap after secondary deformation

The hot rolling of plates on a reversing mill causes a modification of the geometrical characteristics of the plate at each pass. This paper treats the evolution of two of them, the flatness and the crown, both of which are closely connected being two effects of the same cause—the deformation of the rolls of the rolling mill. The flatness characterizes the shape of the main faces of the plate. A plate is considered flat if its median surface is cylindrical. The crown characterizes the shape of the cross-section of the plate, as well as being a dimension of this section. The crown is defined as the difference between the thickness of the plate at the axis and at the edge. The models of the flatness and crown of plates have been developed in the context of a research program of IRSID on the automation and optimization of hot rolling on a reversing mill. This research has been performed in co-operation with the Longwy rolling mills of Usinor.

At the time of the conference, the authors were with IRSID, France

PURPOSE OF THE MODELS

Rolling experience shows that a plate after a rolling pass does not always remain flat. Frequently undulations along the edges (wavy edges) or along the axis (wavy centre) are observed. The models of flatness and crown of the plate aim at making the relations explicit between the rolling conditions and the state of the plate before the pass, and the state of the flatness and crown of the plate after the pass. These models only apply in the case of plates which are flat before the pass under consideration. They describe the phenomenon of the plastic deformation of the plate after leaving the roll gap, which sometimes results in wavy edges or in wavy centres.

REASON FOR THE MODELS

The automation and optimization of hot rolling of plates on a reversing mill requires determination of the deformation cycle of the plate from the process control system. This deformation cycle, which leads to the final desired dimensions, is the rolling schedule. This schedule must be optimal and to achieve this the control system must foresee the optimal deformation and thus the optimal rolling force which is compatible with the imposed safety limits for mill operation, together with the behaviour of the slab during rolling and the desired characteristics of the plate. Two of these limits are represented by the flatness of the finished plate.

IMPORTANCE OF THE MODELS

The flatness and crown of the plates are two geometrical characteristics for which the customers' specifications are becoming more and more severe. Therefore it has become necessary to understand the phenomena that determine the characteristics. The models of flatness and crown are necessary elements of this process of understanding.

Observation and interpretation of the rolling phenomena with respect to flatness and crown of plates

Observation of rolling practice shows that:

  (i) after each pass, the plate can be 'buckled' (wavy edges or wavy centre)
 (ii) the appearance of the phenomenon is related to the thickness and width of the plate, the rolling force, the wear of the rolls, and the rolling speed
(iii) the phenomenon, when it occurs, extends itself up to the exit of the roll gap and appears practically as soon as a small length of the plate has been rolled
 (iv) the state of flatness may be restored to a buckled plate by a cycle of convenient passes during which further buckling may be tolerated
  (v) the plate is buckled at the edges after a pass with too high a rolling force, and buckled in the centre with too little force
 (vi) the ends of the plate are not much deformed during rolling if a reduction cycle is employed

such that buckling at the edges or the centre is avoided at each pass. The end faces then become cylinders with vertical axes and very great radii

(vii) taking the plate as a composite of parallel fibres in the rolling direction, it can be noted that, for a buckled plate, the length of the fibres developed along the edge is different from that developed in the centre.

The occurrence of buckling can be explained by a combination of the phenomena of elastic deformation of the rolls during the pass and the phenomena of deformation and bending of the plate at the exit of the roll gap. The crown of the plate leaving the roll gap results from the deformation of the rolls at the exit from the roll gap. This roll deformation results from the rolling force and its distribution over the roll gap, which in turn results from the characteristics both of the plate before the pass, and of the rolling mill during the pass. Generally, the condition relating the profile of the plate before and after the pass is not held to, and consequently the elongation of fibres along the edge and along the centre differs. If the fibres were independent, they would slip along each other and leave the roll gap with different velocities. The end of the plate leaving the roll gap would become more and more cylindrical as the length of the emerging plate increased. But, as the fibres are linked by the cohesion of the metal, a shearing stress is set up in the plate that has left the roll gap, opposing slipping of the fibres. This shearing stress is held in equilibrium by a state of shearing stress perpendicular to the direction of the fibres and by a state of tension and compression in the direction of the fibres. In the perpendicular direction, the fibres on the edge are under compression and in the centre under tension for rolling conditions close to the appearance of wavy edges, or inversely for conditions of a wavy centre of the plate.

In this way, the profile of the roll gap creates a heterogeneous stress on the fibres at the exit of the roll gap, and imposes a deformation on the fibres of the plate after leaving the mill. We designate this by secondary deformation, with respect to the primary deformation that gives the plate the profile of the exit of the roll gap. It compresses, thickens, and widens the edge fibres and lengthens, reduces, and contracts the centre fibres for rolling conditions approaching the appearance of wavy edges and inversely for conditions approaching the appearance of wavy centres. The nature of the secondary deformation develops with the length of plate that has already left the roll gap. When the length is small compared to the thickness, the fibres slip with respect to each other. When the length increases the slipping becomes more difficult till it is blocked and then the fibres will be compressed or stretched. Thus, the secondary deformation is dependent on the length of plate which has left the mill. In the stationary state the fibres of the plate have the same speed at the roll bite, and different speeds at the exit of the roll gap and before the secondary deformation, and again equal speeds after secondary deformation. A straight section of the flat plate at the entry to the roll bite will be deformed at the exit before secondary deformation and will be straight again after secondary deformation. Thus, the secondary deformation is only determined by the crown of the plate at the entry to the roll bite and the profile of the rolls at the exit from the roll gap.

The secondary deformation of the central fibres is the inverse of the deformation of the edge fibres, and the variations in width will compensate each other so as to leave the total width of the plate practically unchanged. The same is valid with respect to the thickness for which the variations are such that the mean thickness remains unchanged. The secondary deformation in the stationary case will determine the state of stress of the plate at the exit of the roll gap and vice versa. This state of stress will be assumed one-dimensional, whether compressive or tensile, and in order to obtain equilibrium of the part of the plate that already has left the mill, the resultant of the summation of the stresses at the exit of the roll gap will be zero. This state of stress created in the plate undergoes relaxation by the complex phenomenon of structural transformation of the metal. It meets its limits in the equally complex phenomenon of buckling of the part of the plate which has left the roll gap. The first phenomenon is governed by variable kinetics according to the physical state of the metal of the plate, i.e. essentially the temperature, the chemical composition, the grain structure, and the work hardening. The second phenomenon has a variable threshold according to the width and the thickness of the plate, the mechanical characteristics of the metal which depend on temperature, the chemical composition, the grain structure, etc.

The warping of the plate is produced when the state of stress exceeds a certain critical threshold and the plate becomes buckled. The critical threshold is, for a state of uniform stress, an inverse function of the length of the plate which has left the roll gap, until this length gets of the order of one-fourth of the width of the plate. The critical threshold then becomes fairly independent of the length of emergent plate. The warping, i.e. buckling, of the edge fibres of the plate shows up effectively as the number of half-waves that minimizes the energy state of the plate. The wavelength is of the order of the width of the plate and is small with respect to the usual plate lengths. We limit our study to the stationary state and to a plate length more than one-fourth of the wavelength of the buckles. The manifestation of the buckling phenomenon is related to the state of stress of the portion of the plate which has left the roll gap and is of a length equal to a fourth of the wavelength of the buckles. Warping may or may not be experienced depending on the values of the secondary deformation, the resistance against deformation, the rolling speeds, the relaxation of stresses, and the critical threshold for warping. Several cases must be considered:

1   The velocity of relaxation of the stresses is zero. The state of stress in the critical portion of the plate is determined by the secondary deformation and the resistance against deformation of the metal. A limit value exists for the secondary deformation which characterizes the onset of the phenomenon of buckling of the plate. This limit value will depend on the secondary deformation effected at previous passes, and the state of stress of the critical portion of the plate will be approximately the sum of the variations of the state of stress introduced at each secondary deformation. Summation of the stresses will take place and after several rolling passes the limit value for secondary deformation will have become zero.

2   The relaxation velocity of the stresses is sufficiently low, with respect to the rolling speed, so as not to cause relaxation of the stresses in the critical portion of the plate during rolling, but sufficiently high for partial relaxation to occur between passes. A limit value exists for the secondary deformation, which characterizes the onset of the phenomenon of buckling of the plate. Although this limit value will depend on previous secondary deformations there will not be an algebraic addition of the growth of the state of stress introduced at each pass by the secondary deformations, but a summation with exponentially declining weight factors. The limit value will not depend on the characteristics of the relaxation of stresses at the pass under consideration.

3   The relaxation of stresses is sufficiently low, with respect to the rolling speed, in order not to cause relaxation in the critical portion of the plate during rolling, but sufficiently high to result in complete relaxation between passes. As before there exists a limit value for secondary deformation, which characterizes the onset of the buckling phenomenon of the plate, but the stresses are not summated. This limit value does not depend on previous secondary deformations nor on the stress relaxation characteristics.

4   The velocity of the relaxation of stresses is sufficiently high, with respect to the rolling speed, in order to cause partial relaxation of the stresses in the critical portion of the plate during rolling and complete relaxation between passes. A limit value for the secondary deformation exists which characterizes the onset of the buckling phenomenon of the plate. This limit value does not depend on previous secondary deformations. It will be higher than the limit value of the preceding case and it will be a function of the characteristics of the relaxation of stresses.

5   The velocity of the relaxation of stresses is infinite. The state of stress in the critical portion of the plate is zero and warping cannot take place. The plate remains flat independent of the secondary deformation. This case appears rather improbable, as it is well known that plates do buckle whatever their chemical composition.

The preceding analysis can be summarized in Table 1. Case 1 corresponds to cold rolling. Case 2 corresponds to hot rolling on a reversing mill of high-carbon high-alloy steel plates and of steel with dispersed elements. Cases 3 and 4 would correspond to hot rolling of low-carbon low-alloy steel. Case 5 does not correspond to real hot rolling conditions at a reversing mill.

TABLE 1 Analysis of cases where warping may or may not be experienced

Dependence	Case 1	2	3	4	5
Primary and secondary deformation at the considered pass	yes	yes	yes	yes	no
Velocity of stress relaxation at the considered pass	no	no	no	yes	no
Primary and secondary deformations at previous passes	yes	yes	no	no	no
Velocity of stress relaxation at previous passes	no	yes	no	no	no

The theoretical case, in which the stress relaxation velocity is sufficiently high (with respect to the rolling speed) in order to cause partial stress relaxation at each rolling pass but which is insufficiently high for total relaxation to occur between passes, has no practical equivalent. A limit value of secondary deformation exists, which characterizes the onset of the phenomenon of buckling of the plate edges. Although this limit value will depend on previous secondary deformations, there will be no complete summation of the state of stress introduced at each pass by the secondary deformation, but a summation with exponentially declining weight factors. The limit factor will depend on the stress relaxation characteristics of the pass under consideration. This case is hardly likely in practice because the ratio of the duration of travel of the critical portion of the plate, at rolling speed, to the duration of the time between two passes of the same portion of metal is great, and the law of stress relaxation is an exponential function of time. Thus, the limit value of the secondary deformation which characterizes the onset of the buckling phenomenon is a more or less complex function, as the case may be, of the width and the thickness of the plate, the temperature and chemical composition of the metal, the primary deformation, the rolling speed and, in certain cases, the previous primary and secondary deformation and also of the instants at which the deformations are performed. The secondary deformation will affect the crown of the plate differently depending on whether there is warping of the plate or not. If there is no warping, the crown of the emergent plate after secondary deformation is intermediary between the crown determined by the rolls at the exit of the gap and the value derived from the crown at the entry of the roll bite by a relation involving the ratio of the mean thicknesses. When a stationary process has been established, the secondary deformation along the direction of rolling produces a deformation across the width and over the thickness, both equal to one half a wavelength. If warping occurs, the crown of the plate approaches the profile of the rolls controlling the exit of the roll gap.

Mathematical expression describing the phenomena of the flatness and the crown of plates

Warping is a phenomenon which creates waves along the edges or along the centre of the plate. As the complete treatment of the phenomenon is complex, we introduce hypotheses and restrictions to facilitate establishing the mathematical models. Thus we:

(i) limit ourselves to cases in which the plate enters the pass flat and without stresses. This imposes the condition that the plate must be flat at each rolling pass as achieved by an optimal control system. This could result in an increase of the number of necessary passes, but improves the surface of the finished plate. In the case of a buckled plate, the millscale formed between two passes collects in the hollows of the waves of the upper surface to form pockets of greater thickness than the layer of millscale from which they originate. The pockets form crusts on the plate at the following pass and emboss the surface of the plate with their impression. Moreover, the wavy edges run through the roll-gap following a complex movement of translation and rotation. The slip marks on the plate consequently show fanshaped streaks in addition to the usual longitudinal streaks

(ii) assume that the width of the plate in the roll-gap remains constant. The widening is a negligible effect in the regions of the plate in which the state of flatness holds good

(iii) assume that the metal is isotropic and homogeneous

(iv) assume that during secondary deformation a linear relation exists between the stress σ and the deformation $\epsilon : \sigma = \mu\epsilon$ and that after secondary deformation, stress relaxation takes place according to a law of the type $\sigma = \sigma_0 e^{-ct}$, in which t is time, σ_0 the initial stress (immediately after secondary deformation), c and μ characteristic parameters of the metal

(v) assume that the transverse profile of the plate can be represented by the relation $h(y) = ky^n + h(0)$, h being the thickness and y the transverse abscissa with its origin at the symmetry axis of the plate. This hypothesis has been verified experimentally in all the rolling cases considered for the establishment of the model with plastic deformation of the rolls ($n \neq 4$)

(vi) assume that the secondary deformation takes place instantaneously immediately after leaving the roll gap and that the stress relaxation takes place subsequently without deformation of the plate. The assumption leads to a dissociation of the phenomena of the evolution of the stresses and the evolution of the secondary deformation. This makes the calculations easily accessible to a schematic representation, which can be treated with the classical theories of deformation. The result of the calculations leads to an overestimation of the state of stress, and thus to the absence of a critical secondary deformation which corresponds to the onset of warping. This is satisfactory for the establishment of a practical rule for rolling operation.

Three successive states of the same portion of the plate are to be considered, i.e. the state at the entry of the roll bite, with index 'minus', the state at the exit of the roll gap before secondary deformation, index 'prime', and the state after secondary deformation, with index 'plus'. The plate is referred to with a system of axes 0, x, y, z. The x-axis is parallel to the rolling direction, the z-axis is vertical, and the y-axis is perpendicular to these directions.

Models of flatness and crown of plates at zero secondary deformation

When the crown of the plate in the states 'minus' and 'prime' are comparable, the longitudinal fibres of the plate are lengthened by the same distance and no secondary deformation takes place. Thus the plate remains flat. This condition is sufficient and generally is not necessary except for steels with a very low stress relaxation velocity. This condition is written as:

$$b' = b^+, \quad \overline{H}' = H^+ \quad \text{and} \quad \frac{b^-}{\overline{H}^-} = \frac{b'}{\overline{H}'} \qquad . \qquad . \quad (1)$$

with $\overline{H}$ = mean thickness of the cross section, and b = crown of the cross section. The crown b' can be expressed as a function of the rolling force after the model of the plastic deformation of the rolls (see Appendix 1), when no secondary deformation has occurred after the preceding pass (see Fig. 1):

$$b^- = A(F_{-1} - F_0)$$
$$b^+ = A(F - F_0)$$

with F = rolling force of the pass under consideration, F_{-1} = rolling force of the preceding pass, F_0 = rolling force at which the elastic deformation of the rolls compensates the crown of the rolls at the roll gap giving a rectangular aperture at the exit; (CDP) is the curve of plastic deformation of the plate at the pass under consideration, i.e. the relation between the rolling force and the absolute reduction of the mean thickness. Thus the rule for rolling operation with zero secondary deformation is obtained which is usually called the rule for rolling with constant relative crown.

$$F = \frac{F_{-1} - F_0}{\overline{H}^-}\overline{H}^+ + F_0 . \qquad . \qquad . \qquad . \qquad . \quad (2)$$

This rule is given in the graph $(F, \overline{H})$ in the case of rolls of a concave shape $(F_0 < 0)$.

In Fig. 1, $(F, \overline{H})$ it can be noted that the model for flatness at zero secondary deformation requires that the point $(F, \overline{H})$ lies on a straight line (LPO), called limit of flatness at zero secondary deformation. It also lies on the plastic deformation curve of the plate (CDP), which determines the point corresponding to the pass. If the rule for rolling operation at zero secondary deformation is applied for the following passes, the corresponding points in the graph $(F, \overline{H})$ will also be on the straight line (LPO). The rule for rolling at zero secondary deformation severely limits the rolling force for ordinary steels,

and leads to an increase of the number of passes in comparison with current practice. Therefore it is of interest to apply, at each pass, a rolling force greater than the one meeting this condition, but without exceeding that which leads to warping. When barrel-shaped rolls are used, the number of passes can be reduced and the first passes, for which there exists no flatness problem, are executed at maximum rolling force. If the rolling mill is equipped with an installation of roll bending, the value of b' can be chosen such that:

$$\frac{b^-}{b'} = \frac{\overline{H}^-}{\overline{H}'}$$

the rule for rolling mill operation at zero secondary deformation, can be applied whatever the rolling force F chosen, obviously within the mechanical limits of the installation.

Models of the flatness and the crown of plates at non-zero secondary deformation

Construction of the models of flatness and crown of plates consists, on the one hand, of seeking the existing states of deformation and stress in the plate (assumed to be flat after secondary deformation) at a rolling pass as a function of the data of the pass (which can be calculated or measured) and, on the other hand, of investigating which threshold this state of stress exceeds to give rise to warping of the plate.

STATE OF SECONDARY DEFORMATION AND STATE OF STRESS IN THE PLATE AFTER SECONDARY DEFORMATION

In the stationary mode of operation the fibres of the plate do not slip. The state of stress of the plate after secondary deformation is assumed uniaxial along the z-direction. The state of secondary deformation ϵ of the plate is determined by the classical application of the theory of mechanics of continuous media (see Appendix 2).

$$\epsilon_x = \frac{\overline{H}^-}{\overline{H}^+} \cdot \frac{h'(y)}{h^-(y)} - 1 = -2\epsilon_z = -2\epsilon_y$$

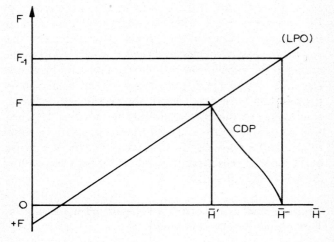

1   Models of flatness and crown of plates at zero secondary deformation

These relations applied to all fibres of the section determine the dimensions, width w, thickness $\bar{H}$, crown b:

$$w^+ = w' \qquad . \qquad . \qquad . \qquad . \qquad . \qquad . \qquad (3)$$

$$\bar{H}^+ = \bar{H}' \qquad . \qquad . \qquad . \qquad . \qquad . \qquad . \qquad (4)$$

$$\frac{b^+}{\bar{H}^+} = \frac{1}{2}\left(\frac{b^-}{\bar{H}^-} + \frac{b'}{\bar{H}'}\right) \qquad . \qquad . \qquad . \qquad . \qquad (5)$$

Equation (5) describes the evolution of the crown of the plates. Its validity is limited to the last passes for which the widening in the roll gap is negligible. During the first passes the widening of the plate is not negligible and in certain cases this can help to reduce the magnitude of the secondary deformation. The state of stress σ of the plate immediately after secondary deformation is governed by a law of the type $\sigma = \mu\epsilon$, as already menrioned, and so

$$\sigma(y) = \mu\left(\frac{\bar{H}^-}{\bar{H}^+} \cdot \frac{h'(y)}{h^-(y)} - 1\right)$$

It can be seen that the fibre under most compression is the fibre at the edge when the primary deformation is more severe for this fibre than for the fibre at the centre, and *vice versa*. The state of stress in the same portion of plate after secondary deformation is determined by the time elapsed since the secondary deformation according to the stress relaxation law $\sigma = \sigma_0\, e^{-ct}$, c being a characteristic of the metal of the plate depending on its temperature, its structure, and its chemical composition.

$$\sigma(y) = \mu\left(\frac{\bar{H}^-}{\bar{H}^+} \cdot \frac{h'(y)}{h^-(y)} - 1\right) e^{-ct}$$

If x is the abscissa of this portion with respect to the exit of the roll gap and V^+ its velocity:

$$\sigma(x, y) = \mu\left(\frac{\bar{H}^-}{\bar{H}^+} \cdot \frac{h'(y)}{h^-(y)} - 1\right) e^{-c(x/V^+)} \qquad . \qquad . \qquad (6)$$

CRITICAL STATE OF STRESS IN THE PLATE AFTER THE PASS

S. P. Timoshenko in his book 'Theory of elastic stability' has studied the phenomenon of warping for different solids, mainly beams and flats, submitted to different states of stress. None of the cases treated corresponds exactly to the case of interest here. However, the case of rolling can be approached partly by the warping of flats submitted to axial compression at one end and to tension at the other and partly by the warping of beams submitted to a distributed loading and to an elastic reaction. The study of warping of flats shows us that the wavelength of the deformed plate is of the order of the width and that the critical state of stress is proportional to h^2/w^2, the proportionality factor K being a function of the physical characteristics of the metal of the plate and of the distribution of the loading on the flat. The value K_a for the buckling along the axis of the plate is of the order of 1·5 times the value K_r for the buckling of the edges, or $K_a = jK_r$ with a value for j of about 1·5. Therefore, the length of the plate to be con-

sidered after the mill is one-fourth of the wavelength, i.e. a length of the order of one-fourth of the width of the plate since the plate can be considered as fixed in the roll gap. This length can be expressed as w/i with i around four. The study of the warping of beams shows us that the representative value of the state of stress for the onset of warping is very close to the mean value of the state of stress over the considered length. The critical threshold of the state of stress is:

$K_r(h^2/w^2)$ for the onset of wavy edges and $jK_r(h^2/w^2)$ for wavy centres, in which K_r depends on the physical characteristics of the plate metal. The representative value for the state of stress for the onset of warping is:

$$\frac{i}{w}\int_0^{w/i} \mu\left(\frac{\bar{H}^-}{\bar{H}^+} \cdot \frac{h'(y)}{h^-(y)} - 1\right) e^{-c(x/V^+)} \mathrm{d}x \quad \text{with } y = w$$

for the buckling of the edges of the plate and 0 for the buckling in the centre. The model of flatness determines the geometrical characteristics of the secondary deformation for which warping sets in for the most loaded fibre. Those geometrical characteristics can be obtained by equating the representative value of the state of stress to the critical threshold, thus:

$$\frac{i}{w}\int_0^{w/i} \mu\left(\frac{\bar{H}^-}{\bar{H}^+} \cdot \frac{h'(y)}{h^-(y)} - 1\right) e^{-c(x/V^+)} \mathrm{d}x = K(y)\frac{h^2(y)}{w^2}$$

in which $K(y) = K_r$ for the buckling of the edges of the plate and $K(y) = K_a$ for the buckling of the plate along the centre. If K_r/μ is set equal to k and by replacing $H - h$ by $(n/n + 1)b$ the equation of the crown of the plate can be written as (*see* Appendix 2):

$$\frac{b'}{\bar{H}'} \leqslant \frac{b'}{\bar{H}'} \text{ near edge} = \frac{b^-}{\bar{H}^-} \frac{kch^{+2}}{i\left[1 - \exp\left(-\dfrac{cw}{iV^+}\right)\right]V^+w}$$

$$\cdot \frac{h^-}{\bar{H}^-} \cdot \frac{n+1}{n} \qquad . \qquad . \qquad . \qquad . \qquad (7)$$

$$\frac{b'}{\bar{H}'} \geqslant \frac{b'}{\bar{H}'} \text{ near centre} = \frac{b^-}{\bar{H}^-} \frac{jkcH^{+2}}{i\left[1 - \exp\left(-\dfrac{cw}{iV^+}\right)\right]V^+w}$$

$$\cdot \frac{H^-}{\bar{H}^-} \cdot (n+1) \qquad . \qquad . \qquad . \qquad . \qquad (8)$$

k and c are functions of the physical characteristics of metal, i.e. the temperature, the structure and the chemical composition. A particular case must be considered, i.e. the relaxation velocity is not high enough to cause relaxation at each pass, but sufficiently high to cause it between two passes. Thus, c is very small and the Eqs. (7) and (8) become:

$$\frac{b'}{\bar{H}'} \leqslant \frac{b'}{\bar{H}'} \text{ near edge} = \frac{b^-}{\bar{H}^-} + \frac{n+1}{n}k\frac{h^{+2}}{w^2} \qquad . \qquad . \qquad (9)$$

$$\frac{b'}{\bar{H}'} \geqslant \frac{b'}{\bar{H}'} \text{ near centre} = \frac{b^-}{\bar{H}^-} - j(n+1)k\frac{H^{+2}}{w^2} \qquad . \qquad (10)$$

HOT ROLLING IN AN OPTIMAL MODE WITH RESPECT TO THE FLATNESS AND CROWN OF PLATES

The optimal mode of rolling is determined by expressing the crown b' in the model of flatness as a function of the rolling force after the model of the plastic deformation of the rolls (see Appendix 1), $b' = A(F - F_0)$. In the particular case in which the relaxation velocity is so low that stress relaxation does not take place at each pass, but is completed between two passes, the optimal mode is expressed as:

$$ F \leqslant F_0 + \frac{b_{-1}^+}{A\bar{H}_{-1}^+} \cdot \bar{H}^+ + \frac{(n+1)k}{An} \cdot \frac{\bar{H}^{+3}}{w^2} \quad . \qquad (11) $$

$$ F \geqslant F_0 + \frac{b_{-1}^+}{A\bar{H}_{-1}^+} \cdot \bar{H}^+ - \frac{j(n+1)k}{A} \cdot \frac{\bar{H}^{+3}}{w^2} \qquad (12) $$

The Eqs. (11) and (12) fix the regions in which the working point of the rolling pass must be found in the graph of force v. thickness, such that the plate will be flat, or buckled at the edges or at the centre. The plate will be flat if its mean thickness $\bar{H}^+$ after the pass lies between the two values $\bar{H}_s^+$ and $\bar{H}_1^+$ defined by the intersection of the curve of plastic deformation with the limits of the region for flat plates (see Fig. 2). The two limit curves of this region meet in $(0, F_0)$ where they have as tangent the straight line that would represent the rolling pass with zero secondary deformation and for which the plate thickness would be H_0^+. The slope of this straight line gives the relative crown of the plate after the pass -1 except for the factor A. This straight line intersects the vertical line $\bar{H}^-$ at a point with ordinate F_{-1}^* which will coincide with the working point of the pass -1 with the ordinate of the force $F - 1$, if the secondary deformation at this pass is zero. $F - 1$ is a fictitious force, which if applied to the rolls over the width w^+. would give a profile of the loaded rolls at the exit of the roll gap equal to b_{-1}^*, thus:

$$ F_{-1}^* = F_0 + \frac{b_{-1}^+}{A} $$

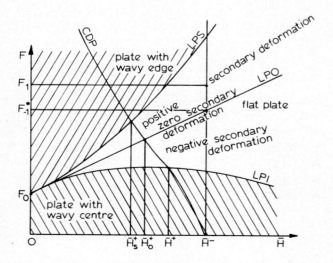

2   *Hot rolling in an optimal mode with respect to the flatness and crown of plates*

$(F_{-1}^* - F_0)$ depends only on the crown of the plate before the pass. The upper and lower limits for flatness are situated independently of F_0 with respect to the limit of flatness at zero secondary deformation. Thus, rolling at maximum secondary deformation allows the thickness to be diminished from $\bar{H}_0^+$ to $\bar{H}_s^+$ for the pass under consideration, compared with rolling at zero secondary deformation. The thickness $\bar{H}_0^+$ is fixed by the value of relative crown of the plate before the pass. It is the smaller the greater the relative crown is before the pass. The relative crown increases from pass to pass in the practical case of rolling with maximum secondary deformation without roll bending. At reduction of the mean thickness there exists a double summation of increments, the first at each pass relative to the thickness which would already be obtained at zero secondary deformation, the second by the increase from pass to pass of the value of the relative profile. In the case of roll bending, the system of three limits is displaced vertically by a value equal to the variation in F_0, due to roll bending. (It must be remembered that F_0 is the force that must be applied on the rolls over the width of the plate so that the profile of the roll gap at the exit will be zero.) This translation is upward when the roll bending force is increased. From these considerations regarding rolling with maximum secondary deformation, an optimal rolling mode is deduced for a mill not equipped with a roll bending installation. The practice of rolling has three aspects:

(i) the productivity of the installation as represented by the minimum number of passes
(ii) the yield of the semiproduct and its quality, as determined by tolerances on its dimensions (width, thickness at the edge, crown, flatness) and by its mechanical and metallurgical properties
(iii) the proper use of the electrical and mechanical equipment of the mill during the rolling passes as determined by the limit of the rolling force, the rolling torque and the loading of the mill drives.

Various rolling modes fully satisfy the last two aspects. They differ from one another by the number of passes involved. Among these modes, the rule for rolling at constant relative crown, i.e. at zero secondary deformation, has been described already. Experience and the theory of flatness itself show that it leads to a high number of passes. A near optimal mode would be the following:

(i) the crown of the non-loaded rolls (mechanical and thermal) must be appreciable in order to make the limit for flatness at each pass less restrictive. However, this crown must be sufficiently small so that the crown of the plate will be positive at each pass. This is brought out in Fig. 2 by the fact that F_0 must be as close as possible to the minimum permissible rolling force for the considered case
(ii) the first passes must be rolled at maximum reduction since they are not limited by the

requirements for flatness, but by the proper use of the equipment. The rolling force is the highest possible together with the relative crown, and the requirements for flatness will be such that they will be least restrictive when they start to limit the deformation

(iii) the later passes, for which the reduction is limited by the flatness, must be rolled at maximum secondary deformation. However, it must be taken into account that the thickness after the last pass must have a given value, and that the relative crown must not exceed a certain limit. In general, it will not be possible to finish rolling with a maximum secondary deformation. The last pass and sometimes the last passes will be made at minimum secondary deformation. The number of passes at minimum secondary deformation will vary, but the rule requires that this number is minimal.

CONCLUSION

The study of the phenomena to which the flatness and crown of plates are related has brought forward the existence of a secondary deformation at the exit of the roll gap. This secondary deformation, caused by the incompatibility of the crown of the plate at the entry to the roll gap with the profile of the roll gap at its exit, consists of a transformation of the section of the plate when this incompatibility is small, and a buckling of the plate, on the edges or centre, when the incompatibility is great. The models for the flatness and the crown presented are limited to the case of rolling without buckling. They give the effect of secondary deformation on the dimensions of the section of the plate, as well as defining the limits to the incompatibility of the crown of the plate at the entry to the roll gap with the profile of the roll gap at its exit. The optimal modes of rolling operation presented make use of the existence of the secondary deformation. They consist of achieving at each pass the optimal deformation which does not change the state of flatness of the plate. This deformation corresponds to the upper limit given by the flatness model. However, the crown of the plate after rolling might become too great and in this case the deformations for the last pass or passes would be determined by the lower limit given by the flatness model. These optimal modes considerably decrease the number of passes compared with certain normal schedules which seek to achieve the deformation that keeps the relative crown proportional to the thickness for each pass, i.e. keep the secondary deformation equal to zero. These models and rules have been incorporated in the optimal automatic control system for hot rolling of plates on a reversing rolling mill by IRSID in co-operation with the Longwy plant of USINOR and have been tested at the rolling department of this plant.

The results obtained to date cover 500 plates of ordinary steel in various dimensions (from 5·5 to 200 mm thick, from 1 800 to 3 800 mm wide). They are most satisfactory with respect to the flatness and the crown of the plate on the one hand, and to the productivity of the mill on the other. The plate has proved flat at each pass, the crown has never exceeded the commercial limits, and the number of passes was always less than the number of passes obtained by the mill operator for comparable cases, even though the operator had the opportunity to 'buckle' the plate during rolling and to flatten it at the last pass. This paper summarizes the results of the first phase of the research involving the flatness and crown of plates. The second phase of this will study the influence of the widening on the limits of flatness during primary deformation, and the influence of the chemical composition of the steel on these limits.

APPENDIX 1

Model of the elastic deformation of rolls

The model is established based on the following hypotheses and simplifications:

(i) the mill is not equipped with roll bending

(ii) the axes of the rolls are parallel to each other

(iii) the effects are neglected of modifications of the crown of the rolls by thermal expansion and wear on the load distribution on the contact between work roll and supporting roll

(iv) the effects are neglected of the weight of rolls and mountings, as well as the influence of the counterweights for the upper rolls

(v) the effects are neglected of the changes in mechanical characteristics of the work rolls and the supporting rolls

(vi) the effect of the elastic flattening of the rolls is neglected

(vii) the effect is neglected of the transverse variation of the primary plastic deformation of the plate

(viii) it is assumed that the bending of the rolls can be described by the bending of a single round bar on simple supports

(ix) it is assumed that the work rolls and the supporting rolls are in contact for the usual rolling forces.

The model describes the profile b' of the rolls at the exit of the gap before secondary deformation as:

$$b' = b_c + \left[1 - \frac{2d_n^3}{a_3 D_n^4 + d_n^4}(2d_n - d_i - d_s)\right.$$
$$\left. - \frac{2a_3 D_n^3}{a_3 D_n^4 + d_n^4}(2D_n - D_i - D_s)\right]$$
$$\cdot \frac{[w + a_4 L_v]a_3 w'^2 F}{(a_3 D_n^4 + d_n^4)} + \left[1 - \frac{d_n}{a_6 D_n^2 + d_n^2}\right]$$
$$\cdot (2d_n - d_i - d_s) - \frac{a_6 D_n}{a_6 D_n^2 + d_n^2}(2D_n - D_i - D_s)\right]$$
$$\cdot \frac{a_7 \cdot w' F}{a_6 D_n^2 + d_n^2} \cdot \quad . \quad . \quad . \quad . \quad (3)$$

which can be reduced to:

$$b' = A(F - F_0)$$

where

F_0 = the force to be applied to the rolls over the width b' so that the section of the roll gap at the exit is rectangular. F_0 is negative if the rolls are concave in form, positive if they are barrel-shaped

b_c = function of the profile of the gap of unloaded rolls

w = width of the plate

F = rolling force

$d_n, d_i, d_s, D_n, D_i, D_s$ = nominal diameter of the upper, the lower, the work, and the supporting rolls

L_v = interaxis of the screws

a_3 to a_7 = coefficients depending on the composition, the structure, and the dimensions of the rolls.

The model describes the transverse crown of the rolls as $h(y) = ky^n + h(o)$, $(n \# 4)$.

APPENDIX 2

Calculation of the state of secondary deformation

In continuous operation the fibres of a plate do not slip with respect to each other and have equal velocities. The state of stress at the exit of the roll gap is uniaxial, either compression or tension. We use the notation $\sigma(y)$ for it. The equilibrium of the external stresses applied to the portion of plate which has left the roll gap manifests itself in the equilibrium of the stresses in the section of the plate after leaving the mill and after secondary deformation:

$$\int_{-(w/2)}^{+(w/2)} \sigma(y)h^+(y)\,dy \# \bar{H}^+ \int_{-(w/2)}^{+(w/2)} \sigma(y)\,dy = 0$$

The deformation ϵ_x along the x-axis can be deduced from the stress $\sigma(y)$ according to a law of the type $\sigma = \mu\epsilon$; thus $\epsilon_x = [\sigma(y)/\mu]$ and the deformations ϵ_y along the y-direction and ϵ_z along the z-direction are both equal to half the deformation ϵ_x. So it can be deduced that the width w^+ at the exit of the roll gap after secondary deformation is equal to the width w' at the exit of the roll gap before secondary deformation, and so to the width w^- at the entry of the roll gap:

$$w' = \int_{-(w/2)}^{+(w/2)} dy' \# \int_{-(w/2)}^{+(w/2)} (1 + \epsilon_y)\,dy^+$$

$$= w^+ + \int_{-(w/2)}^{+(w/2)} \frac{\sigma(y)}{2\mu}\,dy^+ = w'$$

The mean thickness $\bar{H}^+$ of the plate at the exit of the roll after secondary deformation is equal to the mean thickness $\bar{H}'$ of the plate at the exit of the roll gap before secondary deformation

$$\bar{H}' = \frac{1}{w}\int_{-(w/2)}^{+(w/2)} h'(y)\,dy = \frac{1}{w}\int_{-(w/2)}^{+(w/2)} (1 + \epsilon_z)h^+(y)\,dy^+$$

$$= \bar{H}^+ + \int_{-(w/2)}^{+(w/2)} \frac{\sigma(y)h^+(y)\,dy^+}{2\mu l} = \bar{H}^+$$

In concurrence with the conservation of mass, the mean thickness $\bar{H}^-$ of the plate at entering the mill and $\bar{H}^+$ at leaving it after secondary deformation are inversely proportional to the corresponding velocities:

$$\bar{H}^- x w^- x V^- = \bar{H}^+ w^+ V^+ \quad \text{at} \quad \bar{H}^+ V^+ = \bar{H}^- V^- \quad (6)$$

The deformation ϵ_x along the x-direction can be expressed as a function of the geometrical characteristics at the entry of the roll gap and at the exit of the roll gap before secondary deformation:

$$\epsilon_x = \frac{dx^+}{dx'} - 1 = \frac{dx^+}{dx^-} \cdot \frac{dx^-}{dx'} - 1$$

$$\frac{dx^+}{dx^-} = \frac{V^+}{V^-} = \frac{\bar{H}^-}{\bar{H}^+} = \frac{\bar{H}^-}{\bar{H}'}$$

because all the fibres have the same velocity after secondary deformation and

$$\frac{dx^-}{dx'} = \frac{h'(y)}{h^-(y)}$$

because there is no widening in the roll gap, so

$$\epsilon_x = \frac{\bar{H}^-}{\bar{H}'} \cdot \frac{h'(y)}{h^-(y)} - 1$$

The relative crown $b^+/\bar{H}'$ of the plate at the exit of the roll gap after secondary deformation can be expressed as a function of $b^-/\bar{H}^-$, the relative crown at the entry of the mill and $b'/\bar{H}'$ the relative crown at the exit of the mill before secondary deformation:

for

$$\epsilon_x = -2\epsilon_z$$

let

$$\frac{\bar{H}^-}{\bar{H}'} \cdot \frac{h'(y)}{h^-(y)} - 1 = -2\left(\frac{h^+(y)}{h'(y)} - 1\right)$$

which can be written for a fibre at the edge as

$$\frac{\bar{H}^-}{\bar{H}'} \cdot \frac{h'}{h^-} - 1 = -2\left(\frac{h^+}{h'} - 1\right)$$

and for a fibre at the centre

$$\frac{\bar{H}^-}{\bar{H}'} \cdot \frac{H'}{H^-} - 1 = -2\left(\frac{H^+}{H'} - 1\right)$$

and as

$$H^- - h^- = b^-, \quad H' - h' = b', \quad H^+ - h^+ = b^+$$

so by difference

$$\frac{b^+}{\bar{H}^+} = \frac{1}{2}\left(\frac{b^-}{\bar{H}^-} + \frac{b'}{\bar{H}'}\right) \quad . \quad . \quad . \quad . \quad (7)$$

Performance analysis and optimization of the plate-rolling process

F. Seredynski

This paper is based on theoretical and practical investigations carried out to derive, and then to verify, a mathematical model of a plate rolling mill. The model can be used iteratively for practically any plate rolling mill to produce rolling schedules for maximum throughput consistent with mill constraints and with slab/final plate dimensions. In precision rolling, a requirement for high-dimensional accuracy, particularly suppression of plate crown, adversely affects mill throughput. The investigation includes an analysis of the relationship between throughput and dimensional accuracy and sets up a procedure for the optimum utilization of the rolling plant in the presence of roll camber variations occurring during a typical campaign.

LIST OF SYMBOLS

D	work roll diameter, m
e	conversion factor from torque to current, $\mathrm{NmA^{-1}}$
G	motor torque, Nm
$I_A(t)$	dynamic current, A
I_D	deformation current, A
I_F	friction current, A
$I_k(t)$	current in kth state, A
I_L	load current, A
I_{NOM}	motor nominal current, A
I_R	sum of $(I_0 + I_D + I_F)$, A
I_{RMS}	armature RMS current required to complete a schedule, A
I_s	motor starting current, A
J	moment of inertia of mill roll, $\mathrm{Mms^2}$
l	slab length, m
n	speed, rev/min
n_b	base speed, rev/min
n_e	entry speed, rev/min
n_p	peak speed, rev/min
n_x	exit speed, rev/min
N	number of passes
r	reduction
j	pass number

t_e	time at which slab enters the roll gap, s
t_x	time at which slab leaves the roll gap, s
t_1	time at which weak field is commenced, s
t_2	time at which weak field is terminated, s
t_i	inter-pass time, s
2τ	time required to complete one cycle, s
α	ratio of entry speed to base speed
β	ratio of exit speed to base speed
γ	ratio of peak speed to base speed
m	ratio of I_s/I_{NOM}
η	ratio of I_{RMS}/I_{NOM}
T	absolute temperature of the plate, K
T_a	ambient temperature, K
K	thermal diffusivity, $\mathrm{m^2s^{-1}}$
t	time, s
E	emissivity
S	Stefan–Boltzmann constant, $5.66 \times 10^{-8}\,\mathrm{Jm^{-2}s^{-1}K^{-4}}$
k	conductivity, $\mathrm{Jm^{-1}K^{-1}s^{-1}}$
A	area of radiating surface, $\mathrm{m^2}$
V	volume of plate, $\mathrm{m^3}$
σ	specific heat of steel, $\mathrm{Jkg^{-1}K^{-1}}$
ρ	density of steel, $\mathrm{kgm^{-3}}$
w	plate width, m
P	rolling load, MN
γ_w	camber of work rolls, mm
c	plate crown, mm
δ	correction in screwdown setting, mm

The author is with BSC, Corporate Engineering Laboratory

A full assessment of any potential improvement in rolling practice involves the knowledge and experience of a number of specialists. If the efficiency of rolling is to be increased, the specialists (ranging from plant designers to pulpit operators) must examine the factors which appear to be relevant to the specified circumstances. The most common recommendations for increased throughput are to speed up the drives and to increase both the mechanical and the electrical loading. It is, however, difficult to assess quantitatively the full effect of any particular modification proposed. For example, high rolling loads tend to affect adversely plate cross-sectional profile and plate flatness. Furthermore, the required high accuracy of plate thickness makes it necessary to apply low rolling loads towards the end of a rolling schedule, to minimize the error in the estimated mill stretch. Exploration and experimentation by trial and error, involving the capital-intensive rolling plant, must be restricted because of possible adverse effects on production. Besides this, the cost of plant modifications can be very high. The inevitable result is that managers find it very difficult to form an opinion or to take a rational decision about the plant potential and the value of any proposed improvements. Such a situation presents a considerable obstacle to plant modernization and to the investigation of technical efficiency. To evaluate and quantify the performance of the mill or to assess the value of changes in mill design or the effect of automation, it is necessary to write down and collate rules which govern mill performance. Thus, for instance, an estimation of rolling load combined with a knowledge of the dynamics and constraints of the plant could be used to devise an appropriate rolling schedule. Analytical expressions can be derived for the entire rolling process, as will be shown. In this way, a mathematical model of the process can be compiled to derive either a schedule for maximization of the throughput or to establish the effect of any changes in plant or rolling practice before putting such changes into effect.

In the course of rolling plate two distinct stages are observed. The aim of the initial stage is to reduce the slab thickness as rapidly as possible, in some cases imparting correct width to the plate, making sure that the mill is not overstressed. In the second stage of rolling, particular attention is given to the final dimensional aspects of the rolled product. During this final stage, the mill variable parameters are generally well below their constraints. The objective is to produce a plate to the required thickness accuracy with allowable crown, good degree of flatness and minimum loss of material. When, in addition, a particular finishing temperature is specified, the rolling schedule must be correspondingly modified, even if the mill throughput is in consequence reduced. This paper describes a comprehensive mathematical model of the hot reversing rolling process and explains how the model can be used to derive rolling schedules for maximum throughput. The elements of the model are illustrated in Fig. 1. They are

(i) mathematical formulae describing the behaviour of the process
(ii) material and plant data
(iii) optimizing processor.

The first element forms a pool of information about the process, e.g. reliable methods for estimating rolling load, stock temperature, time intervals between the passes, etc. The information contained in this element can be readily expanded or modified as necessary. The second element contains the particulars of the rolling mill and its main drive, and also of the slab and finished product data. The third element contains the processor of the totality of information provided. The processor offers a high degree of flexibility in the calculations involved in deriving the rolling schedules required. This paper shows how these elements are constructed, how they can be integrated into a rational and practical method of representing mill performance, and how such a method may be applied to the determination of optimum rolling schedules for a hot reversing plate mill.

FACTORS AFFECTING THROUGHPUT

Optimum rolling conditions

It is convenient to subdivide the problem of specifying optimum conditions into four stages

(i) optimization of the speed pattern of a single pass
(ii) optimization of drafting strategy
(iii) overall schedule optimization
(iv) optimization of mill throughput by means of suitable choice of plate widths rolled during the roll campaign.

Speed pattern

With regard to the first of these, it is well known that the output of dc mill drives is limited mainly by the losses generated in the armature circuit, which raise the temperature of the machine windings. It is shown in

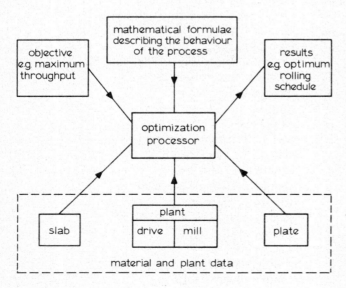

1   Elements of the mathematical model of plate rolling

Appendix 1 that the losses are related to the speed–time pattern employed and it is found that, for minimum losses, the speed–time pattern should be parabolic. In other words, the main drive throughput potential is greatest when a parabolic speed–time pattern is employed. In circumstances where it is inconvenient to impose the parabolic speed–time pattern an alternative pattern, such as a trapezoidal, has to be considered.

Drafting strategy

In the context of this paper an optimum drafting strategy is one which arranges the drafts on successive passes in such a way that the rolling schedule is completed in the shortest possible time. The maximum safe draft in any one pass may be limited by one or more of the following factors

    (i) maximum permissible bite angle
    (ii) maximum permissible roll force
    (iii) maximum permissible instantaneous drive current/torque
    (iv) crown considerations and nominal finished thickness.

The maximum bite angle is a function of the linear velocity of the rolls at the instant of the work piece entry into the roll gap.[1,2] One form of this function is given in Appendix 2.

The maximum roll force is the limiting force which can be tolerated by the mill structure of a particular plant. The reduction taken should never generate a force exceeding this limit. There are usually two armature current peaks which occur, one at the instant of starting the motor and the other at the moment when the piece enters the roll gap. These must not exceed the maximum permissible current (normally 2–3 times the nominal full-load current). During the final stage in plate rolling a gradual reduction of rolling loads is introduced, bearing in mind that

    (i) small rolling loads result in correspondingly small mill deformations and hence more accurate estimation of the screwdown settings to achieve the correct plate thickness
    (ii) small rolling loads, when applied to plain rolls, result in small plate crown
    (iii) the flatness and rectangularity of the plate is improved by the introduction of gradually decreasing rolling loads.

From the above considerations it follows that a compromise must be reached between the throughput and the high dimensional accuracy of the final plate.

Overall schedule optimization

In the previous section the main factors that constrain the drafting strategy have been noted. With given entry, exit and peak speeds and interpass time, the shortest rolling time consistent with these factors may be achieved by proper selection of the draft on each pass. In a similar fashion these parameters may also be varied in an

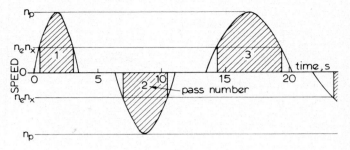

Shaded area shows slab length rolled

2 Parabolic speed pattern, fixed peak speed

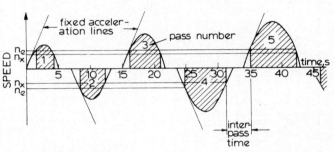

Shaded area shows slab length rolled

3 Parabolic speed pattern, fixed initial acceleration

iterative way and, by suitable permutation, the best values of entry, exit and peak speeds for maximum throughput may be established for the plant/slab/plate data under consideration.

Two approaches to the problem of determining an overall optimum schedule have been attempted. In the first approach a fixed peak speed is maintained throughout any particular schedule, as shown in Fig. 2. A large number of rolling schedules, each with specified entry, exit and peak speeds are calculated according to the optimum drafting strategy already described. The best combination of entry, exit and peak speeds which yields the shortest schedule time is then selected, subject to the motor heating constraint. In the second approach the motor starting current or acceleration is made equal in all passes, as shown in Fig. 3. Here again, the overall optimization is achieved by selecting values of entry and exit speeds and starting current.

Optimization of mill throughput by suitable choice of plate width during a roll campaign

When a variety of plate widths is to be rolled, a conventional 'coffin' sequence of plate widths is usually adopted. It is shown below that such a coffin sequence is in fact the most advantageous for the maximization of mill throughput.

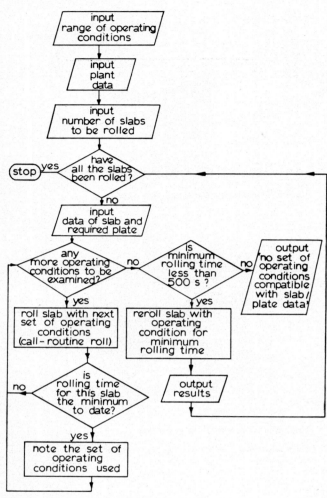

4a   Main program (MARS)

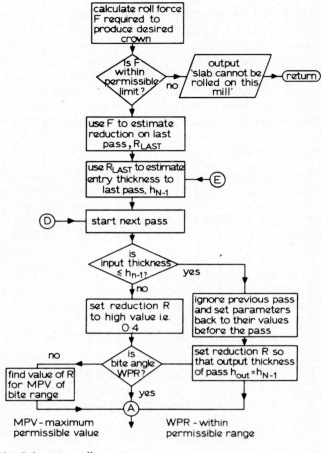

MPV – maximum
permissible value

WPR – within
permissible range

4b   Subroutine roll

FINISHING PASSES

Choice of drafts during finishing passes

The effect of possible inaccuracy in estimation of rolling load and thus in the mill stretch, combined with the requirements for low plate crown and acceptable flatness, makes it necessary for a gradual reduction of rolling loads towards the end of the rolling schedule. In the calculation of optimum rolling schedules the initial drafts are limited by the mill constraints, while the reduction in the final pass is always selected to achieve a rolling load corresponding to the specified plate crown. The reductions for the intermediate passes are then chosen to give a smooth transition between the initial passes and the final pass. This is an iterative calculation involving the last three passes, with provision for the insertion of an extra pass when necessary. The procedure illustrating the method for determining reductions during the finishing passes and the condition of 'smoothness' are shown in the flow diagram in Fig. 4.

Estimation of plate crown

Plate crown is defined as the difference between the thickness of a plate at the centre and at the edges. When the rolls are cylindrical, the roll separating force causes the rolls to flex and gives the crown a positive value

but, when they are convex, the value of the crown could be negative depending on the magnitude of the rolling load. Excessive crown is regarded as an undesirable transverse variation in plate thickness and attempts are made to minimize it. The additional material constituting the crown represents a material loss to the works, since the customer pays for the nominal weight of a plate of uniform thickness. Where plates must be slit and joined, crown leads to problems of matching and, in certain cases, matching cannot be achieved. The crown is a function of rolling load, plate width, and roll camber. In stands fitted with roll bending facilities the crown could be controlled by application of hydraulic pressure to the roll bending jacks. Based on the work listed in Ref. 3, the parameters affecting plate crown have been combined by means of regression analysis into a simple expression of the following form:

$$c = a_0 + (a_1 + a_2\sqrt{w})P + (a_3 + a_4w^{1\cdot25})\gamma_w$$
$$+ \left[a_5 + a_6\left(\frac{w}{\ln_e w/10}\right)^3\right]J_B \qquad . \qquad . \qquad . \quad (1)$$

where

c = plate crown, mm

a_0 to a_6 = coefficient appropriate to a particular rolling stand

P = total rolling load, MN

w = plate width, mm

γ_w = work roll camber, mm

J_B = roll bending jack force, MN

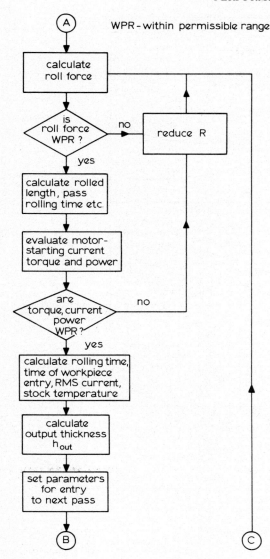

WPR – within permissible range

4c Subroutine roll (cont.)

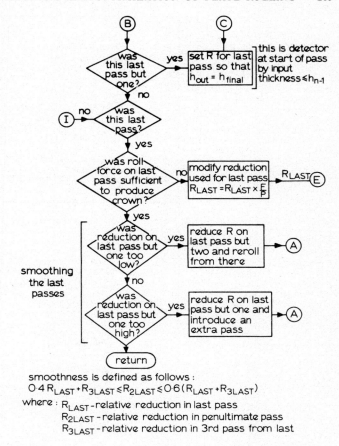

smoothness is defined as follows :
$$0{\cdot}4\,R_{LAST} + R_{3LAST} \leqslant R_{2LAST} \leqslant 0{\cdot}6\,(R_{LAST} + R_{3LAST})$$
where : R_{LAST} – relative reduction in last pass
R_{2LAST} – relative reduction in penultimate pass
R_{3LAST} – relative reduction in 3rd pass from last

4d Subroutine roll (cont.)

Figure 5 shows the relationship between total rolling load and plate width for several different roll cambers. All the curves were calculated for $J_B = O$ and fixed plate crown. It will be seen that, for a fixed value of plate crown, increasing convexity of the rolls implies an increasing rolling load. The rolling load is also a function of plate width. It will be observed that strict control is required to produce a plate to the required specifications. It is interesting to note particular cases where a particular rolling load and roll camber result in producing the same crown for two different plate widths.

Figure 6 shows the latitude of rolling loads as a function of roll camber for the production of a plate with a crown between 0·0625 and 0·125 mm. The diagrams are drawn for five different plate widths. From these diagrams it can be seen that the narrow plate could be rolled to the required crown with convex, cylindrical, or concave rolls: the latitude of rolling load for a wide plate is small and a solution is possible only with the convex rolls.

Combined effect of roll thermal camber and roll wear on plate crown

Let it be assumed that the roll campaign starts with a cold, cylindrical pair of work rolls. The rolling commences and the heat from the rolled stock is gradually absorbed by the work rolls, causing the roll diameter to increase due to thermal expansion. This expansion is greater at the centre of the rolls, since this part of the roll is more frequently in contact with the stock and the bearing ends dissipate the heat faster than the middle part. Hence a nominally cylindrical roll will become convex, i.e. with a positive camber. According to the results of an investigation,[4] the estimated positive camber does not exceed some 0·125 mm (achieved within 3 h after roll change) before it is reduced by roll wear, first to zero and then to some negative value, before the rolls are changed. (It will be appreciated that such idealized uniform roll wear is a convenient approximation.) Assuming that the roll camber first increases and then decreases in a linear fashion, there are two instances during the roll campaign when the rolls are truly cylindrical. To ensure that all plates are rolled with the same specified crown, a rolling load must be used according to the plate width and the instantaneous roll camber. Figures 7a and 7b demonstrate the relationships between rolling load and the described changes of roll camber during a campaign. These relationships have been calculated using Eq. (1) for two typical plate crowns

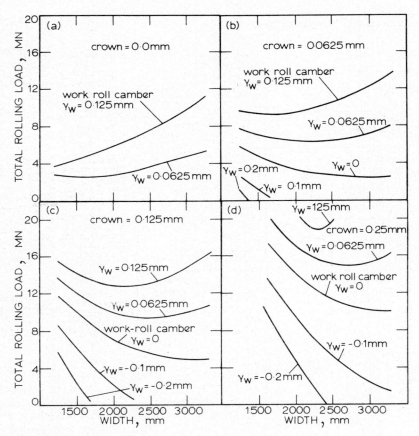

5   *Relationship between total rolling load and plate width*

and five discrete plate widths. It will be seen that, to supress the effect of the prominent positive roll camber to achieve a low plate crown, the rolling load must be correspondingly high. From Figs. 7a and 7b it will be also observed that, while the narrow plate can be rolled throughout the whole roll campaign, the wide plates cannot be rolled with a negative camber.

Relation between plate crown control and mill throughput

In this section it is intended to introduce a new concept which would assist in a rational quantification of mill throughput, particularly while rolling plates of various widths with the specified crown. The low rolling loads required to ensure low plate crown imply a small reduction of plate thickness per pass and so adversely affect mill throughput. The reduction in plate thickness per pass cannot, however, be considered to be fully indicative of the mill throughput. The effective deformation of the workpiece during a rolling pass can be more conveniently expressed as a product of the draft taken and the plate width. This product provides a convenient figure of merit in assessing the effectiveness of rolling. Assuming similar material grade, temperature, and rolling speed, a figure of merit can be derived as follows:

since

$$P = kw\sqrt{(\Delta h)}$$

and

$$M = (\Delta h)w$$

then

$$M = \frac{P^2}{k^2 w} \qquad . \qquad . \qquad . \qquad . \qquad . \qquad . \qquad . \qquad (2)$$

where

P = rolling load, MN
k = coefficient
w = plate width, mm
(Δh) = draft, mm
M = figure of merit, mm^2

For crown control passes the value of rolling load is calculated from Eq. (1) giving

$$M = \left[\frac{c - n_0 - (n_a + a_4 w^{1 \cdot 25}) \gamma_w}{a_1 + a_g \sqrt{w}} \right]^a \frac{1}{k^2 w} \qquad . \qquad . \qquad (3)$$

When plates of various widths are rolled with the objective of achieving the same crown (assuming a constant camber), the figure of merit is highly dependent on plate width. It is evident that a wide plate is more susceptible to crown formation than a narrow one. The figure of merit allows quantitative comparison in the reduction in plate cross-sectional area to be made and thus quantification, at least approximately, of the mill throughput.

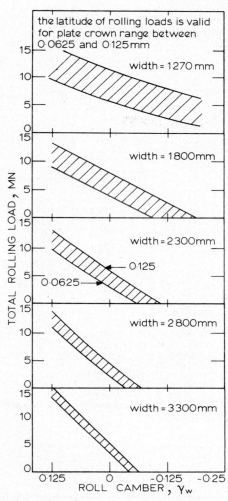

6 *Latitude of rolling loads for specified range of plate crown as a function of roll camber*

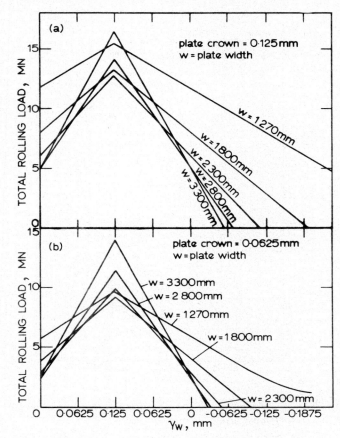

7 *Rolling load variations during a roll campaign to achieve a specified plate crown*

The figure M can be now calculated for any combination of roll camber and plate crown. Figures 8*a*, 8*b*, and 8*c* show the relationship between the figure of merit of mill performance and plate crown calculated for particular plate widths and valid for specified roll cambers. Thus, for example, when the rolls are cylindrical (Figure 8*a*) the figure of merit for 3 300 mm wide plate rolled with 0·125 mm crown is some 12 times lower than the figure for 1 270 mm wide plate. The comparison indicates how much faster the narrow plate could be finished if both widths were made with the identical crown.

Plate width scheduling during a roll campaign

The concept of a figure of merit applicable to rolling a plate to a specified crown has been evolved in the previous section. It has been shown how a quantitative comparison can be made between the rolling of plates of different widths. A plate mill usually has a large range of plate widths to roll and the question arises whether any attempt should be made at width scheduling and, if so, what is the most advantageous sequence of plate widths over a roll campaign. From what has already been described, it is evident that some form of

width scheduling is essential if the objective is to minimize the plate crown and maintain a high mill throughput. To investigate the width scheduling problem three assumptions are made

(i) that in rolling a wide range of plate widths, the changes in work roll camber are taking place as previously described
(ii) that the figure of merit must not be allowed to drop below an accepted value throughout the whole work roll campaign
(iii) that all the plates rolled will have the same crown.

To commence the evaluation, a diagram (Fig. 9) is drawn containing the calculated figures of merit as a function of roll camber and five such curves are shown, each for a particular plate width. All the figures of merit are valid for the same plate crown, i.e. 0·125 mm. Since the figures of merit are highly dependent on rolling load, their peak values correspond to the maximum positive roll camber. Now, a fixed figure of merit is assumed and drawn, so as to embrace all plate widths. It will be noticed that, at the start of the roll campaign, the set figure of merit is exceeded for narrow plates only. For the wider plates the figure at the start of the roll campaign is below this set value. At some positive value of roll camber, the figures of merit for the wider plates attain the set value. By following this graphical procedure a sequence of widths is determined as presented in

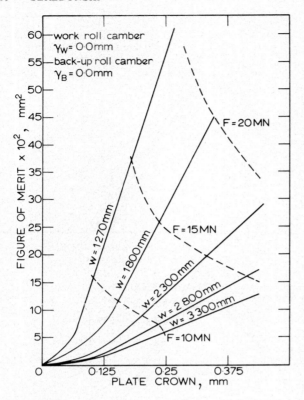

8a   Figure of merit of mill performance as a function of plate crown (plain rolls)

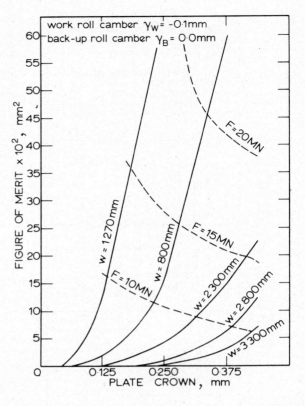

8c   Figure of merit of mill performance as a function of plate crown (concave rolls)

Fig. 10. Referring back to Fig. 9, it is evident that the narrowest plate can be rolled at any time i.e. with up to 0·2 mm negative roll camber. The widest plate must be rolled only when the roll camber is most positive i.e. at least 0·06 mm. Hence, to satisfy the entire consignment of

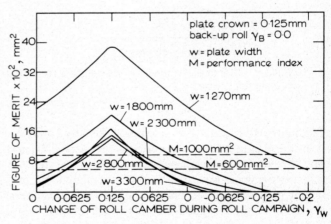

9   Mill performance figure of merit as a function of roll camber during a roll campaign

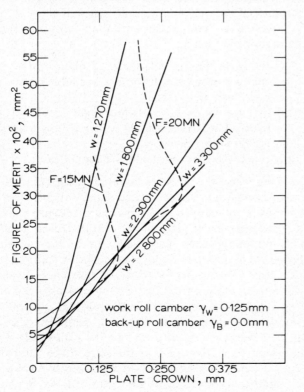

8b   Figure of merit of mill performance as a function of plate crown (convex rolls)

plate widths, the narrowest plate must be rolled at the end of the roll campaign. Figure 10 contains two diagrams to illustrate the situation when the figure of merit is changed. In both cases the classical 'coffin' pattern of widths is evident. A higher figure of merit reduces the effective latitude of the negative roll camber, requiring a camber of $-0·125$ mm instead of $-0·2$ mm at the end of the roll campaign. Application of width scheduling offers three major advantages:

(i) the mill throughput is maximized while the plate crown is kept within a specified tolerance

(ii) the roll campaign might be extended subject to the overall surface quality of the rolls

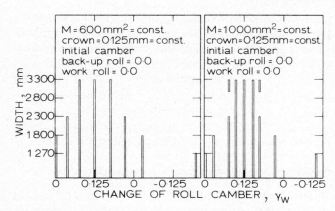

10 *Calculated optimum pattern of plate widths rolled during a roll campaign*

(iii) the 'coffin' pattern of width reduces the possibility of plate surface imperfections, particularly that of 'tramlines'. The 'tramlines' are generated by uneven wear of roll surfaces and are likely to be present on wide plates which are rolled following a consignment of narrow plates.

ELEMENTS OF THE MATHEMATICAL MODEL

The mathematical model combines the equations describing the performance of the various parts of the process, e.g. the main drive, the mill and the slab. Appendix 1 contains the analysis of mill drives. The speed pattern is related to the rolled length of the plate. The heating of the motor is considered during the no-load acceleration and deceleration and also when the deformation of the plate is taking place. The conditions of working within base speed and above, i.e. at field weakening stages, are fully considered. The heating of the motor is calculated for each pass but the overall energy dissipation is referred to the time required for the complete rolling schedule. The calculation of the slab temperature is described in Appendix 3. Since the roll force, torque, and power requirement in a hot rolling process are highly temperature-dependent, accurate estimation of slab temperature is needed to work out these qualities. Two methods have been used. The first is based on the calculation of differences considering unidirectional heat transfer by conduction within the slab and surface radiation, and the second is based on the approximate solution of the Stefan–Boltzmann heat radiation equation. There was no significant difference in the accuracies of these two methods. The estimation of roll force is based on a new method.[5] The roll force is a product of two functions, one describing the geometry of rolling and the other referring to the yield stress of the material. The geometrical function is a simplified version of Sims equations and the yield stress is expressed in algebraic form. The effect of roll flattening on the roll force is considered. The estimation of plate crown is described in the previous paragraph and the estimation of mill stretch is contained in Appendix 4.

DEVELOPMENT OF THE MODEL, ITS VERIFICATION AND SOME OF ITS APPLICATIONS

Systematic investigations into the entire plate rolling process resulted in the establishment of methods for estimation of rolling load, plate cooling, crown control, etc. Each of these methods has been verified statistically by extensive steelworks data trials. The standard deviation of error has been minimized. When it was found necessary, corrections and improvements were implemented. These methods were then incorporated as subroutines into the mathematical model.

Having established these subroutines, the logic of coordination of different calculating procedures was set up, as shown in its most elementary form in the flow diagram in Fig. 4. The computer program, written in FORTRAN IV, consists of modular subroutines to be processed by a 1905 ICL computer. It requires some 12 K core store and takes about 3 min per slab to run. The optimizing procedures described in the earlier paragraphs consist mainly of iterative techniques, since the process is non-linear and discontinuous.

The scope of application of the model is shown in Fig. 11. Given plant and slab data, optimum rolling schedules can be calculated. In its initial applications the model has been extensively used to show how the rolling schedule time is affected by changes in plant operation. Parameters such as motor acceleration, roll gap entry, and exit speeds were deliberately varied in small strips within a wide range. The object of these investigations was to establish whether any general rules could be applied to the flat rolling process. The results of the investigation are described and illustrated. Having established the suitability of the model over a wide range of conditions, the second major stage of model application was directed to a particular wide plate rolling mill.

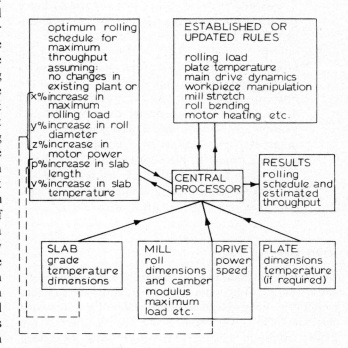

11 *Mathematical model of a plate rolling mill*

In this exercise a comparison was carried out between optimum rolling schedules, generated off-line by the model, and the actual results achieved by highly experienced operators working at their best. The comparision involved a large number of plates and extensive logging. Finished plates were checked for thickness accuracy and plate crown.

PRINCIPAL SCHEDULE VARIABLES

Before discussing the results of computation, the following variables are defined for later use:

(i) schedule time t_s This is the time required to roll a workpiece from some specified initial dimensions to the desired final product. It includes both the rolling time and the time during which the workpiece is outside the roll gap between successive passes

(ii) heating factor   This is defined as the ratio of I_{RMS}/I_{NOM}, where I_{RMS} is motor RMS current calculated over the schedule time and I_{NOM} is the nominal rated motor current. To avoid overheating of the motor the heating factor should not exceed unity, calculated over the complete rolling schedule

(iii) entry speed ratio, exit speed ratio, and peak speed   Entry speed ratio is defined as the ratio of the roll speed at the instant of piece entry into the roll gap to motor base speed. Similarly, exit speed ratio is the ratio of roll speed at the instant of piece exit from the roll gap to the motor base speed. The peak speed ratio is the ratio of peak roll speed during a pass to the motor base speed

(iv) starting current or acceleration ratio m This is defined as the ratio of the current required to overcome the friction and to accelerate the motor from stop, to the nominal motor current. Since the friction current is relatively constant, m can be taken as a measure of acceleration

(v) inter-pass time t_i This is defined as the time interval between the exit of the workpiece and its re-entry into the roll gap. During this interval the operator slows down and reverses the main mill drive, adjusts the roll gap for the next pass and manipulates the workpiece. The duration of the inter-pass time depends on a number of factors such as turning the plate for broad-side passes or squaring a short piece before re-entry into the roll gap. In the present investigations a constant inter-pass time has been arbitrarily selected.

RESULTS

The model has been used to assess the performance of a plate rolling plant under various rolling practices and conditions and also to determine the conditions for most efficient rolling. To demonstrate the validity of the model, optimum schedules for several slabs have been derived and the effects of various parameters on through-

put have been examined. It is important to state that the figures quoted, and the comparisons presented of various parameters and their effect on the rolling schedule, refer to a particular rolling plant and to particular slab and plate combinations. It is not the object of this paper to derive general rules which would be valid for any combination of plant, slab and product, although it is intended to provide guidelines for assessing the relative merits of different rolling practices.

Minimum schedule time and heating considerations

In this section the effect on the schedule time and heating factor of peak rolling speed (in the first optimization approach) and of acceleration (in the second optimization approach) will be discussed.

FIXED PEAK ROLLING SPEED

It may be thought that the shortest schedule time is obtained when the rolling speed is as high as possible. This is not, however, necessarily true for an optimum rolling strategy, because the roll force and the current both increase with speed. Consequently, at higher speeds, a lighter reduction has to be taken to maintain these parameters within permissible limits. The consequence of lighter reduction is an increase in the number of passes and the schedule time. This argument suggests that there exist rolling speeds at which the total rolling time is minimal. Evidence of this is shown in Fig. 12. On the same figure the heating factor is plotted. There are two boundaries on the figure which should not be transgressed. The horizontal hatched line is the limit beyond which the motor temperature rise is in excess of the safe

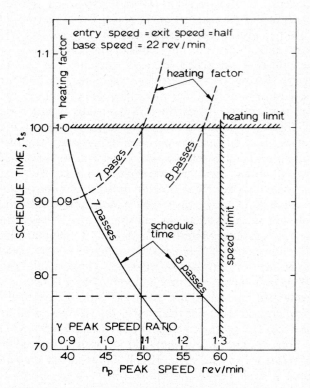

12   Variation of schedule time and heating factor with peak speed ratio for slab no. 1

value. The vertical hatched line indicates the maximum permissible speed. Beyond this, the starting current is excessive (i.e. over 2·5 times the nominal motor current).

Figure 12 shows the inherent discontinuity of the process. When the rolling speed is increased from 49 to 50 rpm an abrupt change in the schedule time occurs, due to the increase in the number of passes from seven to eight. It is also interesting to note that the slab under consideration may be rolled to the desired plate in the same minimum schedule time of 78·5 s in seven or eight passes.

FIXED MOTOR STARTING CURRENT

Figure 13 shows the variation of the schedule time with m, the ratio of starting current to nominal motor current. It should be noted that higher starting current corresponds to higher acceleration of the drive. It can be seen that, at particular values of m, the schedule time assumes a minimum value. Here again, discontinuity occurs when the number of passes is changed. The minimum schedule time is 71·5 s as compared with 78·5 s when rolling is performed with constant peak speed. In general, fixed starting current is more readily achieved in practice than fixed peak rolling speed and, in addition, results in a shorter schedule time. In the sections that follow, the fixed starting current approach is subjected to further investigations.

Effect of inter-pass time

It is generally thought that a reversing mill will be working at its maximum throughput when the workpiece is out of the mill for the shortest possible time between the passes. It should be noted, however, that a reduction in the schedule time corresponds to an increase in RMS current and the heating problem may be serious as a result. This means that, to avoid an excessive temperature rise, a smaller draft has to be taken which might correspond to a longer schedule time. Thus, save for the situation where the drive is under-run, the reduction in

inter-pass time does not necessarily correspond to appreciable increase in throughput.

Effect of slab size on throughput

The problem of optimum selection of slab size for maximum mill throughput is of importance, especially for schedules that include broadsiding passes. A plate of specified length, width, and thickness may be produced from variously sized ingots, all with the same specified weight. The slab size will be selected to be comparable with the reheating facilities and at the same time to provide the shortest schedule time. To illustrate this point let it be assumed that a slab of 3·75 tons weight is to be rolled to a plate of 152 cm width and 1·9 cm thickness. Figure 14 shows how the slab thickness and length affect the throughput. It should be noted that the mill under consideration is a universal mill and that the throughput figures refer to the actual rolling time and do not include down time.

Effect of rolling parameters on throughput

The proper selection of the three rolling parameters, i.e. entry and exit speeds and acceleration ratios (or peak speed ratio), is of considerable importance, since the schedule time varies appreciably with these parameters. In Fig. 15 the schedule time is plotted for a range of entry and exit speeds and acceleration ratios. The vertical lines indicate the variation of schedule time for a specified acceleration ratio when the ranges of entry and exit speed ratios $0.25 \leqslant \alpha \leqslant 0.75$, $0.25 \leqslant \beta \leqslant 0.75$ are covered. It can be seen that, for moderate values of acceleration ratio, the schedule time does not vary appreciably with changes in α and β, while at low or high values of m the schedule time is sensitive to the entry and exit speeds. This fact can also be seen in Fig. 16. In this graph the schedule time is plotted against entry speed ratio for an exit speed ratio of 0·75 and for two values of acceleration ratio. It can be seen that the schedule time changes by 40 s (i.e. from 123 to 83 s) for a change of 0·5 in entry

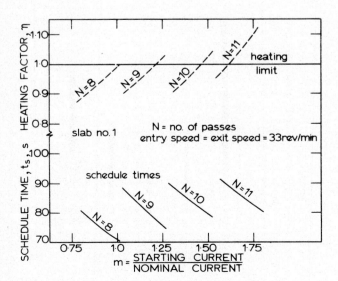

13 *Schedule time and heating factor as a function of motor starting current*

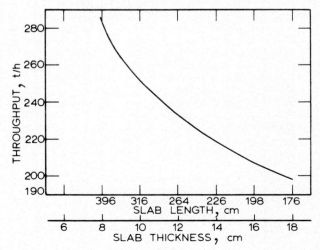

Calculated for a constant slab weight 3·7 t, plate size 1660 × 152 × 1·9 cm

14 *Effect of slab length and thickness on mill throughput*

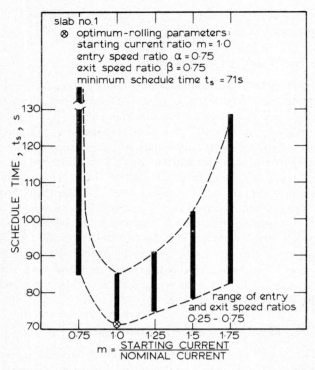

15   Variations of schedule time with entry and exit speed and starting current for slab No. 1

entry speed is always advantageous. In an attempt to verify whether the optimum rolling parameters for maximum throughput remain reasonably constant for a variety of products, three slabs which were thought to cover the common practical sizes were examined. The variation of schedule time with rolling parameters is plotted in Figs. 15, 17, and 18. It will be observed that the optimum value of acceleration ratio in all cases is $m - 1·0$. This indicates that it is advantageous to allocate a torque (or current) equal to nominal motor torque (or current) to overcome friction and to accelerate the drive from stop. It has also been found that the optimum entry and exit speeds lie between $\frac{1}{2}$ to $\frac{3}{4}$ of base speed for the slabs under consideration. In a similar way the optimum values of rolling parameters for any particular mill may be determined for a range of products commonly rolled by that mill.

Comparison between the optimized rolling schedules and the best present steelworks practice

A set of data concerning the production of a large number of plates was recorded. Rolling loads, pass temperature, screwdown setting, rolling speed, etc. were recorded for each rolling pass. When the plates were cold the thickness across the plate edges and across their widths were repetitively measured and recorded. Following correction for thermal expansion, the formulae representing the relationships between plant and process parameters were verified. Using very conservative plant parameters and the initial and final dimensions of the plate, the optimum rolling conditions were calculated.

speed ratio, when $m = 1·75$. However, for the same range of α, the schedule time changes by only 5 s when $m = 1·0$. Thus, provided that acceleration ratio m is properly selected, a tight control of entry and exit speeds is not necessary.

Figure 16 also shows that the schedule time t_s decreases with entry speed for a fixed value of exit speed. However, as shown in the following example, the best combination of entry and exit speeds for shortest schedule time does not necessarily mean that the highest possible

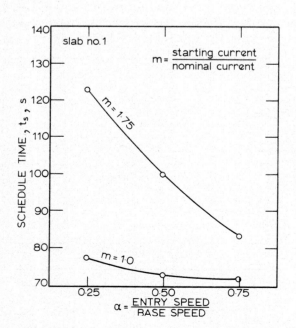

16   Variations of schedule time with entry speed ratio for a fixed exit speed ratio $\beta = 0·75$

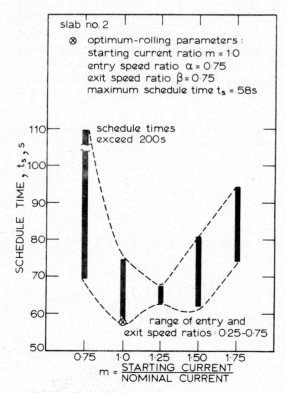

17   Variations of schedule time with entry and exit speeds and starting current ratio for slab no. 2

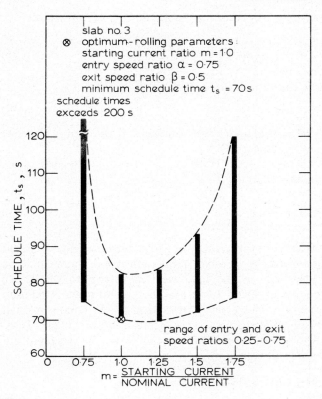

18   Variation of schedule time with entry and exit speeds and starting current ratio for slab no. 3

To make the comparison realistic the values of inter-pass manipulation time and hand plate gauging time were assumed to be the same as in present practice. The results showed that, on average, the throughput would be increased by some 17%. The actual variation in plate rolling time ranged from 45% above to 22% below the optimum scheduled time. When the operator time was lower than the calculated value, investigations showed that some rolling constraint had been transgressed.

CONCLUSIONS

An analytical representation of the hot reversing rolling process, based on a study of the behaviour of the plant and the method by which the rolling is performed, has been described in this paper. A slab may be rolled to the desired finished product in a large number of ways. Many of these, however, may result in excessive mill loading, motor heating, unsatisfactory crown, and gauge of the product, or long schedule time. It has been shown that, with the aid of the model described, optimum methods of rolling can be devised so that all the plant constraints and limitations are satisfied, satisfactory quality of the product is ensured and, at the same time, the throughput is maximized. To demonstrate these aspects, several examples of optimum rolling schedules have been presented.

Since the hot reversing rolling process involves a number of non-linear, discontinuous, and interdependent parameters, general rules for 'best' rolling practice applicable to all plant/slab/plate combinations cannot be established. It has been shown, however, that for any particular plant optimum values of rolling parameters such as speed, acceleration, etc. may be determined for a range of products commonly rolled by that plant. Application of the described model to a particular problem required modification according to the type of rolling involved. The present model is applicable to a single-stand plate mill. For multi-stand mills the analysis for optimum working has yet to be developed. The computer program containing the mathematical model has been assembled in modular form, however, thus providing a high degree of flexibility and permitting such changes to be made with ease.

An important stage in plate rolling, consisting of plate finishing passes, has been investigated to arrive at the desired dimensional accuracy. The relationships between screwdown setting, plate crown, rolling load, roll camber, and plate width have been included to form another module of the mathematical model. It has been shown that the plate crown could be satisfactorily controlled without additional equipment such as roll bending jacks, solely by the use of appropriate rolling schedules. Roll bending jacks, however, give far greater flexibility of operation.

The concept of a mill performance index has been introduced and applied to study the effect of plate crown control on mill throughput. The diagrams illustrating this relationship allow a compromise to be chosen between high throughput and low plate crown. The significance of width scheduling has been elaborated and it has been shown that the conventional 'coffin' pattern of width scheduling is scientifically justified. In addition to its use for the generation of optimum drafting schedules, the model can be used for evaluation and indication of the potentialities of the rolling plant. It can be used to assist mill managers to assess potential plant performance in finding, according to market requirements, a compromise between high throughput and high dimensional accuracy of the plate. For example, it can be used to assess the effects of improvements in plant design on the final product. The mathematical model is eminently suitable for such assessment and calculates, for any particular mill configuration, the minimum number of passes as a function of initial slab size, temperature, and final plate dimension. Alternatively, the model will determine the necessary dimensions of the slab/plate prior to rolling in the finishing stand, to satisfy particular rolling requirements such as finishing plate temperature. Although the present form of the model makes it unsuitable for on-line use, it could form the base for an on-line application.

ACKNOWLEDGMENTS

The author is indebted to his colleagues in General Steels Division and in the Corporate Laboratories for providing and processing large volumes of rolling data.

REFERENCES

1 B. V. KORTZFLEISH: *Stahl Eisen*, 1967, **87** (8)
2 Z. WUSATOWSKI: 'Fundamentals of rolling'; 1969, Oxford, Pergamon
3 K. N. SHOHET AND N. A. TOWNSEND: *JISI*, 1968, **206** (11), 1 088
4 H. TAKANO *et al.*: 'Computer control of a plate mill', AISE Spring Conference, Philadelphia, 1967
5 M. TAROKH AND F. SEREDYNSKI: *JISI*, 1970, **208** (7), 695
6 T. J. TOU: 'Modern control theory', 1965, McGraw Hill
7 J. C. JAEGER: *Proc. Camb. Phil. Soc.*, 1950, **46**, 4
8 E. DOWNS *et al.*: 'Plate mill automation', Bisra Automation Conference, Scarborough 1963
9 F. X. MACEDO AND F. SEREDYNSKI: *J. Inst. Measurement and Control*, 1971, **4**, T117

APPENDIX 1

Mathematical analysis of mill drives

In this appendix the speed pattern for optimum performance of the main drive is derived and a mathematical model of the mill/drive, based on the optimum speed pattern, is developed.

OPTIMUM SPEED PATTERN

The power of main drives is limited mainly by the heat generated in the armature circuit. It is desired to establish the motor speed equation such that a specified slab length is rolled in the least possible time and the heat developed in the armature of the drive is minimum. The armature current is:

$$I = \frac{\pi J}{30e} \cdot \frac{dn}{dt} + I_L \quad . \qquad . \qquad . \qquad . \qquad (1)$$

where the first term represents the current required for acceleration or deceleration and the second term, I_L, is the load current. I_L is equal to friction current when the slab is outside the roll gap and is equal to the sum of friction and deformation currents when the material is being rolled. The rolled length is:

$$l = \frac{\pi D}{60} \int_{t_e}^{t_x} n \, dt \quad . \qquad . \qquad . \qquad . \qquad (2)$$

and the heat generated is:

$$= k \int_{t_e}^{t_x} R I^2 \, dt$$

$$= kR \int_{t_e}^{t_x} \left(\frac{\pi J}{30e} \cdot \frac{dn}{dt} + t_L \right)^2 dt \quad . \qquad . \qquad . \qquad (3)$$

The problem stated above can be solved by classical methods of optimal theory, such as Calculus of Variations. The optimal speed equation is the solution to the Euler–Lagrange partial differential equation:[6]

$$\frac{\partial F}{\partial n} - \frac{d}{dt}\left(\frac{\partial F}{\partial \dot{n}}\right) = 0 \quad . \qquad . \qquad . \qquad . \qquad . \qquad (4)$$

Where the function F is the weighted sum of integrands (2) and (3), i.e.

$$F = \left(\frac{\pi J}{30e} \frac{dn}{dt} + I_L \right)^2 + \lambda n \quad . \qquad . \qquad . \qquad (5)$$

where λ is a constant. Substituting (5) in (4) we get

$$\lambda - 2\left(\frac{\pi J}{30e} \right)^2 \cdot \frac{d^2 n}{dt^2} = 0 \quad . \qquad . \qquad . \qquad . \qquad (6)$$

the solution to (6) is of the form:

$$n = at^2 + bt + c \quad . \qquad . \qquad . \qquad . \qquad . \qquad (7)$$

where a, b, and c are constants. If the motor starts at $t = 0$, then $c = 0$.
Assuming motor stops at $t = 2\tau$ and has its peak speed equal to n_p, then (7) is

$$n = \frac{2n_p}{\tau}\left(t - \frac{t^2}{2\tau} \right) \quad . \qquad . \qquad . \qquad . \qquad (8)$$

If the speed varies according to (8) then the heat developed for rolling a specified slab length is minimum. In some cases (e.g. in the field weakening region) the above parabolic speed pattern is not an absolute optimum solution. However, optimization for all conditions will result in speed patterns which are impracticable. Thus, throughout the analysis which follows, the speed pattern of (8) will be assumed.

ROLLED LENGTH

The rolled length is given by Eq. (2). Substituting (8) into (2) we get

$$l = \frac{\pi D n_p}{60\tau} \int_{t_e}^{t_x} \left(t - \frac{t^2}{2\tau} \right) dt$$

$$= \frac{\pi D n_p}{60\tau}\left[(t_x^2 - t_e^2) - \frac{1}{3\tau}(t_x^3 - t_e^3) \right] \quad . \qquad . \qquad (9)$$

Referring to Fig. A1, entry and exit speeds are specified and t_e and t_x have to be found in terms of these. From (8):

$$t_e = a\tau \quad \text{and} \quad t_x = b\tau$$

where

$$a = 1 - \sqrt{1 - \frac{n_e}{n_p}} \quad . \qquad . \qquad . \qquad . \qquad (10)$$

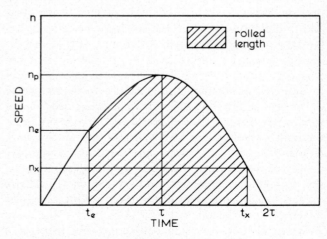

A1   Parabolic speed pattern

and

$$b = 1 + \sqrt{1 - \frac{n_x}{n_p}}$$

Once n_e, n_x, n_p, D and the length to be rolled are specified τ can be found from (9) and (11).

$$\tau = \frac{60l}{\pi D n_p}[(b^2 - a^2) - \tfrac{1}{3}(b^3 - a^3)]^{-1} \quad . \quad . \quad (11)$$

The pass rolling time is: $t_p = (t_x - t_e) + t_i$. However, the parabolic speed pattern requires that if t_e, found from the above equation, is less than 2τ then it is set to 2τ, i.e.

$$(t_p)_{min} = 2\tau$$

The schedule time is:

$$t_s = \sum_{j=1}^{N} (t_p)_j \quad . \quad . \quad . \quad . \quad . \quad (12)$$

MOTOR CURRENT EQUATIONS

The motor current consists of three main components, namely friction current, acceleration or deceleration current, and deformation current. The latter is present only during the interval between the piece entry and exit from the roll gap. Three important cases will be dealt with as follows:

Case 1 *Rolling below or at base speed*
The torque G in this case does not vary with the speed. The dynamic current can be found from the speed by the following equations:

$$G = eI_A \quad . \quad . \quad . \quad . \quad . \quad . \quad (13)$$

$$= \frac{J\pi}{30} \cdot \frac{dn}{dt} \quad . \quad . \quad . \quad . \quad . \quad (14)$$

$$I_A = \frac{\pi J}{30e} \cdot \frac{dn}{dt} \quad . \quad . \quad . \quad . \quad (15)$$

or substituting n from (8) into (15)

$$I_A = I_0\left(1 - \frac{t}{\tau}\right) \quad . \quad . \quad . \quad . \quad (16)$$

where

$$I_0 = \frac{J\pi n_p}{15e\tau} \quad . \quad . \quad . \quad . \quad . \quad (17)$$

The three components and the resultant currents are shown in Fig. A2. Three regions or states can be distinguished as follows:

(i) state 1 Motor accelerates from zero speed to entry speed. The armature current consists of two components in this state, friction and dynamic currents

$$I_1 = I_F + I_0\left(1 - \frac{t}{\tau}\right) \quad 0 \leqslant t \leqslant t_e \quad . \quad (18)$$

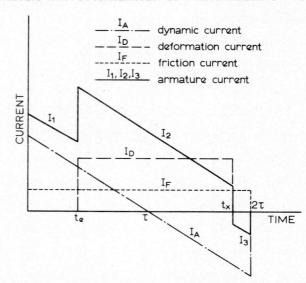

A2 *Current components and resultant current when rolling at a speed below base speed*

The maximum current in this state which is the motor starting current is

$$I_{1max} = I_s = I_F + I_0 \quad . \quad . \quad . \quad (19)$$

(ii) state 2 The workpiece enters roll gap and deformation takes place. The current in this state is

$$I_2 = I_F + I_D + I_0\left(1 - \frac{t}{\tau}\right) \quad t_e \leqslant t \leqslant t_x \quad (20)$$

The maximum current which occurs at the instant of piece entry into the roll gap is

$$I_{2max} = I_F + I_D + I_0\left(1 - \frac{t_e}{\tau}\right) \quad . \quad . \quad (21)$$

(iii) state 3 The workpiece exits from the roll gap and motor decelerates until it stops. The current is now

$$I_3 = I_F + I_0\left(1 - \frac{t}{\tau}\right) \quad t_x \leqslant t \leqslant 2\tau \quad . \quad (22)$$

The maximum current is at the instant when the motor stops, i.e. at $t = 2\tau$

$$I_{3max} = I_F - I_0 \quad . \quad . \quad . \quad . \quad (23)$$

Case 2 *Rolling above base speed*
The torque drops with speed in accordance with the equation

$$G^1 = G\frac{n_b}{n} \quad . \quad . \quad . \quad . \quad . \quad (24)$$

Assuming that the entry and exit speeds are not greater than the base speed, the weak field is entered and is left at some interval in state 2 as shown in Fig. A3. The times at which this happens can be found from Eq. (8):

$$t_1 = \tau\left(1 - \sqrt{1 - \frac{n_b}{n_p}}\right) \quad . \quad . \quad . \quad (25)$$

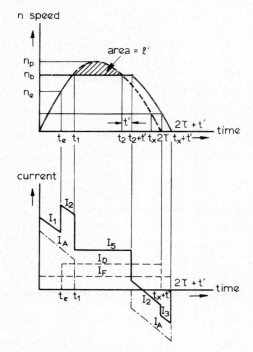

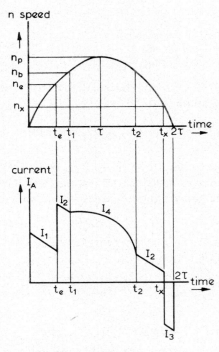

A3   Rolling at base speed   *A4   Operation in field weakening region*

$$t_2 = \tau\left(1 + \sqrt{1 - \frac{n_b}{n_p}}\right) \qquad . \qquad . \qquad . \qquad . \qquad . \qquad (26)$$

(iv) state 4   This is defined for the time interval $(t_2 - t_1)$. The current in this state is related to the current in state 2 by

$$I_4 = I_2\frac{n}{n_b} \qquad . \qquad . \qquad . \qquad . \qquad . \qquad (27)$$

when I_4 and n are substituted from (20) and (8) into (27) the result is

$$I_4 = \frac{15eI_0}{J\pi\tau^3 n_b}[I_0 t^3 - \tau(2I_0 + I_R)t^2 + 2\tau^2 I_R t] \tag{28}$$

where

$$I_R = I_0 + I_D + I_F$$

The current equations in state 1, 2, and 3 in this case are as in the Case 1. However, in this case the time interval $t_e \leqslant t \leqslant t_x$ of Eq. (20) is modified to $t_e \leqslant t \leqslant t_1$ and $t_2 \leqslant t \leqslant t_x$ (see Fig. A4).

OPERATION WITH FIXED STARTING CURRENT

If instead of the peak speed the starting current is fixed for each pass of the schedule the rolling time may be calculated as follows: The starting current is given by (19)

$$I_s = I_F + \frac{J\pi n_p}{15e\tau} \qquad . \qquad . \qquad . \qquad . \qquad (29)$$

Let us define

$$m = \frac{I_s}{I_{NOM}} \qquad . \qquad . \qquad . \qquad . \qquad . \qquad . \qquad (30)$$

Substituting (30) in (29) gives

$$\tau = \frac{cn_p}{m - m_F} \qquad . \qquad . \qquad . \qquad . \qquad . \qquad (31)$$

where

$$c = \frac{J\pi}{15eI_{NOM}} \quad \text{and} \quad m_F = \frac{I_F}{I_{NOM}}$$

The rolled length given by (9) in terms of m is

$$l = \frac{\pi D}{60}\frac{m - m_F}{c}[(t_x^2 - t_e^2) - \tfrac{1}{3}\tau(t_x^3 - t_e^3)] \quad . \qquad . \qquad (32)$$

t_e and t_x are given in (10). Substituting τ from (31) in (10) results in

$$a = \frac{cn_p}{m - m_F}\left[1 - \sqrt{1 - \frac{n_e}{n_p}}\right] \qquad . \qquad . \qquad . \qquad (33)$$

$$b = \frac{cn_p}{m - m_F}\left[1 + \sqrt{1 - \frac{n_x}{n_p}}\right]$$

The only unknown is (32) and (33) is peak speed n_p which is found by a suitable iterative method. Once n_p is determined the problem reduces to that already described and the analysis given remains valid for both fixed peak speed and fixed starting current.

Heating considerations and utilization of the motor

The ratio of RMS current required to complete a rolling schedule to the nominal motor current provides information regarding the heating and utilization of the drive. The value of RMS current for a multipass operation can be found from the following equation:

$$I_{RMS} = \sqrt{\frac{\sum_{i=1}^{N}(X_j + Y_j + Z_j)}{\sum_{j=1}^{N}(t_p)_j}} \qquad . \qquad . \qquad . \qquad (34)$$

where

X_j = integral of square current in jth pass during time interval from motor starting to the instant of piece entry into roll gap

Y_j = the same as X_j but during the interval when material is being rolled

Z_j = the same as X_j but during the interval between the time when piece exits and the instant when motor stops.

Now

$$X_j = \int_0^{t_e} I_1^2(t)\, dt \qquad . \qquad . \qquad . \qquad . \qquad (35)$$

Substituting (18) into (35) and integrating gives

$$X_j = I_s^2 t_e^2 - I_0 I_s \frac{t_e^2}{\tau} + I_0^2 \frac{t_e^3}{3\tau^2}$$

and

$$Z_j = \int_{t_x}^{2\tau} I_3^2(t)\, dt$$

where

$I_3(t)$ is given by (22).

$$Z_j = I_s^2(2\tau - t_x) - \frac{I_0 I_s}{\tau}(4\tau^2 - t_x^2) + \frac{I_0^2}{3\tau^2}(8\tau^3 - t_x^3)$$

The value of Y_j is different for each of the previously mentioned three cases. For Case 1, the current equation in this case is given by (20)

$$Y_j = \int_{t_e}^{t_x} I_2^2(t)\, dt$$

$$= I_R^2(t_x - t_e) + \frac{I_0 I_R}{\tau}(t_x^2 - t_e^2) + \frac{I_0^2}{3\tau^2}(t_x^3 - t_e^3)$$

For Case 2, the value of Y_j in this case is (*see* Fig. A4)

$$Y_j = \int_{t_e}^{t_1} I_2^2(t)\, dt + \int_{t_1}^{t_2} I_4^2(t)\, dt + \int_{t_2}^{t_x} I_2^2(t)\, dt$$

The sum of first and third integrals is

$$\sigma = \int_{t_e}^{t_x} I_2^2(t)\, dt + \int_{t_2}^{t_1} I_2^2(t)\, dt$$

$$= I_R^2[(t_1 + t_x) - (t_2 + t_x)]$$

$$- \frac{I_0 I_R}{\tau}[(t_1^2 + t_x^2) - (t_2^2 + t_e^2)]$$

$$+ \frac{I_0^2}{3\tau^2}[(t_2^3 + t_x^3) - (t_2^3 + t_e^3)]$$

The second integral after evaluation is

$$\int_{t_1}^{t_2} I_4^2(t)\, dt = \left(\frac{15 e I_0}{J \pi n_b}\right)^2 \left[\frac{I_0^2}{7} \cdot \frac{(t_2^7 - t_1^7)}{\tau^6} - \frac{(2I_0 + I_R)I_0}{3}\right.$$

$$\times \frac{(t_2^6 - t_1^6)}{\tau^5} + (4I_0 I_R + (2I_0 + I_R)^2) \times \frac{(t_2^5 - t_1^5)}{\tau^4}$$

$$- I_R(2I_0 + I_R) \cdot \frac{(t_2^4 - t_1^4)}{\tau^3}$$

$$\left. + \frac{4}{3} I_R^2 \cdot \frac{(t_2^3 - t_1^3)}{\tau^2}\right]$$

where

$$I_R = I_0 + I_D + I_F$$

Thus, having calculated X_j, Y_j, and Z_j, the value of RMS current may be found from (34) and the heating factor η is then determined:

$$\eta = \frac{I_{RMS}}{I_{NOM}}$$

APPENDIX 2

The maximum permissible bite angle is a function of roll velocity at the entry of the workpiece into the roll gap. This angle has been determined experimentally and is plotted in Fig. A5 in three straight line segments. Referring to the figure one can write

$$\theta = 25 \cdot 5 - 2\, VE \qquad \text{for } V_E < 1 \cdot 5\, \text{m/s}$$

$$\theta = 32 \cdot 6 - 6 \cdot 75 VE \quad \text{for } 3 \cdot 6 > V_E > 1 \cdot 5\, \text{m/s}$$

$$\theta = 8° \qquad\qquad\quad \text{for } v > 3 \cdot 6\, \text{m/s}$$

where

$$V_E = \frac{\pi D n_e}{60}$$

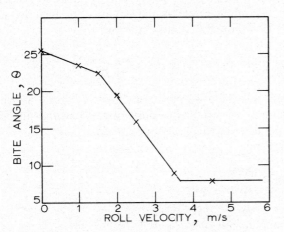

A5 Variation of bite angle with linear velocity of rolls at the instant of workpiece entry

Thermal properties of steel

In the numerical calculation references are made to the following functions:

EMISSIVITY

The emissivity may vary greatly depending upon such factors as the amount of scale present on the surface. The true value of emissivity is often modified to include the effect of other heat losses, particularly when these losses are not separately estimated. The emissivity of hot plate as a function of temperature can be expressed by the following equation:

$$E = \frac{T - 273\cdot15}{1\,000}\left(0\cdot12491\frac{T - 273\cdot15}{1\,000} - 0\cdot38012\right)$$
$$+ 1\cdot0948$$

DIFFUSIVITY

Although the steel most commonly used in plate rolling is BS15, the thermal data for this steel are not readily available. However, such data have been compiled for En 3 (1), a similar steel with somewhat higher carbon content. The diffusivity is approximated by two straight lines:

for the temperatures below 875°C and above 700°C

$$K = 0\cdot15\,.\,10^{-7}(T - 273\cdot15) - 0\cdot07825\,.\,10^{-4}$$

and for the temperatures above 875°C

$$K = 0\cdot02667\,.\,10^{-7}(T - 273\cdot15) + 0\cdot02966\,.\,10^{-4}$$

where

  T the absolute plate temperature (K)
  K thermal diffusivity (m² s⁻¹)

CONDUCTIVITY

In the same manner as diffusivity, the thermal conductivity of En 3 is approximated by two straight lines: for the temperatures below 1 083 K (810°C)

$$k = -58\cdot6\,.\,10^{-3}(T - 273\cdot15) + 72\cdot5$$

and for the temperatures above 810°C

$$k = 10\cdot75\,.\,10^{-3}(T - 273\cdot15) + 16\cdot8\,(Jm^{-1}\,K^{-1}\,s^{-1})$$

where T is the absolute plate temperature (K). The numerical solution of heat flow as applied in predicting the temperature drop of plate during rolling is rather involved, although it is useful when the temperature gradient inside the plate has to be known. For the thin plate such as is rolled by the plate finishing stand, a simpler and faster method as described in Appendix 3b is preferable.

APPENDIX 3a

Numerical solution of the partial differential equation

The temperature drop of the plate is a function of heat losses which in turn depend on the heat conduction within the plate. Since the length and the width of the plate are very large with respect to its thickness, it can be assumed that the heat flow takes place between the flat surfaces only. In circumstances where unidimensional flow takes place the conduction could be expressed by the following equation:

$$\frac{\partial^2 T}{\partial x^2} = \frac{1}{K}\frac{\partial T}{\partial t} \qquad . \qquad . \qquad . \qquad . \qquad . \qquad . \quad (1)$$

At the surfaces of the plate the heat radiation follows the Stefan–Boltzmann equations:

$$k\frac{\partial T}{\partial x} - ES(T^4 - T_a^4) \qquad . \qquad . \qquad . \qquad . \quad (2)$$

where

  T absolute temperature of the plate, K
  T_a ambient absolute temperature, K
  x the distance, m
  K thermal diffusivity, m² s⁻¹
  t time, s
  E emissivity factor
  S Stefan–Boltzmann constant, 5·66 10⁻⁸ Jm⁻² s⁻¹ K⁻⁴
  k conductivity, Jm⁻¹ K⁻¹ s⁻¹

The solution of Eq. (1), particularly when the initial temperature distribution is given, is achieved by using a numerical method proposed by Jaegar.[7] This method is based on the calculation of differences. On substitution of infinitely small changes ∂T, ∂x, etc. in the heat conduction Eq. (1) by the finite values ΔT, Δx, etc. the equation becomes:

$$\frac{\Delta T(x = \text{const})}{\Delta t} = K\frac{\Delta^2 T(t = \text{const})}{\Delta x^2} \qquad . \qquad . \qquad . \quad (3)$$

To solve this equation it is necessary to assume that the plate is divided into a number of imaginary slices each Δx thick and also that the test time interval is divided into small increments Δt. The heat transfer takes place between the slices and, from the heat balance, the temperature of each slice can be calculated. From the temperature gradient the effective plate temperature is then evaluated. The heat flow into node (i) from the adjacent nodes (i − 1) and (i + 1) is equal to the heat stored at node (i). Thus the equation of heat balance leads to a finite difference equation:

$$\frac{K}{(\Delta x)^2}[T_{(i+1)} - 2T_{(i)} + T_{(i-1)}] = \frac{1}{\Delta t}(T_{(i)}^1 - T_{(i)}) \quad . \quad (4)$$

where T_i is the absolute temperature of slice i at time t (assumed constant over slice) and T_i^1 is the absolute temperature of slice i at time $t + \Delta t$

  Writing

$$M = \frac{(\Delta x)^2}{K\Delta t} \qquad . \qquad . \qquad . \qquad . \qquad . \quad (5)$$

$$T_{(i)}^1 = \frac{1}{M}[T_{(i+1)} + T_{(i-1)} + T_i(M - 2)] \qquad . \qquad . \quad (6)$$

The value of M must be selected in such a manner as to

ensure the stability of solution. At the surface of the plate the radiation takes place. The surface temperature is calculated from the combined Eqs. (2) and (4):

$$\frac{k\Delta x}{2K\Delta t}(T_b^1 - T_b) = \frac{k}{\Delta x}(T_{b-1} - T_b) - ES(T_b^4 - T_a^4)$$

where T_b is the temperature of the boundary node at the time t and T_b^1 is the temperature of the boundary node at the time $t + \Delta t$.

APPENDIX 3b

Approximate method of calculation of plate temperature drop

The solution of the Stefan–Boltzmann equations pertaining to plate cooling

$$\frac{dT}{dt} = -\frac{2AES}{\sigma V\rho}(T^4 - T_a^4) \qquad . \qquad . \qquad . \qquad (7)$$

can be simplified subject to three conditions:

  (i) $T \gg T_a$ (ambient temperature neglected)
  (ii) $w \gg h$ and $l \gg h$ (geometrical representation of a plate)
  (iii) Δt, the finite time interval, must not be too large

where w, l, and h are the width, length, and thickness of the plate respectively. A finite difference approximation to dT/dt can be written into Eq. (7)

$$\Delta T = -\frac{2SE}{\rho\sigma h}T^4 \Delta t \qquad . \qquad . \qquad . \qquad (8)$$

If the initial temperature is T_0 the new temperature T can be calculated from

$$T = T_0 + \Delta T \qquad . \qquad . \qquad . \qquad (9)$$

Alternatively, solving Eq. (8) analytically:

$$\int dt = -\frac{\rho\sigma h}{2SE}\int \frac{dT}{T^4} \qquad . \qquad . \qquad . \qquad (10)$$

gives

$$t = \frac{\rho\sigma h}{6SE}T^{-3} - C_0$$

where C_0 is a constant at $t = 0$, $T = T_0$ (initial conditions)

$$C_0 = -\frac{\rho\sigma h}{6SE}T_0^{-3}$$

$$t = \frac{\rho\sigma h}{6SE}\left(\frac{1}{T^3} - \frac{1}{T_0^3}\right)$$

$$T = \frac{T_0}{\sqrt[3]{1 + (6SE/\rho\sigma h)T_0^3 t}} \qquad . \qquad . \qquad . \qquad (11)$$

To simplify the above equation further, the values of emissivity E, specific heat σ and the density ρ are considered constant, independent of the temperature T. The difference between the first method (Eqs. (8) and (9)) using small time increments Δt, and the analytical solution, has been found to be negligible. Even with $\Delta t = 10$ s the percentage difference between the numerical and analytical solutions was only 0·1 %. Equation (11) is very convenient to use and it yields accurate prediction of the temperature drop in plate rolling.

APPENDIX 4

Estimation of mill stretch

Because of the effects of rolling load on the rolls and mill housing, there is an appreciable difference between the roll gap setting and the resulting plate thickness. The increase in roll gap due to rolling load is caused by a number of factors such as elongation of the mill frame, compression of the screws and bending of the rolls. The mill stretch must be correctly estimated each time the rolls are set, to ensure high accuracy of the plate thickness. The following expression has been evolved as a result of the investigations[5,8]

$$\delta = a_1 + (a_2 + a_3\sqrt{w})P + (a_4 + a_5 w^{1.25})\gamma_w + a_6 N$$

$$. \qquad . \qquad . \qquad . \qquad (1)$$

where

δ	correction in screwdown setting to compensate for mill stretch, mm
a_1 to a_6	are the coefficients appropriate to a particular instant during work rolls campaign
w	plate width, mm
P	rolling load, MN
γ_w	camber of the work rolls, mm
N	number of the plates rolled

The correction in screwdown setting ensures that the edges of the rolled plate will be correct at the expected rolling temperatures. Further correction is required to allow for thermal contraction of the plate, so that the thickness of the finished plate is accurate at normal temperatures. (The hot metal thickness measurement problems are outside the scope of this paper. The analysis of some errors resulting from the application of isotope gauges is described in Ref. 9.)

Theoretical predictions of plastic flow in hot rolling including the effect of various temperature distributions

G. C. Cornfield and R. H. Johnson

A numerical method of solving a standard hot-working equation has been developed for the purpose of making theoretical predictions of the strain, strain rate, and hydrostatic stress distribution in material subjected to deformation by rolling. Illustrations of the local variation of each deformation parameter with position in the roll gap are presented for a uniformly heated mild steel slab undergoing a 50% reduction in thickness. The changes to the distribution of deformation caused by typical non-uniform temperature conditions existing before deformation were explored using a temperature profile representative of a hot surface and cold interior and a temperature profile representative of a cold surface and hot interior.

SYMBOLS

ϵ_{ij}	strain tensor
$\dot{\epsilon}_{ij}$	strain rate tensor
σ_{ij}	stress tensor
σ'_{ij}	reduced stress tensor
$\bar{\sigma}$	equivalent stress
$\sigma_x, \sigma_y, \sigma_z,$ $\tau_{xy}, \tau_{yz}, \tau_{xz}$	stress tensor in Cartesian coordinates
A, n, Q	constants in the deformation law
v	Poisson's ratio
E	Young's modulus
T	temperature, K

Deformation at temperatures above $0.7 \times$ their absolute melting temperature, that is 'hot working', is probably the most convenient method of rapidly shaping metals, in both small and large tonnages, with minimum expenditure of energy. At such temperatures deformation occurs without hardening, thus enabling large strains to be accomplished without detriment to the basic mechanical properties of the final product. Although through-heated stock may be essential for hot working there is

The authors are with the Electricity Council Research Centre, Capenhurst, Chester

no detailed knowledge, particularly from a theoretical standpoint, of how the distribution of temperature within the stock affects workability and the quality of the worked product. This paper describes some first steps taken in an attempt to examine the effect of temperature distribution on mechanical working behaviour.

Several methods of applying heat can be adopted according to requirements dictated by either the material itself or the working process. Of these it is well accepted that electrical methods give rapid heating with an accurate control over temperature and that features such as the ability to generate heat internally in the stock are unique. One incidental aspect of this paper is to find out if electrical furnaces, e.g. induction furnaces, should produce a similar distribution of temperature to that attained in fuel-fired furnaces. More important, however, is the value of this theoretical approach in helping to discover if specially tailored profiles convey new benefits. This paper, therefore, is first concerned with calculations of specific temperature distributions in heated stock. Second, an interpretation of the strain and strain rate distribution during rolling deformation is given, and this is combined with the third aspect of this study, namely how particular temperature patterns affect deformational behaviour.

CHOICE OF PROCESS AND MATERIAL

Of all the mechanical working processes, rolling is the most common and was therefore chosen in preference to other working processes as the mode of working to be analysed in the context of contoured temperature requirements. On the basis of annual tonnage of materials rolled in the UK, steel was selected for study and considered in slab form to facilitate computations. Temperatures at which steel is hot rolled usually fall in the range 1 000°C to 1 350°C, the slabs being preheated initially to the upper end of this range in order to compensate for heat losses during subsequent stages of reduction. The precise preheat temperature, however, is usually not known, nor are any details of the pattern of temperature distribution within the stock. Temperature values, such as the approximate furnace temperature, the surface temperature of the stock, or a predicted temperature based on the fuel consumption and rate of stock throughput, are frequently quoted. The inadequacy of such values has become particularly apparent in recent years with the advent of the computer-controlled hot strip mill, where accurate control of slab temperature is desired.[1]

An impression of the diversity of opinion regarding reheating requirements for steel slabs, supporting the above contention, is provided by the following comments, taken from the 1966 BISRA Slab Reheating Furnace Conference.[2,3,4]

(i) the most important factor was not the temperature distribution in the slab leaving the furnace, but the final rolling temperature of the strip to be made out of the slab

(ii) the true temperatures of a slab being heated within, or leaving, the furnace, are unknown. Temperature variations through the slab thickness and 'end' to 'end' variations are unknown

(iii) uniformly well-heated slabs could be the most important single factor in obtaining improved quality of product.

At the present time operating experience in a generally unquantified form is relied upon heavily. It is not surprising therefore, that an accurate description of the temperature pattern within a slab of metal, which is known from practical experience to roll well, is not available and because handling inevitably produces some changes, various opinions exist as to the ideal temperature profile required. Several basic forms of temperature profile must, therefore, be examined.

TEMPERATURE PROFILES IN HEATED SLABS

Three primary forms of temperature profile existing across a section of a slab can be identified, i.e. a hot surface with cold interior, a cold surface with hot interior and a uniform temperature. As discussed next, these profiles take into account various aspects of industrial practice, such as relative positioning of furnace and mill

with its effect on heat loss in handling, as well as the heating practice employed.

In fuel-fired continuous multi-zone furnaces, the temperature of slabs leaving the final heating zone is not uniform, although the heat content may approach that necessary for rolling. In order to attain an effectively uniform temperature level, normal practice is to pass the slabs through a soaking zone before discharge, enabling heat to soak into the centre from the hotter surface layers. This equalization of temperature is then disturbed and the original pre-soak temperature pattern reversed when the slab loses heat to a cold background during handling from furnace to mill. This final temperature distribution is represented in basic form by the cold surface–hot interior profile (Fig. 1*a*).

It is generally evisaged that a high rate of heating, a small and compact furnace structure, and the absence of bulky ancillary equipment to supply fuel and air for combustion, all contribute towards the feasibility of locating an induction heating unit close to the mill. Thus, with the additional features of automatic control and the facility to make instantaneous adjustments to the power input, it is possible to achieve correct rolling temperature with a minimum of superheat and time for soaking. Despite these attributes, however, induction heating was chosen in this paper to provide the example of a hot surface–cold interior profile. It is implicit in the profile illustrated in Fig. 1*b* that thermal soaking to

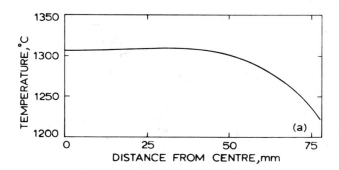

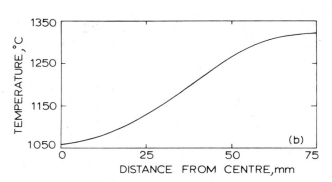

The temperature gradient is shown in (*a*) a surface-heated slab allowed to cool by radiation for 60 s and (*b*) an induction-heated slab immediately after the power has been switched off and before any temperature redistribution from soaking or cooling has taken place; further details are given in the text

1 Calculated temperature profiles across a section from centre to surface of a slab 152·4 mm (6in) thick

achieve uniform temperature was purposely omitted from the final stages of the heating cycle. Although inherently different in the outer surface layers, such a profile can be assumed also to represent one typical of inadequate heating using conventional surface heating methods. This form of profile has important implications irrespective of heating method for all cases where furnace and working operation are so close together that the heat input–metal throughput balance prevents significant heat conduction and the soaking time to equalize centre and surface temperatures is shortened or omitted.

The non-uniform temperature distributions were computed for a typically sized mild steel slab, using a finite difference approximation to the one-dimensional heat-transfer equations because the thickness (6in) of the slab is small compared with its width and length. (In practice widths of 25–75in and lengths of 15–35 ft are typical so this assumption is quite satisfactory.) The hot surface-cold interior profile was calculated for mains frequency (50 Hz) heating to an average temperature of $1\,200°C$ in 390 s from a base temperature of $800°C$. The centre and surface temperatures are $1\,060°C$ and $1\,325°C$ respectively. The induction furnace was assumed to comprise the stock surrounded and separated by refractory insulation from the water-cooled coils. It was also assumed that coil end effects were negligible over most of the stock length, the outside of the refractory was maintained at a constant temperature by the water-cooled coils, and that the electrical conductivity was constant which implies that, for a slab above Curie temperature, the form of the power distribution through the slab does not change, only its total magnitude. The cold surface–hot interior profile was modelled by a slab which had its outside surface raised instantly from $800°C$ to $1\,350°C$, the heat then conducting inwards into the core until a $50°C$ temperature differential was achieved. This was followed by a cooling period of 60 s, approximating to free radiation to a cold background from adherent layers of scale equal to 2% of the total thickness.

DEFORMATIONAL BEHAVIOUR DURING SLAB ROLLING

Earlier work

Previous theoretical treatments of hot rolling deformation have limited usefulness in the context of the present paper. Here, the major interest is in the strain and strain rate distribution within the deforming material in which a particular temperature pattern exists. Early development in the theory of rolling[5] was directed towards the calculation of rolling loads and torque. The method of predicting these parameters was based on slip line field solutions[6] for a rigid plastic (constant yield stress) material which sticks perfectly to the rolls. Only isothermal conditions were considered. Alexander's original solution was limited in application due to its statically indeterminate nature but it has since been adapted somewhat to broaden its usefulness.[7,8,9] This,

and other analytical methods, however, are unlikely to be of much assistance in solving the present problem where strength varies due to non-isothermal conditions.

A situation analogous to a non-isothermal distribution of temperature is where materials of different strength, but at the same temperature, are sandwiched together for rolling. Early work[10] examined the practical aspects of rolling mild steel between $700°C$ and $1\,200°C$ when sandwiched between either copper or stainless steel. It was concluded that the rolling pressure for such composites was made up from the pressures for the individual layers in the ratio of their thicknesses. Arnold and Whitton[11] later confirmed this work and analysed the overall plastic deformation of sandwich materials in terms of an 'effective' yield stress. More recent work[12] on similar lines has indicated that load and torque can also be predicted for rolling materials with continuously varying strengths.

Mathematical method

A numerical approach using iterative methods and based on the 'TESS' stress–strain program, is adopted. Full details of this and the method used are given in Appendix 1. Assumptions made in the present theory are summarized as follows:

1. At hot-working temperatures, the material obeys a relationship between stress, strain rate, and temperature similar to that used to describe multiaxial secondary creep.

$$\dot{\epsilon}_{ij} = A\bar{\sigma}^{n-1} . \sigma'_{ij} . \exp(-Q/kT) \qquad . \qquad . \qquad . \qquad (1)$$

This is also similar to the general relation correlating the strength of hot steel with strain rate and temperature proposed by Sellars and Tegart[13] and is a reasonable representation of numerical data.[14] The value of A and n used in the equation were in fact calculated from this numerical data, using the uniaxial form of Eq. (1). It must be emphasized that the constants A and n can be estimated easily only from numerical data supplied from tests which employ a simple uniaxial deformation such as simple compression or simple shear. By use of the multiaxial creep Eq. (1) data from such tests can then be used, in principle, to investigate deformation in any geometry. Tests based on torsion or indentation have a relatively complicated biaxial nature and as pointed out by Moore[15] it is difficult to see how data from such tests can be used to predict results in a significantly different geometry. One drawback of Eq. (1) is that it assumes strain rate to be independent of strain. From Cooks' data[14] this appears to be a good approximation for temperature above $1\,200°C$ and strains above 5%. Below 5% strain Cook does not present any data. The torsion tests of Rossard and Blain[16] indicate that in the strain region below 5% the stress may drop by a factor of 3 or 4. The indentation work of Weinstein and Matsufuji[17] shows a much smaller variation of about 0·8 although the strain rate varied in their tests. For the reasons quoted above it is not clear how relevant these experimental results will be in determining the true uniaxial stress–strain rate–strain behaviour. It is implicit in the use of Eq. (1) above that steel is not well represented by a plastic rigid material when hot-rolling deformation is being considered.

2. It is assumed that sticking friction occurs, i.e. no slipping takes place, although in practice slipping must occur at the first and last points of contact with the roll surface. With this assumption the surface layers tend to expand immediately to their final dimensions near to the point of entry, thus concentrating the first stages of deformation in a thin surface layer.

3. The surface boundaries of the stock material are assumed to be at fixed positions and, except when in contact with the rolls, stress-free. This introduces errors as the theoretical problem involves free boundaries just ahead of the rolls. Consequently, an apparent mass imbalance will result and non-zero velocities normal to the boundary will exist if the fixed and free boundaries do not coincide. The deformation pattern, however, cannot be too inaccurate as most strain takes place between the rolls.

4. The heat generated by the work of deformation is negligible (in the example considered here the average temperature rise is $\approx 10°C$). It is also assumed that there is no heat conduction to the rolls. This is a good approximation for normal rolling speeds, where the contact time is $\leqslant 1$ s.

Effect of temperature profiles on deformation behaviour

The effect of three temperature distributions on the strain and strain rate distribution are examined. These include a uniform temperature throughout and two temperature patterns representative of the heating routes discussed previously and shown in Fig. 1. In each case, results are in the form of contour maps* showing the distribution of the longitudinal, shear and effective strain rates in the deforming material. One example (for uniform temperature) is presented of the distribution of areas where the material suffers hydrostatic tension. It was calculated from the assumption of plane strain where the hydrostatic stress

$$\sigma_z = \tfrac{1}{2}(\sigma_x + \sigma_y) \qquad . \qquad . \qquad . \qquad . \qquad . \qquad (2)$$

The diagrams were all compiled from on-line plots obtained as part of the computer output using the

---

* As a consequence of the assumption that the fixed and free surface boundaries must coincide the percentage of slab reductions for the uniform temperature slab and the handled slab is not the same as that for the induction-heated slab. This is explained as follows. The thickness and shape of the workpiece ahead of the rolls is not known and has to be estimated. In general the estimated value will not be correct, and a normal velocity will exist at the stress-free surface resulting in an apparent mass imbalance. This can be eliminated by calculating the pre-roll thickness of the workpiece. The actual thickness strain on the central axis is found by integrating back through the calculated velocity field starting at the exit plane where the true thickness corresponds closely to the minimum roll gap (calculations indicate a slight thickening after exit). The extra material needed to preserve the mass balance is shown in Figs. 2, 3, and 4 by the blank areas ahead of the rolls. In the induction-heated slab this extra material is negligibly small and therefore not shown in Fig. 5

program described in the Appendix. The numbers ascribed to each contour line represent the strain rate expressed as a fraction of the main strain rate calculated in the manner described by Larke.[18] The strain pattern within the material is demonstrated by illustrations of the distortion caused to a regular mesh grid. Some confidence in our numerical assessments is provided indirectly by the good agreement between the strain pattern deduced from the analysis and those obtained experimentally from multi-layer plasticine models or from the use of imbedded markers.[19]

Slip line fields for the hot-rolling process, such as those calculated by Alexander and others, show zones of 'unplastic' or rigid metal bounded on one side by the roll/metal interface and protruding wedge-fashion towards the neutral axis. These zones are generated by frictional forces at the interface, but arise primarily because slip line theory assumes that the material deforms with a constant yield stress. In the present study, where a more realistic approach to the hot strength characteristics has been adopted, it should be noted that these rigid metal zones are absent. The strain rate contour diagrams indicate that straining extends well in front of the rolls, and to some extent behind them. The distance affected is difficult to estimate as the section length adopted in the calculations was not quite long enough. From the sections considered, however, it would appear that some strain occurs in the material over a length approximately equal to the workpiece thickness both in front of and behind the rolls. This observation that plastic deformation extends beyond the geometric limits of the roll-gap zones has also been made by Tarnovskii *et al.*[20]

UNIFORM TEMPERATURE

The variation in longitudinal strain rate is illustrated in Fig. 2a. Prominent features in all the strain rate contour diagrams are the position and relative size of the zones where the rate of deformation is a maximum. In this case a high rate of longitudinal straining occurs adjacent to the first point of contact with the rolls and is subsequently constrained within a zone which moves towards the centre as reduction proceeds. Nowhere, however, does the maximum rate of straining exceed $\approx 2.5 \times$ the mean strain rate. In the compressive region on the exit side, the material is attempting to increase in thickness with the result that a slight positive thickening of the stock must occur immediately the roll constraint is removed.

The shear strain rate distribution is shown in Fig. 2b. As expected the material between the rolls exhibits a positive shear strain rate, i.e. the outside layers are moving faster than the inner layers. On the entry and exit side of this region there are zones of negative shear strain rate which are equivalent to backward extrusions of metal. The effective strain rate distribution over the whole of the roll-gap section is given in Fig. 2c. In reflecting the characteristics of both the longitudinal and the shear strain rate distribution, Fig. 2c effectively summarizes the basic pattern of the deformation. In this case it is seen that the areas bounded by contours where the strain

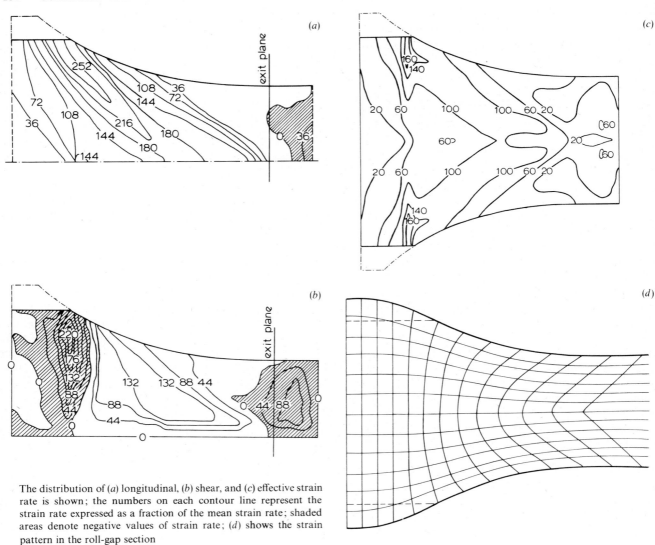

The distribution of (*a*) longitudinal, (*b*) shear, and (*c*) effective strain rate is shown; the numbers on each contour line represent the strain rate expressed as a fraction of the mean strain rate; shaded areas denote negative values of strain rate; (*d*) shows the strain pattern in the roll-gap section

2   *Contour map of half-sections in the roll gap of a 152·4 mm (6in) thick slab uniformly heated to 1 350°C*

rate is equal to the mean strain rate extend towards the centre and slightly overlap, about midway through the roll gap. The strain distribution given in Fig. 2*d* follows closely the grid distortion obtained with plasticine models[21] and the experimental results of Kasz and Varley.[19] It is noteworthy, however, that whereas the overall strain pattern is essentially uniform, the rate at which the strain has occurred is distinctly non-uniform. The example (Fig. 3) given of the distribution of tensile and compressive hydrostatic stress for uniform temperature is interesting for showing areas of tension under the rolls. This is a somewhat surprising result and confirms that a complex system of forces exists in the central regions.

COLD SURFACE–HOT INTERIOR

The variation in longitudinal strain rates during the rolling of a slab with the temperature profile shown in Fig. 1*a* is illustrated in Fig. 4*a*. The contour map is not significantly different from that deduced for the case of uniform temperature. The zone with the fastest rate

of straining has moved a short distance from the surface as a consequence of the increased deformation resistance of the surface layer. There is almost no change in magnitude of the peak deformation rate. Similarly, the shear strain rate pattern (Fig. 4*b*) and the mesh grid pattern (Fig. 4*d*) are nearly identical to those obtained for a

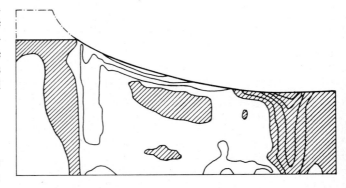

3   *Contour map of half-section in roll gap showing areas (shaded) of tensile hydrostatic stress in a uniformly heated 152·4 mm (6in) thick slab*

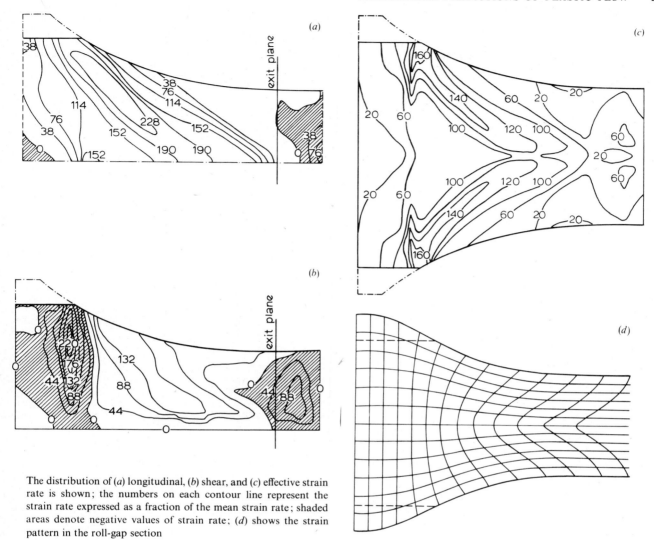

The distribution of (a) longitudinal, (b) shear, and (c) effective strain rate is shown; the numbers on each contour line represent the strain rate expressed as a fraction of the mean strain rate; shaded areas denote negative values of strain rate; (d) shows the strain pattern in the roll-gap section

4   Contour maps of half-sections in roll gap of the conventionally surface-heated 152·4 mm (6in) thick slab after 60 s cooling (see the temperature profile shown in Fig. 1a)

uniform temperature. The effective strain rate distribution (Fig. 4c) on the other hand, although possessing some similarity with the uniform temperature case shows the higher strain rate contours now extending deep into the central region. The cold surface–hot interior temperature pattern is likely to be typical of most ferrous stock at the point of mill entry.

HOT SURFACE–COLD INTERIOR

Figure 5a indicates that deformation in terms of the longitudinal strain rate is an order of magnitude higher in the hot outer layer, where it first contacts the rolls, than that found anywhere else in the bulk of the material. The shear strain rate pattern (Fig. 5b) and effective strain rate pattern (Fig. 5c) similarly show high rates in the hotter surface layers. These high deformation zones are restricted to the surface layers in contrast to the previous examples where they extend deep into the material. The strain pattern (Fig. 5d) also shows very heavily sheared surface layers. A slab having a cold interior therefore undergoes the most inhomogeneous

strain, a well-known penalty of inadequate heating. Our example confirms that little shear deformation of the interior layers takes place and most of the strain energy is absorbed at the surface.

RESULTS

Three specific temperature profiles were chosen in order that examples of theoretically deduced plastic flow patterns could be illustrated in this paper. Only general comments, therefore, are possible. In most rolling operations uniformity of working is believed to be desirable. If this uniformity is interpreted as equal amounts of deformation in each layer, then the present theoretical study confirms the accepted practical viewpoint that the cold surface–hot interior type of profile is required. It is now possible, however, to define more closely the profile shape desired at the working stage and thus deduce the profile required at the heating stage. In most circumstances it will be necessary for electrical furnaces to achieve a near-uniform temperature

The distribution of (*a*) longitudinal, (*b*) shear, and (*c*) effective strain rate is shown; the numbers on each contour line represent the strain rate expressed as a fraction of the mean strain rate; shaded areas denote negative values of strain rate; (*d*) shows the strain pattern in the roll-gap section

5   *Contour maps of half-sections in roll gap of the 50 Hz induction-heated 152·4 mm (6in) thick slab with the temperature profile shown in Fig. 1b*

distribution in the workpiece before handling commences. This answers the question posed early in the paper on the matching of heating routines for different furnace types. It should be noted from sandwich rolling calculations that the cold surface–hot interior profile is associated with a higher roll pressure compared with a slab uniformly heated to the same heat content level. If it is essential to minimize roll pressures and yet maintain this working pattern then an increase in the temperature of the inner layers is necessary.

IMPLICATIONS OF THE PRESENT STUDY

The ability to analyse deformation in the manner illustrated in this paper points to the possibility in the future of directly using temperature as a means of controlling deformation and, ultimately, the metallurgical condition of the final product. Already there are indications that such a sophisticated approach is not far away and that it may find use in such fields as grain size control, inclusion size control and spheroidization control. Several workers, e.g. Dewsnap[22] have demonstrated that structural control is highly dependent on the hot-working conditions such as temperature, strain, and strain rate. Where conditions have to be defined fairly

precisely, then it must be important also to ensure that the most appropriate distribution of deformation is achieved. In addition, details of the stress distribution may be relevant to structural control. In particular the stress conditions at or near the plane of exit are considered to have a major influence on ultimate structure.[16] A further application of this knowledge of stress distribution lies in examining aspects of fracture during hot-working. Although only a few systematic studies have been reported[23] it is recognized that some quantitative assessment of shear and hydrostatic stress would be valuable when ductility problems are encountered.

CONCLUSIONS

It has proved possible by computer solution of a standard hot-working equation to obtain a theoretical prediction of the stress–strain–strain rate distribution during rolling deformation. These predictions provide, at the present time, the best available data on the plastic flow behaviour in this working operation. On the basis of the results shown in the present study, temperature profile tailoring should be a means of further improving process control in the metallurgical route.

ACKNOWLEDGMENT

The authors thank the Electricity Council for permission to publish.

REFERENCES

1 D. J. RAY: *JISI*, 1969, **207**, 907
2 I. F. HOLLANDER: 'Slab reheating furnaces', 1966, **2**, Bisra Pe-Conf. Proc./1/68
3 A. MASSEY *et al.*: *ibid.*, 15
4 H. H. DINEEN: *ibid.*, 64
5 H. FORD: *Met. Rev.*, 1957, **2**, 1
6 J. M. ALEXANDER: *Proc. IME*, 1955, **169**, 1 021
7 H. FORD AND J. M. ALEXANDER: *J. Inst. Met.*, 1963–4, **92**, 397
8 F. A. A. CRANE AND J. M. ALEXANDER: *ibid.*, 1968, **96**, 289
9 J. M. ALEXANDER: *Proc. Roy. Soc.*, 1972, **A326**, 535–63
10 A. POMP AND W. LEUG: *Mitt. K.W.Inst. Eisenf.*, 1942, **24**, 123
11 R. R. ARNOLD AND F. W. WHITTON: *Proc. IME*, 1959, **172**, 241
12 A. G. ATKINS AND A. S. WEINSTEIN: *Internat. J. Mech. Sci.*, 1970, **12**, 641
13 C. M. SELLARS AND W. J. MCG. TEGART: *Rev. Met.*, 1966, **63**, 731
14 P. M. COOK: Proc. Conf. Properties of Materials at High Rates of Strain 86; 1957, Inst. Mech. Eng.
15 P. MOORE: 'Deformation under hot working conditions', 103; 1968, London, The Iron and Steel Institute
16 C. ROSSARD AND P. BLAIN: *Rev. Mét.*, 1958, **55**, 573
17 A. S. WEINSTEIN AND A. MATSUFUJI: *Iron and Steel Eng.*, 1968, **45**, 121
18 E. C. LARKE: 'The rolling of sheet, strip, and plate', 297; 1957, London, Chapman and Hall
19 F. KASZ AND P. C. VARLEY: *J. Inst. Met.*, 1950, **76**, 407
20 I. YA. TARNOVSKII *et al.*: 'Deformation of metals during rolling', 86; 1965, Oxford, Pergamon Press
21 E. OROWAN: *Proc. IME*, 1943, **150**, 140
22 R. F. DEWSNAP: *JISI*, 1970, **208**, 727
23 W. J. MCG. TEGART: 'Ductility', 133; 1968, Ohio, ASM
24 F. FITZGERALD AND A. T. SHERIDAN: 'Mathematical models in metallurgical process development', 123; 1970, London, The Iron and Steel Institute

APPENDIX 1

Strain distribution in the rolled slab

The deformation problem reduces to the solution of the following equations, completely identical to the commonly used secondary creep equations.[13]

$$
\left.
\begin{aligned}
\dot{\epsilon}_{xx} &= A\bar{\sigma}^{n-1} \cdot (\sigma_x - \sigma_y) \exp(-Q/kT) \\
\dot{\epsilon}_{yy} &= -\dot{\epsilon}_{xx} \\
\dot{\epsilon}_{xy} &= 2A\bar{\sigma}^{n-1} \cdot \tau_{xy} \exp(-Q/kT)
\end{aligned}
\right\} \qquad (A1)
$$

where $\bar{\sigma}$ is given by

$$
\bar{\sigma}^2 = \tfrac{3}{4}(\sigma_x - \sigma_y)^2 + 3\tau_{xy}^2
$$

The boundary conditions are prescribed strain rates or stresses over the boundary. Some of the boundary conditions are 'free' as the position of the surface immediately ahead of and behind the rolls is not known beforehand. These surfaces must be such that the material has a zero normal stress and zero normal velocity on the surface. Only one of these conditions can be prescribed, the position of the surface being adjusted to satisfy the other. In practice this would have been too costly in both real time and computer time, and small approximations were introduced into the solution by allowing the stress-free surface to be non-coincidental with the actual surface ahead of the rolls. The problem was solved by an iterative method, which relied on a finite element, elastic stress-strain program developed by the CEGB and run on their IBM 360/65 computer. The program solves the elastic stress–strain equations

$$
\left.
\begin{aligned}
\epsilon_{xx} &= \frac{1}{E}[(1 - v^2)\sigma_x - v(1 + v)\sigma_y] \\
\epsilon_{yy} &= \frac{1}{E}[(1 - v^2)\sigma_y - v(1 + v)\sigma_x] \\
\epsilon_{xy} &= \frac{1 + v}{E}\tau_{xy}
\end{aligned}
\right\} \qquad (A2)
$$

where E is Young's modulus input as a function of space. Using the correspondence $\epsilon \to \dot{\epsilon}$ and displacement $\to$ velocity, and putting $v = 0.5$ and $E = \{\tfrac{4}{3}A\bar{\sigma}^{n-1} \cdot \exp(-Q/kT)\}^{-1}$ Eqs. (A2) are completely analgous to Eqs. (A1). Solutions to these equations required an iterative procedure at each step, where E is calculated for each element as a function of the equivalent stress and is then re-introduced to calculate a new value of the equivalent stress. An over-relaxation factor of

TABLE 1   Tables used to evaluate the temperature dependent thermal conductivity and diffusivity by linear interpolation

Conductivity, W/Km	Temperature, °C	Diffusivity, mm²/s	Temperature, °C
51·5	0	14·4	0
50·3	110·0	13·5	105·0
31·3	705·0	5·0	670·0
25·3	800·0	2·9	725·0
29·3	1 200·0	3·5	775·0
		4·5	875·0
		6·0	1 300·0

Thermal conductivity of refractory material	1·1 W/Km
Thermal diffusivity of refractory material	0·4 mm²/s
Thermal conductivity of scale	1·0 W/Km
Effective emissivity between refractory and steel	0·8
Electrical skin thickness at 50 Hz for steel above the Curie point	76 mm (3in)
Slab thickness during heating prior to rolling	150 mm (6in)
Slab thickness after rolling	
(i) uniformly heated slab	75 mm
(ii) uniformly heated slab with 60 s cooling	75 mm
(iii) induction-heated slab with no cooling	90 mm
Roll diameter	0·965 m (38in)
Deformation law for steel in uniaxial tension (valid between 1 100° and 1 350°C)	

$$
\dot{\epsilon} = 7 \cdot 1 \times 10^4 \cdot \sigma^6 \exp(-2 \cdot 9 \times 10^4/T)
$$

where the units of $\dot{\epsilon}$ are s^{-1} and σ is in MN/m^2

$(n - 1)/n$ was used, giving the ith iterate of E as

$$E^{(i)} = \frac{n-1}{n} E^{(i-1)} + \frac{1}{n} \{A(\bar{\sigma}^{(i)})^{n-1} \cdot \exp(-Q/kT)\}^{-1}$$

$$\qquad \qquad \qquad \cdot \quad \cdot \quad \cdot \quad \cdot \quad \cdot \quad \text{(A3)}$$

A finite element mesh with 180 elements was used and the equivalent stress and $E^{(i)}$ calculated from the data output. As this was a production program no modifications were allowed and the above calculations for the equivalent stress were tackled separately on a Univac 1108 computer.

APPENDIX 2

Thermal properties of steel

The temperature dependent thermal conductivity and diffusivity were evaluated by linear interpolation from Table 1. The values were read from graphs presented by Fitzgerald and Sheridan.[24]

Research on the optimization of the operation of wide strip mills

S. Wilmotte, J. Mignon, and M. Economopoulos

This paper deals with finding an algorithm that allows parameters for control of the finishing train to be calculated aimed at improving the flatness and the transverse crown of the hot-rolled strip. Four main types of mathematical models are discussed, i.e. energy models, thermal models, the model of evolution of the crown of the rolls during a rolling schedule, and models for the deformation of the stand and of the rolls in use. Optimization criteria for load distribution are then determined for transformation of the strip into a product of prescribed characteristics. Finally, the optimization at the level of the mill is discussed, to determine the crowns to be given to the rolls.

SYMBOLS

T	temperature
V	temperature of the external medium
t	time
τ	time interval
θ	duration of the revolution of a work roll
v	strip velocity
u	linear velocity of the work roll
a	diffusivity
k	conductivity
g	transfer coefficient
h	strip thickness
B	strip width
L	length of the roller table
R	radius
D	diameter
l	length of contact zone
s	thickness of the oxide layer on the strip
F	rolling force
C	rolling couple
P	electric power
K	factor describing the type of steel
Σ	crown index of the strip
ρ^*	flatness index of the strip
σ	partial roll crown = difference between the diameter of the roll in the centre and just at the edge of the strip
σ, t	total crown of the roll = the difference between the roll diameter in the centre and at the edge of the roller table
S	equivalent roll crown
$m, n, p,$	parameters

Indices

e	entry of the mill
s	exit of the mill
g	roll gap
b	supporting roll
w	work roll
m	centre of the strip
r	edge of the strip
c	contact zone between work rolls and supporting rolls
o	surface
M	maximum

The object of studies undertaken over several years at CRM in the field of hot strip mills is to maximize, or at least to improve the 'value' of the production by properly choosing the value of the control parameters. The production of a strip mill consists of the transformation

The authors are with CRM, Belgium

of the collection of slabs into coils within a given period. The collection of coils produced within the considered period of time can be divided in two groups:

    (i) the first choice is of those that have been treated according to schedule

    (ii) the coils affected by a fabricating defect.

The latter can be divided in several categories after the nature of the defect so that we can represent the production of a wide strip mill as in Fig. 1. The 'value' of the production of a wide strip mill depends on the total throughput and on the distribution of the produced coils over the four categories given in Fig. 1. The control actions that can be undertaken for maximizing the value of the production of a hot strip mill are manifold. In this paper we only consider the selection of parameters for the finishing train. We suppose that the rolling schedule, the rolling sequence and the characteristics of the bar at the entry of the finishing train are known. The paper deals with finding an algorithm that allows us to calculate parameters for controlling the finishing train, aiming at the improvement of the flatness and the transverse crown of the strip. Therefore, we are really after improving the quality of production, as it is defined above. Among the control parameters for the finishing train can be discerned:

    (i) those corresponding to the collective of a rolling schedule, i.e. the crowns to be given to the work rolls at the grinding bay.

    (ii) those that can be chosen for each coil, i.e. the roll speeds, the position of the screws, and the forces to be applied on the roll bending system for the mills that are equipped with it.

The optimization must therefore be performed at two levels. One, at the level of the preparation of the mill considered as part of the system and next at the level of the coil, also in accordance with the total system. The problems encountered in practice can be formulated more precisely:

    (i) regarding the optimization at the level of the coil, the aim is to determine the optimal values for the crowns of the rolls and the ideal load distribution between the stands for each coil. In the case that the stands are equipped with a roll bending system, the determination of the values of the crowns of the rolls can be translated into the calculation of forces to be developed in these installations. As particular cases of this problem can be considered the determination of the optimal crowns for the rolls, the load distribution being given, and on the other hand the calculation of the ideal load distribution, the actual crowns being given

    (ii) considering the optimal preparation of the mill one tries to find the optimal crowns for the rolls to be ground.

For applying the various algorithms, mathematical models must be derived describing the physical phen-

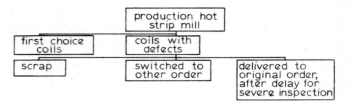

1 *Classification of the production of a hot strip mill*

omena that play a role during rolling. Because they are so important, we shall discuss them first.

THE MATHEMATICAL MODELS

In general, four main types of mathematical models can be discerned:

    (i) energy models, that allow the calculation of the rolling force and couple, as well as the electric power taken up by the mill motors

    (ii) the thermal model, giving the temperature history of a point of the strip between entry of the first stand and exit of the last stand of the finishing train

    (iii) the model of the evolution of the crown of the rolls during a rolling schedule taking the roll wear and the thermal expansion into account

    (iv) models for the deformation of the stand and of the rolls in use determining the roll gap and the state of flatness at the exit of the stand.

We shall not describe the energy models as they are the classic ones. After making some remarks about the thermal model, we shall treat in more detail the models of the evolution of the crown and the deformation of the stand.

Model of the temperature evolution of the strip

The establishment of this model is made in two stages. In a first phase we have constructed a complex model describing the evolution of the temperature distribution

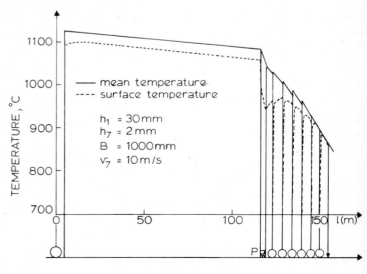

2 *Evolution of the temperature of the strip*

over the thickness of the strip along the finishing train. In this model is incorporated the fall in temperature by cooling the surfaces outside the stand, the temperature rise in the roll gap due to the work done and the cooling due to the contact with the work rolls in the roll gap. An example of the result obtained with this model is given in Fig. 2. With this model is also calculated the development of the thickness of the scale layer from the scale breaker till the exit of the last finishing stand. This model is too complex to be used in an algorithm in which the calculation of the temperatures must be repeated a great number of times. Therefore in a second phase we have derived from the complete model a simplified model requiring only a limited calculation time. This model consists of three relations that achieve the calculation of the evolution of the mean value of the temperature distribution over the thickness of the strip:

(i) between stands, the evolution of the mean temperature is given by the relation

$$\frac{\overline{T} - V}{(\overline{T} - V)_{\text{init}}} = \exp\left[-\tau \frac{2}{h} \frac{a}{k} \frac{g}{1 + \frac{h}{6} \frac{g}{k}}\right] \qquad . \quad (1)$$

(ii) the increase of the temperature in the mill is given by

$$\Delta \overline{T}_{\text{d}} = m_1 \frac{a}{k} \frac{F}{B\sqrt{l_{\text{g}}}} \ln \frac{h_{\text{e}}}{h_{\text{s}}} \qquad . \qquad . \qquad . \quad (2)$$

(iii) the fall of temperature due to contact with the rolls can be calculated with

$$\Delta \overline{T}_{\text{f}} = -m_2 \frac{\overline{T} - V'}{h_{\text{e}} + h_{\text{s}}} \left(\frac{l_{\text{g}}}{u}\right) m_3 \qquad . \qquad . \qquad . \quad (3)$$

A numerical calculation method has been established for determining the values of the coefficients of these relations which minimize the sum of the squares of the differences between calculated and measured values of the temperature falls between the exit of the last rougher stand and the exit of the last finishing stand. This study has been made on a population of more than 1 000 coils of all dimensions and rolled in different cooling conditions. The histogram of the results is shown in Fig. 3.

Mathematical models of the evolution of the crown of the rolls, of the transverse crown, and the flatness of the strip

The notions of crown and flatness of the strip and crown of the rolls are strongly interrelated. The flatness of the strip depends effectively on the evolution of the transverse profile of the strip. The profile at the exit of a stand is itself a function of the shape of the descriptive of the roll, taking in account wear and thermal crown. The models of profile, flatness, and crown cannot be verified separately. They have to be treated simultaneously. Moreover, at present neither the crown of the strip between the stands, nor the crown of the rolls during rolling are accessible to direct measurements. Many test campaigns have been made on a finishing train of a hot strip mill

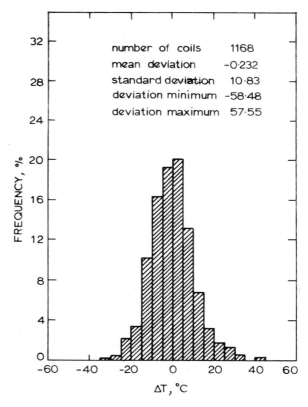

3   Histogram of the results obtained with the thermal model

with the object to check the validity of the projected models. Each test has consisted of assembling during a complete rolling campaign the values of all quantities necessary for the calculation of the crown of the rolls and the crown of the strip. The results of the calculations have been compared with the measured crowns of the strips after the last stand, the roll crowns after the campaign and the observations with respect to the strip flatness. Before analysing the results of these tests, we first shall elucidate the way in which the models have been established.

Establishing the models

CROWN OF THE ROLLS

During a hot rolling campaign the crown ground on the rolls changes rapidly due to wear and dilatation. For determining the descriptive of an unloaded work roll two models must be employed

(i) one for calculating the thermal field inside the roll and from that of the dilatation of the roll surface
(ii) one for calculating roll wear of each point along its length.

If it is assumed that the phenomena of dilatation and wear are not interdependent, the determination of the descriptive of the roll at each moment leads to the superposition of the thermal and worn crowns.

Model of the thermal evolution of the crown of the rolls
Calculation of the temperature field
Figure 4 represents schematically a work roll in its surroundings:

(i) the roll heats up when in contact with the strip, and taking into account the presence of ample quantities of vapour and smoke it can be assumed that the contribution of radiation from the strip may be neglected

(ii) part of this heat is removed

(a) by cooling water under pressure and moreover by the running water
(b) by the supporting roll at the zone of contact
(c) by the air
(d) by the bearings.

A point on the surface of a roll can be exposed to different types of external circumstances within one revolution, e.g. a point on the circumference at $Y = 0$ is during rolling successively in contact with pressurized water jets, running water, the supporting roll, and the strip. As we are only interested in the average temperature over a revolution, we replace these external circumstances by an equivalent homogeneous environment, exchanging the same amount of heat with the roll. This equivalent environment is characterized by

(i) an equivalent temperature V^*
(ii) an equivalent transfer coefficient g^*.

The heat flow at the surface can be written as

$$\phi = g^*(T_0 - V^*) \quad . \quad . \quad . \quad . \quad . \quad . \quad (4)$$

Therefore, we have reduced the problem to a two-dimensional relation in (x, y) for calculating the temperature distribution in the section AOB. Knowing the thermal state the dilatation at the surface can be determined. To obtain the temperature distribution in the roll we have solved with a finite difference method the equation of heat propagation, that is written in two dimensions and in cylindrical coordinates:

$$\frac{1}{a'}\frac{dT}{dt} = \frac{\partial^2 T}{\partial x^2} + \frac{1}{x}\frac{\partial T}{\partial x} + \frac{\partial^2 T}{\partial y^2} \quad . \quad . \quad . \quad . \quad (5)$$

More information about the calculation method can be found in Ref. 9. For calculating the heat exchange between strip and roll in the roll bite we have used a solution for the case in which the bodies are homogeneous, of different initial temperatures, put in contact across an insulating layer consisting of the oxide layer.[1]

Calculation of the field of displacement at the surface
The calculation of the values of the displacements at the surface from the temperature field has been made in an approximate fashion assuming that each section of the roll deforms independently of the adjacent sections. This hypothesis holds if one is only interested in the thermal crowns for the head ends of the strips. In fact, during the interval between the rolling of consecutive strips the important thermal gradient at the edge of the strip will decrease appreciably.

Model of roll wear
The model used for describing the development of the work roll wear is simple. It is based on the two following hypotheses

(i) only the part in contact with the strip wears
(ii) the degree of wear is proportional to the length of strip with which it has been in contact.

These hypotheses could be verified by comparing for a great number of rolls the profiles of wear at the end of a campaign with the programmed decrease of widths in the campaign's rolling schedule.

Composite model of the evolution of the crown of rolls
Adding up the profile of wear and the thermal profile the shape of the descriptive of the work roll is found. In Fig. 5 the shapes of the descriptive of the last finishing stand are given, calculated at the moment of entry of a certain number of coils during a test campaign. It can be seen that the form of the crown can strongly vary during a rolling schedule as a function of the rolling sequence and the dimensions of the strip.

CROWN OF THE STRIP

During the rolling of a strip the work rolls and supporting rolls undergo plastic deformation by bending and flattening. Supposing that no deformation occurs when the strip leaves the rolls, the transverse crown of the strip coincides with the transverse profile of the roll gap under load in the exit plane. The descriptive of the work roll in contact with the material at that instant will be called 'active descriptive' according to the definition proposed by B. Fazan.[2] Therefore, the study of the crown of the strip has been converted to the study of the shape of the active descriptive of the work roll. In the same way as for the thermal model, we have made a complete model in the form of a numerical calculation program. From this we derived a simplified algebraic expression between the various relevant parameters.

Complete model
The determination of the deformations of the rolls under load is a three-dimensional problem of elasticity. This complex problem has been approached by considering

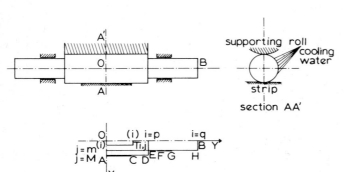

4   Schematic view of a work roll in its surroundings

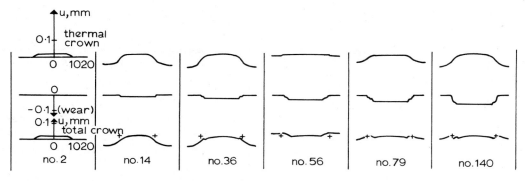

The crosses indicate the widths of the strips

5 *Thermal crown, wear, and total crown at the time of rolling several coils in F6 (sixth stand of finishing train)*

the displacement of a point on the roll surface as a resultant of

(i) the displacement of the whole roll, considered as a rigid body
(ii) the deformation of the axis due to bending and shearing
(iii) the deformation of the straight section due to bending and to flattening.

The boundary conditions are defined by taking into account the displacements at the interfaces of

(i) work roll and strip
(ii) work roll and supporting roll
(iii) supporting roll and mill frame.

The complete expression for the displacements and the calculation method have already been explained in a previous paper.[3] In this paper can also be found comparisons between calculation results and experimental data.[4,5,6] Since this paper has appeared we have changed the theory for calculating the flattening of the rolls in contact with the strip so as to obtain a better agreement between measured and calculated crowns near the edges of the strip.

Simplified model
The model we developed gives good results but requires an appreciable calculating time. In order to obtain a more serviceable model we have tried to derive, from a series of results obtained with the complete model, a simple algebraic relation. It appears that the following relation can be applied:

$$\Sigma_s f(h) = n_1 \frac{L}{D_b} \left(\frac{B}{D_w}\right)^2 \left(n_2 + \frac{B}{L}\right) F - \left(\frac{B}{L}\right)^2 S + n_3 \quad . \quad (6)$$

with

$$f(h) = h \quad \text{for } h > 3 \text{ mm}$$

$$= \frac{n_4}{1 + n_5 \log h} \quad \text{for } h \leqslant 3 \text{ mm}$$

Σ_s is defined as the relative difference between the thickness in the centre and the thickness at a certain

distance d from the edges. In this paper this term will be referred to as 'crown index'. The first term of the second member gives the influence on the transverse crown of the strip of the rolling force and the geometry of the strip and of the rolls. S is the equivalent crown of the rolls. In this term are included the crown ground on the work rolls and the supporting rolls, the wear and the thermal crown as well as the force U developed in the roll bending system, if that has been installed. In the case that the rolls have a parabolic crown and in which $U = 0$, the expression for S becomes

$$S = n_6 \sigma_{w,t} + n_7 \sigma_{b,t} \quad . \quad . \quad . \quad . \quad (7)$$

that can be written as, the values of the coefficients n_6 and n_7 being known

$$S = \sigma_{w,t} + n_7(\sigma_{w,t} + \sigma_{b,t}) \quad . \quad . \quad . \quad (8)$$

The first term of this relation describes the form of the roll gap when the mill is not loaded; the second term the interval existing between the work rolls and the supporting rolls. It can be seen from the results of Fig. 5 that the form of the active descriptive can differ appreciably from the parabolic curve. In this case it is still possible to use the simplified model by defining the equivalent crown of the rolls by:

$$\left(\frac{B}{L}\right)^2 S = PS + n_7 \left(\frac{B}{L}\right)^2 (SW + SB) \quad . \quad . \quad . \quad (9)$$

In this relation

(i) *PS* is the difference of the ordinates of the point in the centre and of the corresponding point at the edges of the strip, taken on the parabola, that best fits the active descriptive in contact with the strip
(ii) *SW* is the difference of the ordinates of the point in the centre and of the point at the edge of the table, taken on the parabola best fitting the complete profile of the active descriptive of the work roll
(iii) *SB* is the same as *SW*, but referring to the supporting roll.

FLATNESS OF THE STRIP

Two fibres are considered over the width of the strip, one in the centre and one at the edge. Representing the thickness of a fibre by the notation H and the length by L, both before deformation in a stand and by h and l after rolling, the relative lengthening of the fibres at the exit is, assuming no widening occurs:

$$\frac{\Delta l}{l} = \frac{H_m}{H_r} \frac{h_r}{h_m} \frac{L_m}{L_r} - 1$$

Introducing the crown index $\Sigma_s = 1 - h_r/h_m$, it is found that

$$\frac{\Delta l}{l} = \frac{1 - \Sigma_s}{1 - \Sigma_e} \frac{L_m}{L_r} - 1$$

or

$$\frac{\Delta l}{l} = \frac{\Sigma_e - \Sigma_s}{1 - \Sigma_e} + \frac{\Delta L}{L} \frac{1 - \Sigma_s}{1 - \Sigma_e} \quad . \quad \quad . \quad \quad . \quad \quad . \quad (10)$$

The ideal condition for flatness is the case for which at the exit of the stand, the relative lengthening for all fibres is zero, i.e. $\Delta l/l = 0$. Under these conditions it can be calculated with relation (10) that the profile at the exit of the stand is:

$$\Sigma_s = \frac{\Sigma_e + (\Delta L/L)}{1 + (\Delta L/L)}$$

In the case of a tandem mill the relative lengthening at the exit of the last stand may be expressed as a function of the exit profile and of the characteristics at the entry of a stand i:

$$\left(\frac{\Delta l}{l}\right)_f = \frac{(\Sigma_e)_i - (\Sigma_s)_f}{1 - (\Sigma_e)_i} + \left(\frac{\Delta L}{L}\right)_i \frac{1 - (\Sigma_s)_f}{1 - (\Sigma_e)_i}$$

If the bar is flat at the entry of stand i, the relative lengthening of the fibres at the exit of the train will be:

$$\left(\frac{\Delta l}{l}\right)_f = \frac{(\Sigma_e)_i - (\Sigma_s)_f}{1 - (\Sigma_e)_i} \quad . \quad \quad . \quad \quad . \quad \quad . \quad (11)$$

The relative lengthening of the fibres at the exit of a train has a relation to the final flatness of the strip. This is termed $\rho*$

$$\begin{cases} \rho* > 0 \text{ corresponds to a tendency to develop waves} \\ \quad \quad \text{in the centre} \\ \rho* < 0 \text{ corresponds to a tendency to develop wavy} \\ \quad \quad \text{edges.} \end{cases}$$

It must be noted that this simplified model is based on the hypothesis that the fibres lengthen independently of each other. It only can give approximate information on the development of flatness defects. On the other hand, however, it is found in practice that $\rho*$ need not be exactly equal to zero for the strip to be flat. There exists a region of values for $\rho*$ within which no waves appear.

Experimental verification

The crown of the rolls and the crown and the flatness of the strip have been calculated and measured for a campaign.

CROWN OF THE ROLLS

We have calculated the evolution of the thermal field and of the crown during the period of cooling in air after building out of the rolls of the last stand. These results have been compared to measurements of the surface temperatures with iron-constantane thermocouples.

(i) the temperature at the middle of the table of the upper roll has been recorded continuously for a period of 20 to 100 min after the exit of the last strip from F6

(ii) the thermal crown of the lower roll has been determined 40, 60, and 90 min after the exit of the last strip from F6.

It can be seen from the curves in Figs. 6a and 6b that the agreement between the calculated and measured values is very good. The calculated temperature in the centres is at the end of the campaign 2°C higher than that measured. At the edges the temperatures coincide. The crowns of the work rolls of stand 6 also have been measured 40 min after rolling the last strip. Figure 7 presents the comparison between the measured values (average of the upper and lower roll, at the operator and the drive sides) and the calculated values taking into account the thermal crown and the wear.

CROWN OF THE STRIP

With the model we have calculated the crown of the head ends of the strips of all 164 coils rolled during a campaign. The crown computed at the exit of a preceding stand is used as crown of entry at the consecutive stand. In this way the crown can be followed from the exit of F1 to the exit of F6. In order to judge the results it was necessary to obtain a large number of crown measurements. The crowns of about 100 samples taken at 5 m from the head end of the strip have been measured on a VOLLMER type profilometer. In order to be certain of the reproducibility of the results several measurements have been made of each sample.

In Fig. 8 can be found the comparison between the measured and calculated results for several coils. The agreement is very good. It is shown particularly that with the model the gradient at the edge is reproduced to an extent as corresponds with practice. After this qualitative verification we have compared the calculated and measured crown indices at 40 mm from the edges. Inspection of the curves of Fig. 9 shows that the agreement of these values is excellent.

FLATNESS OF THE STRIP

During all our tests we have never found flatness defects before the exit of the third stand. So stand F2 can be taken as reference stand for characterizing the state of flatness of the strip at the exit of the tandem mill. The flatness index of the strip is defined by the following expression:

$$\rho* = \frac{(\Sigma_s)_2 - (\Sigma_s)_6}{1 - (\Sigma_s)_2} = \frac{\Sigma_3 - \Sigma_7}{1 - \Sigma_3}$$

From the values of Σ_3 and Σ_7 as calculated by the profile

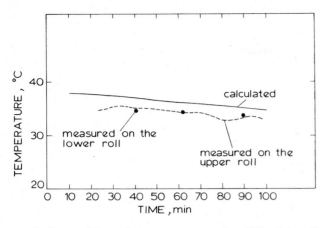

6a Evolution of the surface temperature at the middle of the roller table of the work rolls of F6 building out

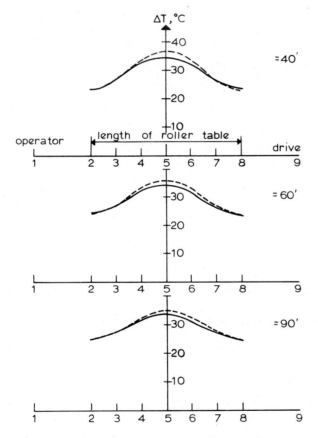

6b Temperature distribution calculated (indicated by the broken line) and measured (indicated by the unbroken line) at the surface of the lower work roll of F6 at different instances after building out

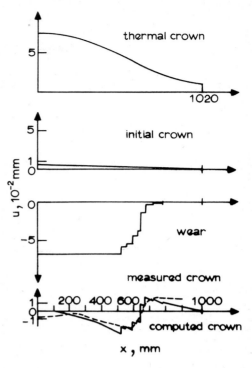

7 Comparison between calculated and measured roll crown 40 min after F6 building out

can be superposed, if a change of origin is made for the values of ρ^*. It is likely that the necessity for the translation of the curve arises from poor estimation of the value of Σ_3. The calculated values of the crowns at the two first stands will be lower than the actual values as

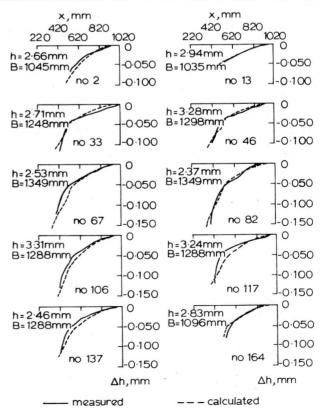

8 Comparison between some calculated and measured strip crowns during campaign no. 3

model we have drawn the curve giving the value of ρ^* for each coil of the campaign (Fig. 10a). To this curve we can compare the curve that qualitatively represents the state of flatness at the exit of the finishing train (Fig. 10b). The determination of the state of flatness has been performed both from direct visual observation and from photographs taken 3 s after the head end of the strip had left F6 (it can be seen that the results obtained in the two cases are in good agreement). The comparison of the two curves is made in Fig. 10c. It can be seen that the curves

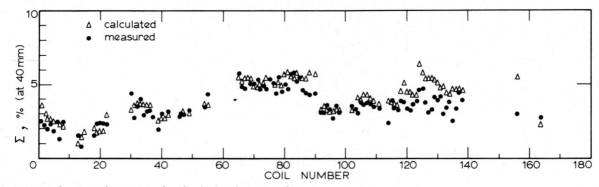

9   *Comparison between the measured and calculated crown indices*

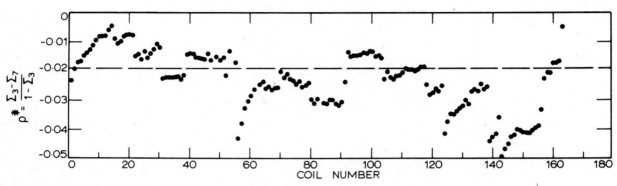

10a   *Calculated values of the flatness index at F6*

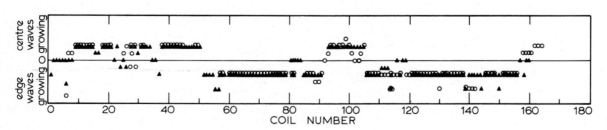

10b   *State of flatness observed of the head end*

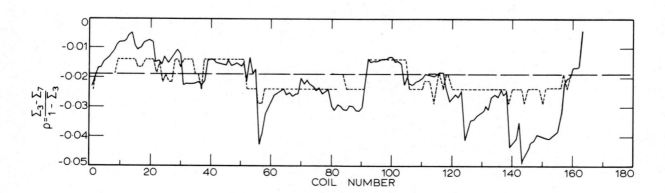

10c   *Comparison between the state of flatness as calculated and as observed*

the model does not take into account the transverse flow of material. This point must still be looked into. However, it is established that the parameter ρ^* can successfully be used for characterizing qualitatively the state of flatness at the exit of the finishing train. Having shown the validity of the various models, we will now examine how it will be possible to solve with them the problem that interests us.

OPTIMIZATION AT COIL LEVEL

Let us recall which problems arise in practice:

(i) in general the distribution of the load between the stand of the finishing train and the forces to be developed in the roll bending equipment must be determined

(ii) a particular case of the general problem is to determine the forces to be developed in the roll bending system, when the law for the load distribution between the stands is prescribed

(iii) another particular case is to seek the ideal load distribution in the case that roll bending equipment is not available.

The two first problems only have a limited applicability. We shall not consider them here. The problem of the load distribution, on the contrary, is very important. It is known that in the classical system of computer control of continuous hot strip mills the calculation of the presetting is performed on the basis of coefficients of load distributions that are stored in the memory of the computer. The span left to the operator for modifying these coefficients is limited. These systems suffer from a too great rigidity. They do not allow the actual state of the mill to be taken into account. Among the disadvantages of the systems can be mentioned the difficulty to control the flatness of the strips. The algorithm that we propose makes it possible to calculate from data characterizing the state of the mill at the considered instant the reduction schedule for transforming a known product in a strip of prescribed characteristics, taking into account the limitation of the mill and providing a best fit to an optimizing criterion.

Defining the problem

The known characteristics of the product to be rolled are:

(i) the thickness h_1
(ii) the temperature T_1
(iii) the width B
(iv) the quality K.

The specifications are given as:

(i) the final thickness h_7
(ii) the final temperature T_7
(iii) the final crown index Σ_7.

The state of the finishing train is characterized by

(i) the diameters of the work rolls and the supporting rolls

(ii) the equivalent crowns of the work rolls and the supporting rolls.

The presetting of the train can be translated into the determination of the following parameters

(i) the thickness h_{i+1} at the exit of the stand 1 to 5 (5×)
(ii) the crowns Σ_{i+1} at the exit of the stand 1 to 5 (5×)
(iii) the velocities v_{i+1} of the strip (7×)
(iv) the velocities u_i of the rolls (6×)
(v) the temperatures T_i in the stands 2 to 6 (5×)
(vi) the rolling forces F_i (6×)
(vii) the rolling couples C_i (6×)
(viii) the electric power taken up by the drive motors P_i (6×)

In total the value of 46 parameters has to be determined. For calculating the values of these parameters the following relations are available

(i) the conservation of mass flow $h_i v_i = $ constant
(ii) a relation between the velocity of the strip and the velocity of the roll $v_{i+1} = f(u_i, h_i, h_{i+1})$
(iii) the profile model
(iv) the force model
(v) the temperature model
(vi) the power model
(vii) the couple model.

In total there are 42 relations. Therefore, the system possesses four degrees of freedom. The limitations are of two types:

(i) the limitations of the mill

$$P_i \leqslant p_1 P_{Mi}$$
$$C_i \leqslant p_2 C_{Mi}$$
$$F_i \leqslant p_3 F_{Mi}$$
$$u_i \leqslant p_4 u_{Mi}$$
$$v_7 \leqslant v_{M7}$$

The coefficients $p(p < 1)$ have been introduced for taking into account the fact that the parameters are calculated for the head end of the strip and that the limit values may not be exceeded at the tail end. The last limitation is determined by the phenomenon of flying of the strip between the finishing train and the coiler.

(ii) the limitations with respect to the flatness of the strip. Good flatness of the strip is required between the stands and at the exit of the finishing train. The flatness condition at the exit of the finishing train is met, if the following expression has been adhered to for all stands (i)

$$|\rho_i^*| = \left| \frac{\Sigma_i - \Sigma_7}{1 - \Sigma_i} \right| \leqslant \rho_{cri}^*$$

The fact that a limit flatness index exists sets the suitability of the crown of the strip to adapt itself to the profile of the roll gap. It can be shown that the expression of the critical value of the flatness index can be expressed as:

$$\rho_{cri}^* = f(i) \left(\frac{h_7}{B} \right)^2$$

The value of the function $f(i)$ increases with increasing strip thickness and temperature. Therefore, it is a decreasing function of the stand number.

As the system has four degrees of freedom an infinite number of solutions exist. Among this collection of solutions those that best meet an optimization criterion can be determined. Various optimization criteria can be chosen. We have selected three:

(i) criterion 1 concerns the distribution of electric power between the stands. The function that has to be minimized is the following:

$$\epsilon_1 = \sum_{i=1}^{6} \left(\frac{P_i}{P_{Mi}} - \frac{1}{6} \sum_{i=1}^{6} \frac{P_i}{P_{Mi}} \right)^2$$

(ii) criterion 2 concerns strip flatness. The following function must be minimized:

$$\epsilon_2 = \sum_{i=2}^{6} |\rho_i^*|$$

(iii) criterion 3 is a mixed criterion. The function to minimize is:

$$\epsilon_3 = q_1\epsilon_1 + q_2\epsilon_2$$

The coefficients q are weight factors.

Solution method

In order to solve the problem shown, we used the method of dynamic programming. First, the range of variation which is permitted for the thickness at the exit of each stand is determined. Among all ways that lead to obtaining the desired values (thickness, crown, temperature) that is selected that satisfies best the applied optimization criterion. In the case that it is not possible to attain the prescribed value, the solution is kept that approaches most that value.

OPTIMIZATION AT THE LEVEL OF MILL SET UP

A problem equally important as the previous is the determination of the crowns to be given to the rolls at the grinding shop. We have just seen how it was possible to calculate for each coil the load distribution for the various stands of the train. When the finishing train has run in it is possible to join to each format (required width x thickness) a 'typical' load distribution. We assume that these 'typical' load distributions are known for all formats of the rolling schedule under consideration.

Defining the problem

To solve the problem four types of data are necessary.

(i) all characteristics at the entry and the exit for all coils of a rolling schedule
(ii) the rolling sequence defined by the time interval between the rolling of consecutive strips

(iii) the crowns of the supporting rolls must be known and are assumed to remain unchanged during a campaign
(iv) the desired final crown, that imposes the profile of the roll gaps after running in for a reference format Σ_7.

We have tried to find a solution for the problem that has a great versatility while being as general as possible, which was not the case with the already proposed methods.[7,8] Also it is easily possible to modify one or more input variables to study directly the influence of this variation on the ideal values of the crowns of the rolls.

Solution method

The solution method is composed of three parts. First from the characteristics at the entry and the exit of the strips are calculated: the rolling parameters for the different stands corresponding to the 'typical' load distributions and in particular the forces, the thicknesses and the temperatures, and the duration of rolling. Second, the profile is determined of the active descriptive of the work roll of each stand and for each coil, taking account of the wear and the thermal field, starting from a zero initial roll crown. S^* is the value of the equivalent corresponding roll crown. If the initial roll crown would be equal to $S \neq 0$, the value of the equivalent roll crown would have been:

$$S' = S^* + n_6 S \qquad . \qquad . \qquad . \qquad . \qquad (10)$$

Therefore, the problem consists in determining the initial values of the roll crowns at each stand that allow rolling under the optimal conditions for flatness for all coils of the rolling schedule. The algorithm is the following:

(i) with relation (6) is calculated the roll crown, after running in S' at the last stand, that leads to the prescribed value of the crown of the strip at the exit for the reference format. The initial value S is determined corresponding to it according to relation (10) as well as the values of the roll crowns, after running in S' for all coils and the values of the crowns of the strip at the exit.
(ii) the limits between which the crown of the strip must be at the last stand but one, so that the strip will be flat at the last stand, are given by

$$\Sigma_7 - \rho_{cr6}^* \leqslant \Sigma_6 \leqslant \Sigma_7 + \rho_{cr6}^*$$

Using the profile model, the limit values can be found of the actual roll crown at the last stand but one:

$$S'_{m5} \leqslant S'_5 \leqslant S'_{M5}$$

Knowing the value of S^* for the considered coil, the limits of the span of variation of the initial crown are given by:

$$S_{m5} \leqslant S_5 \leqslant S_{M5}$$

These limits exist for each coil. Next the common zone

of all these spans is determined, which defines the possible margin of the crown to give to the last stand but one. Finally, within this margin is sought the value that meets the following optimization criterion

$$\sum_{\text{coils}} \left(\frac{\rho_i^*}{\rho_{\text{cri}}^*}\right)^2 = \text{minimum}$$

These calculations have to be repeated for all stands.

REFERENCES

1 CARSLAW AND JAEGER: 'Heat conduction in solids', 1959, Oxford
2 B. FAZAN: *Rev. Mét.*, Nov., 1960
3 S. WILMOTTE et al.: Metallurgical Reports CRM, Mar., 1972
4 B. FAZAN AND J. C. ALBERT: *Rev. Mét.*, Jan., 1963
5 O. PAWELSKI AND H. SCHROEDER: *Arch. Eisenh.*, Oct., 1968
6 Y. MISAKA AND T. YOKOI: ICSTIS Congress, Sept., 1970, Tokyo
7 V. P. VOLEGOV et al.: *Stal in English*, 1966, **6**
8 K. H. WEBER: *Neue Hütte*, Jan., 1971
9 S. WILMOTTE AND J. MIGNON: Metallurgical Reports CRM, to be published

Calculation of temperature distribution in a hot-rolled sheet on the run-out table, with emphasis on the α–γ transition

R. Wartmann and H. Mertes

On the run-out table of a hot strip mill, a rise in the temperature of the strip may take place because of the α–γ transition in the region of 600°C. If this is not completed before the strip is coiled, texture defects will be caused. A mathematical model has been developed, based on the behaviour of an 8 mm strip, and taking into account the cooling conditions on the run-out table, the temperature dependence of the material constants and the heat of the α–γ transition. This model makes it possible to calculate the location, and the degree of completion of the transition from pyrometer readings at two points only. The model has been applied to a 20 mm strip, passing along the run-out table at a lower speed. It is found that, although the surface cools, and the transition occurs, the centre does not cool sufficiently, and the transition does not take place until the strip has been coiled.

SYMBOLS

c	specific heat of steel
d	strip thickness
Δd	thickness of a volume element
k	specific heat averaged over the volume element
n	number of layers over the strip thickness
t	time
t_u	duration of transition
Δt	length of time interval
u	heat of transition at the α–γ point
$\dot{u}_v$	transition velocity
α_0, α_n	heat-transfer coefficient strip-cooling medium
ϑ_i	temperature of the point i in the strip at the beginning of the time interval
ϑ_i^*	temperature of the point i in the strip at the end of the time interval
$\vartheta_{A0}, \vartheta_{An}$	temperature of the cooling medium
ϑ_u	temperature of the start of transition
λ	heat conductivity of steel
ρ	density of steel

The authors are with Hoesch Hüttenwerke, Dortmund

Cooling of the hot-rolled strip on the run-out table not only aims at obtaining the correct coiling temperature, but also at controlling the cooling rate such that the steel attains its required physical poperties. This paper does not attempt to elucidate the technological aspects of the problem, as has been done for a hot strip mill by Hoogovens.[1] The emphasis will be on the influence of the heat of recrystallization at the α–γ transition point on the temperature distribution in the strip, when the start and the duration of transition is varied. Also a method will be developed, with which from two measurements of the surface temperature at the end of the run-out table the start and the duration of the transition can be determined. The basis of these studies is a mathematical model describing the temperature distribution in a strip as a function of time.

DEFINITION OF THE PROBLEM

On the run-out table of the hot strip mill of the West-falenhütte two pyrometers, sighted at the strip surface, have been installed at 83·60 m (pyrometer 1) and at 108 m (pyrometer 2) from the last finisher. Many measurements indicate that the temperature sensed by pyrometer 2 is higher than that sensed by pyrometer 1. At first sight, these surprising results can be explained by assuming that between the pyrometers, part of the $\alpha-\gamma$ transition takes place. This possibility is important because if in the majority of cases the transition takes place at the end of the run-out table, there is a danger that it will continue in the coil and so lead to texture defects.

To obtain insight into the problem, all available data at the hot strip mill of the Westfalenhütte were assembled for several coils. With the help of a mathematical model for this set of data, the temperature at which the $\alpha-\gamma$ transition started and its duration were determined. The mathematical model calculates the temperature distribution in the strip as a function of time. The boundary conditions take into account cooling on the run-out table, e.g. air or water cooling, the temperature dependence of the material constants and the heat of recrystallization of the $\alpha-\gamma$ transition.

Among the most important parameters is the heat-transfer coefficient from strip to water. Unfortunately although this coefficient can be estimated theoretically, due to many operational influences, it cannot be accurately calculated. Therefore, it must be deduced from the test data together with the start and the duration of transition. To obtain the unknown quantities, start of transition, duration of transition, and heat-transfer coefficient from strip to water, they were varied systematically in the model till the measured results were reproduced. This method will be elucidated below. On the basis of the results so obtained it will be very simple to use the model for calculating the behaviour of much thicker strips (16–20 mm) in order to predict their metallurgical properties.

FUNDAMENTALS OF THE MATHEMATICAL MODEL

In order to make the model generally applicable, all data necessary for calculating the temperature distribution in the strip are introduced from the outside. Among these are:

(i) material constants of the rolled steel including the heat of transition, the temperature of the start of transition and the transition time (both these last quantities usually take the shape of parameters, of which the value must first be determined by the model)

(ii) the length of the run-out table, the position, and the characteristic heat-transfer coefficient of all installed cooling elements

(iii) thickness, velocity, and final rolling temperature of the strip

(iv) indication of which cooling elements are in use

(v) various basic data for the mathematical model, e.g. the value of the time interval and the number of layers over the strip thickness.

When more calculations are made consecutively for each

case only those data that are different from the preceding case have to be put in. So a significantly easier operation is obtained, especially as the data under i and ii do not change for one steel quality and one hot strip mill. The originally planned input of the complete temperature–time transition diagram had to be abandoned, as this diagram also depends on the rolling pressure. The mechanism of the $\alpha-\gamma$ transition is represented in the model in the following way. The transition starts in a volume element, when its temperature decreases below the transition temperature. During the time given by the transition period, the volume element liberates the heat of transition uniformly. This means that the centre and the surface of the strip in particular undergo transition at different times.

The calculation of the temperature distribution in a strip becomes a three-dimensional transient heat-conduction problem. Owing to the required calculation effort, that is even too much for a large type computer, it will be necessary to reduce the number of dimensions, which in the considered case is possible without introducing appreciable errors. The temperature gradient transversely to the direction of movement is practically zero, as the strip is very wide with respect to its thickness. The temperature gradient in the direction of movement can be taken as zero, owing to the strip's high velocity (2–4 m/s). So a one-dimensional transient heat-conduction problem is left with time-dependent boundary conditions, temperature-dependent material constants, and with a temperature- and time-dependent heat source. Such a problem can be solved with a modern large computer in a reasonable time. The calculating time for the case of an IBM 370/165 is about 15 s. The explicit treatment of radiation can be neglected as a rough calculation shows that the contribution of radiation in the case of water cooling remains below 2%. In the case of air cooling the strip radiation can be taken into account by increasing the heat transfer coefficient correspondingly.

MATHEMATICAL MODEL

The transient heat-conduction problem reduced to one coordinate in space has no analytical solution as the material constants depend on temperature and the boundary conditions on time. Therefore, for solving the heat-conduction equation the Crank–Nicholson method[3] has been used with iteration of the matrix of coefficients. The derivation is performed directly from the heat-balance equation of a volume element. Like most methods for numerically solving partial differential equations, the Crank–Nicholson method works by discretization of the independent variables of place and time. When the strip is divided over its thickness in n equal layers of thickness Δd, $n + 1$ points are obtained P_i, $i = 0, \ldots, n$. The inside points $P_1, \ldots, P_{n-1}$ are supposed to correspond with a volume element of thickness Δd, the outside points P_0 and P_n with a volume element of thickness $\frac{1}{2}\Delta d$. For each point P_i the temperature ϑ_i^* at the end of the time interval is calculated from ϑ_i, the temperature at the beginning of the time interval, with the help of the equations that follow. The points inside the strip $P_1, \ldots, P_{n-1}$ satisfy the balance equations.

$$[k_i^*\vartheta_i^* - k_i\vartheta_i]\,\Delta d = \left[\frac{\vartheta_{i-1}^* + \vartheta_{i-1}}{2} - \frac{\vartheta_i^* + \vartheta_i}{2}\right]$$
$$\times \lambda_{i-}\frac{\Delta t}{\Delta d}$$
$$+ \left[\frac{\vartheta_{i+1}^* + \vartheta_{i+1}}{2} - \frac{\vartheta_i^* + \vartheta_i}{2}\right]$$
$$\times \lambda_{i+}\frac{\Delta t}{\Delta d} + \varkappa_i\dot{u}_v\,\Delta t\,\Delta d. \qquad (1)$$

For point P_0:

$$[k_0^*\vartheta_0^* - k_0\vartheta_0]\frac{\Delta d}{2} = \left[\vartheta_{A0} - \frac{\vartheta_0^* + \vartheta_0}{2}\right]\alpha_0\,\Delta t$$
$$+ \left[\frac{\vartheta_1^* + \vartheta_1}{2} - \frac{\vartheta_0^* + \vartheta_0}{2}\right]$$
$$\times \lambda_{0+}\frac{\Delta t}{\Delta d} + \varkappa_0\dot{u}_v\,\Delta t\frac{\Delta d}{2} \qquad (2)$$

and for point P_n:

$$[k_n^*\vartheta_n^* - k_n\vartheta_n]\frac{\Delta d}{2} = \left[\frac{\vartheta_{n-1}^* + \vartheta_{n-1}}{2} - \frac{\vartheta_n^* + \vartheta_n}{2}\right]$$
$$\times \lambda_{n-}\frac{\Delta t}{\Delta d}$$
$$+ \left[\vartheta_{An} - \frac{\vartheta_n^* + \vartheta_n}{2}\right]\alpha_n\,\Delta t$$
$$+ \varkappa_n\dot{u}_v\,\Delta t\frac{\Delta d}{2} \qquad (3)$$

The heat conductivities $\lambda_{i\pm}$ between the points P_i and $P_{i\pm1}$ are averaged over time and place. Averaging over place is carried out using the equation

$$\lambda_{i\pm} = \frac{2\lambda_i\lambda_{i\pm1}}{\lambda_i + \lambda_{i\pm1}} \qquad (4)$$

Averaging over time is realized by considering λ_i and $\lambda_{i\pm1}$ as a function of $(\vartheta_i^* + \vartheta_i)/2$ resp. $(\vartheta_{i\pm1}^* + \vartheta_{i\pm1})/2$. The temperatures $\vartheta_{A0}, \vartheta_{An}$ of the cooling medium (air or water) and the heat-transfer coefficients α_0 and α_n are functions of time, or, which is the same, functions of the position on the run-out table. The average specific heats k_i per volume element satisfy the equation

$$k_i = \frac{1}{\vartheta_i}\int_0^{\vartheta_i} c_i\rho_i\,d\vartheta . \qquad (5)$$

in which the specific heat c_i and the density ρ_i at point P_i are functions of temperature. This way of defining k_i has been chosen to obtain an expression which is linear in the temperatures ϑ_i^*. The terms $\varkappa_i\dot{u}_v\,\Delta t\,\Delta d$ resp. $\varkappa_0\dot{u}_v\,\Delta t\,\Delta d/2$ or $\varkappa_n\dot{u}_v\,\Delta t\,\Delta d/2$ represent the heat flow that results at the $\alpha-\gamma$ transition at the considered point. The quantity $\varkappa_i$ is equal to 1, when at point P_i the transition is just

in progress otherwise it is equal to zero. For the transition velocity $\dot{u}_v$ the following relation is valid

$$\dot{u}_v = \frac{u\rho}{t_u} \qquad . \qquad . \qquad . \qquad (6)$$

in which u is the heat of transition and t_u the duration of the transition. When the material constants k_i^* and $\lambda_{i\pm}$ are taken as temperature independent the Eqs. (1)–(3) form a set of $n + 1$ linear equations in ϑ_i^* with $n + 1$ unknowns. In the matrix of coefficients only the main diagonal and both the adjacent diagonals are occupied. When its coefficients are represented by a_{ij}' and the components of the vector on the right side by b_i', then follows:

$$a_{00}'\vartheta_0^* + a_{0,1}'\vartheta_1^* = b_0',$$
$$a_{i,i-1}'\vartheta_{i-1}^* + a_{ii}'\vartheta_i^* + a_{i,i+1}'\vartheta_{i+1}^* = b_i',$$
$$i = 1, \ldots, n-1$$
$$a_{n,n-1}'\vartheta_{n-1}^* + a_{nn}'\vartheta_n^* = b_n' . \qquad . \qquad (7)$$

with

$$a_{00}' = k_0^*\frac{\Delta d}{2} + \frac{1}{2}\cdot\frac{\Delta t}{\Delta d}[\alpha_0\,\Delta d + \lambda_{0+}], . \qquad . \qquad (8)$$

$$a_{ii}' = k_i^*\,\Delta d + \frac{1}{2}\cdot\frac{\Delta t}{\Delta d}[\lambda_{i-} + \lambda_{i+}] \qquad i = 1, \ldots, n-1 \qquad (9)$$

$$a_{nn}' = k_n^*\frac{\Delta d}{2} + \frac{1}{2}\cdot\frac{\Delta t}{\Delta d}[\lambda_{n-} + \alpha_n\,\Delta d] . \qquad . \qquad (10)$$

$$a_{i,i-1}' = -\frac{1}{2}\cdot\frac{\Delta t}{\Delta d}\lambda_{i-} \qquad i = 1, \ldots, n \qquad (11)$$

$$a_{i,i+1}' = -\frac{1}{2}\cdot\frac{\Delta t}{\Delta d}\lambda_{i+} \qquad i = 0, \ldots, n-1 \qquad (12)$$

$$b_0' = \left[k_0\frac{\Delta d}{2} - \frac{1}{2}\cdot\frac{\Delta t}{\Delta d}(\alpha_0\,\Delta d + \lambda_{0+})\right]\vartheta_0 + \alpha_0\,\Delta t\vartheta_{A0}$$
$$+ \frac{1}{2}\cdot\frac{\Delta t}{\Delta d}\lambda_{0+}\vartheta_1 + \varkappa_0\dot{u}_v\,\Delta t\frac{\Delta d}{2}, \qquad . \qquad (13)$$

$$b_i' = \left[k_i\,\Delta d - \frac{1}{2}\cdot\frac{\Delta t}{\Delta d}(\lambda_{i-} + \lambda_{i+})\right]\vartheta_i + \frac{1}{2}\cdot\frac{\Delta t}{\Delta d}\lambda_{i-}\vartheta_{i-1}$$
$$+ \frac{1}{2}\cdot\frac{\Delta t}{\Delta d}\lambda_{i+}\vartheta_{i+1} + \varkappa_i\dot{u}_v\,\Delta t\,\Delta d \qquad i = 1, \ldots, n-1$$
$$(14)$$

and

$$b_n' = \left[k_n\frac{\Delta d}{2} - \frac{1}{2}\cdot\frac{\Delta t}{\Delta d}(\lambda_{n-} + \alpha_n\,\Delta d)\right]\vartheta_n$$
$$+ \frac{1}{2}\cdot\frac{\Delta t}{\Delta d}\lambda_{n-}\vartheta_{n-1} + \alpha_n\,\Delta t\vartheta_{An} + \varkappa_n\dot{u}_v\,\Delta t\frac{\Delta d}{2} \qquad (15)$$

If

$$a_{ij} = \frac{a_{ij}'}{a_{ii}'} \qquad . \qquad . \qquad . \qquad . \qquad . \qquad (16)$$

and

$$b_i = \frac{b_i'}{a_{ii}'} \qquad . \qquad . \qquad . \qquad . \qquad . \qquad (17)$$

then the following expression results

$$\vartheta_i^* = b_i - a_{i,i-1}\vartheta_{i-1}^* - a_{i,i+1}\vartheta_{i+1}^* \quad i = 0,\ldots,n \quad (18)$$

The temperatures ϑ_{-1}^* and ϑ_{n+1}^* as well as the coefficients $a_{0,-1}$ and $a_{n,n+1}$ have only been introduced formally and are put equal to zero at the start of the calculation. As has already been mentioned the matrix of coefficients only takes the shape of a tridiagonal matrix and so is not fully occupied and as the temperatures ϑ_i^* are not much different from ϑ_i, it seems a good choice to utilize the Gausz–Seidel method for solving the set of Eq. (18) with as start vector $\{\vartheta_0,\ldots,\vartheta_n\}$. The convergence of the method is ensured as

$$|a_{i,i-1}| + |a_{i,i+1}| < 1 \quad i = 0,\ldots,n \quad . \quad . \quad (19)$$

This is valid for each time interval. Therefore, the limitation existing in the Schmidt method[2] of the choice of the time interval in relation to the thickness Δd is avoided. Of course, this does not mean that the Crank–Nicholson method produces sufficiently accurate results for each arbitrary time interval. Only the permissible time interval becomes appreciably greater. In our case the permissible time interval is increased by a factor of 10. This obviously leads to an appreciable reduction in computer time.

In Fig. 1 the number of iterations of the temperature vector per time interval is shown for the whole cooling stretch as a function of the duration of the time interval. A decrease of the number of iterations can be noted for the cooling stretch, when increasing the time interval, although the number of iterations per time interval increases.

Acceleration of the convergence of the Gausz–Seidel method is obtained by the application of successive overrelaxation. In Fig. 2 the number of iterations of the temperature vector for the total cooling period is shown as function of the overrelaxation factor ω. The greater the time interval chosen, the greater becomes the acceleration of convergence.

In order to include the temperature dependency of the material constants in every time interval Δt the coefficients of the set of Eq. (18) must be iterated. This is performed by first making ϑ_i^* equal to ϑ_i, which results in a matrix of coefficients from which an approximate solution is obtained for the temperatures ϑ_i^*. Then, the material constants and so the matrix of coefficients is calculated again, from which again follows an approximate solution of ϑ_i^* etc. This method is continued until the results for ϑ_i^* do not change any more within a predetermined error limit.

RESULTS

In this section some results obtained with the model will be treated. In Fig. 3 is represented the characteristic

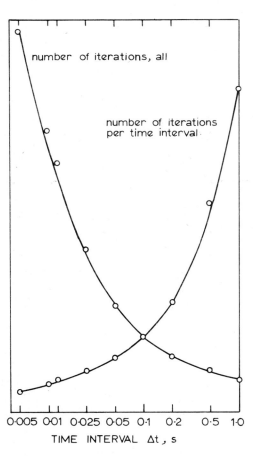

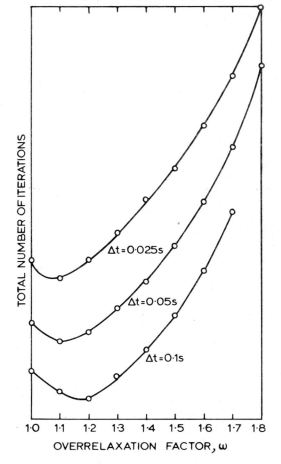

1 Number of iterations of the temperature vector for the run-out table and per time interval as a function of the length of the time interval

2 Number of iterations of the temperature vector for the run-out table depending on the overrelaxation factor for several time intervals

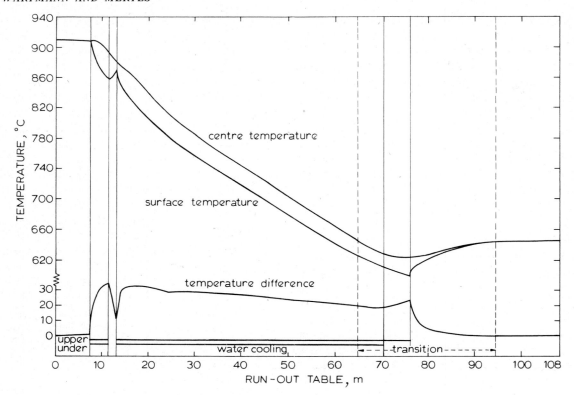

The start of transition is at 630°C, the duration of transition is 6 s

3   *Curves of the centre and surface temperatures as well as their difference along the run-out table for an 8 mm strip at a velocity of 4 m/s*

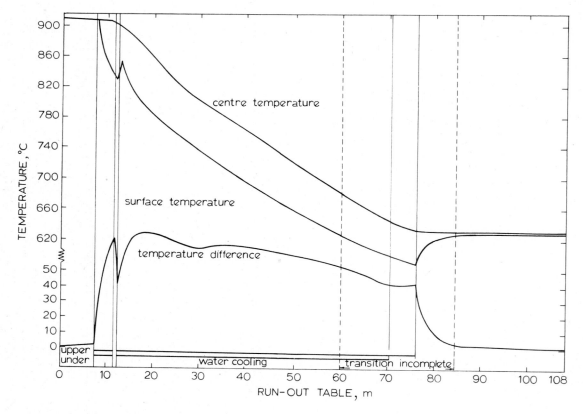

The start of transition is at 630°C, the duration is 6 s

4   *Curves of the centre and surface temperature as well as their difference along the run-out table for a 20 mm strip at a velocity of 1·6 m/s*

evolution of the surface and centre temperature of an 8 mm thick strip along the cooling table. Along the abscissa it has been marked where water cooling has been used on the table. In these zones, high-temperature gradients appear. When the strip enters a stretch without water cooling, these gradients decrease rapidly to a small value and actually an increase of the surface temperature takes place by heat flow from the centre. The minimum that appears in the temperature gradient at around 24 m is caused by the temperature dependency of the material constants. At around 65 m the α–γ transition starts, first in the outer layer, later in the centre of the strip. The result is a general increase of all temperatures by the heat of transition liberated. The transition is finished inside the strip at around 95 m.

In Fig. 4 the evolution of the surface and centre temperature of a 20 mm strip along the cooling table at equal cooling power is shown. Owing to the greater amount of heat to be removed the strip moves with only 40 % of the velocity of the 8 mm strip. A comparison of the temperatures of both strips shows the phenomena to be expected, i.e. low surface and high centre temperature for the 20 mm strip and so much greater temperature differences. Therefore the transition sets in at the surface earlier. It cannot penetrate into the strip, as there the temperatures do not sink below the temperature of start of transition, so that the transition is limited to the outside layers of the strip. Therefore, the transition of the centre part has to take place after coiling. Owing to the incomplete transition of the 20 mm strip, its surface temperature at 108 m remains below that of the completely transformed 8 mm strip, an expected result.

In Fig. 5 is shown the course of the surface temperatures as measured by both pyrometers and their difference with the temperature ϑ_u of the start of transition for transition durations of 6 s and 10 s at otherwise equal conditions. At the transition temperature $\vartheta_u = 580°C$ no transition takes place on the run-out table. The small temperature difference between the two pyrometers is caused by a heating of the surface by heat flow from the centre. With a growing ϑ_u the temperatures of both pyrometers rise as now the transition starts on the run-out table. These temperatures reach their maximum, when the transition ends at the corresponding pyrometer. The subsequent temperature drop is caused by the increased heat removal in the water cooled part of the cooling stretch, as there an ever greater part of the transition takes place with increasing transition temperature ϑ_u. When the complete transition takes place before pyrometer 1 is reached, as is shown in Fig. 5 for the case of a transition duration of 6 s, then a similar situation exists as at $\vartheta_u = 580°C$. The temperature difference has come back to a small amount. The temperature level lies about 35°C higher. This temperature difference is also found by calculation, when the heat of transition is divided by the specific heat of steel. The shape of the curves of the temperature difference between the two pyrometers can be explained by the fact that at low values of ϑ_u the transition in the strip is still incomplete as the centre is not transformed. For growing ϑ_u finally the transition is completed. At the same time the position of the start of transition shifts upstream, so that the part of the transition that takes place between the pyrometers, becomes ever smaller, until finally all transition takes place before pyrometer 1. For a duration of the transition t_u, that corresponds to the retention time of the strip on the run-out table, this last phenomenon obviously cannot occur.

In Fig. 6 are shown the surface temperatures measured with both pyrometers and their difference against the duration of the transition for transition temperatures of 600°C and 620°C at furthermore equal conditions. It is conspicuous that at small values of t_u the temperature difference between both pyrometers is negative. This effect is caused by the high transition velocity $\dot{u}_v$, that strongly increases the surface temperature of the strip and so blocks the heat flow from the centre to the cooling water. Therefore, the transformation of the centre does not take place. On the stretch between the two pyrometers the heat flows from the outside layers of the strip to the outside and to the centre, so that a negative temperature difference is found. With increasing duration of the transition this blockage disappears and finally again positive differences are obtained between the two pyrometers.

In general, the pyrometer temperatures themselves pass through a maximum, when the transition has be-

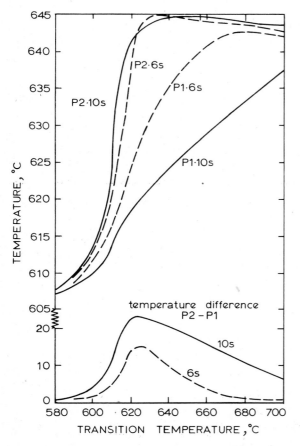

5 *Curves of the temperature at both pyrometers P1 (at 83·6 m) and P2 (at 108 m) and their temperature difference depending on transition temperature and the duration of the transition of 6 and 10 s*

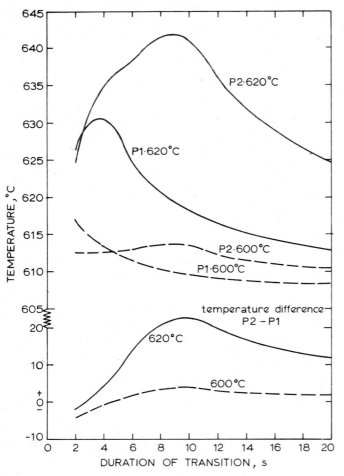

*6   Curves of the temperature at both pyrometers P1 (at 83·6 m)
      and P2 (at 108 m) and their temperature difference depending
      on the duration of the transition at transition temperatures of
      600 and 620°C*

come complete before the considered pyrometer. For
the pyrometer 1, mounted closer to the finishing train,
this happens at a shorter duration of transition as for
pyrometer 2. After reaching the maximum the temperature curve falls again as an ever greater part of the heat
of transition is liberated behind the pyrometer. This state
of affairs also causes the increase to a maximum of the
temperature differences with growing t_u. If the transition
were to start without delay over all the strip, then this
maximum must be found at the same duration of transition at both pyrometers. However, as the transition starts
later in the centre of the strip than on the surface, a shift
is found of the position of both maxima with respect to
each other.

The relations just shown between the start and duration of the transition on the one hand and both the
pyrometer temperatures on the other hand can be
utilized to calculate the first from the last. Several solutions exist. Let us for example assume that at pyrometer
1 a temperature of 617°C has been measured and at
pyrometer 2, 637°C. The temperature difference is 20°C.
In Fig. 7 two intersections are found of the temperature
difference curve for $t_u = 10$ s at $\vartheta_u = 616$°C, and $\vartheta_u =
642$°C. Only the first intersection can be used and it gives

exactly both the measured temperatures of 617 and
637°C. If the same method is applied for Fig. 8, then
also two intersections are found on the temperature difference curve for $\vartheta_u = 620$°C at $t_u = 7·7$ s and $t_u = 11·9$ s.
In this case the second point results in both the temperatures measured by the pyrometers. Therefore, two solu-
tions exist: $\vartheta_u = 616$°C, $t_u = 10$ s and $\vartheta_u = 620$°C,
$t_u = 11·9$ s. This does not prove that more solutions
always exist. Also it will not be attempted here to prove
this. Some comments may be sufficient.

The temperatures measured with both pyrometers
can be considered as functions of the start ϑ_u and duration t_u of transition. Geometrically therefore, the temperatures can be represented as surfaces over the (ϑ_u, t_u)
plane. The curves shown in Fig. 7 and Fig. 8 then are
intersections through these surfaces parallel to both coordinate axes. It is found that the surface of the temperature differences between both pyrometers possesses a
maximum and from there on falls monotonously in all
directions. For this reason the geometrical locus of
constant temperature difference is a continuous curve
without intersections. The geometrical locus of constant
temperature at pyrometer 2 is also a continuous curve
without intersections.

Except in special cases two continuous curves intersect each other always in at least two points, if they have

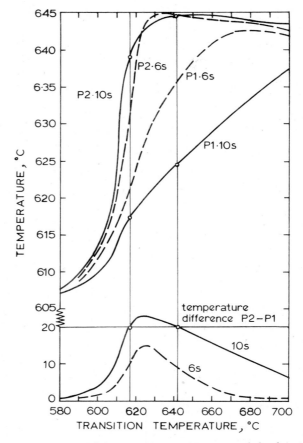

*7   Determination of the transition temperature and the duration
      of transition in a hot-rolled strip from two pyrometers measure-
      ments (see Fig. 5)*

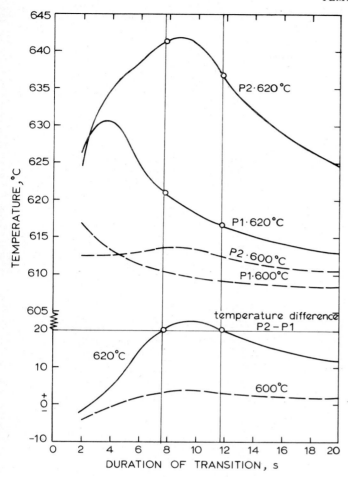

8   *For the determination of the transition temperature and the duration of the transition in a hot-rolled strip from two pyrometer measurements (see Fig. 6)*

an intersection at all. When more solutions for the start and duration of the transition have been found, it will be necessary to exclude some by other calculations or for technological or metallurgical reasons. When it happens that both the previously mentioned curves have no intersection, an incorrect heat-transfer coefficient strip-water can be the reason, as it influences the temperature curves of Fig. 7 and Fig. 8. For the heat-transfer coefficient strip-water a value can easily be estimated, as the temperature measured at pyrometer 2 can only differ by 35°C from that at pyrometer 1. This means a width of variation of about 10% for the heat-transfer coefficient strip-water. By evaluating several measurements on different strips this span of variation can be decreased.

REFERENCES

1   F. HOLLANDER: 'Design and control for advanced processing on the run-out table', AISE Rolling Mill Conference, 1970, Baltimore
2   GRÖBER *et al.*: 'Wärmeübertragung', Berlin 1963
3   J. CRANK AND P. NICHOLSON: *Proc. Camb. Phil. Soc.*, 1947, **43**, 50–67

Modelling of a tandem cold-strip rolling mill

M. A. Foster and S. A. Marshall

Consideration of the cold-strip rolling mill process shows that there are many areas where mathematical models of various types, and data analysis, can contribute significantly to process operation and increased yield. A data logging trial can be carried out to collect relevant data to highlight facets of rolling practice needing special attention, to determine unknown parameters required for the models, and to evaluate the models themselves. From a literature survey of the various rolling theories, a number of modelling techniques suitable for on-line use were chosen and compared, amongst them those of Ekelund, Bland and Ford, Stone, and Roberts. In the paper a linearized mill model and data analysis are discussed also, and some applications of the non-linear model are given.

SYMBOLS

W	width of strip
H	thickness of ingoing strip
h	thickness of outgoing strip
M	rigidity of mill stand
F	total roll force
f	roll force per unit width
T	total roll torque
t_f	forward tension per unit area
t_b	backward tension per unit area
u	speed of ingoing strip
v	speed of outgoing strip
L	distance between stands
E	Young's modulus of steel
D	torque characteristic of main motor
S	roll gap opening or screw setting
hf	backup roll film thickness
μ	coefficient of friction
R	undeformed work roll radius
R'	deformed work roll radius
l	undeformed arc of contact $= \sqrt{R\delta}$
l'	deformed arc of contact
h_{av}	average thickness in roll gap $= (H + h)/2$
δ	draft $= H - h$
r	reduction $= 1 - h/H$
$\tilde{h}$	new estimate of outgoing gauge

$\bar{k}$	mean yield stress
k_s	yield-reduction relationship
$\dot{\epsilon}$	strain rate
Z	tension factor
r_b	total reduction on entry
r_m	total reduction on exit
λ	Poisson's ratio of work roll
V_R	roll speed
V_S	set roll speed
i	suffix for number of stand
Δ	symbol which denotes the small deviation

The cold-rolling process usually consists of a number of process stages such as threading, running, welds, and accelerating. During this process it is possible to produce almost any gauge having a surface finish varying according to customer requirements from a relatively coarse to a mirror condition, and with gauge controlled, if needed, to extremely fine limits. In addition, it is possible as the process continually work hardens the material to effect by inter-annealing and varying degrees of cold reduction a range of hardness without actual heat treatment as generally recognized. The process involves a number of disturbances such as uneven thickness or hardness of incoming hot raw material, wear, and thermal expansion of the rolls. Over recent years there has been an increasing demand for the cold strip mill to improve in gauge accuracy, productivity, and product yield, and to meet such requirements control systems have to be developed. The aim of the present work is to investigate a number

M. A. Foster is with BSC, Swinden Laboratories, Rotherham and S. A. Marshall is with University of Sheffield, Dept. of Control Engineering

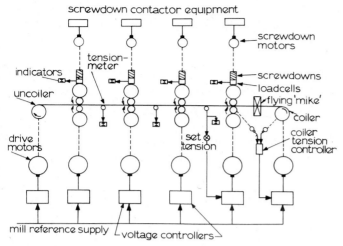

1 Schematic of tandem rolling process

of problems encountered on rolling mills and present certain methods including data acquisition and analysis and mathematical modelling which attempt to overcome them.

The paper is considered in five main sections dealing with the tandem-mill rolling process, literature survey, data acquisition, development of model, data analysis, and applications.

TANDEM-MILL ROLLING PROCESS

The rolling mill (*see* Fig. 1) considered in this paper is a four-high tandem cold mill designed to roll steel strip and comprises the drive motors and equipment for four stands, uncoiler, and coiler and has motor operated screwdowns. Each stand is fitted with 10in diameter direct driven work rolls and supported rigidly by two 22in diameter undriven backing rolls. Details of the electrical main drives are given in Table 1. The stand drive motors are supplied by individual mercury arc-converter sets. Two six-anode rectifiers and one six-anode inverter are connected back-to-back to provide 600 V dc power for acceleration, rolling and regeneration. More details of the mill and its equipment are given by Gifford and Bray.[1] The mill is designed to roll a wide range of material from mild steel to 1·3% carbon steel and strip up to 18in wide may be reduced by up to 85% in thickness. The finished product thickness ranges from 0·01 to 0·14in with tolerances up to ±0·0005in and the mill is capable of finishing speeds up to 2 000 ft/min. Descaled

TABLE 1   Drive equipment

Main drives	HP rating	Voltage rating	Speed range, rev/min
Stand 1 drive	1 000 hp	600	168/436
Stand 2 drive	1 000 hp	600	212/551
Stand 3 drive	1 000 hp	600	241/627
Stand 4 drive	1 000 hp	600	291/764
Coiler	300 hp	350	126/440
Uncoiler	25 kW	350	250/880
Screwdown	2 × 15 hp	230	1 125/2 200

hot-rolled strip is manually fed off the vertical uncoiler and through the four stands of the mill being continuously reduced in thickness with the last stand producing the required product thickness before strip is finally coiled on the vertical coiler. The heat generated by the rolling process is removed by soluble oil squirted on to the roll faces which also increases the mill rolling efficiency. The tandem mill rolling cycle can be split into five operations or parts.

Mill set-up

The operator must set each stand roll gap or screw position and main drive speed so that when he threads the strip through the mill the correct stand gauges and tensions are established. This operation is influenced by three major factors:

(i) there is some variability in the gauge and hardness at the head of successive hot-rolled coils

(ii) gauge along the first 50 ft of the hot-rolled coil will vary unless the coil has been mill dressed

(iii) when the mill is accelerated from thread speed to full rolling speed (typically 1 500 ft/min) the finished gauge changes rapidly by some 0·008–0·01in, a change which cannot be readily corrected manually.

The objective, therefore, is to set up the mill so that correct finished material will be achieved at full rolling speed. This is the most important operation of the whole of the rolling cycle from the point of view of establishing correct product thicknesses with the minimum length of material rolled out of tolerance.

The required percentage reductions at each stand are determined by the metallurgical qualities of the finished product required by the customer, the roll cambers, and the limitations on rolling load and drive power. From these percentage reductions the required interstand gauges at each stand can be determined. In order to find the correct roll gaps to achieve these stand gauges, the operator must know the roll force or mill stretch required to give the desired reductions at each stand and must make an allowance for the gauge change produced during acceleration. The required strip speeds may be calculated from the required finishing speed, the required gauge and the condition that mass flow through the mill must be constant. For regular orders, the screwdowns and speed settings can be given to the roller on a job-card. However, a great deal still depends on the skill of the operators, in particular because of the variation in gauge and hardness at the head-end and along the first 50 ft of hot-rolled coil.

Mill threading

In this operation, the strip is entered manually into each stand in turn, threaded on to the coiler after the last finishing stand, and a length of strip is rolled at thread speed while the roller ensures the mill set-up is correct. The flying micrometer will be moved on to the strip to record finished gauge. During this phase, roll force indication will inform the roller of the approximate interstand gauges. Interstand tension is checked at this stage since, when the mill is accelerated, there will be rapid changes through the mill which could lead to tearing of the strip or complete loss of tension and a cobble.

Acceleration

As soon as the roller is satisfied that the threading operation is completed and the strip is gripped on to the coiler, the mill is accelerated to full rolling speed. To accelerate the mill, all the mill-drive armature voltages are increased linearly at the same rate. The ratios of the speeds are determined by the motor field current settings and the motor speed-load characteristics. During this phase the exit gauge at each stand falls rapidly and the finished gauge falls by up to 0·01in for a 1 500 ft/min speed change. It is not possible to control manually this gauge variation since all screwdowns would have to be rapidly moved at precise moments to ensure safe working tension levels. Therefore, since all the strip rolled at considerably less than full rolling speed is well outside commercial tolerances, the minimum yield loss is achieved by maximum acceleration, i.e. 5 s for a change from 150 to 1 500 ft/min. Here, it is very important, particularly on thin strip, that the tension does not rise to a point at which the strip tears or does not fall to zero so that a loop is thrown and the mill cobbles.

Constant speed rolling

When the desired rolling speed is reached the operator holds the mill at that level. The finished gauge, as measured on the flying micrometer, should ideally be correct at this point. If there is a small error in finished gauge the roller will correct for this by changing the coiler applied tension and the tension between the last two stands by varying stand 4 speed. Larger errors will be corrected by adjustment of one or more screws.

Deceleration

As the tail end of the strip approaches the first stand the roller decelerates the mill in typically 3s for a change of 1 500 to 150 ft/min. The main drive armature voltages are reduced linearly at the same rate to ensure that the relative speeds maintain the correct ratios to keep the interstand tensions constant. The last few feet of strip are rolled at thread speed and the gauge increases rapidly.

Application of modelling to the tandem process

It can be seen from the above brief resumé that there are a number of areas where modelling (and data analysis) can contribute significantly to process operation, increased yield and a better understanding of the rolling process. In many cases a good model will give insight into the behaviour of certain variables which are difficult

to measure. Various aspects of mill operation may be investigated and presented below is a summary of the types of model that may be developed and used to assist this investigation.

MILL SET-UP MODELLING

The basic form of this type of model is shown in Fig. 2. The drafting model provides the required draft pattern in response to product requirements and production constraints and is often based on power considerations. From this given pattern, the roll forces and hence screwdown positions are calculated. Such a model can be implemented on plant in a number of ways either by:

(i) producing detailed tables to aid the roller in obtaining good set-up. Here, the information is based upon 'nominal' input specifications and no account for batch variations can be made

(ii) using an on-line computer in advisory mode and with interstand information to update current advice. With this mode of operation the required specification is input via suitable peripheral devices and advisory mill settings are continually output via digital displays

(iii) using an on-line computer in fully automatic set-up. The procedure is extended one step further and the advisory outputs in (ii) are coupled to the mill servos in order to adjust mill speeds, screwdowns, etc, automatically.

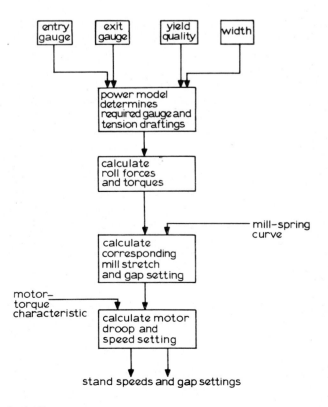

2   *Mill set-up*

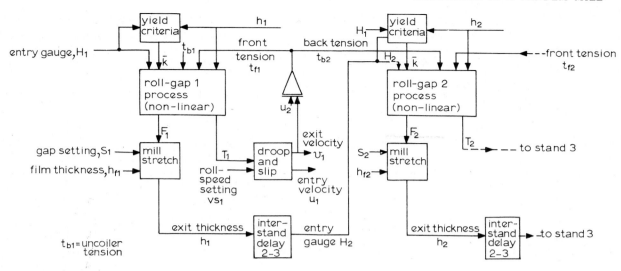

3 Generalized non-linear rolling model

GENERAL NON-LINEAR MODEL

The basic form of this type of model is shown in Fig. 3. When used to determine only steady-state solutions, it can be employed to investigate:

(i) accuracies required for good set-up
(ii) new mill reduction schedules
(iii) adaptive set-up algorithms
(iv) speed effect phenomena
(v) the steady-state interactions of various control schemes.

When the necessary mill dynamics are included, the model permits the evaluation of differing automatic gauge control (AGC) schemes at thread and full speeds and during acceleration.

LINEARIZED MILL MODEL

The basic form of this type of model is shown in Fig. 4. This model, although restricted to small changes, can be

4 Linearized model (simplified)

used to analyse and possibly synthesize new control systems using modern design techniques including, for example, the Inverse Nyquist Array[2] and Optimal Control.[3]

THERMAL MODEL

Concerned with the determination of minimum rolling and coiling temperatures by appropriate selection of reduction schedules and coolant temperatures (*see* Roberts[4]). This type of model may form part of the overall drafting model mentioned above.

For the above models it is necessary to determine roll force and torque from mill data and the following section considers how this can be achieved.

LITERATURE SURVEY

The aim of the survey was to determine the nature of available rolling theories and existence of any special techniques found to be particularly successful and efficient in the solution of these theories when applied to the multistand cases.

Early works by von Karman[5] and Siebel[6] were based on the theoretical analyses of the mechanics of rolling, and von Karman produced a theory which assumed plane deformation and slipping friction and resulted in the formation of the von Karman equation which cannot be integrated directly. Later works by Trinks[7] and Tselikov[8] proposed, respectively, a graphical solution and simplification by replacing the arc of contact by two chords. Underwood[9] gives a detailed account of both approaches. In 1927 Ekelund[10] analysed the forces in the roll gap and produced an equation for roll force which has recently been found to give remarkable agreement with the experimental work of Ford.[11] Larke[12] has shown that with minor modification the Ekelund equation could be used in place of more complex equations. A significant contribution to the development of rolling theory was made in 1943 by Orowan[13] and an excellent account of his work may be found in Underwood. Orowan's theory is considered to be the most accurate of the rolling theories and is usually used as a yardstick by which simpler theories may be assessed. Hockett[14,15] describes a computer scheme for the solution of Orowan's equations which uses a reiterative process, and Golton and Rees[16] have developed a technique which completes an iteration of Orowan's equations allowing for roll flattening in 10 s using a hybrid computer. Owen and Griffins[17] have recently presented a paper describing the solution using a PDP8/Solartron 247 hybrid computer. Cosse and Economopoulos[18] carried out a detailed mathematical study of cold rolling which included elasto-plastic strain effects and used a modified fourth order Runge–Kutta integration scheme to solve the resulting differential equations. The procedure is complex but has a high accuracy over a wide range of operating conditions. In the same manner, Lugovski[19] proposed an algorithm using an Euler integration scheme and claimed that the method was suitable for on-line use.

Later work was concerned with deriving simplified equations to permit rapid roll-force calculations. Bland and Ford[20,21,22] modified Orowan's theory by regarding the compression as homogeneous and introduced several mathematical approximations resulting in the derivation of equations for roll force and torque with or without tension. Hill[23] proposed an analytical approximation to the above in the case of rolling without tension and Hessenberg and Sims[24] and Larke provided corrections to permit the use of tension. Cooke and Parker[25] considered the calculation of roll force by using a series of dimensionless curves derived using numerous measured roll forces and reductions.

Two more recent works which offer significant simplicity to make them suitable for on-line use are by Roberts[26] and Stone.[27] Roberts extends the accepted rolling theory approach to incorporate strain rate effects as a result of extensive experimental work carried out at the United States Steel.[28]

Green, Sparling and Wallace[29] have presented rolling equations based upon the shear-plane theory and this is compared with the Bland–Ford method by LeMay and Nair.[30] Witt[31] compares experimental data with a mathematical model and indicates that consideration should be given to relating gap friction to the yield stress criteria of the model. The majority of the above mentioned theories are defined as functions of deformed roll radius or arc of contact. The usual procedure is to compensate for this roll flattening by the inclusion of Hitchcock's roll-flattening formula[32] which introduces a reiterative process. Kobasa[33] presents experimental evidence using high speed photography which suggests that the actual contact length is greater than that calculated by Hitchcock's formula. Roberts and Stone present alternative equations for the deformed arc of contact. It is, however, important to distinguish whether some theories presented have elongated or exaggerated the arc of contact to compensate for the friction hill, i.e. the calculations for the arc of contact are not necessarily interchangeable. Normally, the inclusion of the deformed arc of contact expression leads to a reiterative process since roll force is

a function of deformed radius and *vice versa*. However, it is often possible to make appropriate analytical approximations which remove the problem (*see* Gessler[34] and Sutton[35] for example).

Friction conditions and their resulting forces in the roll gap are not well understood and it is necessary to postulate the existence of an effective coefficient of friction along the arc of contact between the workpiece and rolls. The value of the friction coefficient is dependent upon the rolling lubricant used,[36,37] the surface condition of the strip,[38] roll diameter, roll finish,[31] roll speed[27,39] and the reduction given to the strip.[40,41] Roberts[42] reviews the problem of friction and indicates that the friction coefficient may vary between 0·01 and 0·15. MacQueen[43] on the other hand has compared a number of rolling theories and has rejected the physical meaning of the friction term and uses it simply as a constant in the roll force and torque equations.

Some examples of papers dealing with the state of the art of mill hardware and automatic gauge control schemes are given below. Tack and Strebel[44] describe the type of electrical equipment now available for cold-rolling mills using thyristor field and armature voltage control systems. Draper[45] describes a number of AGC schemes incorporating interstand tension control by main drives and screwdown overspill. DeYoung and Dolphin[46] describe an AGC system based on the design of stiff motor drives and tension overspill on to the succeeding screws. The problem of combined gauge and shape control is considered by Tarokh,[47] Bravington,[48] Saxl,[49] and Haraguchi.[50]

A number of plants have considered the use of mill set-up algorithms to produce better tolerance material. Butterfield[51] describes a mill set-up scheme which relies upon the interpolation between a small number of standard set-ups. Bryant *et al.*[52] present a scheme based on an analytical model including frictional and thermal considerations and permitting stand-to-stand updating or feed forward. Yoshitanti *et al.*[53] incorporated a scheme using a combination of data banks and an updating algorithm based upon a coil-to-coil principle which assumes that the primary cause of set-up variation comes from the mill operation. MacQueen states that theory-based set-up models are erratic and has thus incorporated a scheme based upon steel energy curves derived from plant data. It is reported that a high degree of success has been achieved, presumably owing to the various unknown parameters, e.g. friction, yield, etc., being lumped together into a single experimental curve. Lapham[54] describes the use of computers in the set-up of an 80in tandem mill. A power model is used to determine drafting and tension levels which distribute the load on all working stands and yet achieve the maximum possible delivery speed. Given this required drafting pattern, a Bland–Ford roll force model is used to determine the roll load and hence screwdown positions. Bryant *et al.*[55] present a paper concerning optimal scheduling based on roll force, shape, and thermal crown considerations.

DATA ACQUISITION

The purpose of the data logging trial was to collect relevant data to:

  (i) assess the accuracies of present mill set-up
  (ii) permit the evaluation of the proposed model
  (iii) highlight any facets of current rolling practice which require special attention
  (iv) locate the various sources of yield loss on the mill
  (v) permit the determination of the unknown parameters required for the model.

A mobile Ferranti Argus 500 process computer (*see* Fig. 5) was used to log a number of plant variables, and software (requiring 4K core) was specially written to carry out the actual trials together with providing test routines to aid the calibration of the interface hardware between the computer and plant transducers. Data output was punched directly on to paper tape in a compressed alphanumeric code so as to reduce tape length, and then subsequently written onto a magnetic tape for data analysis on an ICL computer. By using the alphanumeric code no character manipulation was required on the data processor. A fast punch was employed.

At certain times during the logging, the volume of output data could exceed the speed of the punch and so an intermediate 4K core buffer area was utilized permitting up to 100 s of logged data to be held awaiting punching. Each output record of data, including the 26 analog, 8 digital, and 5 external interrupt derived signals, was output every 0·5 s with an appropriate time marker. The overall limitation on high sampling rates was determined by the speed of the analog-digital scanner, which allowed 100 points/s, and the output facilities. Consequently, each analog plant variable was scanned every 0·5 s. Owing to the lack of scanning speed, no digital filtering was possible and therefore RC networks provided the pre-computer processing. Signals requiring continuous tracking, e.g. screwdown position, were input via the faster digital interface. The logging program was controlled by the operation of a manual control box situated on the plant and the sampling of the coils was carried out during the periods when the mill was being threaded or accelerated and when any coil welds passed through the mill. Spot checks were also made as the body of the coil passed through the mill.

Analog inputs

Table 2 lists the analog process variables measured, together with the method of pre-computer processing. Most signals from the transducers were in the range of 0–10 volts, thus simple resistor divider networks and RC filters constituted the pre-computer processing. Special provisions were required for the signals associated with the motor drives and it was necessary to use direct current isolators (DCI) to provide isolation from the high voltages encountered. Interstand tension was measured by single-roll tension-meters using ac displacements differential transducers driven from a 400 Hz supply. Coiler current was used as an indirect measure of coiler applied tension. Roll force was measured using Davy-United load cells which are part of the standard mill complement and use was made of the spare strain gauge bridges provided on these cells. However, signal levels are small, about 0–10 mV, and the required pre-amplification is provided by integrated circuit amplifiers

TABLE 2 Analog inputs

No.	Variable	Transducer output	Conditioning
8	Roll force	0–35 mV	Amplify (×100)
5	Armature current	(0–200 mV) (0–400 mV)	Isolate and scale
1	Armature voltage	0–600 V	Scale, isolate, scale
2	Flying micrometer	0–±8 V	Offset and scale
1	Backup pressure	0–10 mA	Load
5	Speed	0–250 V dc	Scale
3	Tension	0–4 V dc	Scale

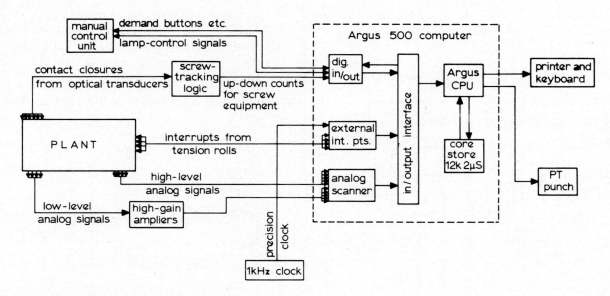

5 *Data logging using Ferranti Argus 500 process computer*

each fed from separate power supplies to ensure high common mode rejection.

The Taylor flying micrometer was part of the standard mill instrumentation for measuring output thickness and has a differential gauge range of ±0·0025in. Since the measured gauge change during acceleration can be as much as +0·010in, a Vollmer micrometer gauge, giving a range of ±0·012in, was used to supplement the Taylor micrometer. This provided the opportunity of carrying out a comparison test between the two measuring gauges over a wide range of rolling conditions.

Digital inputs (including interrupts)

Table 3 lists the digital inputs measured. The computer digital input hardware is based on the 'sense contact-closure' mode; thus throughout the plant interface mercury wetted reed relays were used to prevent contact bounce. Interstand gauges were measured by two methods:

(i) application of the gauge meter equation to each stand
(ii) direct measurement of interstand speed and the application of the constant mass flow expression. (Note that the finished gauge can be accurately measured using the flying micrometers.)

The interstand speeds were measured by counting the number of 1 KHz clock pulses received during one revolution of the tension roll, it being appreciated that

TABLE 3   Digital inputs

No.	Variable	Signal
8	Screw position	Photocell unit mounted about screwdown motor drum produces separate pulses for 0·5 thousand movements up and down
4	Strip velocity	1 kHz signal gated by pulse train derived from tension roll, count so obtained gives inverse of speed
1	Footage counter	Pulse train supplied from final stand work rolls

the method was only applicable when the mill was under steady-state conditions; i.e. no slippage occurring between the tension rolls and the strip (*see* Fig. 6). Mounted on each tension roll were magnets and in their close proximity are mercury wetted reeds mounted on the roll support frames. The signals from the reed switches were used to drive the computer external interrupt circuitry and associated software was arranged to carry out the pulse counting. Owing to the different construction of the last stand exit roll, the strip speed equipment was transferred to the final stand work roll shaft (slip between work rolls and strip is small on this stand). A measure of strip length passing through the final stand was obtained using a microswitch mounted on the final stand work roll shaft and the signal fed via an interrupt.

Finally, the screw position transducers were of a digital type with the Argus 500 carrying out the necessary pulse counting, tracking, and scaling. It was considered impossible to install transducers making direct use of the existing Selsyn screwdown position indication equipment. An optical method was selected due to its simplicity and low cost. Two optical pick-ups, each consisting of lamp unit and photocell were mounted 90° apart about the periphery of the screwdown drive motor brakedrum (Fig. 7). The drum surface was covered with 180° dark and 180° translucent material and as it rotated caused the cells to generate near squarewave signals displaced by ±90°, the sign of which depends only upon the direction of rotation. By suitable logic circuitry, the signals from the cells may be decoded into two pulse trains dependent upon direction and giving a frequency rate proportional to screwdown velocity. In this way it is possible to enter all screwdown signals (two per stand) via one 24 bit digital input word. The above technique of screwdown position tracking is obviously incremental and requires initially some fixed position datum, this being provided by either:

(i) preloading the stand to 50 tons each side and zeroing the relevant tracking counters by operation of a suitable button provided on the control box
(ii) transferring the current position value as read on the mill position equipment into the tracking counter via the keyboard.

In practice (ii) was adopted since it did not interfere with production.

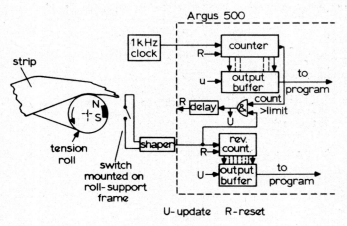

6   *Schematic of strip-steel measuring equipment*

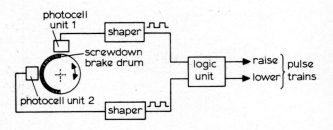

7   *Schematic of screwdown-position measuring equipment*

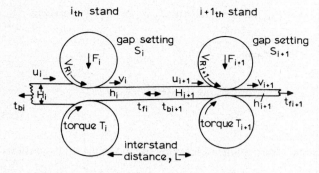

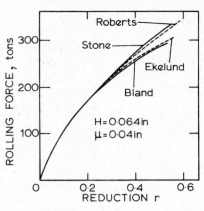

9 *Comparison of methods*

DEVELOPMENT OF NON-LINEAR MODEL

From the literature survey a number of theories which appear suitable for on-line use were chosen and compared using theoretical data. Figure 8 illustrates the roll gap nomenclature. Figures 9 and 10 show the results for two specific schedules, for stand 1 only, using the methods of Ekelund, Bland–Ford, Stone, and Roberts. Several observations may be made regarding this comparison:

(i) the techniques of Ekelund and Bland–Ford give good agreement as shown in Fig. 9

(ii) the choice of the coefficient of friction greatly influences the results and the individual methods vary considerably in sensitivity to this term, as shown in Fig. 10

(iii) although there are many more methods of calculating rolling force it is essentially very difficult to determine which is the best. It seems, however, that the accuracy of the models depends more on the values adopted for the yield stress and coefficient of friction than on other parameters

(iv) the methods by Ekelund, Bland–Ford, and Stone can be combined with their respective roll flattening expressions to eliminate the need for equation reiteration:

(a) *Ekelund roll force equation*

$$f = \bar{k}l' \cdot \left\{1 + \frac{1 \cdot 6\mu\sqrt{R\delta} - 1 \cdot 2\delta}{H + h}\right\} \qquad . \quad (1)$$

Hitchcock's roll flattening equation

$$R' = R\left(1 + \frac{2cf}{\delta}\right) \qquad . \qquad . \qquad . \qquad (2)$$

where $c = 8(1 - \lambda^2)/\pi E$. Manipulating (2) gives

$$f = \left(\frac{R'}{R} - 1\right) \cdot \frac{\delta}{2c} \qquad . \qquad . \qquad . \qquad (3)$$

Substituting for f in Eq. (1) gives the quadratic

$$R'\delta\left(\frac{1}{2cR} - \frac{1 \cdot 6\mu\bar{k}}{H + h}\right) - \bar{k}\left(\frac{1 - 1 \cdot 2\delta}{H + h}\right)\sqrt{R'\delta}$$

$$- \frac{\delta}{2c} = 0$$

from which R' may be readily determined, and f is found from (2).

(b) *Bland–Ford roll force equation*

$$f = \bar{k}l'\left\{1 \cdot 08 + 1 \cdot 79\mu r\sqrt{\frac{R'}{H}} - 1 \cdot 02r\right\} \quad . \quad (4)$$

Substituting for f in Hitchcock's Eq. (3) as above gives

$$R'\delta\left(\frac{1}{2cR} - \frac{1 \cdot 79\mu\bar{k}\sqrt{r}}{H}\right)$$

$$- \bar{k}(1 \cdot 08 - 1 \cdot 02r)\sqrt{R'\delta} - \frac{\delta}{2c} = 0$$

from which R' may be determined.

(c) *Stone's roll force equation*
Given Stone's expression including roll flattening (e.g. Eq. $(17)^{27}$)

$$\left(\frac{\mu l'}{h_{av}}\right)^2 = \left[\exp\left(\frac{\mu l'}{h_{av}}\right) - 1\right]\frac{2a\mu \cdot \bar{k}}{h_{av}} + \left(\frac{\mu l}{h_{av}}\right)^2 \tag{5}$$

where $a = 8(1 - \lambda^2)/\pi E \cdot R$. It has been observed that in general

$$\frac{\mu l'}{h_{av}} \leqslant 0 \cdot 9$$

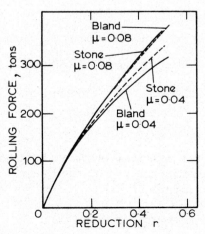

10 *Variation of μ*

Thus expanding

$$\exp\left(\frac{\mu l'}{h_{av}}\right) \approx 1 + \frac{\mu l'}{h_{av}} + \frac{1}{2}\left(\frac{\mu l'}{h_{av}}\right)^2$$

Equation (5) becomes

$$\left(\frac{\mu l'}{h_{av}}\right)^2 = \left[\frac{\mu l'}{h_{av}} + \frac{1}{2}\left(\frac{\mu l'}{h_{av}}\right)^2\right]\frac{2a\mu\bar{k}}{h_{av}} + \left(\frac{\mu l}{h_{av}}\right)^2$$

Rearranging and solving the resulting quadratic gives

$$\frac{\mu l'}{h_{av}} = \frac{1}{2}\left\{\frac{B}{1 - B/2}\right.$$

$$\left. + \sqrt{\frac{B^2}{(1 - B/2)^2} + \frac{4A}{(1 - B/2)}}\right\}$$

where

$$B = \frac{2a\mu\bar{k}}{h_{av}} \quad \text{and} \quad A = \frac{\mu l}{h_{av}}$$

and which explicitly defines the flattened arc of contact in terms of the undeformed arc of contact, and f may be determined from

$$f = \frac{\left(\exp\left(\frac{\mu l'}{h_{av}}\right) - 1\right)}{\frac{\mu l'}{h_{av}}}0 . l'\bar{k} \qquad . \qquad . \quad (6)$$

(v) the technique of Bland–Ford is probably the most used of all the theories and can be presented in form suitable for on-line computation. Hence, its choice in the scheme below:

(vi) *Proposed mill equations and comments*
   The model combines the following equations:

   (a) roll force and torque equations including Hitchcock's flattening expression,[2] i.e.

$$F = \bar{k}l'W\left\{1.08 + 1.79\mu r\sqrt{\frac{R'}{H}} - 1.02r\right\} \quad (7)$$

$$T = \bar{k} . R . W(H - h)\left\{1.05\right.$$

$$+ (0.07 + 1.32r)\mu\sqrt{\frac{R'}{H}} - 0.85r\right\}$$

$$+ R . W . (H . t_b - h . t_f) \qquad . \qquad . \quad (8)$$

   (b) mill spring or stretch equation:

$$h = \frac{F}{m(F)} + S - hf \qquad . \qquad .. \qquad . \quad (9)$$

   (c) slip equations of Bland–Ford giving the neutral angle and relating entry-exit strip velocities u and v to the roll peripheral speed, V_R

   (d) motor droop characteristic:

$$V_R = V_S + D . T \quad . \qquad . \qquad . \quad (10)$$

   (e) elastic deformation of strip between the stands:

$$tf_i = \frac{E}{L}\int_0^t (u_{i+1} - v_i) . dt \qquad . \qquad . \quad (11)$$

   (f) interstand transport delay:

$$H_{i+1} = h_i . e^{-s(L/v_i)} \qquad . \qquad . \qquad . \quad (12)$$

Some observations concerning the use of the mill equations

MILL SPRING

The mill spring characteristic is denoted by the term $m(F)$ and is shown graphically in Fig. 11. It is determined by forcing together the driven work rolls and measuring the resulting roll forces for differing screw or roll gap position; it is seen that the resulting curve exhibits some hysteresis. Since F is often greater than 100 tons, $m(F)$ can be reduced to a linear relationship of the form, $ax + b$.

BACK-UP OIL FILM

The back-up roll oil film thickness, hf, is determined from experiments of the type described by Cosse and Economopoulos[56] and yields an expression of the form:

$$hf = \alpha . V_R^{\frac{1}{2}} . (1 + \beta F + \gamma F^2) . \qquad . \qquad . \qquad . \quad (13)$$

In practice the film thickness varies only 20% over a working roll force range of 100 to 250 tons, and is usually in the range 0·005 to 0·008in.

MEAN YIELD STRESS, $\bar{k}$

Both the roll force and torque equations require the mean yield stress characteristic which comprises the yield stress-reduction curve, tension stress and strain rate. From mill data it has been shown that the yield stress-reduction curve has the form:

$$k_s = y_b + 32r^{\frac{1}{2}} \qquad . \qquad . \qquad . \qquad . \qquad . \quad (14)$$

for low carbon steels, where y_b is the initial input yield stress, lying in the range 14–23 tons/in², and is dependent on previous working and chemical analysis. Equation (14) requires appropriate modification for strain rate and tension, thus:

$$\bar{k} = \left\{1.15k_s + \frac{A'}{k_s^{\frac{1}{2}}}\log(\dot{\epsilon})\right\} . Z \qquad . \qquad . \qquad . \quad (15)$$

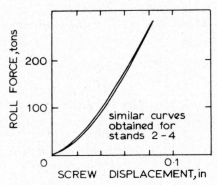

11   Mill spring curve

where

$$\dot{\varepsilon} = \text{strain rate} = V_r \cdot \sqrt{\frac{Rr}{H} \cdot \frac{2}{(2-r)}}$$

$$Z = \frac{1 - (\alpha_1 - 1)t_b + t_f}{\alpha_1} \quad \begin{array}{l} \alpha_1 = 3 \text{ for rf} \\ \alpha_1 = 10 \text{ for roll torque} \end{array}$$

and k_s is evaluated at the mean reduction, $\bar{r}$, where $\bar{r} = 0{\cdot}4r_b + 0{\cdot}6r_m$, $r_b = 1 - H/H_1$ and $r_m = 1 - h/H_1$.

DROOP CHARACTERISTIC

The unknown parameter, D, within the motor droop equation, was determined by inspection of the mill hardware and details and motor loading patterns taken during the threading of the stands. Of course such derived droop curves, that is curves which show the relationship between stand speed and torque (*see* Fig. 12), are applicable only at thread speeds and have to be extrapolated to high speeds in the light of circuitry details. The drives in use are not based on a constant rev/min load droop, but employ circuitry which effectively overspills onto the field such as to soften the drives as the operating speed is raised.

COEFFICIENT OF FRICTION

The values of coefficient of friction used in the model were determined by examination of the logging data. By parameter fitting it is possible to develop a friction model which supplements the main rolling force model. This work yields similar results to those in the paper by Kawamata,[57] i.e.

$$\mu \approx a + bH \qquad . \qquad . \qquad . \qquad . \qquad (16)$$

where a and b are determined by curve fitting.

SOLUTION OF STRIP DEFORMATION AND MILL SPRING EQUATIONS

The above model gives the rolling force as a function of the outgoing thickness, which is itself a function of both unloaded roll gap setting and roll force because of the stretch in the mill supporting structure. It is not normally possible to combine these relationships to obtain an explicit expression and hence a solution has to be obtained using an iterative scheme. The method of successive approximations was considered in some detail and found to lack sufficient stability and also be slow to converge; both factors are closely dependent on the ratio between $\partial P/\partial h$ and $\partial M/\partial h$ which may vary within the range $\frac{1}{2}$ to 10, thus imposing severe restrictions on the choice of convergence parameters. As a result of this, a method based upon geometrical considerations was developed and found in practice to exhibit rapid convergence. The method entailed calculating a new estimate for the outgoing gauge, $\tilde{h}$, from the expression:

$$\tilde{h} = \frac{H \cdot Sk}{Sk + M} + \frac{S \cdot M}{Sk + M} \qquad . \qquad . \qquad . \qquad . \qquad (17)$$

where Sk is the estimated steel strip spring ($= F/H - h$), and M is the slope of the mill spring characteristic ($= 6\,000$ tons/in for $F > 100$ tons). Figure 13 shows the geometric interpretation of the above equation. If an analytic estimate of $\partial F/\partial h$ is available[60] then Eq. (17) may be rewritten thus:

$$\tilde{h} = \frac{F + S \cdot M - h \cdot (\partial F/\partial h)}{M - \partial F/\partial h} \qquad . \qquad . \qquad . \qquad (18)$$

which leads to a rapidly convergent scheme.

In contrast to the above, Sharpe[58] described a scheme for the solution of strip deformation and spring relationships by local linearization and combining with the mill spring characteristic to give an initial estimate of the output thickness for use with a single step Newton–Raephson scheme.

SOLUTION OF COMPLETE MODEL

The resulting model consists of a set of non-linear differential equations and algebraic equations, the latter being implicit in nature. The steady-state solution may be found by setting $H_{i+1} = h_i$, and simultaneously integrating the resulting tension differential equations by a Runge–Kutta Merson variable step integration routine. This method is fast since the integration scheme automatically adjusts the operating step length to ensure accuracy of solution and steady state is reached when no further changes in tension occur. Where only steady-state solutions are required then use of this exclusive digital approach of solution is applicable and rapid in operation. However, when considering the dynamic behaviour of the mill, the choice of analog or digital computer solution may be considered. Arimura et al.[59]

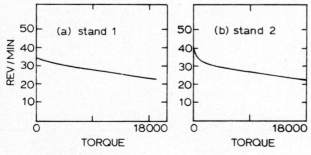

Taken at thread spreads

12   Motor droop characteristics

13   Geometrical interpretation of iterative scheme

consider the solution of the dynamic model of a 5-stand mill using the digital simulation language DSL/90. Sharpe on the other hand considers the use of a hybrid computer system. The solution of the steady-state model was carried out on the University of Sheffield, Department of Control Engineering's AEI CONPAC 4020 process computer with a Tektronix display providing the necessary man/machine interface. By inputting suitable parameters via the display keyboard, the model may be used to determine mill set-up parameters, assess set-up accuracies and so on. Typical solution times were found to be about 10 s.

The complete dynamic model was solved on the Department's CONPAC 4020/Applied Dynamics AD4 hybrid system. The digital computer carries out the solution of the non-linear rolling equations and digital integration of the tension differential equations, while the dynamics of the motors and screwdowns were patched onto the analog machine. Interstand transport delays were held as tables in the digital machine.

LINEARIZED MILL MODEL

The basic non-linear equations require iterative solution for a given set of rolling conditions, but for the purpose of simulating a given schedule, the steady-state equations may be linearized about the mill set-points to yield for example, linearized equations of the form:

$$\Delta F = \left(\frac{\partial F}{\partial S}\right)\Delta S + \left(\frac{\partial F}{\partial t_b}\right)\Delta t_b + \ldots \left(\frac{\partial F}{\partial H}\right)\Delta H \qquad . \quad (19)$$

which when combined with the linearized spring expression, gives:

$$\Delta h = \frac{\Delta S \cdot M}{[M - (\partial F/\partial h)]} + \frac{\Delta H \cdot \partial F/\partial h}{[M - (\partial F/\partial h)]}$$

$$+ \Delta t_f \cdot \frac{\partial F/\partial t_f}{[M - (\partial F/\partial h)]} + \ldots \qquad . \quad (20)$$

Similar linearized relationships may be defined for roll torque, roll slip, etc.[59] Figure 4 shows the form of this type of model.

The partial derivatives may be obtained analytically (*see* Misaka[60]) or numerically by changing each variable by a known (small) amount around the mill set-point about which the process is being linearized and evaluating the resulting change in the computed variable. Such an approach has been adopted to investigate both the static and dynamic performance of the tandem mill. Its usefulness in mill set-up probably lies in its aid to predict and correct for set-up errors when the mill is being threaded. Misaka[60] and Courcoulas and Ham[61] consider the use of linearized models to determine numerically the relationships between control inputs, i.e. speeds and gap settings and product dimensions (and tensions); i.e. by setting $H_{i+1} = h_i$ and $tb_i = tf_{i-1}$, the linearized equations may be expressed in the form:

$$\mathbf{y} = A\mathbf{u}$$

where the input vector $\mathbf{u} = [\Delta S_1 \ldots \Delta S_4, \Delta Vs_1 \ldots \Delta Vs_4]$

and response vector $\mathbf{y} = [\Delta h_1 \ldots \Delta h_4, \Delta tf_1 \ldots \Delta tf_4]$, from which the open loop sensitivities of the elements of the response or output vector $\mathbf{y}$ can be readily ascertained.

Phillips,[62] Bryant,[63] and Arimura[59] use linearized-mill equations for the simulation of the dynamic performance of a tandem mill under differing modes of gauge and tension control. Cumming,[64,65] outlines experimental work using a Hewlett–Packard correlator to estimate the individual mill sensitivity coefficients. This type of work is particularly valuable in assessing the variation of such sensitivities with speed. Smith[66] indicates how the linearized dynamic model may be solved using matrix expansion techniques and briefly reviews the methods available for the rapid matrix solution of the interstand transportation delays.

DATA ANALYSIS

This section is concerned with the analysis of data to investigate the causes of strip loss, and to examine the current rolling practice. A preliminary scan of data, being primarily limited to low carbon steels, was carried out to test its reasonableness and comparisons were made between the desired reduction schedules and the actual reductions achieved in practice; these indicated that generally a larger reduction (by about 0·004in) was made at the first stand. The breakdown of strip loss is shown in Fig. 14, the results of which led to the instigation of a further trial geared specifically to track yield losses on a larger number of coils. Preliminary results of combined trials suggest that:

(i) on average a large amount of strip is lost before acceleration occurs which has been subsequently ascribed to excessive screw activity before acceleration, suggesting that set-up is not correct, the tension exerted by the coiler not being properly established, and damaged first turns on the ingoing coil. Of the above, the second is considered the primary cause and work is currently being carried out to remedy this problem

(ii) a number of coils suffer from excessively large losses (> 100 ft) and are usually associated with large corrections on the screw positions after

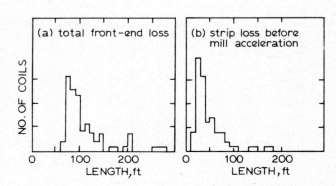

14   Breakdown of strip loss

mill acceleration. Again several reasons are possible, i.e. the target gauge is not going to be reached, and the reduction distribution causes some concern, e.g. excessively high or low tensions predominate in the mill

(iii) the scheduled mill speed is not always achieved because of the nature of the material, and any further increase may cause gauge undershoot. It is here that mill set-up would be particularly useful since it would permit the scheduled production speeds to be achieved more consistently.

Examination of the mill data for empirical relationships

Calculations were carried out on the data in order to determine if any obvious trends were present. For example, if the loading/inch for each individual stand is correlated the histogram in Fig. 15 is obtained, where it will be seen that the spread in loading on stand 1 is small and suggests that, for low carbon steels, a specific value of P/W is aimed for ($\doteqdot 15$ tons/inch). By substituting this value into the mill spring equation it can be shown that for stand 1

$$S_D = h - 2\cdot5(W - 8\cdot0)\qquad\qquad(20)$$

where h is the target exit gauge for stand 1 and S_D is the difference between the true unloaded roll gap displacement and the pre-load calibration point (in fact S_D is the displayed reading upon the roller's gap monitoring equipment). This equation has been confirmed by discussion with the rolling personnel and, since the variation in the width of strip rolled is kept to a minimum during a work shift, if a new schedule requires h to be changed from h_{11} to h_{12} the new screw setting is obtained from

$$S_D(\text{new}) = S_D(\text{old}) + (h_{12} - h_{11})\qquad(21)$$

i.e. $\Delta S_D = \Delta h$.

The use of these incremental variations eliminates the need for accurate screw calibration provided the screws track correctly and, in practice, once the roller has established a datum for his screw position, he will then choose new screw positions (as the batch specification changes) in an incremental manner. Further, when the complete model is used to evaluate set-up inaccuracies and variations in strip properties the screw set-points

are initially determined by the above empirical relationship. The scheduled stand speeds are determined by using mass flow considerations, that is, V_{S1} is used as the pivot stand and the remaining stands are calculated using

$$V_{Si} = V_{S1}\frac{h_1}{h_i}\qquad i = 1\ldots4$$

Under these circumstances the interstand tensions between stands 1 to 3 are left to find their own levels.

APPLICATIONS OF THE NON-LINEAR MODEL AND SOME RESULTS

Mill set-up

The rolling forces (RF) required to give measured mill reductions were calculated using the gauge, yield, and tension data. This was carried out for all low carbon steel orders and the % errors between the calculated RF and actual RF are shown in the histograms of Fig. 16 (coefficient of friction taken as 0·04). From these it will be observed that a considerable spread in error occurs on the first stand, and better RF estimates are achieved for stands 2, 3, and 4. It can be shown that the RF errors may be reduced to $\pm5\%$ by the introduction of the frictional model given in Eq. (16). The scatter observed on the first stand is primarily caused by relatively small variations in both strip hardness and gauge, the latter of which will be eliminated on later stands since a reliable estimate of the gauge leaving stand 1 is known, while the entry gauge is only known within 'nominal' limits. Even within a single batch of coils, the RF estimates can show considerable scatter, the errors being caused by variation in the raw material yield strength which may be estimated to be of the order of ±4 tons/in^2 by examining the actual mill RF. It is interesting to note that such a yield strength variation does not adversely affect the output gauge, but inspection of mill data (and confirmed by the model) shows that the resulting tension variations are excessively high and thus this is more of an operational inconvenience. Investigations are at present being conducted into the introduction of tension control in order to improve this aspect of mill operation.

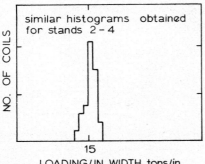

15 Roll force loading/inch width for stand 1

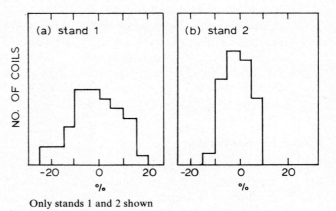

Only stands 1 and 2 shown

16 Histograms for % error between calculated and measured roll forces

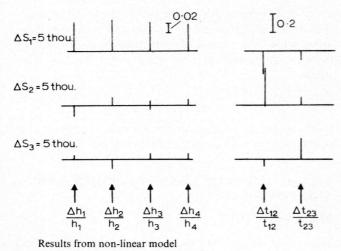

Results from non-linear model

17   Sensitivities to screw position

Sensitivities to screw positions and speeds

Figure 17 shows the sensitivities of the dependent variables to changes in each of the control input variables, i.e. screw gap and speed settings, for an open loop mill. The order considered is a standard low carbon 0·064–0·019in product with input yield stress of 20 ton/in². It can be seen that

(i) by increasing the roll opening of the first stand, the gauges increase and interstand tensions at all stands decrease. Note that the fractional gauge decrease at each stand is approximately equal for each stand, i.e.

$$\frac{\Delta h_1}{h_1} \approx \frac{\Delta h_2}{h_2}$$

(ii) by increasing the speed of the first stand, all the stand gauges increase whilst the interstand tensions decrease. Increasing set speeds on stands 2 or 3 result in only marginal changes in exit gauge but lead to an increase in back tension and decrease in front tension

(iii) on stands 2 and 3, relatively small variations in gap position cause significant variations in interstand tension, particularly the back tension. Thus, it can be seen that large gauge errors cannot be readily removed by operation of stands 2 or 3 alone, due to the high risk of tension collapse (in practice all the screws have to be adjusted to ensure safe tension working levels)

(iv) the factors which influence the finished gauge are changes in speeds of the first and last stands and the roll gap setting on the first stand.

Main drive motor droops

Under normal mill operations, the output gauge sensitivities to screw movements are typically 0·25, 0·18, 0·12, and 0·1 for stands 1–4 respectively. If however the droop coefficients, D, are reduced by 30%, i.e. the motor drives are 'stiffened', these sensitivites become 0·2, −0·1, 0·13, and 0·11 respectively, indicating a reversal in sign for

stand 2. Such an effect is pointed out by Courcoulas, and thus there is a need for correct selection of mill droops if undesirable mill characteristics are to be avoided and adequate mill stability achieved. With the mill in question, some special orders lead to an apparent gauge insensitivity on stand 2 and ideally require the drives to soften slightly.

Speed effect

The mill is threaded at between 80 and 180 ft/min and as soon as all the stands and coiler are suitably engaged the mill speed is raised to full production speed. As the speed is raised the strip output thicknesses drop by up to 0·008in, an effect often referred to as the 'speed effect'. Figure 18 shows typical interstand gauges obtained during a normal mill acceleration. The possible causes of this speed effect are the back-up roll bearing oil film thickness[56], which Eq. (13) shows is highly speed dependent, the frictional properties in the roll gap, and the inadequate matching of the individual stand speed ratios at thread and production speeds.

The contribution by the bearing film can be readily evaluated by the non-linear model by running the simulation at thread and full speeds. Such work has led to the conclusion that up to 0·003in may be contributed by this cause. It is interesting to note that when employing tension control by main drives, the contribution owing to film thickness is greater than 0·003in, presumably due to the loss of the inherent gauge attenuation afforded by the 'open tension' operation. However when using tension-control by correction on successive screw-downs, the contribution tends to be reduced to about 0·002 in, since the film variations on the latter stands are effectively 'absorbed' within the controlling loops, leaving only the open operation on stand 1 (in practice dynamic effects will reduce this effectiveness but nevertheless the result will still be satisfactory). In line with Ref. 57, no significant variations in the coefficient of friction with roll speed have been observed.

In practice, large increases in tension between stands 1 and 2 are observed, although the foregoing suggests that tension decreases should be experienced. Analysis of the mill data shows this tension change is often very

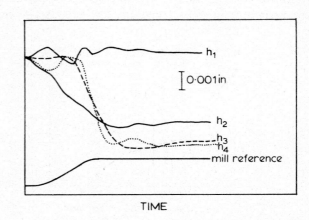

18   Typical interstand gauge variations during mill acceleration

large and must therefore present considerable operational difficulty. Discussions held with the rolling personnel suggest that they have considerable difficulty in establishing sufficient tension at thread speed and to overcome this either more reduction should be introduced on stand 1 or the speed of stand 1 should be reduced by up to 30 ft/min from the scheduled values. Both approaches however cause the tension to rise to excessive levels at full speed suggesting that the motor speed ratios are not being kept constant as the mill is increased in speed. By further data analysis and application of the model the probable cause of this 'ratio' effect has been located, shown to introduce up to 0·004in speed effect, and has led to a re-appraisal of the method of control of mill speed. A further 0·002in speed effect has been shown to be introduced by an offset in the motor droop characteristic, which was in turn shown to be the primary cause of the large tension variations mentioned above. It is interesting to note that the rolling personnel point out that when a bias is introduced into the speed controller to eliminate this offset the overall speed effect is reduced by about 0·0015 to 0·002in and the large tension variations are significantly reduced thus confirming the theoretical findings. Using tension control by screws or main drives significantly reduces the contribution due to the 'ratio effect', leaving essentially only the variations due to back-up film.

With respect to the possible reduction of the 0·003in speed effect caused by the back-up oil film, several methods may be considered: the use of screw position pattern generators,[67] i.e. raise the screws in some predetermined fashion as the mill speed is increased, and the introduction of tension control via screws and/or main drives. The former is being evaluated with due consideration being given to the effect of bad mill set-up.

CONCLUSION

A better understanding of the rolling process and of the problems encountered by the rolling personnel has been obtained from the work described in this paper. In particular, the errors introduced in the output gauge during the acceleration period have been thoroughly analysed and their causes discussed. This has led to the preparation of firm recommendations concerning modifications to the existing hardware in order to increase strip yield.

ACKNOWLEDGMENTS

The authors express thanks to the Special Steels Division, BSC, for permission to undertake this investigation and appreciate the cooperation given by Mr J. D. Gifford of Swinden Laboratories.

REFERENCES

1 J. D. GIFFORD AND D. B. BRAY: 'Control of a multi-stand cold strip mill', IEE Symposium, Sept., 1966
2 H. H. ROSENBROCK: *Trans. IMC*, 1971, **4**, 9–11
3 A. R. M. NOTON: 'Introduction to variational methods in control engineering', Pergamon Press, 1965
4 W. L. ROBERTS: *Iron Steel Eng.*, May 1968, 128–35
5 T. VON KARMAN: *ZAMM*, 1925, **5**, 139
6 E. SIEBEL: *Stahl Eisen*, 1925, **45**, 1 563
7 W. TRINKS: *Blast Furnace Steel Plant*, 1937, **25**, 1 005
8 A. I. TSELIKOV: *Metallurg*, 1939, **6**, 61
9 L. R. UNDERWOOD: 'The Rolling of Metals—Theory and Experiment', (1), Chapman and Hall Ltd, 1950, London
10 S. EKELUND: *Steel*, 1933, **93**, 27
11 H. FORD: *Proc. IME*, 1948, **159**, 115
12 E. CLARKE: 'The rolling of strip, sheet, and plate', Chapman and Hall Ltd, 1957, London
13 E. OROWAN: *Proc. IME*, 1943, **150**, 140–67
14 J. E. HOCKETT: 'The rolling pressure of uranium sheet and plate', Los Alamos Sci. Lab. Report No. LA-2233, 1959
15 J. E. HOCKETT: *Trans. ASM*, 1960, **52**, 675
16 J. W. GOLTON AND D. REES: *IEEE Trans. Elec. Comp.*, 1967, **16**, 717
17 A. G. OWEN AND A. W. J. GRIFFIN: *Proc. IEE*, 1972, **119**, 1 510–6
18 P. COSSE AND M. ECONOMOPOULOS: *CNRM*, 1968, **17**, 15–32
19 V. M. LUGOVSKI AND K. YU. ARKHANGEL'SKAYA: *Stal in English*, 1970, **9**, 713–5
20 D. R. BLAND AND H. FORD: *Proc. IME*, 1948, **159**, 144
21 H. FORD et al.: *JISI*, 1951, **168** (I), 57–72
22 H. FORD et al.: *Ibid.*, 1952, **171** (II), 239–49
23 R. HILL: 'The mathematical theory and plasticity', Clarendon Press, Oxford, 1951
24 W. C. F. HESSENBERG AND R. B. SIMS: *JISI*, 1951, **168**, 155
25 M. COOKE AND R. J. PARKER: *J. Inst. Met.*, 1953, **82**, 129
26 W. L. ROBERTS: *Iron Steel Eng.*, Oct., 1965, 75–87
27 M. D. STONE: *Iron Steel Eng.* (II), Dec., 1956, 59–76
28 R. J. BENTZ AND W. L. ROBERTS: 'Speed effects in the second cold reduction of steel strip', Mechanical Working and Steel Processing V, Metallurgical Society Conferences 1966, **50**, 193–216
29 J. W. GREEN et al.: *J. Mech. Eng. Sci.*, 1964, **6**, 219–35
30 I. LE MAY AND K. D. NAIR: *Journal of Basic Eng.*, Mar., 1967, 69–75
31 F. A. WITT: *Iron Steel Eng.*, Jun., 1965, 121–8
32 J. H. HITCHCOCK: ASME Report of Special Research Committee on Roll Neck Bearings, Jun., 1935, 33–44
33 D. KOBASA AND R. A. SCHULTZ: 'Experimental determination of the length of the arc of contact in cold rolling', AISE Yearly Proceedings, 1968, 283–8
34 YU. V. GESSLER: *Stal in English*, 1968, **9**, 816–18
35 R. W. SUTTON: *IFAC*, 1966, **1** (2), Paper 17C, Session 17, Jun., 1966
36 S. N. VOJNOVIC et al.: *AISE Yearly Proceedings*, 1964, 333–9
37 J. M. THORP: *Proc. IME*, 1961, **175** (11)
38 P. W. WHITTON AND H. FORD: *Proc. IME*, 1955, **15G**, 123–33
39 R. B. SIMS AND D. F. ARTHUR: *JISI*, Nov., 1952, 285–95
40 R. J. BENTZ AND W. L. ROBERTS: *Blast Fur. Steel Plant*, Aug., 1970
41 T. MIZUNO et al.: *Bull. JSME*, 1969, **12**, 50, 359–67
42 W. L. ROBERTS et al.: *Iron Steel Eng.*, Aug., 1970, 77–84
43 A. J. F. MACQUEEN: *Iron Steel Eng.*, Jun., 1967, 95–109
44 J. P. TACK AND E. STREBEL: *Brown Boveri Rev.*, 1971, **58**, 65–77
45 D. W. DRAPER AND R. J. GOODRIDGE: *Proc. IEE*, 1968, **115**, (10), 1 513–21
46 D. R. DEYOUNG AND T. J. DOLPHIN: *Iron Steel Eng.*, Sept., 1966, 119–27
47 M. TAROKH: SIMAC 70 Conference, IMC, Sheffield, Oct., 22–3, 1970
48 C. A. BRAVINGTON AND C. N. CHECK: *ibid.*
49 K. SAXL: *Proc. IME*, 1958, **172**, 727–42
50 S. HARAGUCHI et al.: *Bull. JSME*, 1971, **14**, 104–12
51 M. H. BUTTERFIELD: *Trans. Soc. Inst. Tech.*, 1965, Sept., 76–85
52 G. F. BRYANT et al.: *JISI*, Nov., 1971, 869–75
53 Y. YOSHITANTI et al.: 'Computer Control of Cold Rolling Mills', International Eisenhuttentagung Automatisieriag in Huttenwerken, 1970

54 G. G. LAPHAM: *Iron Steel Eng.*, Nov., 1972, 39

55 G. F. BRYANT *et al.*: Chapter 6 in 'Automation of tandem mills', 1973, London, The Iron and Steel Institute

56 P. COSSE AND M. ECONOMOPOULOS: *CNRM*, 1969, **18**, 41–7

57 T. KAWAMATA *et al.*: *Iron Steel Eng.*, Aug., 1972, 79–86

58 J. E. SHARPE: 'Hybrid modelling for a cold rolling mill', Colloquium on why hybrid computers, IEE Control and Automation Division

59 T. ARIMURA *et al.*: *Automatica*, 1970, **6**, 601–7

60 Y. MISAKA: *ISI Japan*, 1968, **8**, 86–96

61 J. H. COURCOULAS AND J. M. HAM: *Trans. AIEE*, 1957, **76**, 363–70

62 R. A. PHILLIPS: *Trans. AIEE*, 1957, **76**, 355–63

63 G. F. BRYANT AND M. H. BUTTERFIELD: *Proc. IEE*, 1964, **3** (2), 393–405

64 I. G. CUMMING: *JISI*, Aug., 1972, 570–80

65 I. G. CUMMING: 'Experimental Models in the Steel Industry', Colloquium on statistical model prediction and control, IEE Colloquium Digest 1971/12

66 H. W. SMITH: *Automatica*, 1969, **5**, 183–90

67 W. GREGORY AND R. GRIFFITHS: '4-stand tandem cold mill AGC and computer set-up', Third BISRA Automation Conference, 1969, PE/CONF/22, 96–108

Process design criteria for the cooling of a cold strip mill

L. W. Koot

The technical progress in the field of deep drawing and other mechanical deformation processes has caused an increasing interest in producing high quality strips with better shape and profile properties. Thus, the cold strip mill for sheet and tin plate must achieve these high standards. Also, when rolling a strip, its quality has to be maintained constant. At some cold strip mills the operators control the shape and profile of the rolled stock by varying the thermal crowns of the work rolls. In this case, a number of valves connected to sections of cooling water headers are installed. These valves control the volume of coolant which is distributed by nozzle sprays over the work-roll surface. The thermal conditions and the effectiveness of heat removal from the work rolls or from the strip depend on a number of parameters that are part of the cold rolling process, i.e. slip conditions in the roll bite, reduction scheme of the mill, lubricating conditions, type of emulsion and rate of application, arrangement of the coolant sprays, and production rate. For given operating conditions we were able to calculate pressure distribution between the work rolls and the strip (friction hill), slip velocity variation along the arc of contact, and temperature increase of the strip resulting from the deformation work. By using our mathematical model on cold rolling, which describes the deformation process in the bite, we could qualify and quantify each of these factors. This model was verified by measurements at a new 5-stand cold strip mill and by measurements at a small experimental stand. Subsequently a lay-out of the cooling sprays was designed for a 5-stand cold strip mill for tinplate and was installed in August 1972. The heat transfer problem in the roll bite of a stand, including the friction heat source, has been solved with our model, provided the strip temperature before entering the gap is known. This last temperature is a result of heat losses of the strip during its travel from one stand to the next, implied by other boundary conditions. The calculations are repeated for each subsequent stand until the last stand is passed by the strip section under consideration. The temperature level of the rolls in the several stands and the rate of expansion of the diameters are of interest in relation to the controllability of the thermal camber. Also the temperature history of the strip, in relation to the effective lubricant layers on it, are important factors. At higher strip temperatures the deformation resistance is decreased to some extent. On the other hand, the strip temperatures, lubricant temperatures, and lubricant properties are to be considered in relation to the effect of the rolling friction and the strip surface quality.

SYMBOLS

$\dot{\varepsilon}$	strain rate, 1/s
r	reduction
$\Delta\sigma_{v_e}$	increment of deformation resistance caused by strain rate, kgf/mm^2
vT	increment of the deformation resistance caused by a temperature increase, kgf/mm^2
R	work roll radius, mm
R', R''	effective radius of deformed work roll, mm
φ_n	arc between entry and neutral point in the roll bite
φ_{tot}	total arc of contact between strip and work roll
h_{in}	strip thickness on the entry, mm
h_{out}	strip thickness at the exit, mm
Δh	draft, mm
b	strip width, mm
p	roll pressure, kgf/mm^2

The author is with Hoogovens IJmuiden BV, IJmuiden

P roll force, kgf/mm
V_{se} strip speed at the exit of the bite, mm/s
V_{st} strip speed, mm/s
V_s slip speed, mm/s
V_r roll speed, mm/s
S slip coefficient
T torque, (kgf m)/mm
q_f friction energy dissipation, W/mm^2
q_r heat flow to the work rolls, W/mm^2
q_d deformation energy, W/mm^3
q_c heat flow by conduction, W/mm^2
q_{cw} heat flow to cooling water, W/mm^2
T_{ss} strip-surface temperature, °C
T_{rs} roll-surface temperature, °C
T_{lu} lubricant temperature, °C
T_{cw} cooling water temperature, °C
U_c roll radius expansion at the centre of the strip, mm
U_{ss} roll radius expansion at the side of the strip, mm
E Youngs modulus, kgf/mm^2
v compression modulus
μ friction coefficient
α_1 local heat transfer coefficient, W/mm^2 °C
t time, s
ρ_r radial coordinate in the work roll, mm
z axial coordinate in the work roll, mm
a thermal diffusivity of the work roll, mm^2/s
$(\rho c)_{lu}$ heat capacity of the lubricant, J/(°C mm^3)
λ_{1u} heat conduction coefficient, J/(°C mm)

Cold rolled products have many applications and even more are to be expected. At the same time cold strip product consumers are demanding higher quality of sheet and tinplate, especially with respect to a reproducible flatness. These demands affect the processing of the older cold strip mills, which are not equipped with up-to-date tools for control. Therefore, every improvement in the process control of a cold strip mill is important as the economic lifetime of the mill will be extended. Any improvement of the strip quality involves the following physical phenomena:

(i) the expansion of the work roll as a consequence of the temperature distribution, thermal camber
(ii) wear
(iii) roll pressure distribution between the work rolls and the back-up rolls accounting for the roll bending
(iv) deformation resistance of the stock
(v) friction conditions in the roll bite
(vi) transfer of surface roughness from work roll to strip.

Generally, four main measures can be taken to improve cold strip mill performances with regard to the strip quality.

(i) Entry-strip geometry: Only hot rolled strips which have a defined profile and flatness are accepted. Although most operators of hot strip mills try to fulfil this requirement, it may be concluded that in the hot strip mill process also shape control is not yet completely attained. Even when the cold strip mill is computer operated the strip entry profile remains relevant

(ii) Composition of the rolling programme: Gauge range tables are made in ranges of delivery strip thickness in conjunction with the required total reduction. A gradual decreasing in the width of the strips which are to be rolled in a campaign is envisaged. Therefore, both the effects of thermal camber variation and the wear of the work rolls have been taken into account

(iii) Rolling practice: The definition of reduction schemes, the distribution of strip tension over the mill and roll speeds are the main methods of control. The skill of the operators is very important in this connexion. It seems that, based on practical experience, the roll forces in the different stands are maintained at the same level. There are limitations of course, owing to the design of the mill i.e. roll diameters, mill stretch, maximum roll force, and installed motor powers. The application of a particular lubricant or emulsion is a boundary condition for the process and not a means of control

(iv) Shape control facilities: These facilities are often installed in the newer mills. In particular, the roll bending equipment and the possibility to manipulate the cooling and lubrication of the work rolls is intended. It should be understood that the operation of the mill with these facilities is rather more complicated, requiring much experience and skill on the part of the operating crew. Having taken all these process and control aspects into consideration, it is amazing that the operators are, in the majority of cases, rolling a good product. Although they have no quantitative physical relations at their disposal, many final results of these relations are applied. The experience on which their practice is based must envelop very much of the complicated physics involved. However, real problems may arise when extrapolations are made. This may be the case in engineering and use of new mills or when the equipment is removed. Also, changes in the steel grade of the rolled stock may increase the number of problems. This paper deals with the description and evaluation of some process mechanisms which determine the conditions of the cooling water flow effectively and the temperature conditions to which the lubricant is subjected.

DESIGN CRITERIA FOR THE TINPLATE MILL

It was decided that the cooling system of the cold strip mill had to be replaced. From a practical point of view, the installed pump capacity had to be maintained constant. Only the distribution of coolant over the stands and the spray arrangements around the work rolls were the subjects for calculations. Having designed the water flows to each roll, the temperature level and

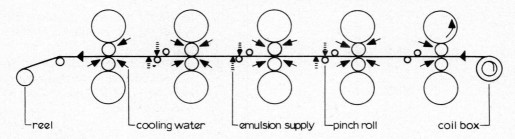

1 Cooling water on a 5-stand cold strip mill

the dynamics of it are computable. The cold strip mill to which the calculations were applied consists of 5-stands, lubricated with a 6 resp. 12% tinnol emulsion, maximum strip width 1 100 mm, work-roll diameters 580–480 mm, back-up roll diameter 1 300 mm, maximum mill speed 5 150 ft/min, installed power per stand, respectively 2 000, 4 000, 4 000, 4 500, 5 400 hp. The general situation of the water flow is shown in Fig. 1. Figure 2 gives schematically a closer view of the equipment which is relevant with respect to the heat-transfer phenomena. The three following questions, concerning the reconstruction of the cooling system of this particular mill, were:

(i) at what rate is the transition of mechanical work into heat distributed over the five stands? In relation to this, the question arises of what proportion of the developed heat is transferred to the work rolls, the rest being removed from the bite with the strip and the lubricant layers

(ii) at what speed can we anticipate the thermal camber of the work rolls to be influenced when the flow rate of the cooling water is changed? This flow rate can be controlled by varying the water pressure in the headers or by switching header sections provided with nozzles on and off

(iii) what maximum strip and tinnol emulsion temperatures may be present in the redesigned situation?

Is it possible to greatly decrease the emulsion temperature by applying supplementary water sprays directed to the strip?

The answers to these questions were calculated with mathematical models. A description of these models is given next. However, a brief reference to the first and second questions may help to clarify the situation. The temperature increase of the water flow is defined at stationary conditions if the total mass flow of water is known. The distribution of the total flow over the mill is based on the answer to the latter part of the first question. Hence, the number of nozzles of a chosen type is determined per stand. The headers and the sprays are positioned around the surface of the work roll, and are based on maximum effectiveness for cooling, taking into account the design limits. This implies that the temperature level of the roll is determined. From this starting point it is possible to evaluate the supplementary influence of additional water flows on the roll camber variations.

Models

The questions which are formulated have been answered by using mathematical models. Figure 3 shows a brief flow chart of the applied models and their relationships. The models are checked by measurements. This is done to some extent in practice on full scale. For some aspects

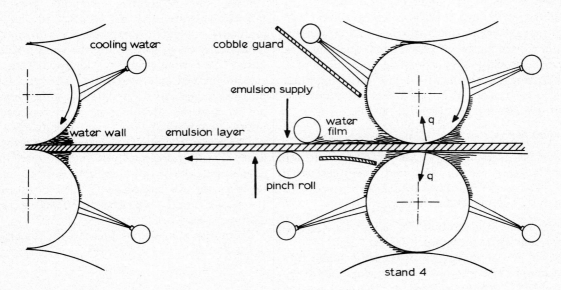

2 Details of cooling and lubrication

3 Flowchart of the model

laboratory simulations were used. The deformation model results are the basic parameters for the heat distribution model. This model makes it possible to calculate the strip and lubricant temperatures. The heat transfer to the work roll is also determined with this model and consequently answers the first question. The output of the model makes it possible to calculate with two subsequent models the answers to the second and third questions, respectively, roll camber variations and lubricant temperatures between the stands.

Deformation model

This model describes the deformation process in the roll bite and is based on an advanced one-dimensional theory.[1,2] The assumptions involved in the theory of the model may be summarized as follows:

(i) plane strain conditions in all cross sections perpendicular to the work-roll length

(ii) strain hardening of the material is taken into account. The strain hardening curve is determined in the way that Ford[1] proposed, i.e. tension tests after subsequent rolling reductions

(iii) the elastic recovery is taken into account as a part of the arc of contact on the exit side of the gap

(iv) the strain rate is included in the model as a variable effect on the deformation resistance of the material. The data of Roberts[3] and Atkins[4] have been used

$$\Delta\sigma_{v\dot\varepsilon} = c . f(r) . \log(1\,000\,\dot\varepsilon)$$

(v) a small temperature effect on the deformation resistance of the material is introduced. The influence of the temperature is based on the figures of Pawelski[5]

$$\Delta\sigma_{v_t} = -12\cdot5\,\text{kgf/mm}^2/100°C$$

(vi) the friction coefficient, μ, has a constant value along the arc of contact

(vii) the tension is homogeneously distributed over the cross sections of the strip at entry and exit side of the bite.

It is possible to use the model in different ways depending upon the questions which have to be answered. The following inputs were required:

(i) material constants such as yield stress, strain hardening, strain rate effect, temperature effect, Youngs modulus, contraction modulus

(ii) stand parameters such as work-roll diameters, D

(iii) process constants, strip geometry such as entry thickness, exit thickness, initial thickness, width and strip tension between the stands, strip temperature at the entry of the bite, roll speed, and friction coefficient.

The execution of the computer program is illustrated in Fig. 3. The calculation begins with an estimation of the position of the neutral point, φ_n. The roll flattening is not yet known and hence the deformed roll radius, R', is also estimated. The calculation is continued determining the pressure, p, along the arc of contact, $R' . \varphi_{tot}$. Two simultaneous differential equations, concerning the normal pressure and the stresses in the strip, are gradually integrated along the arc of contact. This is numerically carried out using the Runge–Kutta procedure. These calculations are followed from the entry side to the exit side of the bite. The resulting normal pressure at the exit of the bite has to be zero. If this is not the case, the calculation has to be repeated using an improved approximation for φ_n. Eventually a sufficient accuracy for the pressure was achieved. Now the roll force, P, is determined with the integration of the vertical components of the roll pressures and shear stresses. At this stage the roll flattening is calculated according to the Hitchcock formula,[6] which is corrected because of the elastic recovery zone.

From the analyses of Prescott Longmans[7] can be derived:

$$\frac{R''}{R} = 1 + \frac{16(1-v^2)}{\pi E\Delta h[1 + \sqrt{(\Delta h_{el})^2}]/\Delta h}\frac{P}{b}$$

TABLE 1   Calculation results of the cold-rolling process model

Stand number		1		2		3		4	
		Calculated	Measured	Calculated	Measured	Calculated	Measured	Calculated	Measured
Cold strip mill	Power, kW/mm*	—	0·145	2·07	2·00	2·39	2·33	2·55	2·63
	Friction coefficient	—	0·115*	0·040	0·045*	0·036	0·030*	0·045	0·028*
	Slip, %	—	—	0·66	1·31	0·80	0·59	0·73	0·50
	Roll force, tf/mm	—	0·68	—	0·68	—	0·71	—	0·68
Laboratory stand	Torque, kgfm/mm	2·5	3·1	3·1	3·5	3·2	3·4	1·9	2·1
(No strip	Friction coefficient	0·050	0·138*	0·040	0·050*	0·030	0·030*	0·035	0·028*
tensions)	Slip, %	0·32	—	0·04	—	−0·23	—	0·26	—
	Roll force, tf/mm	—	0·47	—	0·59	—	0·61	—	0·54

* Values published by Davy United[8]

This relation is applicable to more cases than the original Hitchcock formula:

$$\frac{R''}{R} = 1 + \frac{16(1 - v^2)}{\pi E \Delta h} \frac{P}{b}$$

The new relation is especially relevant for cold rolling. The elastic recovery zone can be an appreciable part of the arc of contact in that process. The whole calculation is repeated in order to make the difference between R'' and R' negligible. Having reached this stage, the program is continued with calculations of torque, rolling power, tension work, deformation work, and friction work. These latter quantities of work must satisfy the energy balance referred to in the next section. The first model described has been checked by measurements on a new cold strip mill and in some aspects by measurements on a two-high laboratory stand. Reductions, roll forces, strip tensions, torque, and slip were measured on the stands. The strip material constants were determined according to Ford's proposals. Having adequately checked the model, then were calculated rolling powers, torques, T, and slip coefficients

$$S = \frac{V_{se}}{V_R} - 1$$

assuming different friction coefficients. These calculations were repeated for as long as the too large differences between the calculated and measured values of the roll forces at the measured reductions occurred. The checking results are given in Table 1. A reasonable agreement is shown between the measured and calculated values of the torques and powers. The resulting friction coefficients agree very well with those which are normally found,[8,9] taking into account the usual dispersion. The conditions on the laboratory stand are far different from those in practice (roll diameter 230 mm, maximum roll speed 90 ft/min). Nevertheless, the model was capable of predicting the measured values.

Heat-transfer model

The calculation results of the deformation model are the input parameters of the heat transport model, as is shown in Fig. 3. The computer program is based on the solution of the Fourier's differential equation for heat diffusion in one direction. The integration is executed using the numerical implicit finite difference method. The grid system encloses half the strip thickness, the very thin oxide layer, the lubricant layer and the shell of the work roll. At points of the grid system inside the strip and in the lubricant layer, heat sources are introduced. The boundary conditions are symmetry in the centre of the strip and a constant temperature of the bulk of the work roll. The model is based on a number of assumptions:

(i) the deformation work is partially (85%) dissipated into heat and the accumulated dislocation energy is about 15%[10]

(ii) heat is transferred in the thickness direction of the strip, considering symmetry with respect to the upper and lower work rolls. Regarding the mass flow rate in the bite, the heat conduction in the strip length direction may be disregarded

(iii) deformation work is homogeneously dissipated over the thickness of the strip

(iv) friction work is dissipated in the lubricant layer, which is considered as an emulsion. The equivalent thickness of the layer is assumed to be equal to half the sum of the surface roughness of the roll and the mean roughness of the strip in the bite, using CLA values. The physical constants are calculated proportionally to the concentration of tinnol in water at the existing temperature

(v) temperature distribution in the shell of the roll is assumed to be uniform at the moment of entry into the roll bite

(vi) there is no net heat generation because of elastic deformations in the work roller in the elastic recovery zone of the strip

(vii) when defining the heat-transfer process, a particular problem arises because the work roll slips over the strip surface. This means that at the entry side of the neutral point, relatively more roll surface is available for contact conduction, whereas at the exit side less roll surface receives the heat flow. This effect must be taken into account when calculating the roll temperatures per time step. Figure 4 illustrates this difficulty which further complicates the calculations.

The calculation with the heat-transport model begins

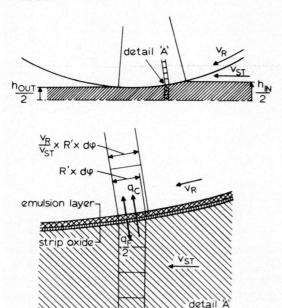

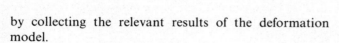

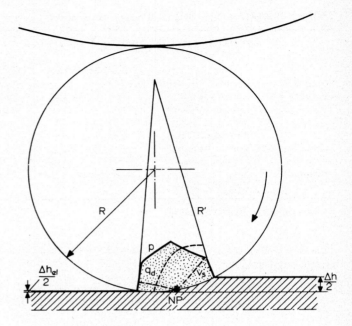

4   *Analysis of the heat-transfer mechanism in the roll bite*

5   *Deformation mechanisms*

by collecting the relevant results of the deformation model.

(i) the normal pressure, p, along the arc of contact, 'friction hill'

(ii) slip velocity, v_s, on entry and exit side of the neutral point. The local heat generation by friction is $q_f = \mu \cdot p \cdot v_s$

(iii) heat generation, in the strip, q_d, because of the plastic deformation during the passage through the bite.

Figure 5 gives an example of these parameters. In particular the values of v_s, p, and q_d, as a function of the position on the arc of contact, are shown in the picture. The calculation continues gradually through the roll bite regarding one cross section of the strip. The time intervals are unequal owing to the variable strip speed. The temperature distribution over strip, oxide layer, lubricant layer, and work-roll shell comes from the numerical solution of the differential equation. The energy balance can be used as a check at the end of the last time step. The sum of the integrated and dissipated deformation work, friction work and heat transport to the work rolls must be equal to the heat accumulation in the strip. The calculations have been carried out for a

test case of a reduction of strip thickness 2·40 mm to 0·33 mm. The main data of this rolling procedure are given in Table 2. The most important results with respect to the heat exchanging processes in stand 4 with regard to heat flows and temperatures are shown in Figs. 6 and 7.

The relatively large temperature increase of the lubricant on the interface is rather surprising. It is questionable whether the lubricant properties of interest for friction are still present at the severe conditions of pressure and temperature. The calculation results attained if different thermal properties of the emulsion are assumed in stand 4 are illustrated in Fig. 8. It must be emphasized here that only a small amount of literature describing the thermal and frictional properties of lubricants at the particular conditions which are present in the gap of a cold rolling mill is available. The heat flow to the work roll is a result of the described calculations and also an input of the temperature model of the work roll. The strip temperatures at the exit of the bite are the starting conditions of the following model.

Strip cooling between stands

The heat losses of the strip and those of the emulsion layers on it are calculated in order to determine the

TABLE 2   Data of the cold rolling procedure of a strip

Stand	1	2	3	4	5	Reel
Entry thickness, mm	2·40	2·00	1·32	0·78	0·49	0·33
Entry tension, kgf/mm²	1·0	10·5	9·3	11·8	13·0	4·0
Roll speed, ft/min	600	1 000	1 700	2 700	4 000	
Roll force (calculated), tf	1 075	1 185	1 345	1 085	1 170	
Roll power (measured), kW	300	2 250	2 670	3 150	3 680	

Strip width, 811 mm
Work-roll diameters, 535–590 mm
Yield stress, 25·2 kgf/mm², strain hardening, 70 kgf/mm² at 85% red

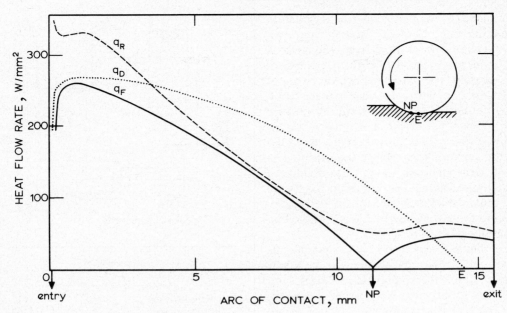

6   *Heat-flow distribution in the roll bite of stand 4*

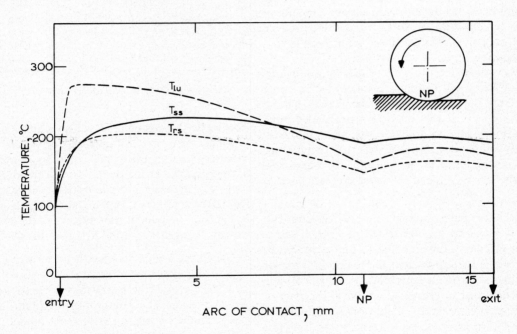

7   *Temperature variation along the arc of contact at stand 4*

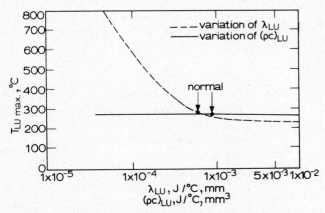

8   *Maximum interface temperature depending on the thermal properties of the lubricant*

temperature conditions at the entry of the next roll bite. The program exists for the solution of the Fourier differential equation for one dimension (strip thickness) and is executed using the numerical implicit finite difference method. The basic assumptions of this model are the boundary conditions of the differential equation

(i) the problem is one-dimensional, neglecting the heat flow in the strip length direction for the same reasons as are mentioned in the former model. Three stages can be distinguished. The pass time in each stage is divided into a number of time steps at which the temperature distribution of the cross section of the strip under consideration is calculated

(ii) the strip moves in the first stage from the bite to the damming rolls. Cooling water flowing over the work rolls is swept along with the strip. A cooling-water layer is formed at the upper side of the moving strip. The film thickness can be about 2 mm. The heat-transfer coefficient between emulsion and cooling film is measured, mean value $\alpha = 0.8$ [W/cm^2 °C]. The heat transport at the other side of the strip is caused mainly by radiation to the surroundings. Hence the heat flow is very much dependent on the temperature level of the radiating surface. The emulsion layers, of about 1 μm in thickness, remain on both sides. The cooling-water film, however, is stripped off by the damming rolls

(iii) assuming that no heat losses to the pinch rolls occur, because of their rapidly achieved stationary temperature level, the second stage ranges from these rolls up to the water wall located in front of the next roll bite. A new emulsion layer of homogeneous thickness is formed just behind the damming rolls by the lubricant supply. The supply has a temperature of 70°C. In addition to the redistribution of temperature, some heat is lost by radiation on both strip surfaces

(iv) the water wall is the result of the cooling water flow on the work roll surfaces at the strip entry side. This is the last stage to be passed by the cross section of the moving strip under consideration. The cooling over this small range is slightly improved because of the turbulating water at the entry of the roll bite. It is assumed that the existing lubricant layers remain in this stage.

Calculations have been carried out concerning the process conditions and are illustrated in Figs. 1 and 2 and given in tabular form in Table 2. The strip speed, related to the exposure times and the temperature level are the dominant factors in determining the heat losses. In Fig. 9, a diagram is presented showing the energy flows of this particular study. Additional calculations have been made to estimate the advantage of applying cooling-water sprays directed on to the strip in the first stage. The calculations of strip temperatures have been undertaken for some rolled strips. The strip temperatures at the reel have been compared with measurements taken in actual practice and they are in good agreement. However, more measurements are required and envisaged.

Roll-cooling model

This model is based on two main computer programs. One describes the heat-flow phenomena in an element of the skin in the central cross section of the roll during a revolution and the second describes the temperature distribution in the central part of the work-roll body. The first program involves the implicit numerical integration of Fourier's differential equation. The shell of the roll can be considered as an uncurved surface if it is allowed to take its thickness small enough. The prob-

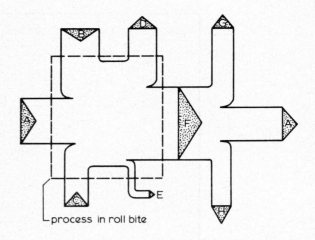

Energy, W/mm^2	Stand				
	1	2	3	4	5
A Latent heat in strip	560	1 360	2 610	3 820	4 200
B Deformation	760	2 230	3 160	2 710	2 480
C Friction work	220	610	1 440	1 100	1 540
D Heat flow to work rolls	90	350	890	1 010	1 330
E Dislocation	120	340	490	410	370
F Latent heat in strip	1 330	3 510	5 830	6 210	6 520
G Heat flow to cooling water	−10	790	1 440	1 570	—
H Heat flow to surrounding	−20	130	570	440	—

9   *Energy-flow diagram with tabled data*

lem is one-dimensional, as is also stated by Pawelski.[11] The heat flow in the tangential direction is negligible with respect to surface speed. The most important part of the program is the definition of the boundary conditions. The element under consideration passes gradually the different sectors I, II, III, and IV which are illustrated in Fig. 10. The temperature history of the element on the work-roll surface of stand 4 is also presented:

(i) From A to B: Contact between strip, intermediate emulsion and roll surface. The heat flow rate to the work roll, q_r, is caused by friction and conduction. The values of q_r are quantitatively determined by the heat-transport model

(ii) From B to D: Cooling by water jets on the roll surface. This sector extends from the exit of the roll bite to the first contact of the work roll with the back-up roll. The heat-transfer coefficient, α, is related to the roll-surface temperature and the temperature of the cooling water by:

$$q_{cw} = \alpha(T_{rs} - T_{cw})$$

The values of α are dependent on a number of water spray conditions. Experimental measurements with water sprays at half scale have provided much information on the cooling effectiveness of these jets

(iii) From D to E: Material contact with the back-up roll. Heat is conducted across the interface for as long as the surface element to be studied is passing the flattening arc, which is caused by the roll force

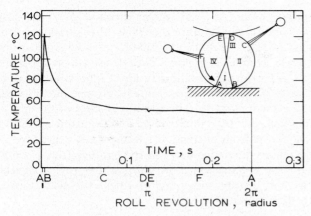

10 Temperature history of a point on the roll surface during one revolution

(iv) From E to A: Cooling by water jets. The remarks relating to sector B to D are applicable to this sector.

The calculations are continued for each revolution of the work roll during the passage of the whole strip in that particular stand. The results are the boundary conditions of the second program. This program is based on the solution of Fourier's differential equation in cylinder coordinates. The problem can be considered as radial symmetric, i.e. the radius, ρ_r, and the axial coordinate z, are the only independent variables

$$\frac{\partial T}{\partial t} = a \frac{\partial^2 T}{\partial \rho_r^2} + a \frac{\partial^2 T}{\partial z^2} + \frac{a}{\rho_r} \frac{\partial T}{\partial \rho_r}$$

This program is analytically executed. By means of this program it is also possible to calculate the expansions of the roll in several cross sections. It is rather a good approximation to state that the diameter expansion is proportional to the mean temperature of the cross section, taking into account the tangential and axial stress effects. These calculations can be made for a whole rolling program for each of the work rolls involved. For the determination of the dynamic temperature distribution of a work roll many parameters are involved. The most important parameters with respect to the penetration of heat in the shell are:

(i) cooling water temperature, T_{cw}
(ii) location of jet impingements on the roll surface
(iii) production rate and roll speed.

Both programs of the model have been checked. Surface temperatures of work rolls of a hot strip mill were measured 20 min after exchanging. Also, temperature measurements have been carried out with a thermocouple probe in the centre line of a work roll. These temperatures extended over the barrel length at several points and were registered during some rolling programs. The calculated results were in close agreement with the experimental ones.

RESULTS

Distribution of heat production

Table 3 includes the quantitative results of the calculations of the deformation work per stand under normal stationary process conditions, i.e. mill speed 5 000 ft/min. The dissipated work, which has to be removed from the work roll by cooling water in order to maintain stationary conditions, is also tabulated. These conditions include the temperature levels which the work rolls experience. The figures show the following remarkable effects. The most critical are stands 3 and 5 where the largest quantities of heat/mm strip width have to be removed from the work roll. The heat flow rate to the work rolls of stand 4 is also large. Table 3 shows that the proportion of the deformation work that is transferred to the work rolls increases with the stand number. This trend is not present when the heat losses to the rolls are related to the driving powers. Also, when comparing the deformation work and driving powers of each stand, it becomes clear that an appreciable part of the driving powers of the last stands are transported by tension in the strip to the former stands. The flow rates of cooling water to the stands were chosen proportionally to the heat flows taking into account constructional possibilities, with respect to the headers and nozzles. The calculated strip temperature has the largest value at the exit of the roll bite of stands 4 and 5. This means that problems relating to high lubricant temperatures may be expected to be most critical in these stands.

Thermal cambers of work rolls

An example of the development of the thermal camber of the work roll in stand 4 is shown in Fig. 11. The conditions in the calculations are concerned with a small rolling program of strips which have a width of 811 mm.

TABLE 3 Distribution of energy consumption in a cold strip mill

Stand number	1	2	3	4	5
Deformation work, W/mm*	760	2 230	3 160	2 710	2 480
Driving power (measured), W/mm	370	2 780	3 330	3 880	4 550
Heat flow to the work rolls, W/mm	90	350	890	1 010	1 330
Proportionally to deformation work, %	11·8	15·7	28·2	40·5	53·5
Stationary temperature level of the work roll, °C	55	63	61	62	69
Flow rate of cooling water, m³/h	74	126	200	305	213
Strip temperatures at resp. entry/exit of the roll bite, °C	20/45	46/119	88/197	129/210	142/221

* All energy data are related values per mm strip width

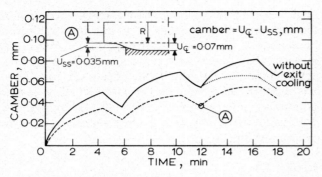

11   Variations of the thermal camber during a rolling program

The thickness and the reduction scheme are given in Table 2. The weight of the strips is about 12 tons and the production rate is 120 tons/h. This means rolling times of 4·5 min per strip and 1·5 min handling times between two successive strips. The roll temperature is 47°C at the start of the program. The diagram shows a rapidly increasing thermal camber if the cooling-water flow on the work-roll surface is minimized at the exit side of the bite. The variations in the camber from head end to tail end of each strip are larger. The variation for the third strip is 0·027, instead of 0·018 mm with normally cooled rolls. The camber differences between the head ends of two successive strips are also larger. It must be remembered, however, that a permanent decrease in the water flow, especially at the exit side, will result in a higher stationary temperature level of the roll. In the diagram it is also demonstrated that an increase in the water flow, starting with the third strip, greatly decreases the thermal camber variation over the strip length. This effect is a result of the temperature level which is much nearer to the stationary level of the roll. Eventually the normal existing thermal camber variations are minimized if this stationary temperature level is as low as possible. However, these variations can be maximally influenced by controlling the coolant flow if it is carried out at a higher temperature level of the roll.

Lubricant temperatures

The variation of this temperature on the way from stand 3 to stand 4 is shown in Fig. 12. The effect of supplementary coolant sprays, directed on to the strip in front of the damming rolls is also presented. The heat-transfer coefficients, relating to the sprays, are known from measurements with water jets on a rotating roll. It is evident from the diagram that the cooling-water film on the strip surface immediately behind the work roll is most effective. The additional effect of the sprays, however, is rather small, about 10°C in front of stand 4 and 5°C in front of stand 3. This is mainly caused by the decreased difference between the temperatures of lubricant and cooling water. In addition, one row of nozzles has a relatively small region where the heat-transfer coefficient has large values.

CONCLUSIONS

The flow rates of cooling water to the stands are designed proportionally with the heat flows to the work rolls of each stand. These proportions are neither related to the deformation work nor to the driving power in the stands. The variation of the coolant flow rate at the exit side is most effective for changing the thermal camber. The flow rates at entry and exit side are proportionally 1:3. The stationary temperature level of the work roll is mainly decreased by designing a high cooling efficiency at the exit side of the roll bites. The conditions of stand 4 are the most critical ones in our normal practice. Stands 3 and 5 are subject to somewhat less severe conditions. The distribution of the load factors and the mechanical work dissipation over the mill are influenced by the distribution of tensile stresses in the strip over the mill. Designing the cooling conditions for upper and lower work roll the same, only very small differences in the roll behaviour may be expected. Efforts to raise the temperature level of the work roll to the stationary level in a short time are advantageous. The thermal camber variations are then earlier reduced. The temperature decrease of the lubricating emulsion at the entry of a roll bite is affected to a small extent by one supplementary row of water sprays. This cooling would be most useful between stands 3 and 4, if more sprays were to be distributed over a longer distance in strip length direction. The highest lubricant temperatures are present in the roll bite. The question is, whether these temperatures are more critical than those at the entry of the bite. More information is required on the properties of the lubricant at the severe conditions in the roll bite in order to be able to criticize the effects of lubricant application.

ACKNOWLEDGMENTS

The research for the determination of the process criteria of the cooling of a cold strip mill was greatly assisted by the cooperation of the mill management and the design office. The author also wishes to mention the work carried out by the various groups of the Process Technology Rolling Mills Department with particular regard to the numerous calculations carried out by Mr H. Bruinsma. Thanks have to be expressed to the

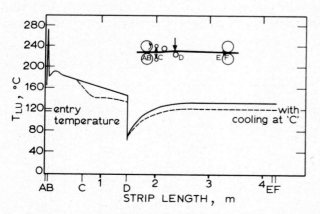

12   Temperature of the lubricant between the fourth and the fifth stand

management of Hoogovens BV IJmuiden for permission to publish this paper.

REFERENCES

1 H. FORD: 'Researches into the Deformation of Metals by Cold Rolling', *Proc. Inst. Mech. Eng.*, 1948
2 P. COSSE AND M. ECONOMOPOULOS: 'Mathematical Study of Cold Rolling', Report of CRM, Liege, 1968
3 R. J. BENTZ AND W. L. ROBERTS: *Blast Furn. Steel Plant*, Aug., 1970
4 ATKINS: *J. Inst. Met.*, 1969, **97**
5 O. PAWELSKI: 'Herstellung von Kaltgewalztem Band', Vol. 1, p. 245, Verlag Stahleisen M.B.H., Düsseldorf, 1970
6 HITCHCOCK: 'Roll Neck Bearings', Am. Soc. of Mech. Engrs. Research Publication, 1935
7 PRESCOTT: LONGMANS: Applied Elasticity, 1924
8 T. J. LAWS AND D. LATHAM: 'A report of the cold rolling trials carried out at the Steel Company of Wales', Davy United; F.R. report: 109, Oct., 1970
9 A. GELEJI: Bildsame Formgebung der Metalle, Akademie-Verlag, Berlin, 1967
10 W. G. BURGERS, Rekristallisation verformter Zustand und Erholung, Akademische Verlagsgesellschaft Becker und Erler kom-Ges./Leipzig, 1941
11 O. PAWELSKI: *Arch. Eisenh.*, 1971, **42** (10)

Discussion on chapter six: Hot and cold rolling

CHAIRMEN: A. E. PENGELLY (BSC, GENERAL STEELS DIVISION, TEESSIDE)
M. ECONOMOPOULOS (CRM, BELGIUM)

The following papers were discussed: *Research on the optimization of the operation of wide strip mills* by
S. Wilmotte, J. Mignon, and M. Economopoulos; *Criteria for hot rolling of plates with respect to the flatness and
the crown of the plate* by G. Fritsch, G. Haralamb, and J. C. Illaire; *Calculation of temperature distribution in a
hot-rolled sheet on the run-out table with emphasis on the α–γ transition* by R. Wartmann and H. Mertes;
Performance analysis and optimization of the plate-rolling process by F. Seredynski; *Theoretical predictions of
plastic flow in hot rolling including the effect of various temperature distributions* by G. C. Cornfield and
R. H. Johnson; *Modelling of a tandem cold-strip rolling mill* by M. A. Foster and S. A. Marshall; *Process design
criteria for the cooling of a cold-strip mill* by L. W. Koot.

Mr F. Hollander (Hoogovens, IJmuiden) introduced the
discussion by referring to cooperative work between
Hoogovens and CRM on the quantitative representation
of shape parameters in the IJmuiden hot strip mill.
This mill has been under computer control for about
four years and the process is optimized by controlling
thread speed and timing in direct relationship to the
heating processes in the furnaces. The next stage is to
improve strip shape from a basis which is advantageous
compared with the conditions described by Wilmotte.
The rolling processes are already well optimized and
easily reproduced. Further, on-line computer control
has been in service for four years and virtually all the
required data are available. Finally, back-up roll bending is available on the last finishing stand.

By combining models describing the mechanics of the
process developed by CRM and models describing the
thermal effect in the rolling process as developed by
Hoogovens, an attempt was made to quantify the shape
of the strip and to compare measured and calculated profiles. In Table 1 Mr Hollander indicated the magnitude
of the various factors affecting shape. Ground crown,
wear, and thermal expansion are basic to the mill before the strip enters the gap. Deflection of back-up and
work roll, roll flattening, frame stretch, and roll neck

movement in the bearing occur only during rolling, and
of these the latter two have no influence on profile of
the gap. Each of the separate phenomena has a magnitude between 0·1 and 0·01 mm. Next, the form of
expansion of work rolls during a schedule was examined
and it was shown that there is a profile to the expansion
resulting from the geometry of contact across the roll;
also that there is a recovery period between strips of
comparable magnitude to the heating cycle. The great
importance of timing sequences emerged strongly.
Figure 1 shows some calculated and measured profiles
at the head end of the strip after the sixth stand of the
finishing train. To obtain the calculated profiles, a set of
calculations was done for each of the preceding five
passes, each output shape being the input for the next
stand. A second graph on the same figure shows the
profile of a strip which was rolled in an asymmetric
gap although the calculated profiles assume a symmetrical process which cannot of course always be guaranteed.

At this stage, edge flattening had not been considered, but it could be concluded nevertheless that the
model was a fair representation of practice with deviations between calculated and measured profiles at
50 mm from the edge symmetrical and smaller than
0·5 mm. It seemed likely to Mr Hollander that by taking

TABLE 1 Factors determining the shape of the rolling gap

	Characteristic values for the strip, mm		
	Middle (M)	Edge (E)	M − E
Ground shape of work roll	0·100	0·088	0·012
Wear of work roll	0·302	0·302	0·000
Thermal expansion of work roll	−0·205	−0·150	−0·055
Deflection of back-up roll	0·333	0·316	0·017
Flattening back-up roll–work roll	0·298	0·142	0·156
Flattening work roll–strip	0·156	0·157	−0·001
Deflection of work roll	0·786	0·684	0·102
Poisson's work-roll deformation	−0·015	−0·010	−0·005
Poisson's back-up roll deformation	−0·012	−0·011	−0·001
Displacement back-up–roll neck	−0·440	0·440	0·000
Stretch of frame	1·187	1·187	0·000

into account edge flattening, this could be improved to between 0·02 and 0·01 mm.

Metallurgical observers quantified strip shape after the finishing stands in five categories, i.e. large or modest centre buckles, flat, and modest or strongly wavy edges. Categorization of this type for a series of coils had been compared with the calculated shape index. Whenever the extreme faults occurred they were confirmed theoretically and generally there was good agreement between theory and practice. During the experimental period there was a short delay during which both the theoretical and observed shape changed from one character to the other. In future it is hoped, after some further quantification, to simplify the models so they can be used to calculate shape index on line, to deter-

mine an acceptable range of mis-shape, and subsequently to correct automatically for shape outside the acceptable band.

Dr J. R. Leigh (BSC, Corporate Engineering Laboratory, UK) asked for details of the strip-shape index discussed by Mr Wilmotte. He referred to his own work on the definition of shape for cold strip, pointing out that it was fortunately possible on cold mills to make detailed measurements of stress in the material. To compute his shape index, he uses a number of inputs suitably weighted and, in all cases, made up of the sums of squares to yield a positive figure which reduces to zero for perfectly flat strip. Dr Leigh was concerned that simple definition of long middle or long edge would be unsatisfactory and would not properly permit the prediction of buckling which is a complicated phenomenon but, nevertheless, is the prime concern of customers. His team had conducted an extensive study with quality control inspectors to define some 42 forms of strip shape and he had attempted to calibrate his index to correspond to these different forms. Dr Leigh wondered whether Mr Wilmotte had considered other inputs to shape index in the case of hot strip.

Replying, **Mr Wilmotte** pointed out that problems of flatness in hot and cold strip are not exactly the same and he agreed that the situation is more complicated with the cold material. After consideration he had concluded that definition in terms of buckled edges or buckled centres was probably best for hot material. Mr Wilmotte also pointed out that the customers for hot and cold strip are quite different, the cold mill usually being a hot mill's customer.

Dr Johnson wondered whether it would be possible to think in terms of shape control by using a rapid and efficient electrical induction heater to control thermal profiles either in the roll or perhaps in the strip itself. He wondered whether this would help in achieving control over shape. **Mr Fritsch** answered this point obliquely by pointing out that on reversible and continuous mills roll camber can already be adjusted partly by grinding and partly by roll bending to control shape. He showed curves which, when superimposed, could yield a substantially flat profile.

Mr Pengelly (Chairman) said that he felt that much of the problem of thermal camber control consisted of

1 Calculated and measured profiles at the head end of the strip

providing adequate cooling rather than using differential heating and although it had been shown that induction heating could cause thermal changes much faster than thermal diffusion, it was difficult to envisage a practicable approach.

Mr Townsend said he was very interested in the paper presented by Fritsch *et al*. He had a question and wished to make a few points about some of his own work,[1] which tended to confirm points made in the previous paper. One assumption made in the paper implied that work-roll camber had little effect on final shape. Mr Townsend was concerned about this since he had found that work-roll camber considerably affected load distribution between work roll and back-up roll, and thus fairly markedly affected flexure of the former and thus flatness. The question concerned Eq. (6) of the paper in which reference was made to an exponential law taking into account relaxation in shape coupled stress as a result of creep. Mr Townsend's view was that creep had little effect because of the short time at rolling temperature and the low strain levels experienced. Regarding recovery and recrystallization effects, which he thought would be more significant than creep, it seemed much more difficult to account for the way these factors affect

longitudinal stresses. Mr Townsend wondered whether the authors have any values for parameter C in Eq. (6).

Unable to account for recovery and recrystallization effects, but feeling that they probably depended on strain rate in the gap, Mr Townsend had adopted strategy which he felt might be of interest. Figure 2 has an ordinate[2] which represents the maximum differential strain as the algebraic sum of compression and tensile strains in the emergent material assuming a symmetrical longitudinal strain distribution (typically parabolic as in Fig. 3). Roughly speaking the total strain to cause buckling is linearly proportional to the ratio of the thickness to the width of the plate squared, i.e. the abscissa of Fig. 2.

By carrying out a range of single pass rolling experiments and measuring crown and gauge of each sample before and after rolling, as well as observing whether the samples were flat or buckled, it was possible to construct Fig. 2. There is a threshold line between conditions which result in good flatness and those which cause long edge or long middle. This is similar to a figure of Mr Fritsch's which showed a combination of operating conditions that ensured flatness. Mr Townsend took the view that since it was not possible to account for recovery and recrystallization and since he regarded creep as negligible, a criterion of good draughting was that conditions should always be within the acceptable region of the graph. Mr Townsend felt that this result also supported Mr Wilmotte's view that some mismatch in the profiles of ingoing and outgoing material was possible without flatness being affected. At large thicknesses this was obviously larger than in the finishing passes.

REFERENCES

1 K. N. SHOHET AND N. A. TOWNSEND: *JISI*, 1971, **209**, 769
2 K. N. SHOHET AND N. A. TOWNSEND: *JISI*, 1968, **206**, 1088

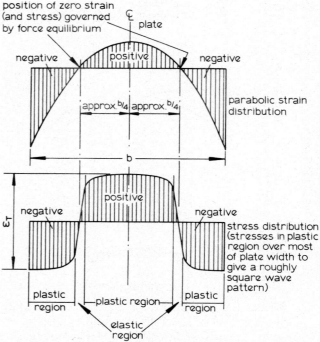

3　*Typical stress and strain distributions in a long-edge specimen*

2　*Relation between crown changes and plate dimensions showing the transition from flatness to bad shape*

Answering, **Mr Fritsch** said that he did indeed take account of work-roll camber although only in a simple fashion by treating the roll as a stressed beam. He ignored phenomena arising from the camber of the rolls themselves, i.e., the results of contact between work rolls and back-up rolls. He realized that this was an incomplete answer to Mr Townsend but said that his objectives had been severely practical and the experimental results appeared to justify the assumptions made. Concerning the question about Eq. (6), tests had been made on 1 000 sheets and creep effects had been accounted for as described in his paper. He was quite convinced that the time between two rolling passes was adequately long to relax all the strains of the previous pass.

Mr Economopoulos (Chairman) had three questions for Mr Fritsch deriving from his own difficulties in working on flatness of sheet. First, he wanted to know how Mr Fritsch measured the two parameters which he used to characterize flatness and shape of the strip between and after passes. Second, he wanted to know how Mr Fritsch obtained numerical values for the parameters which he used in the formula enabling him to determine for each pass the limit force maxima and minima between which flat sheet was obtained. Last, he wished to know Mr Fritsch's opinion of the popularly held view that temperature variation is a major factor affecting sheet flatness.

Mr Fritsch replied that he had done a series of trials on mills in which deliberate buckling of the middle or edges was induced. Since, in hot rolling, these conditions are both readily distinguishable from flatness, boundaries between flat and not-flat could readily be ascertained and in this way numerical coefficients were determined by concurrently logging and data. Concerning temperature variation, obviously this would influence flatness but it was extremely difficult to be quantitative. Subjectively he felt that the factor was more important with strip than with sheet.

Opening the discussion on the paper by Wartmann and Mertes, **Dr Brimacombe** had a practical question which was of interest to people concerned with continuous casting also. He wanted to know how and with what accuracy Dr Mertes measured the heat-transfer coefficients between sprays and the strip.

Replying, **Dr Mertes** said that he felt that most of the heat transfer data which had been deduced from the heat balance was accurate to about 10% although in some cases he would claim 5% where special care was taken. Spray pressure measurements were not accurate enough to improve on this and there had been some difficulty with interference between sprays.

Opening the discussion on the paper by Seredynski, **Mr Fritsch** said that he had for some time been studying optimization problems and had recently been concerned with controlled rolling where, near the end of the sequence, passes have to be made rapidly and at a specific low temperature. Under these conditions many of the normal optimization rules seemed inapplicable. He wondered if Mr Seredynski could comment.

Mr Economopolous (Chairman) intervened, remarking that controlled rolling was a field of considerable interest to many people present and he felt that it would be useful if Mr Fritsch would detail some of the difficulties he had discussed before Mr Seredynski answered. Mr Economopoulos, too, found difficulties during controlled rolling; for example, in one mill acceleration was essentially limited by the ilgner set and he thought that power difficulties of this sort might be common.

Mr Fritsch agreed saying that defining the acceleration at each pass had proved particularly difficult and it seemed that motor power was often the limit to deformation rate. Sometimes it was possible to operate normally, i.e. accelerating until motor power became limiting. Alternatively it might be that motor acceleration had to be limited and the problem was to work within whatever local rules applied and to make the best attempt to achieve the desired final rolling temperature and reduction.

Replying, **Mr Seredynski** said that it was impossible to give other than general answers since the circumstances of the mill concerned would be overriding. He remarked that most electrical machinery is capable of very heavy temporary overloads. Providing that adequate time for cooling was allowed and that the total heat generated was within bounds, overloads of 250% were quite normal.

Dr L. Willner (Betriebsforschungsinstitut des VDEh, Germany) commented that in Germany, various groups are studying means of defining permissible overloads for electrical machines. Although he agreed with Mr Seredynski that very large overloads are permissible under the right conditions, he also pointed out that the result of going too far is an extremely expensive repair. He also had a question about resistance to deformation, and wondered whether Mr Seredynski could offer an approach to classify different steels in terms which would permit accurate predictions. Mr Seredynski was unable to be very helpful about this although he argued that accuracies of perhaps 8% could be achieved.

In his experimental work, Mr Seredynski had generally been concerned to operate with conservative mill loadings but nevertheless had been able to estimate 18% improvement in normal mill throughputs. Thus, there was sufficient room in the optimizing procedure to allow for occasional mistakes in mill operation or material hardness. He pointed out, however, that most of his work had been concerned with conventional rolling rather than controlled rolling where variations would be much greater.

In closing the discussion to allow time for questions on Mr Wilmotte's paper, Mr Economopoulos (Chairman) reiterated points which had been made about variable resistance to deformation. He felt that this lack of data for resistance to deformation as a function of temperature was a major impediment to validation of rolling models. His own laboratories have begun a programme of work on hot extensometer and torsion trials but there remains much to do. There had been considerable discussion about mill loads and he felt that there was a dearth of criteria for the design of mill bearings which are commonly overloaded grossly beyond their nominal specification.

Mr Economopoulos (Chairman) opening the discussion on the paper by Cornfield and Johnson said that he had been particularly interested in this paper which represented a new approach to the computation of deformations in the roll gap. Dr Johnson had concerned himself with the possibility of applying external energy to the material in the gap and thereby influencing the thermal gradients and thus deformations. Mr Economopoulos wondered whether the rolling experts present would regard this as a feasible proposition.

Mr Fritsch also expressed interest in the approach and asked Dr Johnson for his views on phenomena at the entry and exit planes of the rolls. In practice, the strain diagram for sheet rolling, for example, must show considerable strain of both planes, but in practice this is not noticed, and one tends to think of some form of blocking translated in practice into tensile strain at the surface and presumably influenced by temperature gradients through the thickness. In examining the large body of experimental work done, particularly in the UK. Mr Fritsch had frequently been astonished at the differences between results on experimental mills and what can be measured on full-scale production plant. Only when tensile strain at the surface and all other quantifiable effects are taken into account is it possible to reduce the errors of prediction to the order of 5 %.

Dr Johnson agreed that it is important to take into account end effects, but regretted that he had been unable to do so, essentially because his work was part of the electrical industries' research programme rather than being specifically concerned with accurate prediction of rolling parameters. He was currently moving from a model of rolling to one of steel extrusion although he hoped in due course to return to the question of end forces, perhaps following the lines of Russian work of which he had heard.

Mr A. E. Pengelly commented that he felt the approach used by Dr Johnson, which depended particularly on his Eq. (1), was much more realistic than the orthodox plastic flow approaches normally used. He remarked that his own laboratories' work on controlled rolling had shown that there was a clearly exponential relationship between strength and temperature as implied by Dr Johnson. Referring to Dr Johnson's neglect of heat flux from stock to the rolls Mr Pengelly said that he was convinced that in practical rolling this heat transfer was of vital importance. Bradley and Peel had explicitly dealt with this in their paper to the First Mathematical Models Conference. He wondered if Dr Johnson could comment. Referring to the equations given in the appendix, Mr Pengelly said that there seemed to be more unknowns than equations and this implied that some other relationship must have been used to obtain solutions. Was a velocity strain rate

relationship used, and if so could it be explained in more detail? Finally, Mr Pengelly suggested that, whether or not conduction to the rolls has a profound influence on rolling, it certainly leaves the material with a hot middle and thus diminishes the motivation for any form of deep induction heating.

Answering, **Dr Johnson** said that the particular form of the working equations used was subject to the constraints and areas of interest of the problem at hand. For the rolling work he had generally used relationships popular among French and English workers while for his extrusion work he used a different set of laws. He reiterated that generally his objective had been to indicate the form of contour maps to people in the metal industries.

Concerning heat induction to the rolls, Dr Johnson accepted that this must be important but it had not been incorporated in the rolling model since this was essentially set up to establish the techniques. In his extrusion model he was in fact taking it into account.

Concerning the extra relationships used in solving the equations, **Mr F. W. Sharman** (Electricity Council Research Centre, UK) said that the equations he had used related to the displacement velocities in the deforming material and he had assumed no inertia and no acceleration effects on the equilibrium of stresses.

Mr Seredynski pointed out that temperature deviation along the length of slabs resulting from furnace skids led to considerable difficulties with rolling. He wondered if Dr Johnson could comment on the possibility of correcting these temperature deviations electrically. Dr Johnson said that his laboratories were working on a new technique for applying energy transversely and that providing the thickness of the work piece was chosen correctly within a range of up to five inches thick, the centre could be heated at the same rate as the surface. He thought it possible in principle to use this technique to correct variations such as Mr Seredynski described.

Dr Johnson, in response to a question from Mr Koot about the boundary conditions at the contact arc, said that as an approximation, to test the strength of finite element methods in this area, they had assumed sticking friction although they appreciated that this was a distortion of the facts. He hoped to return and tackle the problem with a mixture of sliding and sticking friction.

Mr Townsend asked whether the thermal strains resulting from temperature gradients within the stock had been accounted for and he wondered whether they would be significant.

Mr F. W. Sharman said that they had not taken account of thermal strains. The input temperature profile had simply been convected along the streamlines, being compressed as the stock got narrower but not changing in any other way. Obviously this was a distortion of the truth but it should be fairly simple in principle to correct for conduction effects. Responding to Mr Ouderkerk, who said that the considerable practical temperature variations across the width of slabs would make it interesting to have a three-dimensional model, Mr Sharman said that this was out of the question at present.

Mr Economopoulos (Chairman) opened the discussion on the paper by Mr M. A. Foster and Mr S. A. Marshall by remarking that Mr Foster had presented a rather complete mathematical description of the process of cold rolling, giving a review not only of the static elements associated with the material strength during rolling but also of dynamic aspects of the mill mechanics. It seemed that a number of recommendations for important changes flowed from the work. Mr Economopoulos asked Mr Foster whether he would review the nature of the changes recommended.

Mr Foster said that the most obvious change which he had already mentioned concerned modification of the droop characteristics of the motors to eliminate a kink and thus to reduce tension variations during rolling. This has been achieved by injecting offset voltages into the mag-amp system. This simple modification led to a considerable improvement.

Another major recommendation consisted of introducing tension control via screwdown or via speed. Screwdown control of tension seemed to be more desirable and this was being recommended. Although, in hardware terms, tension control through speed is easier, it tends to result in greater stress variations during rolling.

Dr N. A. Robins (Inland Steel Co., USA) asked about the way in which the coefficient of friction was determined, suggesting that Mr Foster may have worked backwards from the roll force equations based on some prior knowledge of strip properties. He wondered how much of the reported variation in coefficient of friction was really variation in material properties. Mr Foster had been expecting questions on this area. He had a considerable amount of data on yield stress variations for low carbon steel but had to make assumptions about the effect of strain rate on it. After a wide literature survey it was felt that there was a strain-rate effect, and so an assumption was made about this and the equations were worked backward to deduce what turned out to be a simple relationship between friction and incoming gauge. Nevertheless it would be dangerous to presume that this relationsip applied to mills other than that on which the data had been acquired.

Mr Economopoulos (Chairman) commented on Mr Foster's use of Hitchcock's formula (Fig. 5) to calculate roll flattening. He had himself tried various approaches as had people at CRM and he wondered whether Mr Foster had made a comparison of methods. Mr Foster pointed out that methods of calculating roll flattening essentially lead to artificial increases in the arc of contact and by definition this interacts on the assumptions made about coefficient of friction. For this reason he had felt that it was most appropriate to use the roll flattening formula recommended by the author whose basic equations were in use. He did not feel that flattening equations were interchangeable.

Dr N. A. Robins said that in his view friction was a 'fiddle' factor to make equations fit the rolling model. In his view it would perhaps be better to assume coefficient of friction as constant and to develop a correlation method for roll force; this would be as accurate as and more meaningful than going back to calculating a varying coefficient of friction.

Mr Roberts (United States Steel Corporation) had sent a written contribution for the discussion on Mr Koot's paper:

The 'systems approach' taken by Mr Koot in his development and utilization of mathematical models pertaining to the operation of a tandem cold mill is a commendable achievement in that it embodies both the kinematic and thermal aspects of the cold-reduction process. Such an approach is vitally necessary if the shape of commercially cold-rolled sheet and strip is to be improved either through modifications to the design and operating techniques of existing mills or through improved design concepts incorporated into new cold-rolling facilities.

As is the case in the development of virtually all mathematical models, Mr Koot was obliged to make simplifying assumptions. Generally speaking, these assumptions, either explicitly stated or implied, are unquestionably valid, but in some instances, the rationale involved is debatable. For example, temperature distributions occurring in the back-up rolls are not discussed, and yet they are likely to be of greater significance than the thermal effects encountered in the work rolls.[1] Another instance involved the use of a modified Hitchcock equation which establishes an arc length shorter than Hitchcock's original equation, although measurements have shown the latter equation to be too conservative.[2]

Mr Koot states, in effect, that computations using the 'deformation model' were repeated until the calculated and measured values of the rolling force were in reasonable agreement. Presumably, the values of the coefficient of friction that resulted in such agreement were regarded as being correct. Table 1 in his paper indicates that the calculated values for the coefficients of friction for stands 2, 3, and 4 for the cold strip mill were 0.040, 0.036, and 0.045, respectively, but when the rolling conditions at these three stands were simulated on the single stand laboratory mill, the corresponding values for the coefficient were computed to be 0.040, 0.030, and 0.035, respectively. In view of the fact that the laboratory mill had smaller diameter rolls than the production mill (230 mm *v*. 580–480 mm) and was operated at a much slower speed (90 ft/min *v*. 1 000/2 700 ft/min), these results are surprising. It is reported in the literature that decreased mill speed and decreased work-roll diameter both increase the effective coefficient of friction.[3,4]

That the values for the coefficients of friction computed for the commercial mill appear to be too high is indicated by the fact that the values of slip for stands 2, 3, and 4 were measured as being 1·32, 0·59, and 0·50%. Assuming the speeds for these stands were 1 000, 17 000, and 2 700 ft/min, respectively, then using the formula published by Pavlov[5] and cited by Gallai *et al.*[6] (which, incidentally, appears more applicable to cold rolling with low coefficients of friction than to hot rolling with high coefficients), the calculated values for the coefficient would be 0·043, 0·0244, and 0·018 respectively.

The equivalent thickness of the lubricant film in the roll bite is assumed to be equal to half the sum of the surface roughness of the roll and the main roughness of the strip in the bite. From a heat-transfer viewpoint, this appears reasonably satisfactory since, if the strip and roll surface finishes are both assumed to be 10 μin, the equivalent thickness of the oil film would be 10 μin. That layers of such thickness exist in the roll bite has been previously demonstrated.[7,8] However, it should be pointed out that in the case of a typical rolling lubricant emulsion, only the oil phase is carried through the roll bite (and not the emulsion, as assumed by Mr Koot), and that the lubricant film layer is not of uniform thickness, but decreases from the entry to the exit end of the roll bite.

With respect to the distribution of energy in the tandem mill process, as indicated in Table 3 of the paper, the ratios of deformation power to the mill driving power for stands 2 to 5 are as given in Table 2.

TABLE 2 Ratios of deformation power to the mill driving power

Stand no.	2	3	4	5
Ratio deformation power / driving power	0·64	0·80	0·65	0·44

With effective rolling lubricity, the efficiency, ξ, of a mill stand (or the ratio of the deformation power to the mill drive power) may be approximated by the equation[9]

$$\xi = (1 - r/2) \times 100\%.$$

Under these circumstances, and assuming an equal distribution of the frictional energy between the work rolls and the strip,[10] the portion of the mill driving power dissipated as heat in both rolls is about 2/4 × 100%. Thus, the ratio of heat flow to the rolls to that associated with the deformation of the strip is

$$\frac{r}{2(2 - r)} \times 100\%.$$

For stands 2, 3, 4, and 5 this ratio would be expected to assume values of about 10·2, 13·8, 11·3, and 9·8%, respectively. These are considerably smaller than the values presented in Table 3 of Mr Koot's paper.

Regardless of the predictive accuracy of mathematical models like those used by Mr Koot, such models are valuable in that they provide realistic, generalized information and thus establish the most desirable trends to adopt in cold mill operation and design. For example, he has demonstrated the greater effectiveness of cooling sprays on the exit side of the work rolls and the advan-

tages to be gained by raising the average temperature of the work rolls to the equilibrium temperature as rapidly as possible.

To enhance the predictive capacity of mathematical models of the cold-rolling process, much more must be known concerning the yielding behaviour of the strip at high strain rates as well as the lubricity provided by the rolling oil under conditions of high temperature and pressure. However, the design engineer cannot wait until all the detailed information he desires becomes available. Instead, he must utilize the best approximation to scientific truths to which he has access, and he must compensate for any resultant shortcomings in his models by use of empirical corrective factors.

Mr Koot recognizes the lack of information relative to the details of the rolling process (particularly in connexion with the rolling lubricant). In spite of this handicap, however, he has successfully developed a comprehensive model of the cold-rolling process and laid a foundation on which future researchers and development engineers will build when they work in this field.

References

1 M. D. STONE AND R. GRAY: *Iron Steel Eng. Year Book*, 1965, 657–74
2 D. KOBASA AND R. A. SCHULTZ: *ibid.*, 1968, 283–8
3 M. D. STONE: *ibid.*, 1961, 515–25
4 W. L. ROBERTS: Proc. 11th Mechanical Working and Steel Processing Conference, AIMF, 1969, New York, 299–314
5 I. M. PAVLOV: 'Rolling Theory' (Teoriya prokatki), *Metallurgizdat*, 1, 1950
6 YA. S. GALLAI *et al.*: *Steel in the USSR*, 1971, **1**, (10), 806–8
7 R. J. BENTS AND R. R. SOMERS: *Lubrication Engineering*, Feb., 1965
8 W. L. ROBERTS: *Blast Furn. Steel Plant*, May, 1968
9 W. L. ROBERTS: *Iron Steel Eng. Year Book*, 1968, 362–70
10 A. S. WEINSTEIN: *Iron Steel Eng. Year Book*, 1968, 369

In reply, **Mr Koot** said he was grateful for Mr Roberts' contribution and appreciated his support for the importance of the thermo-mechanical approach to cold rolling.

Concerning the point about thermal effects in the back-up roll, Mr Koot said that he found that less than 10% of the heat input per work roll is transferred to the back-up roll. The amount depends on the temperature difference and transfer is mainly at that part of the work-roll surface which also contacts the strip. The large mass of back-up rolls compared with work rolls leads to very slow heating of the former and to a time constant which is much longer than a single rolling schedule. Mr Koot felt that these slow drifts would be automatically accounted for by the operators. Incidentally, heat production in the loaded roll neck bearings is considerable and he had recently completed a model to evaluate this effect.

The modified formula used to calculate roll flattening in deformation model differs from Hitchcock's formula in that it takes proper account of the elastic recovery zone. The original formula results in unreal values of the

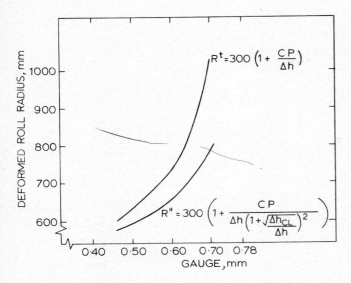

4 *Hitchcock relation at stand 4*

deformed roll radius if the draft is decreasing (Fig. 4). If the modified formula is used more realistic values of the roll forces are predicted.

Replying to the question about oil films, Mr Koot remarked that thermal conductivity of oil is only a fifth of that of the emulsion, a difference which would result (Fig. 8 of Koot's paper) in an increase of 150°C in differential temperature. Obviously, therefore, it is important to examine whether the film is in fact oil or emulsion.

Mr Economopoulos (Chairman) remarked that he had measured back-up roll temperature changes in hot rolling but these were uniform and therefore played no part in problems of profile and flatness. **Mr Wilmotte** commented on the thermal camber model presented by Mr Koot. He had developed several models for the prediction of thermal camber and in each case the result was to predict the temperature rise to an asymptotic value after about two hours. He had examined the magnitudes of various parameters which affected roll temperature rise. The most important of these was what he called 'roll pacing', presumably the ratio of rolling time to total time. A linear change in this factor resulted in a proportional change in camber. Mr Koot confirmed this. Mr Wilmotte had also studied water cooling and had found that a doubling water spray pressure led to a 50% decrease in roll camber.

Dr J. R. Leigh was interested in the possibilities for adjusting roll camber through variable water spray. If emergent strip temperature was non-uniform across the width then there would be a change in the flatness and the temperatures were equalized in the run-out coolers. He was in the course of trying to devise a prediction mechanism for this effect and wondered if Mr Koot could comment.

To adjust roll camber by use of the water sprays it was obviously necessary that the roll temperature be high enough to permit differential heat transfer, but since the general level of temperature rises during the rolling program it would be necessary to take some special account of this if any automatic scheme were proposed. Finally, Dr J. R. Leigh wondered whether Mr Koot intended to fit a shape meter to his mill.

Replying, **Mr Koot** agreed that if temperature differentials existed across the strip width they would certainly be important but he had no evidence on the matter. Concerning roll camber control with water sprays, he disagreed with Dr Leigh about the work-roll temperature history, saying that bulk oil temperature remained fairly constant in the long term although there were, of course, quite rapid changes of surface temperature. He thought that there were no plans for automatic camber control by roll cooling.

Commenting on the point about shape measurement **Mr J. C. Katoen** said that he was considering the addition of shape measurement to the mill, using magnetic, air jet, or tension gauging and in doing so was concerned also to devise a control system which would be coupled to the measurement. Roll bending seemed to be a possibility.

Author index

* Discussion

Subject index

---

* Discussion

---

* Discussion